DEPARTMENT OF SCIENTIFIC AND
INDUSTRIAL RESEARCH

ROAD RESEARCH LABORATORY

RESEARCH
ON
ROAD TRAFFIC

LONDON
HER MAJESTY'S STATIONERY OFFICE
1965

Printed in England for Her Majesty's Stationery Office by J. W. Arrowsmith Ltd., Bristol 3

FOREWORD

This book is the companion volume to Research on Road Safety which was published in 1963. It has grown out of lectures given by Laboratory staff, mainly to senior engineers and police officers, at short courses on road traffic and safety held at the Laboratory since 1952. The main aim of these courses has been to pass on the latest results of research at the Laboratory. The book amplifies the lecture notes and puts them in a more readily accessible form. Some of the information is based on investigations carried out a number of years ago. This follows from the fact that the research has been spread over 17 years, and it is not possible to keep it all up to date. However, the basic relations are likely to continue to be applicable over a long period of years.

Traffic engineering and planning for traffic are becoming increasingly important in Britain. It is desirable that there should be available to practising engineers, planners and others concerned, information which they can use in tackling traffic problems. It is hoped that this book provides a reasonably comprehensive statement of the results of research, up to the time the book was written. Suggestions and criticisms from readers will be welcomed, and will be carefully considered.

Mr. J. B. Behr was responsible for the editorial work; a list of those who contributed to the writing of the book is given on page iv.

W. H. GLANVILLE
Director of Road Research

Road Research Laboratory,
Harmondsworth,
Middlesex.

ACKNOWLEDGEMENTS

The following members of the Traffic and Safety Division contributed to the writing of this Book:

J. Almond, G. Charlesworth, A. W. Christie, T. M. Coburn, R. F. F. Dawson, F. Garwood, C. G. Giles, G. Grime, A. J. Harris, J. A. Hillier, E. M. Holroyd, J. Inwood, V. J. Jehu, J. A. Martin, R. L. Moore, R. F. Newby, S. J. Older, R. J. Smeed, J. C. Tanner, J. M. Thompson, J. G. Wardrop, F. V. Webster, P. D. Whiting.

CONTENTS

LIST OF PLATES

ix

Chapter 1

Introduction

As in other countries, the pressure on the road system of Great Britain is continually increasing. By the end of 1963 there were between 11 and 12 million motor vehicles on about 20 0000 miles of road. It is estimated that by 1980 the total number of motor vehicles will have risen to some 27 million. Congestion on the roads has been estimated to be running at about £300 million to £600 million a year, depending on the valuation placed on non-working time (see Chapter 15). Two thirds of this cost occurs in urban areas, although the mileage run is about equally divided between urban and rural areas. Accidents are estimated to involve the community in losses of some £175 million a year, quite apart from the human suffering caused. About £3700 million is spent annually on road transport in all its forms, excluding taxation; this represents some 13 per cent of the total national income.

The total mileage of roads in the country is increasing at the rate of $0 \cdot 7$ per cent per annum and the mileage of main roads (motorways, trunk and class 1 roads) is increasing at about $0 \cdot 2$ per cent per annum, while the number of motor vehicles is increasing at 7 per cent per annum. From 1958 to 63 the average rate of increase in the number of road casulties has been $3\frac{1}{2}$ per cent. There is clearly a great need for means of reducing both congestion and numbers of accidents, and scientific research provides an effective way of finding them. The Road Research Laboratory of the Department of Scientific and Industrial Research has been working intensively on these problems since 1946. Most of the safety aspects of this work have been described in the companion volume *Research on Road Safety*,[1] and the present book deals mainly with the traffic aspects. Some of the research covered by the two books could be classified as being either "Traffic" or "Safety", and some attention is therefore given to accidents in this book. The effects of roads and traffic on the environment, in terms of appearance, noise and smell, are, of course, important and must be taken into account when planning road systems, but this aspect of the traffic problem is not dealt with here.

In order to deal with traffic problems in a satisfactory way, it has been necessary to build up a scientific discipline. This involves collecting quantitative information about roads and traffic, developing methods and apparatus for studying the problem, focussing attention on the important aspects of traffic operation and finding workable methods of introducing economic considerations. Both practical and theoretical methods are needed.

A relatively new branch of engineering has therefore been evolved, that of traffic engineering. It has been variously defined; the definition adopted by the Institution of Civil Engineers is that traffic engineering is "that part of engineering which deals with the traffic planning and design of roads, of frontage development and of parking facilities and with the control of traffic to provide safe, convenient and economic movement of vehicles and pedestrians''. Early traffic problems were those of control at intersections, and these still form an important part of the work of a traffic engineer. With the growth of traffic is has become necessary for the engineer to look closely at the layout and geometric design of roads. It has also become necessary for him to study the actual and potential patterns and amounts of traffic when considering the design and location of new roads. With the growing urbanization of the country and the increasingly difficult traffic problems arising in urban areas, it is being recognized that a solution to the problems should be sought through co-operation between the traffic engineer, the town planner, the economist and others. Some of these problems have been considered in the Buchanan Report,[2] *Traffic in Towns*, which shows, on certain assumptions, how far it is possible to accommodate travel by car in towns and the likely cost of doing so.

It is sometimes difficult in engineering to separate research from the exercise of the particular art and science involved. It is not so difficult when the engineering concerned is the straightforward application of known and well recognized principles such as the design of a building to conform to an accepted Code of Practice. But where there is no accepted code and the engineer must recognize and evaluate the problem and find a basically new solution, often a unique solution, the dividing line between research and practice becomes indistinct and often quite unrecognizable. Traffic engineering is such a branch of engineering—not only are many of the techniques employed still in the formative stage, but even the field of activity of the traffic engineer is ill-defined, and with the stupendous growth of traffic in recent years its boundaries are wider than they were some years ago. Both the traffic engineer and the research worker are, therefore, to be found working in close association devising and testing out new ideas and new methods.[3]

The aim of the research worker in traffic engineering is to discover methods and principles which the engineer and administrator can use to facilitate traffic flow and reduce accidents. To carry out this task it is necessary to obtain a basic understanding of traffic phenomena and to discover the principles which govern the design of traffic control systems, the layout of roads and junctions and the planning of transport. A large part of the research in traffic engineering in Britain is carried out at the Road Research Laboratory, although an increasing amount is being done by universities, practising engineers, police and others.

The research frequently involves extensive observations of traffic on the roads. Sometimes it is necessary to make experiments on the road which interfere with traffic, but there is clearly a limit to what can be done in this way. There is therefore a need for an area where controlled experiments can be carried out without affecting the public. Until 1960 the Laboratory used Northolt Airport, the Fighting Vehicles Research and Development Establishments at Chobham and a number of disused airfields for this purpose. In that year the Laboratory's Research Track was opened at Crowthorne (see Fig 1.1); it provides unique facilities for studying problems concerned with traffic and safety.[4] The central area is circular with a diameter of 900 ft: its main purpose is to enable controlled traffic tests to be made on a wide variety of experimental layouts (see Plate 1.1).

Much of the research in traffic engineering and certainly much of that carried out by the Laboratory has a definite practical end in view. It is, therefore, very important that the results of research are passed on to those

Research Track, Crowthorne, showing experiment in progress on part of central area

PLATE 1.1

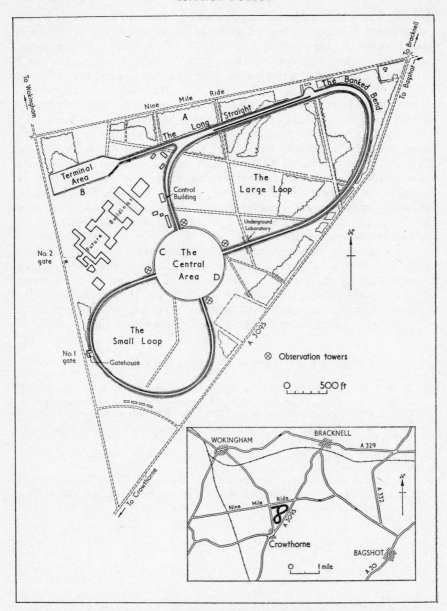

Fig. 1.1. Main features of Road Research Laboratory Track at Crowthorne and sites of proposed buildings

in a position to apply the results and that the findings are also embodied in standards of design and practice generally. A great deal of attention is given to this matter at the Laboratory and close contact is maintained with the Ministry of Transport, highway authorities and others who are directly concerned with traffic matters. The results of researches are published in various forms; these include the Laboratory's own publications, technical papers, road notes and annual reports and articles in the technical press.

Another important means of communicating results of research is by the presentation of papers to learned societies and similar bodies. The present book summarizes the work up to 1963 and gives references to these other publications where appropriate. The science of traffic engineering research continues to advance at an increasing rate, and owing to the time taken to produce a book of this kind, it is inevitable that the latest information cannot always be included. Readers should consult the Laboratory's annual reports and other publications if they wish to be brought up to date.

Research in traffic engineering is carried out in varying degrees in the more intensely motorized countries of the world. At the World Traffic Engineering Conference in Washington in August 1961, several papers on the need for scientific research in traffic engineering and the desirability of international co-operation in promoting it were discussed. There was general agreement that more scientific research was required. It was considered that it was desirable to promote co-operation between the research organizations in various countries.

As a result of the increased use of traffic engineering, facilities for training traffic engineers have been improving. Several universities now include courses in traffic engineering at undergraduate level and more advanced courses at post-graduate level are also available. For the technician and for those engineers who are unable to attend courses at a university the colleges of technology and technical colleges are helping by providing courses.

REFERENCES TO CHAPTER 1

1. DEPARTMENT OF SCIENTIFIC AND INDUSTRIAL RESEARCH, ROAD RESEARCH LABORATORY. *Research on Road Safety*. London, 1963 (H.M. Stationery Office).
2. MINISTER OF TRANSPORT, STEERING GROUP AND WORKING GROUP. *Traffic in Towns. A study of the long term problems of traffic in urban areas*. London, 1963 (H.M. Stationery Office).
3. GLANVILLE, Sir William. Traffic engineering extends its scope. *Traff. Engng & Control*, 1962, **4** (1), 31-3.
4. DEPARTMENT OF SCIENTIFIC AND INDUSTRIAL RESEARCH. *Road Research*, 1960. The report of the Road Research Board with the Report of the Director of Road Research. London, 1961 (H.M. Stationery Office).

Chapter 2

Traffic Flow

SYNOPSIS

Measurement of flow: methods of counting; automatic traffic counters (general description, sites, installation and maintenance of detectors and of counters); turning flows at junctions; distribution of wheel loads. Design and analysis of traffic counts. 50-point traffic census. Trends in traffic on all roads. Distribution of traffic over the road system. Forecasts of future numbers of vehicles.

INTRODUCTION

One of the most important characteristics of a stream of traffic is its *flow*, i.e. the number of vehicles which pass a fixed point in unit time. This is commonly referred to as "volume". Its direct measurement by counting vehicles is therefore fundamental to any systematic approach to road problems. Traffic censuses are needed for many purposes. For instance, they are required for deciding what road widths and junction designs are appropriate; what expenditure on a road is justified; and they are necessary in before-and-after studies of the effect of changes on accidents or delays.

Flows are usually measured by hand or by automatic counters at selected points on the road network. It is easy to collect too much data, or too little, and the design of an efficient programme of counting involves the choice of the appropriate technique and its use in the most economical manner. These points in turn depend on the information required in the work and the desire for accuracy in the results. The arrangement of counts and the analysis of results from them are discussed in some detail in this chapter. Particular attention is paid to the various methods of sampling, since it is very often too expensive to carry out continuous counts at all the points of interest in a project.

A continuous census of traffic flow at 50 points on roads in Great Britain was started in 1956. It covers all roads except motorways and un-classified roads, and the results are used to give information on the hourly, daily, weekly, seasonal and long-term variations in the amount of travel. The continuing data from such permanent censuses are of great value in economic and planning problems.

This chapter also deals briefly with two aspects of traffic behaviour which are closely allied to traffic counting. The traffic distribution at a junction is really a very simple origin-destination pattern but, because of the very short distances involved, turning movements at a junction are usually studied by techniques very similar to those used when making manual counts. Secondly, a convenient method of estimating the distribution of loads on a road, which has an important bearing on pavement design, is to make a classified count and then to assume a distribution of wheel loads for the vehicles in each category.

5

MEASUREMENT OF FLOW

Methods of counting

The simplest method of measuring traffic flow is by means of counts made by observers stationed at the roadside (see Plate 2.1), but for long period counts the expense of manual counting is prohibitive and alternative methods in which use is made of automatic counters are necessary.

Fig. 2.1 shows a typical form used for manual counts. The vehicle classification used should not be more complicated than is required for the job on hand. Normally not more than about ten classes of vehicle should be distinguished, otherwise more enumerators may be needed. Simple

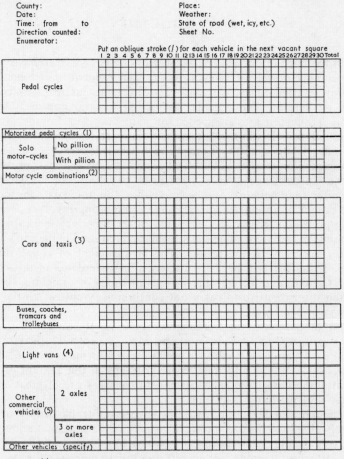

Fig. 2.1. Typical traffic census form

definitions of the classes of vehicle should be chosen, bearing in mind the ability of the enumerators to follow them.

Using this type of form, with up to about ten classes of vehicle, a normal enumerator (e.g. one employed on casual labour from the Employment Exchange) can deal with up to about 800 vehicles per hour, but it is best not to exceed 600 per hour. Intelligent enumerators can, for short periods, count with adequate accuracy up to 2000 vehicles per hour.

Re-settable hand-held counters, usually called hand tallies, are a useful aid to manual counts where a limited number of vehicle classifications is sufficient. These hand tallies consist of a four-figure counter unit actuated by the movement of a push-button. The counters can be used singly or can be linked together in multiple banks as shown in Plate 2.2. The single hand tally is most frequently used for a straightforward count of total flow on a road; for example, when carrying out a comparative check count at an automatic counter site. The multiple hand tally is commonly used for taking a classified count of total flow while other data are being collected, e.g. vehicle speeds or transverse positions. It can also be used in counting and classifying the opposing traffic stream in a journey-time survey by the moving-observer method (see Chapter 3). Vehicles overtaking or being overtaken by the test vehicle can also be counted in the same way.

Automatic counters can be used continuously over long periods and will count the number of axles passing a given point for a fraction of the expenditure in money and manpower required for a manual count. However, it is not yet possible to classify traffic with automatic counters, so that supplementary manual counts must be made when information of this nature is required. The greatest use made of traffic counters has been in the measurement of long-term trends in flow at "permanent" counter sites.

The advantages and disadvantages of automatic counters may be summarized as follows:

Advantages
They cost less and require less labour for counts of 24 hours or more.

Disadvantages
They do not classify vehicles according to type.
They require a certain amount of skilled attention.
They are uneconomic for short counts.

For unclassified counts when more than a "spot check" is wanted the use of automatic counters is desirable. When vehicles need to be classified, it may be worth using a counter to obtain the total flow and to supplement this by manual counts to give the proportions of each type of vehicle.

Automatic traffic counters

GENERAL DESCRIPTION

The essentials of an automatic traffic counter are a means of detecting the passage of a vehicle and a device for counting. Detectors fall into several categories and these are briefly described below:

(1) *Positive contact detector.* In this type of detector the passage of a wheel causes two metal contacts to touch and complete an electric

circuit. Positive contact detectors are difficult to maintain and are rarely used for simple traffic counting.

(2) *Pneumatic detector*. When a wheel crosses one of these detectors an air impulse is sent along the tube at the speed of sound and is used to operate some form of diaphragm switch attached to the end of the detector.

(3) *Hydraulic detector*. Operating in somewhat the same manner as a pneumatic detector, these detectors are best used to detect slow moving vehicles. They are not very satisfactory for detecting vehicles travelling at high speed.

(4) *Magnetic detector*. The vehicle is detected by its effect on the magnetic flux linked with a coil placed in the road surface. Some detectors use the earth's magnetic field; others produce an alternating field with the same coil or a closely adjacent one. The detectors are primarily for permanent installation and are especially useful where snow is common.

(5) *Photoelectric detector*. Light sensitive cells record the interruptions in a beam of light crossing the road. Because of their power requirements and need for accurate alignment these detectors usually form part of a permanent installation.

(6) *Wire detector*. The passage of a wheel sends sound waves down a wire stretched across the road. The wire terminates in a sensitive capsule which translates the sound waves into electrical impulses.

(7) *Capacitor detector*. The weight of a wheel mechanically deforms a coaxial cable or similar strip across the road, causing a change in capacity which is recorded electronically.

(8) *Radar detector*. Moving vehicles in a beam of radio waves are detected by the shift in the frequency of the reflected energy from them.

(9) *Ultrasonic detector*. Pulses emitted by an overhead ultrasonic generator are reflected back from the roof of a vehicle as it passes underneath instead of from the road surface. A receiver adjacent to the generator detects the reduced time taken for the pulse to return.

(10) *Infra-red detector*. Vehicles interrupt a beam of infra-red light reflected on to a photocell from a portion of the road surface illuminated by an overhead infra red lamp.

Since simplicity and reliability are two of the main considerations in the day-to-day operation of portable traffic counters, most use pneumatic detectors consisting of a high quality carbon-black rubber tube of nominal dimensions, $\frac{1}{2}$-inch external diameter and $\frac{1}{4}$-inch internal diameter.

The general requirements of a portable traffic counter are that it should be reliable, easy to handle, economical in power consumption and able to operate for at least one week without attention. Two main types are in use, those which show a simple accumulating total to be recorded by hand and those which automatically record the count at known intervals.

The SYX-RRL Vehicle Counter No. 4A (see Plate 2.3) is an example of the simple accumulating instrument. Impulses from the detector strike a light beryllium-copper diaphragm supported, but not clamped, in a circular housing. Resting on the other side of the diaphragm is a light bow-spring carrying a silver contact. As the diaphragm moves it carries this contact towards another attached to the housing. The initial gap separating the contacts can be adjusted by rotating a spring-loaded cam connected to a knob on top of the counter. The strength of the air impulse depends on the weight and speed of the vehicle, and may close the switch for periods between six and 30 milliseconds.

The counter is powered by two 6-volt lantern cells inverted in the battery compartment and held securely by a rotating clamp. When the contacts close they energize an electromagnet which attracts a spring-loaded pivoted armature carrying a pawl. The pawl drives a small ratchet wheel attached to the counter unit itself which is so arranged that, as the magnet releases, a movement of one tooth on the ratchet increases the number displayed by half a unit. Thus each axle detected records as half a unit and the total shown is in nominal vehicles or axles/2. The counter assembly and batteries are contained in a cast aluminium case which has a small glass window through which the counter may be read.

The Streeter Amet RCH counter (see Plate 2.4) is an example of those instruments which automatically record the count at known intervals. Impulses from the pneumatic detector move a light beryllium–copper diaphragm in the same way as in the simple accumulating counter, but in this case each alternate closure of the contacts advances a bank of four embossed printing wheels by one unit. The counter is powered by a 6-volt lead acid accumulator housed in the lower part of the counter case. A $2\frac{1}{4}$-inch wide paper tape is arranged to pass over the printing wheels, and every hour a spring-loaded hammer sandwiches the paper tape between an inked ribbon and the printing wheels. In this way the reading on the wheels underneath the tape is recorded on the upper surface of the paper. Two further printing wheels are included in the same assembly as the counting wheels; one of the two wheels is marked with the hours up to 12 and the other is marked alternately a.m. and p.m., so that the hour to which the count relates is also recorded on the paper strip. The counter is re-set to zero immediately after each total has been printed.

A similar recording counter which will print every $\frac{1}{4}$-hour is also available. In this model the counter is re-set and the hour wheel is advanced at the end of each hour, but intermediate printings are made each $\frac{1}{4}$-hour. Thus the count recorded in any $\frac{1}{4}$-hour can be obtained by differencing the successive readings.

The Fischer and Porter traffic counter (see Plate 2.5) punches cumulative $\frac{1}{4}$-hour counts in code on a special paper tape $2\frac{1}{8}$ inches wide; the counter uses the normal type of pneumatic detector and diaphragm unit and is powered by a 7.5 volt battery which lasts for several months. Translators are available for converting the special punched tape into punched cards or standard punched paper tape so that the results can be analysed by punched card machinery or by a computer.

The Decca Trafficometry system includes equipment for giving a continuous display of traffic flow in vehicles per hour (see Plate 2.6). Detector impulses from a pneumatic detector and diaphragm unit are sent over a pair of rented G.P.O. telephone lines to a convenient building where the equipment can be housed. Each impulse is weighted by the negative exponential of a number proportional to the time since the impulse occurred; the indicated flow, which can be recorded on a chart (see Plate 2.7), is proportional to the sum of the weighted impulses. The flow at time T minutes is:

$$\frac{30}{a} \sum_i e^{-[(T-t_i)/a]}$$

where a is a constant and the t_i ($i = 1, 2, 3, \ldots$) are the times in minutes at which impulses occurred. The constant a is the effective time over which counts are averaged and the value normally used for it is 10 minutes.

SITES FOR AUTOMATIC TRAFFIC COUNTERS

Selection of the exact site for the instrument will depend to a large extent on the purpose for which the count is required. However, there is usually some latitude and a number of points should be borne in mind so that the detector may be installed in the most efficient position.

Axles rather than individual wheels should be counted and the tube must therefore be placed perpendicularly to the paths of all vehicles. Each wheel of a vehicle that passes obliquely over the detector will be counted as one axle; for this reason it is preferable to use a straight section of road free from junctions and sudden changes in width. Sites near side roads, factory entrances, sharp curves and where vehicles are likely to park or to queue (as, for instance, at the immediate approaches to traffic signals) are not very suitable. The vicinity of bus stops should also be avoided since the tube may inconvenience passengers as they alight from or board the bus, or a bus wheel may stop on the tube and prevent counting; moreover since the road at bus stops is often worn concave by constant braking, a tube stretched across the road at these places may not cling to the surface.

It is very much easier to instal a tube on bituminous materials than on concrete or on stone setts, and this should be borne in mind where a choice of surfacing exists. If a bituminous surfacing is selected, coarse projecting aggregates should be avoided where possible. It should also be borne in mind that some binders become so soft in summer that the tube may be almost completely buried with consequent loss of sensitivity.

In towns the counter is usually padlocked to a lamp post, tree or piece of street furniture situated as near as possible to the kerb. Detector tubes should not cross the footway, because pedestrians may trip over them. In this connexion particular care must be taken to eliminate loops where the tube comes up over the kerb. In rural areas the detector may be buried in a shallow trench where it passes across the verge. If a tree or post is not available the counter can be fastened to a stake specially driven in for the purpose. Care should be taken to avoid sunken power cables if a stake is used; a red light should be provided at night to warn pedestrians of the obstruction.

Before traffic counters are installed the agreement of the highway authority should be obtained. The Ministry of Transport is the highway authority for all trunk roads. County Councils and County Borough Councils are the highway authorities for all other roads in their areas and they are often appointed agent authorities for the trunk roads by the Ministry of Transport. In other areas, where the arrangements are usually more complex, enquiries have to be made locally to find out who is the responsible authority. The police should also be informed of the whereabouts of counters, since the police are frequently the first to learn of damage to the installation.

INSTALLATION AND MAINTENANCE OF DETECTORS

The detector is fastened every three feet by canvas and brass clips (see Plate 2.8) which are in turn nailed to the road surface by hardened cast-steel masonry nails. The tube is stretched by about 10 per cent of its length so that it clings to the road surface, the tension being taken up by special end fixings which are also nailed to the road.

TERMINATION OF DETECTORS. The passage of a wheel (or axle) across the tube sends air impulses in both directions along the tube. If the end of the tube remote from the counter is blocked, a reflection from this blockage returns down the tube and may re-operate the counter, especially if the vehicle is a heavy one; in a similar fashion a reflection is received from an open-ended tube. Because any reflection may cause overcounting the tube has to be terminated in such a way as to prevent reflections of sufficient size to operate the instrument. This is done by inserting into the end of the tube a brass plug about half an inch long drilled with an axial hole. It was found by experiment that this hole should be about $0 \cdot 080$-inch diameter (drill No. 46) for detectors with $\frac{1}{4}$-inch bore, and that if it were materially larger or smaller overcounting would result. Consequently, a detector is no longer reliable when it contains dirt or water, or when the wall is completely pierced at any point.

PREPARATION OF DETECTOR. A suitable length of tube must first be "blown through" to remove dirt and, if necessary, given an application of French chalk. The termination end is then prepared before the detector is fixed to the road. The end of the tube should be bound with one or two turns of insulating tape before pushing the termination plug in, and care must be taken to avoid air leaks past the termination plug when the bound end is clamped in the end fixing. It is important that each terminated tube should be tested for these air leaks. When the intermediate fixings and the second end fixing have been strung on the tube it is ready for installation.

INSTALLATION PROCEDURE. Two men are required, with a 2-lb or 4-lb hammer, a claw case-opener, a supply of cast-steel masonry nails, No. 14 Rawlplugs, and red flags. It is dangerous for one man to attempt to lay a detector single-handed.

The terminal end fixing is secured first in a position where it will not be under water in wet weather. The detector is then stretched across the road so that it is perpendicular to the line of movement of the vehicles. One man stands on the tube to prevent it moving, and diverts the traffic and the other man nails down the second end fixing. This end fixing should be placed as close to the kerb as possible provided the tube is not kinked as it goes up to the counter, and there is not a loop of the tube which could be dangerous to pedestrians. The tube is then stretched until the required tension is obtained, and held in that position by a "collar" of insulating tape bound round it just behind the second end fixing. The intermediate fixings are then spaced out and nailed down.

Masonry nails $2\frac{1}{2}$ inches long should be used for end fixings in high quality road surfaces. On some country roads, a 6-inch wire nail can be hammered in at the edge of the road to give a better grip. A third method of fastening the end fixings is to enlarge the fixing holes to $\frac{11}{32}$-inch diameter and to use $\frac{5}{16}$-inch diameter 4-inch long galvanized-wire pipe-nails.

The intermediate fixings are fastened down with masonry nails of suitable length for the surfacing concerned. If the surfacing is laid on a concrete foundation an overlength nail will bend, causing the surfacing to crack.

When replacing a tube it is usually easier to use the existing nail holes than to make new ones. No. 14 size Rawplugs of the appropriate length slipped into existing holes provide a secure grip.

When a tube has been cut it is best to take up all the fixings and re-lay a complete detector. Intermediate clips and end fastenings can be re-used, but no attempt should be made to pass a replacement tube through clips still nailed to the road.

If a detector has to be moved slightly, or the intermediate fixings are relocated, the old nail holes should be filled with some form of bituminous compound.

WEEKLY MAINTENANCE. The detector should receive a thorough check once a week. Two men are required with a small air pump fitted with the special adaptor designed to push into a detector.

One man disconnects the detector from the counter and "blows through" with the pump from the counter end, the second man observes whether any dirt or water is discharged and ensures that the termination plug is clear. He should then cover the hole in the termination plug with his finger while air is again pumped into the tube. Any leaks around the termination plug or along the tube can be detected when the air escapes through them.

If the location of a cut in the tube is not immediately obvious it can be found by pumping air into the tube while the second man stands on it, first at the termination end and then in steps successively nearer the counter end. When he has passed the cut, the loss of air will cease.

TEMPORARY REPAIRS. Normally a cut tube should be replaced immediately. If the cut is very small and a replacement tube is not readily available the cut may be bound with adhesive tape as a strictly temporary measure for a day or two at the most. Although the tape may last longer in some circumstances, counts made in these conditions cannot be considered absolutely reliable.

STICKY TUBES. Overcounting will also result if the inside of the tube has become sticky and the walls adhere together after the passage of a wheel. This fault can be detected by treading on the tube and listening for the "snap" as the walls separate, and it can be cured by blowing a small quantity of French chalk through the tube. Care must be taken that excess chalk is not left in the tube, where it tends to roll into pellets and block the termination plug.

INSTALLATION AND MAINTENANCE OF COUNTERS

When installing the counter the first step after laying the detector is to insert the battery and switch the counter on.

CONTACT GAP. The adjustment of the contact gap is critical to the sensitivity of the counter and must be carefully checked. The correct setting varies from site to site and counter to counter and can only be found by experiment. However, it usually lies between eight and 15 thousandths of an inch. After making certain that the counter has been *switched on* the contact gap should be reduced until the counter operates, thus giving the effective zero position. The gap is then opened to the desired amount, each "click" usually representing one thousandth of an inch. In practice it is probably best to set the contact gap to ten thousandths of an inch as a starting point when first installing the counter. After connecting the instrument to the detector and securing it with a jubilee clip (which may be necessary in areas where children are likely to pull the detector off the spigot) the operation of the counter should be observed. If the gap is too small the counter will overcount, particularly on heavy vehicles. If the gap is too large the counter will fail to operate when light vehicles pass over the detector.

Contact gaps must be set to miss bicycles but to include fast light cars and it is important that this point should be checked.

CHECK COUNT. A check count should be made before the counter is left; this will show whether the counter is working satisfactorily.

During a check count the performance of the counter is compared with a manual count lasting for 15 minutes or 100 vehicles, whichever is the quicker. The manual count is made in units of nominal two-axled vehicles, any halves being carried over either mentally or on paper. If the counter is working correctly the totals should agree at light flows, while at heavier flows the counter reading may be slightly lower than the manual check because of coincidental wheels on the detector. The counter total should never be higher than the manual check; if this occurs then the counter is overcounting either by multiple pulses from heavy vehicles or by including bicycles. Solo motorcycles are of such varying weights that their effect on the counter cannot be predicted. When solo motorcycles pass during a check count the counter should be watched so that the manual total can be increased by 0, 1 or 2 axles depending on the reaction of the counter. Some genuine differences will also occur if the wheels of lightly sprung vehicles bounce over the detector on a bumpy surface, but a satisfactory check count will rarely show differences of more than three axles in 100 between manual and counter results.

The check count is the most reliable method of testing a counter as it is a direct measure of counting efficiency, and it will reveal errors which are not always apparent on casual inspection. However, the counter should be watched during the check count, as this will help to diagnose the fault if the check count is unsatisfactory.

INSPECTION REPORTS. The results of the check count should be recorded on an inspection report such as is shown in Fig. 2.2. Space is provided for details of the site as well as the date and time of the check count. The information provided by inspection reports is of great value in subsequent analysis of the records and operators should be asked to fill in these forms carefully and accurately.

ERRORS DUE TO CHECK COUNT. At sites where the traffic flow is very low it may be necessary to run a vehicle across the detector in order to study the counter in operation. In these cases the number of extra vehicles recorded on the counter during the check may be large compared with the normal flow, and sufficient notes should be made on the inspection form to allow a correction to be made to that day's total.

BICYCLE CHECK. Counters must be set to miss bicycles but to include fast, light cars, and it it is important that this point should be checked. There are, however, some sites where the flow of bicycles is heavy in the morning and evening but very light during the day when installations are usually

ROAD RESEARCH LABORATORY D.S.I.R.
AUTOMATIC TRAFFIC COUNTER INSPECTION REPORT

DISTRICT		SITE NUMBER	
DATE		DAY OF WEEK	
WEATHER		DIRECTION OF FLOW	

COUNTER SERIAL NUMBER				
CONTACT GAP		CHECK COUNT, IN AXLES DIVIDED BY 2		
		COUNTER	MANUAL	TIME
	START			
CHECK TUBE	END			
CHECK FIXINGS	TOTAL			
CHECK TERMINATION	IS COUNTER RECORDING BICYCLES			

INSPECTION CARRIED OUT BY	

THIS SECTION TO BE FILLED IN ONLY IF THE COUNTER IS
ADJUSTED OR REPLACED

COUNTER SERIAL NUMBER		2ND. CHECK COUNT, IN AXLES DIVIDED BY 2		
CONTACT GAP		COUNTER	MANUAL	TIME
REMARKS :-	START			
	END			
	TOTAL			
	IS COUNTER RECORDING BICYCLES ?			

IF COUNTER IS STILL NOT WORKING PROPERLY, RECORD FURTHER COUNTS
OVERLEAF.

Fig. 2.2. Counter inspection report

made. In these cases it is an advantage if a bicycle can be taken as part of the equipment for the check.

RECORDING COUNTERS. When recording counters are installed it is necessary to set the clock mechanism to the correct time. The recording mechanism should be checked to see that it is working correctly and that it has an adequate supply of paper.

LEAVING THE COUNTER. Before leaving the counter, the instrument should be chained to the street furniture or to a specially installed stake, care being taken that no loops are left in the chain. A check should be made to see that both ends of the chain and the counter hasp have been included in the padlock, it is possible to omit one by mistake and find that the counter has not been fastened down at all. A check should also be made to see that the detector tube near the counter has not been pulled up into a dangerous loop. Finally, it is advisable to make sure that the counter is still working when everything is securely fastened.

INSPECTION OF COUNTER ON SITE. (See Plate 2.9). The operation of the counter should be checked at least once a week using the inspection report described earlier. A check count should be made before altering the counter in any way. This will show whether the counter is working satisfactorily and, if it is not, will give some indication of the accuracy of the counts immediately preceding the inspection. Thus a check count must be recorded even when the counter is obviously not working correctly (although not, of course, if it has failed completely). If the manual count is satisfactory the contact gap should be checked as a precaution. This is done by reducing the gap step by step until the counter operates and counting the number of steps required. If the gap is found to be satisfactory, that is to say within the range 8-15 thousandths of an inch, it is returned to its original position and the remainder of the inspection report is completed. This will involve an inspection of the tube, its fixings, the termination plug and the action of the counter when bicycles pass. If the contact gap is not within the normal range, particularly if it is too small, it may indicate faulty operation of the diaphragm or relays.

If the counter is not operating correctly then the fault must be traced and corrected and then another check count must be made to find out whether or not the remedial measures have been successful. While this is being done it may be necessary to put the counter out of action temporarily and during these periods a manual count should be maintained. At the end of the inspection the counter readings may be adjusted by appropriate stamping on the tube, or, if the required adjustment is too great to be dealt with in this way, a note of the vehicles missed should be made on the inspection report.

The faults that occur at a counter installation can be subdivided into three main groups—under-counting, over-counting and complete failure. Likely causes of these conditions are listed below in a suggested order of checking, although in some cases the fault will be obvious when watching the counter in action. In the event of a faulty count, it is most likely that the fault is in the detector and this should be carefully checked before interfering with the counter. Details of the fault should be noted on the inspection report.

Causes of under-counting:
(1) A cut in the detector.
(2) A partially blocked detector—this can be caused by dirt, French chalk pellets, water (especially if the termination plug is in a puddle during wet weather, in which case it should be moved slightly), a kink in the detector, or a squashed end fixing.
(3) Contact gap too large.
(4) Dirty contacts in the diaphragm unit.
(5) French chalk, rubber dust or dirt behind the diaphragm.
(6) A deformed bow spring.
(7) A kinked or deformed diaphragm which may "snap" like a tin lid.
(8) A faulty counting unit.
(9) Batteries that are run down (most likely with counters that use dry batteries).
(10) Relays that are not working or are out of adjustment (recording counters only).

Causes of over-counting:
(1) An incorrect termination to the tube. The termination plug may be either blocked or missing or there may be air leaks past it when clamped in the end fixing.

(2) A cut in the detector.
(3) A "sticky" detector.
(4) Contact gap too small.
(5) A kinked or deformed diaphragm.

Causes of complete failure:
(1) Counter switched off or a fuse blown.
(2) Battery discharged or disconnected.
(3) Counter mechanism jammed.
(4) Discontinuity or earth fault in the wiring.

Major counter repairs at the site are likely to be unsatisfactory and it is recommended that a faulty counter should be replaced by a spare while it is being repaired in a properly equipped workshop or by the manufacturer. It is unwise to leave a counter open longer than is necessary when making a roadside inspection; passing vehicles stir up dust which is likely to settle between the contacts or in the counter mechanism.

Before the counter is left the battery should be checked to see that it will last until the next inspection. The most satisfactory test for the 6-volt lantern batteries used in simple accumulating counters is to apply an ammeter (10 amps full-scale reading) directly across the terminals for a short while. A new battery will give about six amps. Counters will usually operate on batteries giving as little as three amps on test. Batteries giving less than three amps should be discarded. In addition the batteries should be visually inspected for swelling or signs of "bleeding" which would readily cause corrosion of the case and contact rings.

On some makes of lantern batteries the brass-strip positive contact is long enough to project beyond the side of the battery, particularly when it is pressed down flat. Batteries in this condition should not be used as the projecting positive contact may touch the counter case and short out the battery. The fault can be corrected by folding the end of the strip back upon itself.

Lead-acid accumulators can be checked by measuring the specific gravity of the acid but it is usually simpler to change the batteries at regular intervals.

Recording counters often have hand-wound clocks and it is important that these should be wound at each inspection. Regulation of the clock mechanism may also be required and it has been found that a portable electronic watch timer that produces a printed record simplifies this task considerably.

Turning flows at junctions

It is rarely possible to position a number of automatic counter detectors so that each records a separate stream of turning traffic. Counts of turning flows are therefore usually carried out manually.

Where the junction is small, as with a simple T-junction or cross-roads, the observers can be stationed at ground level and a continuous count can be made of each turning stream. Multiple hand tallies are useful for this purpose.

At roundabouts or complex intersections the observations are best made from a high viewpoint. One method of collecting information on directional patterns involves tracing single vehicles through the intersection. An observer is required for each arm, although all arms need not be studied at the same time. For ten minutes, say, vehicles on an arm are selected, classified and followed through, a fresh vehicle being selected as soon as the last one is finished with. Then for five minutes, say, the total flow on that arm is counted. This cycle is repeated throughout the study period, and the sample counts are expanded to a figure representing the whole period. The proportions of the various turning movements are derived from the data obtained from the selected vehicles. The individual vehicles may be timed as they are traced through the intersection to provide journey time data.

Distribution of wheel loads

In investigating the performance of pavements it is necessary to know the magnitude as well as the number of wheel loads of vehicles using the road. The distribution of wheel loads can be obtained by stopping and weighing a sample of the vehicles. It is not usually necessary to weigh cars as their effect on the road is negligible when compared with the effect of commercial vehicles.

In studies at Baldersby on A.1, and Cambridge, Gloucester on A.38 portable weighbridges calibrated up to 10 000 lbs were used to measure the loads carried by the nearside wheels of commercial vehicles. The loads on the offside wheels were assumed to be the same as those on the nearside wheels.

Because this method is laborious and delays vehicles, suggestions were made, based on the results from these two studies, for simplified methods that could be adopted for future surveys requiring an estimate of wheel loads. It was concluded that the accuracy required in the results governed the amount of weighing to be done and the following three methods, in order of increasing accuracy, were suggested for future surveys:

(1) The wheel load frequency diagram for vehicles of a given axle type (see Fig. 2.3 for details) is assumed to be the same as the mean of the wheel load frequency diagrams observed at Baldersby and Cambridge.

(2) The wheel load frequency diagrams for vehicles of axle type 1.1. and 1.2 are obtained by method (1). A sample of all other commercial vehicles (about a quarter of the total commercial vehicles) are weighed.

(3) All commercial vehicles are weighed.

A classified count for short periods throughout the day to give the proportions of the various axle types in the total flow is required if method (1) or (2) is used.

Some of the wheel load frequencies obtained at Baldersby and Cambridge are given in Fig. 2.4.

Apparatus[1] has now been developed at the Laboratory which automatically weighs vehicles as they travel along the road at normal speeds. The equipment consists of a weighbridge installed in the road and supported on four load cells fitted with resistance strain gauges. The output from the strain gauges when a vehicle crosses the weighbridge is fed to a reflecting galvanometer to give a deflection which is proportional to the load applied. An optical system associated with the galvanometer is used to count the

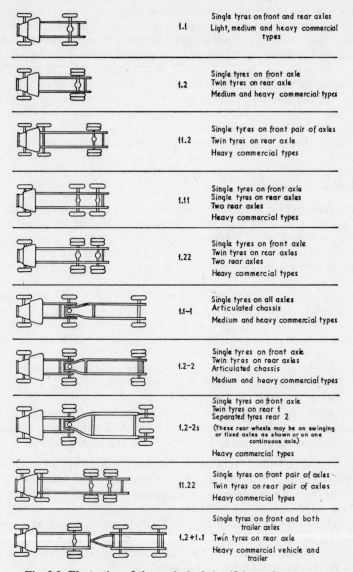

	1.1	Single tyres on front and rear axles Light, medium and heavy commercial types
	1.2	Single tyres on front axle Twin tyres on rear axle Medium and heavy commercial types
	11.2	Single tyres on front pair of axles Twin tyres on rear axle Heavy commercial types
	1.11	Single tyres on front axle Single tyres on rear axles Two rear axles Heavy commercial types
	1.22	Single tyres on front axle Twin tyres on rear axles Two rear axles Heavy commercial types
	1.1-1	Single tyres on all axles Articulated chassis Medium and heavy commercial types
	1.2-2	Single tyres on front axle Twin tyres on rear axles Articulated chassis Medium and heavy commercial types
	1.2-2s	Single tyres on front axle Twin tyres on rear 1 Separated tyres rear 2 (These rear wheels may be on swinging or fixed axles as shown or on one continuous axle) Heavy commercial types
	11.22	Single tyres on front pair of axles Twin tyres on rear pair of axles Heavy commercial types
	1.2+1.1	Single tyres on front and both trailer axles Twin tyres on rear axle Heavy commercial vehicle and trailer

Fig. 2.3. Illustration of the method of classifying axle types

number of wheel loads in predetermined weight groups. The equipment is
in two separate units: (1) The weighbridge, which is permanently installed
in the road at the point where the measurements have to be made, and (2)
the weight classifying and counting equipment, which is moved from site to
site as surveys are required. The equipment is battery operated as sites are
often quite far from a mains supply.

Sometimes it is necessary to know how wheel loads are distributed
transversely across the carriageway. This can be done by recording the
transverse positions of the wheels of each vehicle (to the nearest foot, say,)
and also its registration number, and weighing each vehicle as a separate

operation. A much simpler method, however, is to record transverse positions and vehicle types only, and to apply the previously determined distribution of wheel loads for each type of vehicle, to each transverse location.

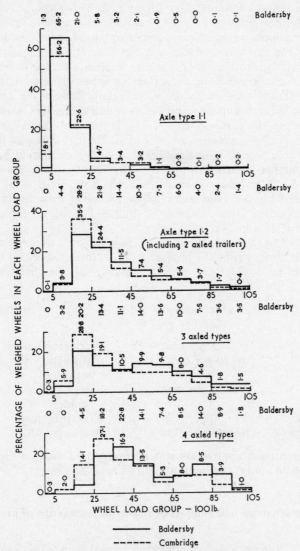

Fig. 2.4. Comparison of wheel load frequency diagrams measured at Baldersby and Cambridge—four vehicle categories

DESIGN AND ANALYSIS OF TRAFFIC COUNTS

Information and accuracy required

The first step is to select the vehicle classification that will be used. This may, for example, be pedal cycles, motorcycles, cars, commercial vehicles and public-service vehicles. If, however, only a general indication of the usage of the road is required, a knowledge of the number of motor vehicles, either with or without a separate count of pedal cycles, would be sufficient. For purposes of estimating capacity it is necessary to be able to express the flow in "passenger car units" (see Chapter 6). This requires classification of the traffic into pedal cycles, light vehicles (motorcycles, cars and light commercial vehicles up to 30 cwt unladen) and heavy vehicles (public-service vehicles and commercial vehicles over 30 cwt unladen).

Before making a traffic count it is also necessary to decide whether one is interested in average flow, peak flow or some variant on these. As a general measure of road usage, the average daily flow, or the annual total, is recommended. For capacity and design studies, however, some measure of peak flow may be required. It would be uneconomic to design a road to carry comfortably the greatest amount of traffic that ever uses it, and it is often suggested, especially in the U.S.A., that a road should be designed for the 30th highest hourly flow per year. This is difficult to observe directly; in the U.S.A., factors have been derived which enable it to be estimated from average daily flow, but it is uncertain whether these factors can usefully be applied in Great Britain. A simpler definition of peak flow is suggested later (see p. 27).

It is difficult to say with any certainty how accurate an estimate of, say, average daily flow will be if obtained from counts at specified times. The best that can be done at present is to classify sampling methods on the following 5-point scale:

Category	Error exceeded with probability of 1 in 10	Interpretation
A	Up to 5 per cent	Very satisfactory
B	5 to 10 per cent	Satisfactory for all normal purposes
C	10 to 25 per cent	Good enough for a rough guide
D	25 to 50 per cent	Unsatisfactory
E	Over 50 per cent	Useless

For any particular application it is necessary to decide on the accuracy required and to select a sampling method accordingly.

Arrangement of counts and analysis of results for estimation of average daily flows

Solutions to the problem of estimating annual flow from sample counts are of two types. In the first place, the counts may be made sufficiently representative of the whole year, i.e. all times of day, all days of the week and all the seasons may occur in appropriate proportions. Secondly, the counts may not be representative of the whole year, this being allowed for in the analysis of the results by applying correcting factors. The first is, in theory, the better solution, but it may be difficult to apply in practice.

For both types of solution, it is desirable that counts should be spread out over the year, rather than confined to a few days, in order to avoid errors due to the effect of such factors as weather. The extent to which this can be done, however, is limited by the practical difficulty of arranging a large number of short counts spread over a period.

Typical applications of the above methods are given in the following examples.

Example 1

If, in order to estimate the average daily flow at a particular point over a year, traffic is counted for two periods of seven days, six months apart, the "obvious" estimate of average daily flow is $\frac{1}{14}$ (flow in week one + flow in week two). No corrections for hour-to-hour or day-to-day variations are required since all hours and days are included in their right proportions. If the seasonal pattern approximates to a sine curve then the pattern will be almost eliminated from the results. In these conditions the estimate has, therefore, the advantage of being free from bias and can be arrived at without information about patterns.

Example 2

If the average daily flow over a year at a point in a rural area is to be estimated from a given total of 500 vehicles in the single hour from 1 to 2 p.m. on Tuesday 14th January, 1964, then the procedure is as follows:

Stage 1. Table 2.15 (p. 44) indicates that in January 1960 the hour 1 to 2 p.m. on Mondays to Fridays contained $5 \cdot 7$ per cent of the day's total traffic. Assuming that the pattern of traffic in 1964 on the rural road concerned is the same as the pattern for all roads in 1960, the estimate of flow for 14th January 1964 is

$$500 \times \frac{100}{5 \cdot 7} = 8772$$

Stage 2. It is estimated that in winter on the road concerned, Saturday traffic is equal to that on a weekday*, while that on Sunday is only three quarters as great. The week's total traffic is therefore estimated as

$$8772 \times 6\tfrac{3}{4} = \underline{\;}59\,211$$

Table 2.13 (p. 42) shows that motor vehicle flow in January at a typical rural site is about 71 per cent of the annual average. The average weekly total for 1964 is therefore estimated as

$$59\,211 \times \frac{100}{71} = 83\,396$$

Multiplying by 52 and rounding off, the estimated number of vehicles using this road in 1964 is 4.3 million.

There is almost no limit to the possible arrangements of counts such as the two just described. The choice in any given circumstances will depend on a variety of factors, such as accuracy required, availability of automatic counters, travelling time to site, type and amount of labour, and whether or not results are required quickly. Suggestions for estimating the average daily flow over a year, either with or without classification by type of vehicle, are given in Table 2.1. For each method the table gives an accuracy category, as defined earlier. This indicates the likely errors when the method is

*In this chapter the word "weekdays" denotes Mondays to Fridays.

TABLE 2.1

Methods of estimating average daily flow
I. Using manual counters only.

Method	Accuracy classification	Possible variations	Comments on analysis	Remarks
(i) Count for 1 hour, on a weekday, between 9 a.m. and 6 p.m.	D	The count could be lengthened by any convenient amount	(i) is similar to example 1 in the text.	These methods and II (i) are the only ones available if an answer is required at short notice.
(ii) Count on one weekday from 6 a.m. to 10 p.m.	C or D		For (iii) estimate week's total as 5 × Friday + Saturday + Sunday.	
(iii) Count from 6 a.m. to 10 p.m. on a successive Friday, Saturday and Sunday.	C	Could be extended to 4 days by including Monday.		
(iv) Count from 6. a.m. to 10 p.m. on 7 consecutive days.	C			
(v) As (i) to (iv) but carried out on 4 occasions at 3 monthly intervals.	C	The number of occasions could be 2, 3 or 6 instead of 4, with appropriate alteration in spacing.	As I(i) to I(iv) to estimate weekly totals; then average the four weekly totals.	
(vi)	C			
(vii) (For (i) and (ii) use different hours and days).	B			
(viii)	B			
(ix) Count from 6 a.m. to 10 p.m. every 52nd day for a year (7 counts in all).	B			These methods are especially useful when counts have to be made at a number of points in the same area. Numerous variations on these methods could be prepared to meet special conditions but it is impossible to list them all here.
(x) Count from 6 a.m. to 10 p.m. every 26 days for a year (14 counts in all).	A or B			
(xi) Count from 6 a.m. to 10 p.m. every 13 days for a year (28 counts in all).	A			
(xii) As (ix) but divide the part of the day of interest into 7 equal parts (e.g. of 2 hours each). On each of the 7 days count successively parts 1, 4, 7, 3, 6, 2, 5.	C	Other similar arrangements of parts are equally suitable e.g. 4, 7, 3, 6, 2, 5, 1.		

TABLE 2.1

Methods of estimating average daily flow. (continued)

Method	Accuracy classification	Possible variations	Comments on analysis	Remarks
(xiii) As (x) but divide the day into 14 equal parts and count successively parts 1, 4, 7, 10, 13, 2, 5, 8, 11, 14, 3, 6, 9, 12.	C			These methods are especially useful when counts have to be made at a number of points in the same area. Numerous variations on these methods could be prepared to meet special conditions but it is impossible to list them all here.
(xiv) As (xi) but again divide the day into 14 equal parts and count successively parts, 1, 6, 11, 2, 7, 12, 3, 8, 13, 4, 9, 14, 5, 10, and then repeat this cycle.	B			

II. Using automatic counters only.

Method	Accuracy classification	Possible variations	Comments on analysis	Remarks
(i) Continuous count for 1 week	C		Expand the whole year as in stage 3 of example 1.	
(ii) 4 continuous counts of 1 week at 3-monthly intervals.	B	Replace 4 counts by 2, 3, or 6 at appropriate intervals.		
(iii) Continuous count for 1 year	A			

TABLE 2.1

Methods of estimating average daily flow. (continued)

III. Combination of manual and automatic counts

Method	Accuracy classification	Possible variations	Comments on analysis	Remarks
(i) to (xiv) As I, but with continuous automatic count for whole year.	A	The continuous count could be reduced to 1, 2, 3, 4 or 6 equally spaced 1-week counts. Accuracy would then be C, C, B B, B.	The manual counts should be analysed in the same way as in I(i) to I(xiv), but the results of this should be solely to give the average percentage composition of the traffic. The actual flows of each type of vehicle should be obtained by applying these percentages to the total flow obtained from the automatic count.	For automatic counts of less than a full year, the associated manual counts need not be taken while the counters are in place, though a useful check is obtained if they are.

NOTES: The total number of vehicles counted divided by the number of hours of counting gives the average hourly flow for the times of day covered. The hours 6 a.m. to 10 p.m. may be extended if desired, but usually it will be sufficient to add 10 per cent. for the night hours 10 p.m. to 6 a.m. Some of the above methods may be adapted when directional counts are required at junctions and the traffic is too heavy for all.

applied in reasonably favourable conditions on a moderately busy road. Although some of the methods are in a low category as regards accuracy, they are included because if they are applied on a number of occasions on the same road the average result will be more accurate; for example, it will be one category higher if it is applied four times.

It should be emphasized that these measures of accuracy are not universally applicable; there may be circumstances in which a method classified as C may be relied on to give perfectly satisfactory results. Each case should be considered individually in the light of local conditions.

As regards the methods in group III (combination of automatic and manual counts) the accuracy category A refers to the estimate of all types of vehicle combined. For individual types the accuracy will depend on the method, and no reliable guidance can at present be given.

It should be noted that each accuracy category covers quite a wide range of accuracies; thus, for example, method I(iv) is obviously better than method I(iii), yet both are classified as C.

Choice of method

Each method given in Table 2.1 is, in certain circumstances, the best one to use. It would not be easy to list the combinations of circumstances appropriate to each method, but some of the relevant considerations are mentioned in the table.

Methods I(xii), I(xiii) and I(xiv) are especially suitable if results are required for a number of sites in the same area since, by displacing the list of times by appropriate amounts, schedules can be evolved which permit the enumerators to visit a number of sites on the same day without much waste of time. For example, suppose there were seven sites (a, b, c, d, e, f and g) and method I(xii) was chosen, then the counts would be arranged as shown in Table 2.2.

TABLE 2.2

Method of counting traffic at seven sites over a period of seven days

| | | | Part of day | | | | |
		1st	2nd	3rd	4th	5th	6th	7th
	1	a	b	c	d	e	f	g
	2	e	f	g	a	b	c	d
	3	b	c	d	e	f	g	a
Day	4	f	g	a	b	c	d	e
	5	c	d	e	f	g	a	b
	6	g	a	b	c	d	e	f
	7	d	e	f	g	a	b	c

If one enumerator carries out all counts in the 1st, 3rd, 5th and 7th parts of the day and another those in the 2nd, 4th and 6th parts, then only 14 man-days work are required to cover all seven sites.

Similar considerations may make methods I(xi) especially suitable. One man or a team could, by proper arrangement of their programme, apply method (ix) at about 30 places per year.

These methods could also be applied when directional counts are required at junctions, each stream being treated as a separate site. However, more satisfactory methods are available in these circumstances. Since there is no travelling time between the various streams at a junction, there is no serious difficulty in changing from one stream to another at frequent intervals. It is suggested that one of methods I(i) to I(xiv) be selected and each hour's counting be divided equally between the various streams. For example, if method I(iii) were used at a cross-roads where the traffic entering on the four arms had to be dealt with separately, then the counts could be arranged as shown in Table 2.3.

TABLE 2.3

Method of counting traffic at an intersection where four streams are to be measured

Time	Stream number		
	Friday	Saturday	Sunday
6·00—6·15 a.m.	1	2	3
6·15—6·30	2	3	4
6·30—6·45	3	4	1
6·45—7·00	4	1	2
7·00—7·15	1	2	3
7·15—7·30	2	3	4
. . .	.	.	.
9·30—9·45 p.m.	3	4	1
9·45—10·00	4	1	2

The same order within the hour is maintained throughout a day, but is changed from day to day. The length of each count could be reduced from 15 to 10 minutes, leaving a 20-minute rest period each hour. When analysing the results of counts of this sort, it would be assumed that each part-hour total was representative of the hour as a whole. Thus in the above example, each quarter-hour total would be multiplied by four and thereafter treated as a one-hour total. The accuracy of the results will, of course, be somewhat less than if a full-hour's count were carried out.

Analysis of results

In many cases the way in which the results of the counts should be evaluated is clear. Table 2.1 gives some comments on the procedure to be adopted in certain cases, but it is more important to keep the underlying principles in mind. These may be expressed as follows:

Rule (i) Decide exactly what quantity is to be estimated, e.g. average daily flow during 1966.

Rule (ii) Apply any corrections to the observed rates of flow that may be required to remove any bias towards particular times of day, days of the week, or seasons.

It is suggested that since traffic on some Bank Holidays tends to be higher than usual and on others to be lower, it should normally be unnecessary to make any special allowance for these holidays in the analysis of the results. Counts on a limited number of days should, of course, avoid public holidays.

Estimation of peak flows

The first problem in the estimation of peak flow is to decide on a satisfactory definition of it, and the second is to find a suitable method of measuring it in practice.

To be acceptable, a definition of peak flow must, as far as possible, be consistent with present usage of the term, it must be inherently reasonable, and it must be capable of measurement without undue difficulty.

When the term peak flow is used in Great Britain, it usually refers to the highest hourly total recorded during a 7-day count made in August for the Ministry of Transport. Since traffic in August is usually very near the summer peak, this definition should give a figure fairly close to the flow during the busiest hour of the year. From this point of view, the definition is a reasonable one. However, it is not altogether satisfactory to define peak flow as the flow in one particular hour, since the weather and other variable influences may make the figure obtained unrepresentative of peak conditions. It is, therefore, suggested that a slightly modified definition should be used. If the average flow for each hour of the week were calculated over all possible consecutive 13-week periods, then the peak-hourly flow is defined as the highest average flow so obtained. For example, the peak-hourly flow might be the average of 13 flows between 8 and 9 p.m. on Sundays in June, July and August, if these were the busiest times and busiest months. This definition gives a figure which is closely related to that obtained by the census carried out by the Ministry of Transport; it is, however, less affected by irregular fluctuations from week to week.

The estimation of peak-hourly flow so defined presents no great difficulty. The first step is to decide which three months carry the highest average hourly flow, and which hour will be concerned. If this cannot be done on the basis of experience, some preliminary counts may be required. Counts should then be carried out for a sufficient number of the 13 peak hours.

For a typical fairly busy road, the accuracy category of this method depends on the number of the 13 hours for which counts are made, as follows:

Number of counts	Accuracy category	
	If on weekday	If at week-end
1	C	C
2 or 3	B	C
4 to 6	A	B
7 or more	A	A

Thus, provided that the time, day and season of the peak hour are known, the determination of the peak-hourly flow requires only a small amount of counting. If August is known to lie in the peak three months, then the highest hourly flow recorded in a one-week August count will, according to the above table, give an estimate of peak-hourly flow with accuracy category C.

Past counts provide some guidance on when the peak hour is likely to occur. The weekday peak hour is normally 5 to 6 p.m. on Fridays. In most places traffic in this hour would be the highest in midsummer, June to August, but it may sometimes be highest in the autumn, or just before Christmas. The week's peak hour is unlikely to occur on a Saturday. On Sundays, the peak hour and season are usually 7 to 8 p.m. from May to August, although it may be 3 to 4 p.m., 6 to 7 p.m. or 8 to 9 p.m. in the same months.

To show how peak flow, as defined, is related to the average flow and to the 30th highest hour, an analysis has been made of traffic at four sites where hourly totals are available for the whole of 1955. For these four sites, the average hourly flow (all times of day, whole year), the peak-hourly flow as now defined, the 30th highest hour, and the absolute peak hour are as given in Table 2.4. The peak-hourly is very similar to the 30th highest hourly flow; at the two urban points (A.4 and A.315) it is 95 and 100 per cent of the 30th hour, and at the two rural points it is 92 and 95 per cent. The peak-hourly flow varies from 170 per cent to 280 per cent of the average hourly flow.

TABLE 2.4

Average flows and peak flows at four sites in 1955

	Average hourly flow	Peak-hourly flow as now defined	30th highest hour	Absolute peak hour
A.4, Hammersmith	1017	1756	1848	2046
A.40, Denham, Bucks.	732	1946	2126	2553
A.41, Aylesbury, Bucks.	196	551	582	1097
A.315, Hounslow, Middx.	512	1068	1068	1370

50-POINT TRAFFIC CENSUS

General description of census

A new system of measuring trends in the amount of road traffic was started in 1956; this involves counting traffic at 50 sites. This section describes the census arrangements, and presents and discusses the results obtained in the first eight years' operation. Further details are given in Road Research Technical Paper No. 63.[2] A set of 50 permanent points was chosen, and at each of them an automatic counter from which daily totals of motor vehicles are obtained was installed. To provide information on the various classes of vehicle, manual counts are carried out at regular intervals at each of the points.

To ensure that counts at a limited number of points would give fully representative results, it was necessary to choose them in an objective random manner, rather than locating them at key points or in any other subjective way.

The general principles of the analysis of the results follow simply from the method of selecting the points. If census points are chosen at random on a set of roads, so that each point on the set has the same chance of inclusion, then the traffic flows in a day, a month or a year at the census points will be a random sample of the flows on that set of roads as a whole. The average traffic flow at the census points thus gives an estimate of the average flow over the set of roads. Therefore the average flow observed on the set of roads, multiplied by the total length of the roads in the set, gives an estimate of the number of miles travelled by vehicles on these roads during the period concerned. Estimates made in this way in successive periods can then be compared to provide an assessment of trends. Traffic on motorways is excluded.

Selection of sample of points

There are in Great Britain about 196 000 miles of road, divided into five classes (excluding motorways); trunk, class I, class II, class III and unclassified. The unclassified roads form about a half of the total mileage of road, but a preliminary survey had shown that they carry less than one-fifth of the total amount of motor traffic. It was therefore decided to omit these roads from the census, both to simplify the selection of points and to save the effort of maintaining continuous counts on roads of little importance.

The decision to use 50 points was governed largely by practical considerations; the maintenance of counts at a greater number was beyond the resources available at the time the census was started, and it was thought that a smaller number might not give sufficiently accurate assessments of trends.

To facilitate the estimation of traffic trends on various classes of road, and to give more weight in the selection of points to the roads in the more important classes, it was decided that separate samples should be drawn for trunk, class I, class II and class III roads in urban and in rural areas separately (urban areas were defined as all boroughs and urban districts in England and Wales, and small and large burghs in Scotland). This decision allowed a free choice of how the 50 points should be allocated to the eight "categories" of road. Since the most important results of the census would be the estimates of trends over the whole country, the allocation of points was intended to maximize the precision of these estimates. On the basis of certain theoretical arguments, used in conjunction with the results of previous censuses, this allocation required that the number of points per mile of road in each category should be proportional to a power, between one half and unity, of the average flow on roads in the category. It was also considered that each category should contain a minimum of three census points. In this way the points were allocated to the eight categories as shown in Table 2.5.

The next and most difficult stage in the selection of the points was the location of the specified number of points at random in each category. The

TABLE 2.5

Miles of road and number of census points on each category of road

Class of road	Urban areas		Rural Areas	
	Miles of road	No. of points	Miles of road	No. of points
Trunk	1729	3	6 541	7
Class I	6313	7	13 422	9
Class II	3925	3	13 675	6
Class III	5465	3	43 384	12
TOTAL	17 432	16	77 022	34

procedure adopted was, to a great extent, dictated by the records of road mileages available and by the administrative organization of roads in Great Britain. For clarity some complications in the selection process have been ignored.

A preliminary allocation[3] ensured that an appropriate number of points should fall in each of the Engineering Divisions of the Ministry of Transport and that within each division the points should be reasonably distributed between the four classes of road and between urban and rural areas. The mileages of road in each category in each local authority area or group of areas were then listed in alphabetical order, and a running total was appended to the list. The roads within local authorities were also assummed to be arranged in a definite order, so that any specified distance down the list of roads determined a specific point on the roads of the category under consideration. One point was then selected at random and the remaining points were spaced at equal mileages up and down the list.

After the positions of all the points had been determined, a few further adjustments were made; some of these adjustments were to reduce the number of points in certain counties that by chance had been allocated too large a proportion of the points; other points were moved short distances because local circumstances made it difficult to maintain a continuous count at the site originally selected.

Organization and analysis of automatic counts

At each site an automatic counter has been in continuous operation since the beginning of 1956. The instruments are of a simple type described above (p. 7). The resulting numbers (axles/2) are usually referred to as numbers of motor vehicles, though these numbers differ slightly from the actual numbers of motor vehicles because of vehicles with three or more axles, and the under-recording of light motorcycles. In general, mopeds do not actuate the counters.

Each counter is read every day at 8 a.m. so that daily totals can be obtained by taking the differences between successive readings. The reading of the counters is usually done by a member of the staff of the local highway authority. This authority is also responsible for checking the accuracy of the apparatus once a week. At some sites, patrolmen of the Automobile Association take the daily readings.

Each month a list of daily counter readings is returned from each census point to the Laboratory for analysis, together with reports on the weekly inspections.

As already mentioned, various internal faults are liable to occur in the counters at present in use, and the detector tubes may be affected by snow, frost, parked vehicles, wilful damage, and so forth. These occurrences present some difficult problems, not only in the estimation of missing values, but also in the assessment of the trustworthiness of the recorded numbers of vehicles.

Taking the latter point first, some of the daily flows recorded can be rejected immediately; in many cases, however, it is not at all certain whether or not the figure is correct. The basic rule followed is that any weekday flow differing from the average for the month by more than 20 per cent is rejected; greater tolerances, 40 and 60 per cent, are allowed for Saturdays and Sundays. However, certain exceptions to this rule have to be made, especially at points with low flows. The accepted daily totals are entered on Cope-Chat cards, one card per point per month.

During the first year, 1956, 21 per cent of daily totals were missing or rejected, but over the last seven years the average has been 12 per cent. Most of the trouble has been experienced in the winter months, especially during the first winter of operation and during the cold spell in January and February 1963. During the whole eight years, three sites have had more than 30 per cent of the daily readings unusable, and twenty sites have had less than 10 per cent unusable. The numbers of lost and rejected daily totals are given in more detail in Tables 2.6 and 2.7.

TABLE 2.6

Percentage of daily totals lost through breakdowns or rejected for other reasons, by month, 1956–63

Month	Percentage lost or rejected								Average 1957—63
	1956	1957	1958	1959	1960	1961	1962	1963	
January	28	20	13	18	16	15	19	35	19
February	31	11	10	11	18	10	12	27	14
March	21	9	9	7	13	5	7	18	10
April	25	14	7	13	10	4	9	9	9
May	20	13	10	11	11	7	10	10	10
June	24	14	12	10	14	8	10	14	11
July	15	18	11	10	13	10	7	10	11
August	22	14	10	12	10	11	12	14	12
September	20	14	9	14	14	14	8	14	12
October	15	11	9	14	13	11	9	10	11
November	11	9	9	13	15	10	6	11	10
December	17	11	11	11	11	12	10	10	11
ALL YEAR	21	13	10	12	13	10	10	15	12

TABLE 2.7

Number of points at which various percentages of the daily totals have been lost or rejected, 1956–63

Per cent lost or rejected	Number of points								Average 1956–63
	1956	1957	1958	1959	1960	1961	1962	1963	
0–5	7	12	15	19	16	24	18	16	9
5–10	11	12	15	12	10	11	14	9	11
10–15	5	13	9	5	9	5	8	5	15
15–20	7	5	5	4	7	1	3	7	6
20–30	7	3	5	6	2	6	4	8	6
30–40	5	3	1	1	5	1	3	2	2
40–50	4	1	0	2	0	1	0	0	0
50–60	3	0	0	1	0	1	0	1	1
60–70	1	0	0	0	0	0	0	1	0
70–80	0	1	0	0	1	0	0	1	0
TOTAL	50	50	50	50	50	50	50	50	50

Two methods are being used to estimate the missing daily totals. The first, which is employed when only a few figures are missing, is to use the average of at least two other days' flow at the same point in the same month to estimate each missing figure. Normally the two days are on the same day of the week as the day with the missing total, and one is earlier in the month and the other later. When a large proportion of a month's daily totals for a site is missing, use is made of data for the same month a year earlier. First an estimate of the trend over the whole country from that month to the current month is made from all those sites for which the record is complete, or can be completed by the first method of estimation. This estimate is then applied to the previous year's average flows per weekday, Saturday or Sunday at the site concerned. This method will thus produce one estimate applicable to all missing weekdays in the month, one applicable to all Saturdays and one to all Sundays.

When all the missing and incorrect values for a month have been estimated, the following totals and averages are calculated for each site:

$$\text{Average daily total, Monday to Friday} = a$$
$$\text{,,   ,,   ,,   Saturday} = b$$
$$\text{,,   ,,   ,,   Sunday} = c$$
$$\text{Traffic flow in a standard week} = 5a+b+c$$
$$\text{Total traffic flow for month}$$

(Public holidays are included in the monthly totals, but not in the averages.) For each category of road, these values are then averaged over all the points in that category and multiplied by the mileage of road in it. Thus an estimate is obtained of the motor-vehicle-mileage for each category in the period concerned. These monthly vehicle-mileages can then be added to give totals for all categories, and trends can be estimated.

Estimates of vehicle-miles for individual days are made by methods similar to those described for the monthly values.

Manual counts

Starting in April, 1957, the Ministry of Transport has arranged for a series of manual counts to be made at each of the sites at which automatic counters are in operation. These counts cover the hours 6 a.m. to 10 p.m. on a consecutive Friday, Saturday and Sunday. Initially one of these counts was held at each site every three months, but starting in January, 1958, a three-day count has been made monthly at each site. The counts are spread over the different week-ends in the month, excluding bank holiday week-ends when special counts are made at some of the sites. The counts are made by the local authorities who are responsible for the maintenance and reading of the automatic counters. The vehicles are classified as follows:

Pedal cycles
Solo motorcycles
Motorcycle combinations
Mopeds (cycles with motors and pedals)
Scooters (motorcycles with small wheels)
Cars and Taxis (including light 3-wheeled cars, invalid carriages, cars with trailers, and dual-purpose vehicles appearing to be used as cars)
Buses and coaches (including works buses)
Light vans (all commercial vehicles of less than 30 cwt unladen weight, including 3-wheeled commercial vehicles, pedestrian-controlled vehicles, and dual-purpose vehicles appearing to be used as commercial vehicles)
Other vehicles (including all heavy commercial vehicles, tractors and traction engines)

Steamrollers, hand barrows, animals, horse-drawn vehicles, and other unusual traffic are not recorded. To facilitate manual counting, the definitions are based on outward appearance of the vehicles, and not on excise licence or carriers' licence categories.

The results of the manual counts are analysed by the Ministry of Transport. The Laboratory uses the results to break down the automatic estimates of vehicle-miles by class of vehicle and trends based on this breakdown are published in the Monthly Digest of Statistics. For this purpose it is assumed that even if 16-hour counts on three days a month do not give as accurate a figure for total motor-vehicle-miles as do continuous counts for the whole month, they give sufficiently accurate estimates of the proportions of different classes of vehicle. All results quoted in this section for particular classes of vehicle are based on the automatic counter results broken down in this way.

While these manual counts are being made, an hourly reading of the automatic counter is taken to serve as a check on the accuracy of both counts. Although at individual sites fairly large discrepancies sometimes occur, the totals for the 50 points agree quite closely; over a six month period there was an average discrepancy of 2 per cent between the two sets of counts.

Results

The figures quoted in this part of the book are estimates of various quantities relating to traffic on trunk and classified roads only. No allowance has been made for unclassified roads or motorways. The estimates

3

given may in some places differ from the true figures by more than might be suggested by the number of significant figures quoted. In general, ratios of similar measurements in different periods are considerably more precise than estimates of absolute vehicle-mileages, such as are given in Tables 2.8, 2.10 and 2.17.

TRENDS FROM YEAR TO YEAR

Table 2.8 shows the variation in annual motor-vehicle-mileage on each category of road since the start of the census.

Each row of the table shows a rising trend of traffic flow since 1957, which is slightly more marked in urban than in rural areas, and on trunk and class I roads than on class II and III roads. Between 1956 and 1963 motor-vehicle-miles on trunk and classified roads (excluding motorways) are estimated to have increased by 66 per cent or 8 per cent compound per year.

TABLE 2.8

Trends from 1956 to 1963 in vehicle-mileage on each category of road

Category of road		Motor-vehicle-miles in year as percentage of 1960 value							
		1956	1957	1958	1959	1960	1961	1962	1963
Urban	Trunk	69	67	81	90	100	109	118	127
	Class I	69	71	83	90	100	107	115	123
	Class II	79	72	87	97	100	108	108	115
	Class III	74	72	90	95	100	107	111	117
	All	71	71	84	92	100	108	114	122
Rural	Trunk	72	71	84	92	100	110	117	124
	Class I	73	73	84	96	100	109	111	115
	Class II	78	74	76	92	100	109	111	112
	Class III	76	74	82	96	100	109	114	119
	All	74	73	83	95	100	109	113	118
All trunk and classified roads		72	72	83	93	100	108	113	120

Table 2.9 shows the trend of traffic flow in urban and rural areas on different days of the week. Sunday urban traffic shows the most marked increase. Sunday rural traffic shows a similar trend until 1959 and then little increase from 1959 to 1960; this was probably due to the very wet summer of 1960.

TABLE 2.9
*Annual average daily vehicle-mileages on trunk and classified
roads, expressed as percentage of values in 1960*

Area	Year	Monday to Friday	Saturday	Sunday
Urban	1956	72	71	69
	1957	71	72	69
	1958	84	84	84
	1959	92	91	93
	1960	100	100	100
	1961	108	108	108
	1962	114	115	113
	1963	123	122	122
Rural	1956	74	72	73
	1957	72	71	74
	1958	82	81	88
	1959	94	94	99
	1960	100	100	100
	1961	110	109	110
	1962	115	113	110
	1963	120	117	115

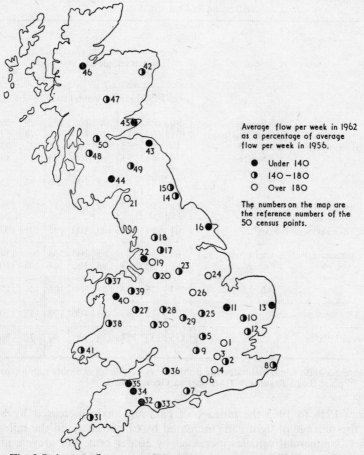

Average flow per week in 1962
as a percentage of average
flow per week in 1956.

● Under 140
◑ 140 – 180
○ Over 180

The numbers on the map are
the reference numbers of the
50 census points.

Fig. 2.5. Average flow per week in 1962 as a percentage of average flow
per week in 1956

Fig. 2.5 shows the approximate location of the census points and the changes in flow at them between 1956 and 1962. Some of the biggest increases in flow were in the Metropolitan Division, where three of the four points showed increases of more than 80 per cent. Some of the smallest increases were in places remote from large towns. The average flows at each point for the years 1956 to 1960 are given in Road Research Technical Paper No. 63.[2]

Table 2.10 shows the variation in annual vehicle-miles since 1956 for the different classes of vehicle for trunk and classified roads. Again, the figures have been expressed as percentages of the average month of 1960 for each class. To obtain these figures it was necessary, because manual counts started in the second quarter of 1957, to estimate vehicle-miles of each class of vehicle for 1956 and the first quarter of 1957. To do this the composition of traffic and trends in composition (estimated from counts at 10 points in most cases) were used to break down the counter totals.

TABLE 2.10

Trends from 1956 to 1963 in vehicle-miles of different classes of vehicle

(All trunk and classified roads)

Class of vehicle		Vehicle-miles in each year as a percentage of 1960 values							
		1956	1957	1958	1959	1960	1961	1962	1963
Motorcycles	Solos	96	101	95	105	100	93	79	69
	Combinations	101	107	111	108	100	91	78	67
	Mopeds	49	62	68	86	100	95	92	83
	Scooters	26	42	55	82	100	106	103	89
	All .	76	84	84	98	100	96	86	75
Cars and taxis . . .		68	67	82	92	100	111	120	129
Public-service vehicles* . .		101	98	98	100	100	102	101	102
Commercial vehicles	Light Vans .	68	70	80	92	100	108	108	114
	Other .	85	82	89	96	100	104	106	110
	All .	77	76	85	94	100	106	107	112
All motor vehicles . . .		72	72	83	93	100	108	113	120
Pedal cycles . . .		135	133	118	113	100	90	76	66

* More accurate trend estimates for public-service vehicles are obtainable from data in the "Public Road Passenger Transport in Great Britain."[5,10]

From 1956 to 1963 the mileage of cars and taxis increased by 89 per cent, the mileage of light vans increased by 67 per cent and the mileage of heavier commercial vehicles increased by 30 per cent. Motorcycle mileage increased until 1960 but since then has decreased. Pedal cycle mileage has fallen steadily, and in 1963 was 51 per cent less than in 1956. Public-service vehicle mileage has been almost constant.

Trends in traffic on all roads are described in a later section (see p. 50).

TRENDS FROM MONTH TO MONTH

Table 2.11 shows the monthly motor-vehicle-mileages expressed as percentages of the average monthly vehicle-mileage in 1960. The well-marked seasonal variation shown is discussed below. The lowest values during the 5-year period occurred in the winter of 1956–57, which was a time of fuel shortage and rationing due to the Suez crisis. In general, the figures show a very consistent upward trend super-imposed on a regular seasonal variation.

TABLE 2.11

Monthly motor-vehicle-mileages expressed as percentages of average monthly figure for 1960

	1956	1957	1958	1959	1960	1961	1962	1963
January . . .	57	44	61	66	75	86	92	84
February . . .	50	44	60	67	78	85	89	81
March . . .	67	56	73	86	92	102	102	109
April . . .	74	72	83	87	100	105	112	120
May . . .	85	77	95	106	107	119	117	129
June . . .	82	87	94	105	117	122	132	139
July . . .	89	91	100	114	121	130	137	146
August . . .	94	98	108	123	126	137	142	150
September . . .	83	83	93	105	110	120	126	134
October . . .	75	75	84	93	97	109	117	127
November . . .	65	68	75	84	89	97	100	113
December . . .	49	66	76	83	88	89	95	108
Average . . .	72	72	83	93	100	108	113	120

The trends shown in Table 2.11 include the seasonal variation, and it is of interest to see whether it is possible to remove this variation to obtain a monthly series of figures showing the underlying long-term trend only. The calculation to be described is based on figures for standard weeks, not monthly totals, and uses data up to February 1963.

The first step was to estimate the normal seasonal pattern as accurately as possible; for this purpose the period November 1956 to May 1957 was excluded, as traffic was affected by the Suez crisis. The figures for the rest of the period were then averaged month by month. The averages were then corrected, to free them from long-term trend, by calculating the average date of the months which had been averaged and correcting by 0·675 per cent for every month by which this date differed from 1st January, 1960. (0·675 per cent per month corresponds to a growth rate of 8 per cent per year.) The individual monthly figures were then divided by their respective corrected seasonal factors; the results are shown in Fig. 2.6. This brings out several features. In the first place, the period of the

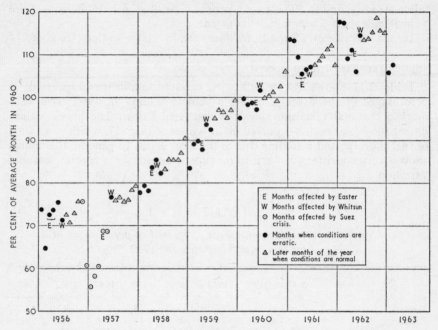

Fig. 2.6. Trends in standard weekly vehicle-miles, freed from seasonal variation (1960 = 100)

Suez crisis shows particularly low figures. Secondly, the figures for the months containing Easter and Whitsun tend to be high compared with the other two months of the period March to June. Thirdly, the figures for January and February tend to be erratic; much of this variation can be explained in terms of the weather of the particular months. The remaining months, normally the last six of each year, which are distinguished in the diagram, generally show a much smoother trend than the whole set of points. This suggests that a series of traffic counts designed to measure long-term trends should be in the second half of the year (unless the whole year can be covered).

SEASONAL VARIATIONS

The effect of the general trend is largely removed by expressing a monthly flow or vehicle-mileage as a percentage of its average monthly value in the same year. Such sets of data averaged over as many years as possible, thus provide the most convenient basis for the study of seasonal variation. Over a period with a tendency for traffic to increase this method tends to inflate data for later months at the expense of earlier ones, but this effect is not usually important.

Table 2.12 shows the seasonal variation of vehicle-mileage on each category of road, the figures being an average over the four years 1959 to 1962. All categories have a well-marked seasonal variation, the amplitude of which is larger on rural than on urban roads. Urban class II roads have the largest seasonal variation of the urban categories and class III the smallest, the former having a pronounced August peak. The fact that all three urban

TABLE 2.12
Seasonal variation of vehicle-mileage on each category of road
(Vehicle-miles per standard week in each month, averaged over 1959 to 1962, expressed as percentage of average over all months)

Month	Urban					Rural					All trunk and class-ified roads
	Trunk	Class I	Class II	Class III	All	Trunk	Class I	Class II	Class III	All	
Jan.	77	81	81	89	81	66	76	58	72	71	76
Feb.	85	90	86	96	89	73	81	64	80	77	83
Mar.	93	94	92	101	94	83	89	73	88	86	90
Apl.	101	99	95	102	99	95	98	87	97	97	98
May	105	104	101	104	104	105	108	101	110	107	105
June	110	110	114	105	110	122	118	135	123	121	116
July	114	109	119	106	111	137	119	153	124	127	119
Aug.	113	110	130	100	112	146	128	178	125	136	124
Sept.	111	109	114	103	109	123	113	130	112	117	113
Oct.	105	103	96	99	102	95	98	85	98	96	99
Nov.	97	87	88	101	96	81	89	71	88	85	90
Dec.	90	93	87	97	92	74	83	65	83	79	86

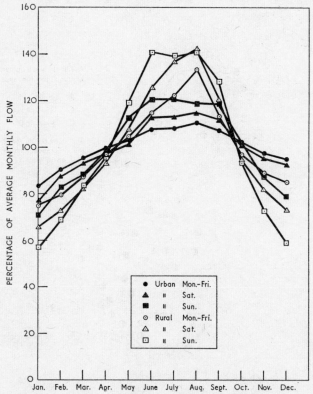

Fig. 2.7. Seasonal patterns on weekdays, Saturdays and Sundays on urban and rural roads (average of 1959, 1960, 1961, and 1962)

class II census points are near the coast, and all three class III points are well inland probably contribute to this effect. Four of the six rural class II points are near the coast and this category of road has the largest seasonal variation of all.

An analysis of variance calculation of the August figures for individual census-points shows significant differences between urban and rural roads, and between the classes of road in rural areas. The differences between classes of road in urban areas are not significant, but appear to follow a similar pattern.

Fig. 2.7 shows the seasonal variation on weekdays, Saturdays and Sundays on urban and rural roads. Week-end rural traffic has the largest seasonal variation and weekday urban traffic the least. A feature of Fig. 2.7 is the summer peak of rural traffic on Sundays; this stays at about the same high level from June to August.

Fig. 2.8 shows the variation from point to point of the August peak. The majority of points at which this peak is low are situated in industrial

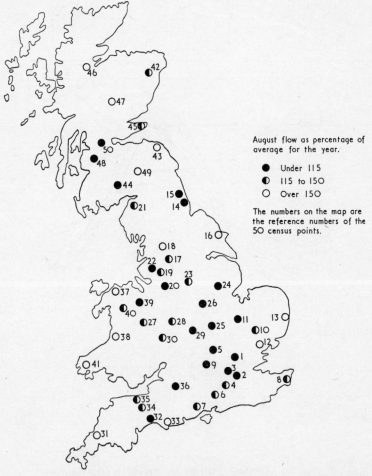

Fig. 2.8. August flow as a percentage of average flow for the year (based on standard weeks 1959–62 combined)

areas, whereas holiday areas contain most of the points with a high August peak.

Seasonal patterns are also found to vary between Ministry of Transport Divisions; Fig. 2.9 shows the patterns for each of the nine Divisions and Scotland. The first part of Fig. 2.9 shows those Divisions with sharp August peaks, and the second part the Divisions with flatter peaks from June to August.

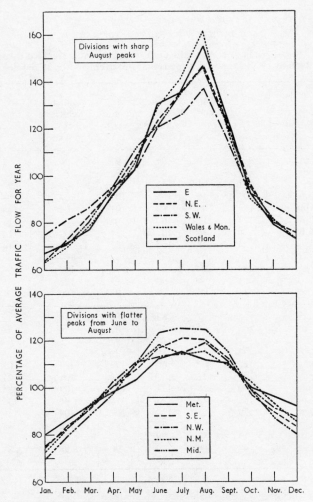

Fig. 2.9. Seasonal variations in each Ministry of Transport Division (based on standard weeks 1959, 1960, 1961 and 1962)

Table 2.13 gives the seasonal variation in urban and rural areas of the vehicle-mileage of different classes of vehicle, averaged over 1959, 1960, 1961 and 1962 and based on standard weekly vehicle-mileages. There are maxima in spring and autumn for heavier commercial vehicles in both urban and rural areas; pedal cycles are less used in urban areas in August than in adjacent months. Table 2.13 shows that motorcycles have the largest

3*

amplitude in both urban and rural areas, and that little variation is shown by public-service vehicles in urban areas and by the heavier commercial vehicles in all areas. Light vans exhibit a secondary maximum in December in urban areas, which is presumably a result of their increased use in the period before Christmas.

TABLE 2.13

Seasonal variation of vehicle-mileage of different classes of vehicle in urban and rural areas

(Vehicles-miles per standard week in each month, averaged over 1959 to 1962, expressed as percentage of average over all months)

Area	Month	Motor cycles	Cars and taxis	Public service vehicles	Light vans	Commercial vehicles other than light vans	All motor vehicles	Pedal cycles
	Jan.	69	79	96	91	94	82	80
	Feb.	78	87	97	95	84	89	89
	Mar.	91	91	97	98	100	93	97
	Apl.	103	96	94	101	103	98	104
	May	113	105	99	101	102	104	110
Urban	June	124	112	107	105	102	111	120
	July	126	116	109	114	102	114	121
	Aug.	124	118	107	107	99	114	111
	Sept.	113	109	102	102	103	108	112
	Oct.	100	100	97	98	107	101	95
	Nov.	88	96	99	93	105	96	88
	Dec.	71	90	98	95	100	91	73
	Jan.	54	67	83	80	88	71	86
	Feb.	65	74	88	87	96	78	78
	Mar.	81	84	89	93	102	87	91
	Apl.	93	93	89	99	104	95	101
	May	122	106	100	106	104	107	116
Rural	June	137	123	120	113	106	121	130
	July	140	128	123	117	103	124	128
	Aug.	148	142	124	118	95	133	126
	Sept.	129	123	109	107	104	119	113
	Oct.	95	97	97	98	102	98	92
	Nov.	73	83	88	92	99	86	76
	Dec.	62	80	90	90	98	83	64

HOURLY PATTERNS

In addition to the manual counts at the 50 points, described earlier, the Ministry of Transport arranged for 7-day 24-hour counts to be made in January and July, starting in July, 1959.

Table 2.14 gives the vehicle-mileage in each hour as a percentage of the total for the day, in July, 1959, for various classes of vehicle. This table is based on counts at 49 points. Table 2.15 presents similar data based on counts at 39 points in January 1960. The most marked difference between the patterns in the two periods is that in July a higher proportion of the day's traffic is carried in the evening hours after 6 p.m.

TABLE 2.14

Daily traffic patterns in summer, 49 points, July, 1959

(Flow in each hour as a percentage of the total flow for the day)

Hour	Motorcycles			Cars and taxis			Public-service vehicles			Commercial vehicles			All motor vehicles			Pedal cycles		
	Mon. to Fri.	Sat.	Sun.	Mon. to Fri.	Sat.	Sun.	Mon. to Fri.	Sat.	Sun.	Mon. to Fri.	Sat.	Sun.	Mon. to Fri.	Sat.	Sun.	Mon. to Fri.	Sun.	Sun.
12– 1 a.m.	0·6	0·8	1·2	1·0	1·0	1·5	0·4	0·2	1·4	0·4	0·7	1·3	0·8	0·9	1·5	0·2	0·3	0·4
1– 2	0·2	0·3	0·5	0·3	0·4	0·6	0·2	0·2	0·5	0·2	0·4	0·6	0·3	0·4	0·6	0·1	0·1	0·2
2– 3	0·2	0·1	0·3	0·1	0·2	0·3	0·1	0·1	0·3	0·2	0·2	0·3	0·2	0·2	0·3	0·1	0·1	0·1
3– 4	0·1	0·1	0·1	0·1	0·2	0·1	0·1	0·2	0·1	0·4	0·5	0·4	0·1	0·3	0·2	0·1	0·3	0·2
4– 5	0·2	0·4	0·3	0·3	0·4	0·2	0·8	0·7	0·3	0·4	1·2	0·7	0·6	0·6	0·2	0·2	0·3	0·9
5– 6	1·2	1·0	0·5	0·9	1·0	0·4	2·9	1·9	1·0	2·3	2·7	1·3	1·5	1·4	0·6	1·2	1·2	1·1
6– 7	2·7	2·0	0·8	3·3	2·2	0·7	5·8	3·7	1·6	5·4	6·0	2·3	4·5	3·0	1·1	4·0	3·4	2·4
7– 8	10·1	4·1	1·7	5·9	3·6	1·7	5·8	5·5	2·9	7·4	8·2	4·1	6·5	4·5	2·0	9·3	7·4	3·1
8– 9	7·0	5·0	2·3	5·7	4·6	3·2	6·2	6·1	2·5	7·5	8·8	4·7	5·8	5·2	3·5	7·8	5·6	5·3
9–10	2·9	3·7	3·5	5·7	5·6	5·1	5·4	5·7	4·7	7·5	8·8	5·9	5·9	6·2	5·7	3·4	5·7	7·1
10–11	2·8	3·8	6·1	5·4	6·9	5·5	5·1	6·1	5·5	7·9	9·5	6·9	5·9	6·9	6·5	2·9	7·1	8·4
11–12 noon	3·1	6·2	3·1	5·4	6·6	6·2	5·1	6·1	5·9	7·9	9·5	6·9	5·9	6·9	6·5	3·5	8·1	8·6
12– 1 p.m.	3·9	8·5	6·3	5·3	6·8	5·5	5·2	6·3	5·1	6·7	8·3	5·6	5·6	7·1	5·6	6·7	10·1	8·3
1– 2	4·1	7·0	5·4	4·7	5·4	4·3	4·7	6·8	5·2	6·5	6·6	4·4	6·3	5·7	4·5	4·7	8·5	7·4
2– 3	3·5	8·0	7·4	6·0	7·3	7·0	5·6	6·6	5·5	7·8	5·7	7·5	6·0	7·1	8·1	3·9	6·4	9·2
3– 4	5·5	7·6	7·6	5·9	8·0	8·2	8·7	6·1	6·8	8·0	4·4	6·8	7·0	6·2	7·2	7·6	6·1	5·9
4– 5	12·5	6·4	6·9	9·1	6·6	9·1	7·5	6·7	5·5	7·7	4·1	5·5	9·0	6·4	7·2	11·9	6·1	6·2
5– 6	9·0	5·9	6·9	8·3	7·3	8·5	7·5	6·7	7·9	5·3	3·5	8·6	7·4	6·5	8·8	7·7	4·0	7·3
6– 7	8·0	5·2	6·4	7·4	7·3	8·8	4·3	5·6	8·1	3·5	3·3	8·1	6·3	5·8	7·9	6·5	3·4	6·4
7– 8	6·2	6·3	6·3	6·3	6·4	8·1	4·7	4·6	7·2	2·6	2·3	7·1	3·9	4·3	5·7	5·0	2·5	4·2
8– 9	5·2	5·0	5·0	6·7	6·7	5·5	4·0	4·7	8·5	1·7	1·8	5·9	3·8	4·0	5·1	4·1	2·1	2·9
9–10	4·9	3·6	4·9	4·7	4·4	5·1	4·0	4·7	5·5	1·3	1·8	3·9	3·8	4·0	5·1	2·4	1·4	2·6
10–11	4·3	3·8	3·0	4·6	4·4	2·5	2·2	3·3	3·5	0·7	1·2	2·2	2·0	3·0	2·5	0·7	—	1·1
11–12 midnight	2·2	2·8	2·4	2·5	3·4	2·5	2·2	3·3	3·5	0·7	1·2	2·2	2·0	3·0	2·5	0·7	—	1·1
	100·0	100·1	99·9	100·0	100·0	100·0	100·2	99·9	99·9	100·2	99·8	100·0	100·2	99·8	100·1	100·1	100·0	100·2
Total 6 a.m.–10 p.m.	90·4	90·7	89·7	91·0	89·8	89·5	92·2	90·3	88·0	95·7	93·3	90·3	92·2	90·2	89·4	95·1	94·4	94·6
Total 10 p.m.–6 a.m.	9·6	9·4	10·2	9·0	10·2	10·5	8·0	9·6	11·9	4·5	6·5	9·7	8·0	9·6	10·7	5·0	5·6	5·6
Day's total as per cent of Monday to Friday average	100·0	125·9	135·8	100·0	139·8	160·2	100·0	125·5	82·3	100·0	63·4	38·9	100·0	118·3	121·3	100·0	85·2	83·1

TABLE 2.15

Daily traffic patterns in winter, 39 points, January, 1960

(Flow in each hour as a percentage of the total flow for the day)

Hour	Motorcycles Mon. to Fri.	Motorcycles Sat.	Motorcycles Sun.	Cars and taxis Mon. to Fri.	Cars and taxis Sat.	Cars and taxis Sun.	Public-service vehicles Mon. to Fri.	Public-service vehicles Sat.	Public-service vehicles Sun.	Commercial vehicles Mon. to Fri.	Commercial vehicles Sat.	Commercial vehicles Sun.	All motor vehicles Mon. to Fri.	All motor vehicles Sat.	All motor vehicles Sun.	Pedal cycles Mon. to Fri.	Pedal cycles Sat.	Pedal cycles Sun.
12–1 a.m.	0·4	1·1	1·9	0·9	1·9	2·5	0·4	0·8	0·9	0·5	0·7	2·0	0·7	1·5	2·4	0·4	0·7	0·4
1–2	0·2	0·2	0·8	0·4	0·8	1·0	0·2	0·3	0·6	0·4	0·4	0·8	0·4	0·6	0·9	0·1	0·1	0·2
2–3	0·2	0·2	0·3	0·2	0·3	0·4	0·4	0·0	0·1	0·3	0·3	1·0	0·2	0·3	0·4	0·1	0·1	0·0
3–4	0·1	0·1	0·2	0·1	0·2	0·2	0·1	0·0	0·1	0·3	0·2	1·2	0·2	0·2	0·3	0·1	0·1	0·0
4–5	0·1	0·2	0·2	0·1	0·1	0·2	0·1	0·1	0·2	0·4	0·4	0·7	0·2	0·2	0·3	0·2	0·2	0·2
5–6	1·6	1·5	1·0	0·3	0·2	0·3	1·0	0·6	0·3	0·6	0·4	1·7	0·5	0·4	0·7	0·9	0·4	0·9
6–7	3·9	2·9	1·0	1·4	2·0	0·5	4·1	2·8	1·2	1·9	2·8	1·2	1·8	2·2	1·7	1·6	4·4	1·6
7–8	13·4	7·3	2·5	4·5	2·5	1·4	7·1	5·6	2·0	8·0	5·9	3·7	5·3	3·6	1·7	11·7	8·8	2·7
8–9	9·1	5·0	2·8	7·5	3·8	2·0	9·7	5·1	2·8	8·2	9·5	3·7	7·9	4·6	2·4	9·2	6·7	4·4
9–10	2·6	2·1	2·1	6·8	3·6	4·2	5·7	5·6	2·8	8·3	9·5	4·7	6·6	5·3	4·5	3·7	5·9	6·5
10–11	2·6	4·4	4·4	5·8	3·8	5·8	4·5	5·4	4·5	8·5	10·2	6·7	6·6	6·3	6·3	3·7	5·9	7·1
11–12 noon	2·4	7·0	7·7	5·5	6·4	5·8	4·5	5·4	4·5	8·7	10·2	9·2	6·4	7·2	6·3	3·8	8·7	11·6
12–1 p.m.	3·8	10·9	7·7	5·9	7·7	7·2	5·0	6·9	7·7	7·8	10·4	8·4	6·4	8·5	7·4	8·7	13·7	10·8
1–2	4·7	9·7	7·8	5·1	7·9	6·4	4·8	9·0	6·7	6·5	7·2	8·5	5·7	7·9	6·7	8·1	8·6	7·8
2–3	3·7	8·6	8·8	6·2	8·5	9·6	4·8	7·1	7·5	8·5	5·4	8·1	8·0	8·4	9·3	4·7	6·0	10·6
3–4	3·5	7·2	9·6	6·7	8·9	11·6	6·4	6·3	7·5	8·8	6·0	9·8	8·1	6·7	11·2	4·3	6·1	10·3
4–5	14·1	6·5	10·6	7·7	7·1	10·9	8·5	9·4	8·4	8·8	4·2	8·7	9·0	6·6	8·7	9·2	5·0	8·7
5–6	11·0	3·7	7·0	7·3	5·8	5·5	4·7	5·3	8·1	3·7	2·3	5·1	6·2	4·4	6·7	10·6	5·0	5·4
6–7	5·5	2·8	3·7	6·8	5·5	5·4	3·3	5·0	6·8	2·2	2·1	2·8	4·8	4·8	5·0	3·1	2·6	3·7
7–8	3·4	2·1	3·8	3·0	3·3	4·4	3·3	4·9	6·7	0·9	1·4	3·1	2·4	3·7	4·2	1·7	0·8	1·8
8–9	3·6	1·6	2·7	3·0	3·3	4·4	3·5	4·2	5·8	0·8	1·1	2·6	2·5	3·5	4·7	1·8	1·0	1·9
9–10	4·2	3·6	4·8	3·3	4·2	4·4	3·5	4·2	5·8	0·8	1·1	3·1	2·4	2·7	4·7	1·8	1·0	1·6
10–11	2·0	3·0	2·7	2·2	3·8	3·0	1·7	1·7	2·4	0·5	1·0	2·2	2·5	3·5	2·9	1·0	1·3	1·2
11–12 midnight	2·0	3·0	2·7	2·2	3·8	3·0	1·7	1·7	2·4	0·5	1·0	2·2	1·6	3·1	2·9	1·0	1·3	1·2
	99·9	100·0	100·1	100·0	100·0	100·0	100·1	99·9	100·0	99·8	100·2	99·9	100·0	100·0	99·9	99·9	100·0	100·0
Total 6 a.m.–10 p.m.	91·1	90·1	88·1	92·5	88·5	87·4	92·7	91·9	89·6	95·9	95·3	87·7	93·7	90·2	87·5	94·9	95·5	95·5
Total 10 p.m.–6 a.m.	8·8	9·9	12·0	7·5	11·5	12·6	7·4	8·0	10·4	3·9	4·9	12·2	6·3	9·8	12·4	5·0	4·5	4·5
Day's total as per cent of Monday to Friday average	100·0	112·2	91·6	100·0	115·9	99·4	100·0	111·2	56·3	100·0	60·4	28·9	100·0	97·0	74·0	100·0	90·1	75·7

DAY-TO-DAY VARIATIONS

Daily motor-vehicle-mileage figures may be used to study the variations of vehicle-mileage with the day of the week. Table 2.16 presents the results of an analysis of this variation. For each alternate month the motor-vehicle-mileage on each day is expressed as a percentage of the average weekday vehicle-mileage. The figures for Monday to Friday were obtained from daily vehicle-mileages in one week in each of the months concerned in each of the years 1956 to 1960; no weeks affected by a public holiday were included. Each weekday mileage was expressed as a percentage of the average of the five weekday mileages in the same week and averaged by month over the five years. The annual average is the average over the months shown. The Saturday and Sunday figures were obtained similarly using monthly and annual averages of weekday, Saturday and Sunday vehicle-mileages over the whole five years excluding public holidays.

Table 2.16 shows, over the year as a whole, a systematic but small increase of traffic from Monday to Friday. This increase also exists in each of the six months examined (except for Wednesday to Thursday in two months), being most marked in July. Annual average Saturday and Sunday mileages are both a little larger than the annual average weekday values. As expected, the figures for both Saturday and Sunday show a well-marked seasonal variation.

TABLE 2.16

Vehicle-mileages on different days of the week expressed as percentages of average weekday vehicle-mileage
(1956–1960)

	January	March	May	July	September	November	Annual average
Monday	99·6	97·6	97·6	96·0	98·4	98·0	97·9
Tuesday	100·7	99·8	99·8	98·2	99·6	99·6	99·6
Wednesday	99·4	99·9	100·1	100·2	100·5	100·2	100·0
Thursday	99·1	100·7	100·4	100·7	100·4	100·6	100·3
Friday	101·3	102·0	102·2	104·9	101·5	101·5	102·2
Saturday	90·7	97·3	103·2	109·4	109·2	98·2	102·5
Sunday	75·1	92·8	116·8	114·8	112·8	85·8	101·4

Traffic during the period just before and just after the English public holidays has been analysed in more detail for five years 1956–60 (Table 2.17). For a week or so on either side of each of the four main holidays, corresponding days in the five years have been averaged. For Easter, Whitsun and August the results are straightforward; in the first place, traffic on the holiday Monday is in each case higher than on any other day within a week in either direction; secondly, the Saturday and Sunday at the holiday week-end have in each case more traffic than the Saturdays and Sundays preceding and following; thirdly, the weekdays immediately preceding and following the holiday week-end (i.e. Friday and Tuesday at Whitsun and August, Thursday and Tuesday at Easter) are somewhat higher than normal weekdays at the same time of year.

The analysis of Christmas figures in Table 2.17 is made in a slightly different way. Apart from December 24th–26th, the days have been classified partly according to day of week, and partly in chronological order. Weekday traffic builds up to a slight peak in the week before Christmas, being highest on the last shopping day but one; there are low traffic flows on Christmas Day and Boxing Day, and also on the Sundays before and after Christmas. Weekday traffic after Christmas increases over the first three working days.

TABLE 2.17

Daily traffic flows at public holidays

(Motor-vehicle-miles, millions per day, average of 1956–1960)

		Easter	Whitsun	August	Christmas	
	Sat	130	163	189		126
	Sun	129	187	185	Previous	128
					five	130
	Mon	133	147	170	weekdays	131
Week	Tue	137	151	181		134
before	Wed	142	155	182		
	Thur	154	156	185	Previous Sat.	123
	Fri	148*	171	190	weekend Sun.	102
Public holiday	Sat	148	181	201	Dec. 24th	131
weekend	Sun	157	204	205	(never Sunday)	
					25th	84*
	Mon	204*	225*	223*	26th	99*
	Tue	163	180	191		
Week after	Wed	144	161	187	Following Sat	†116
	Thur	144	159	184	weekend Sun	‡104
	Fri	143	162	186		
					Following	117
	Sat	143	169	196	three	119
	Sun	150	192	194	weekdays	127

* Public holiday.
† Includes Monday 28th.
‡ Includes Tuesday 27th.

EFFECTS OF WEATHER

This section discusses some of the effects of weather on flow which have been observed from analysis of records for the five years 1956–1960. In 1959 there was much snow and ice in January and February followed by an exceptionally fine summer. The winter of 1959–60 was relatively mild. The summer of 1960 from July onwards was very wet and stormy roughly south of a line from the Mersey to the Humber. This weather sequence accounts for some of the variations of the data in Table 2.18, which shows the amplitudes of seasonal variation of the years 1958 to 1960 of vehicle-miles run by different classes of vehicle in urban and rural areas.

With few exceptions, the amplitude is greater in 1959 than in 1958 or 1960. The average excess of the 1959 amplitude over the average for 1958

TABLE 2.18

Amplitudes of seasonal variation in 1958, 1959 and 1960 of vehicle-miles of
different classes of vehicle in urban and rural areas*

Area	Year	Motor-cycles	Cars and taxis	Public-service vehicles	Light vans	Commercial vehicles other than light vans	All motor vehicles	Pedal cycles
Urban	1958	54	43	15	33	24	35	35
	1959	80	43	15	32	20	38	51
	1960	62	42	13	21	26	35	53
Rural	1958	95	86	42	43	27	71	71
	1959	122	89	58	59	22	78	82
	1960	92	79	33	35	16	64	72

*Amplitudes are the differences between the highest and lowest percentages in the
seasonal patterns.

and 1960 is greatest for motorcycles and least for heavy commercial
vehicles.

An effect caused by the differences between the summers of 1959 and 1960
is illustrated in Fig. 2.10, which shows the estimated vehicle-mileage in the
two years on Sundays on rural roads in England and Wales excluding the
North Eastern and North Western Divisions of the Ministry of Transport.
From July to October traffic in 1960 was less than in 1959. The diagram also
shows that peak Sunday traffic on rural roads in the area in 1959 occurred
in July, August vehicle-miles being 5 per cent less.

To show, in more detail, the effect of wet weather on the 50-point results,
a correlation has been made between the monthly vehicle-mileage figures
and the monthly rainfall figures issued by the Meteorological Office and

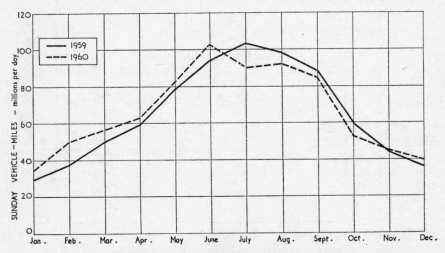

Fig. 2.10. Vehicle mileage on Sundays in 1959 and 1960 on rural roads in England
and Wales excluding North-Eastern and North-Western Ministry of Transport
Divisions

published, for example, in the Monthly Digest of Statistics.[6] The first step is to remove from both the traffic and rainfall data all effects associated with the year or with the month of the year. For traffic, this was done by fitting to the monthly figures, by the method of least squares, a relation of the form:

$$\log (\text{traffic in } j\text{'th month of } i\text{'th year}) = a_i + b_j$$

in which there are five constants a_i for the five years and 12 constants b_j for the twelve months. The period November, 1956 to May, 1957, was excluded from these calculations. The deviations of the logarithms of the traffic from the "expected" values $a_i + b_j$ were then calculated. A similar calculation was then made with inches of rainfall in place of the logarithm of the traffic.

Fig. 2.11 shows the relation between the percentage traffic deviations and the rainfall deviations. The Suez period has been excluded, and so have all Januarys and Februarys, which showed rather more erratic results, no doubt owing to such factors as ice and snow. The months that were wetter than normal tended to have less traffic than normal, but the effect was not large (though it was statistically significant). A detailed study of the points showed that there was a tendency for those months in which Easter or Whitsun fell to have an appreciably higher traffic flow than expected, and in fitting the straight line shown on the diagram allowance was made for this. For example, the two points with traffic more than 4 per cent below expectation were in an April and a May which did not contain either holiday. The fitted line on the diagram shows that the range of rainfall encountered causes the traffic flow to vary over a range of about 3 per cent.

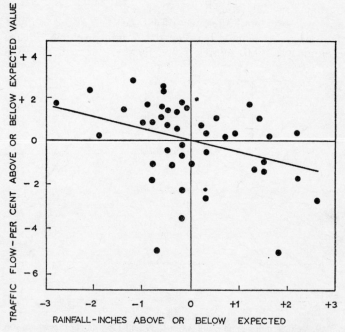

Fig. 2.11. Effect of rainfall on monthly index of motor-vehicle-miles, 1956–60. Januarys, Februarys and Suez period excluded

TABLE 2.19

Trends in traffic flow between various periods, and standard errors of the trends

Pairs of periods		Trend*	Standard error of trend
	1956,57	99	1·6
	57,58	116	2·1
	58,59	112	1·7
	59,60	107	1·3
	60,61	108	1·2
Years	56,58	115	2·8
	57,59	130	2·9
	58,60	120	2·0
	59,61	116	1·9
	56,59	129	3·4
	57,60	139	3·0
	58,61	130	2·6
	56,60	138	3·7
	57,61	151	3·3
	56,61	150	4·1
	1956,57	105	2·6
	57,58	110	2·3
	58,59	113	2·8
	59,60	103	2·2
	60,61	108	1·5
	56,58	116	2·9
	57,59	125	3·3
	58,60	117	2·7
Augusts	59,61	111	2·5
	56,59	131	4·0
	57,60	128	3·2
	58,61	126	3·4
	56,60	135	4·1
	57,61	139	3·5
	56,61	146	4·3
	January	115	2·0
	February	109	2·1
	March	112	2·0
	April	105	2·1
Months	May	111	2·3
(1960 and 1961)	June	104	1·9
	July	107	1·2
	August	108	1·5
	September	109	1·4
	October	112	2·4
	November	109	2·1
	December	102	2·2

* Vehicle-miles in second period as percentage of those in first period.

Accuracy of trends

A discussion of the theory on which the assessment of the accuracy of the trends in vehicle-mileage is assessed appears in Road Research Technical Paper No. 63, pp. 27–35,[2] and some results are given in Table 2.19 for various pairs of periods. The interpretation to be put on the standard error is, roughly, that there is only a one in 20 chance that the true value of the trend will differ from the observed value by more than about twice the standard error. It will be seen that year-to-year trends are more accurate than those from August to August, but either is sufficiently accurate for changes to be measured with reasonable precision. For years two years apart or more, the standard error of the change is normally less than 10 per cent of that change (e.g. the change was 38 units from 1956 to 1960 and the standard error was 3·7 units).

TRENDS IN TRAFFIC ON ALL ROADS

So far the discussion has been dealing with trends and variations of traffic on trunk and classified roads. In this section it is extended to include all roads except motorways. Vehicle-mileage is then related to the numbers of vehicles of each category in use.

In addition to the 50-point census described above, a number of other sources of data are relevant, and these are listed below.

Vehicle-miles travelled in 1960

Fairly reliable estimates of the miles travelled in 1960 by each class of vehicle have been obtained from a sample survey described on pp. 59–63.

In that survey short traffic counts were made during 1960 at each of more than 1000 sites representative of all classes of road in both urban and rural areas, and the results were scaled up to represent the vehicle-miles on all roads in Great Britain by multiplying the average flow on each class of road by the mileage of each class.[4]

Trends in vehicle-miles, 1938–56

These are given for the period up to 1955 by MacNaughton-Smith and Tanner,[7] who combined the results of several series of traffic counts to give the best available estimates of trends. Similar methods have been used to extend their results to 1956,[8] when the 50-point census was started, and to supplement the 50-point census in 1956 and early 1957, when no manual counts were made at the 50 points. Estimates of trends before 1956 are of necessity less accurate than those of trends since that date.

Numbers of vehicles in use

These have been obtained almost entirely from the annual returns[9] published by the Ministry of Transport. These refer to vehicles licensed at any time during the quarter ending in September, and so include vehicles licensed only for the summer months. A certain amount of other information has also been used for government and military vehicles.

Public-service vehicles

The Ministry of Transport publish an annual return[5,10] showing, among other quantities, the total miles run by public-service vehicles while on passenger service. These figures, with some adjustment, are used as a basis of the miles travelled by buses, etc.

Sample survey of commercial vehicles

In 1952, and again in 1958, surveys were made by the Ministry of Transport of samples of commercial-vehicle operators (Glover and Miller,[11] Ministry of Transport.[12]) In each year for one week, records were kept of all journeys made by a sample of vehicles with carriers' licences. These surveys provided estimates of miles travelled by commercial vehicles in the two years, but this information has not been used here, mainly because of the difficulty of relating carriers' licences to a visual classification of vehicles on the road.

Vehicle-Mileages

Table 2.20 gives the estimate of the total vehicle-miles rounded to the nearest hundred million, that were travelled year by year by each class of vehicle on all roads except motorways. The figures were obtained in the following manner.

The 1960 column is taken from the 1000-point census results, except for buses, etc., for which the 1000-point figure is 2·60. The figure for buses etc., in Table 2.20, 2.45, which lies well within the 95 per cent confidence limits of the 1000-point figure, is a compromise between the latter and the figure of 2·36 in the published return for public-service vehicles.[10] The figure is not intended to include mileages of minibuses and microbuses unless they are licensed as public-service vehicles. The 4 per cent difference between 2·45 and 2·36 is an estimate for the mileage that buses travel empty, and the mileage of works, government, and armed forces buses. The 1960 column of Table 2.20 is thought to give the best available estimates of miles travelled by each class of vehicle in 1960, and it is also considered that the estimates are, with the exception of that for public-service vehicles, appreciably more accurate than the best estimates which could be made of the same quantities for earlier years. In addition they are thought to give the most reliable estimate of traffic composition that is obtainable for 1960 or for any other years.

Figures for 1956 to 1959, and 1961 to 1963 were obtained by applying the trends (working to at least five figures) from the 50-point census to the 1960 figures, except for buses, etc., for which trends shown by the published statistics for public-service vehicles were used. For motorcycles and commercial vehicles, the scaling back was carried out on the sub-classes, the totals for the main classes being obtained by addition. The totals for all motor vehicles were obtained by addition of the classes.

The rounding of the final figures is the cause of slight discrepancies between some of the totals and the sums of the constituent items in Table

TABLE 2.20

Total miles run per year by vehicles of different classes on all roads except motorways

Class of vehicle	Thousands of millions of miles															
	1938	1949	1950	1951	1952	1953	1954	1955	1956	1957	1958	1959	1960	1961	1962	1963
All motorcycles .	1·9	1·9	2·7	3·5	3·7	4·2	4·3	4·7	4·6	5·2	5·2	6·1	6·23	6·00	5·37	4·69
Solo motorcycles .									3·1	3·3	3·0	3·4	3·22	3·01	2·54	2·22
Scooters .									0·4	0·6	0·8	1·2	1·51	1·60	1·56	1·34
Mopeds .									0·4	0·5	0·5	0·7	0·79	0·75	0·73	0·66
Motorcycle combinations .									0·7	0·8	0·8	0·8	0·71	0·65	0·55	0·47
Cars and taxis .	17·3	12·6	15·9	18·2	19·0	20·7	23·1	26·3	28·7	28·1	34·4	38·6	42·02	46·73	50·26	54·20
Buses, coaches, trolley-buses and trams .	1·9	2·5	2·5	2·6	2·6	2·6	2·6	2·6	2·6	2·5	2·4	2·5	2·45	2·47	2·47	2·49
All commercial vehicles	7·9	11·8	11·8	12·3	12·4	12·8	13·4	14·3	14·3	14·2	15·8	17·6	18·66	19·79	20·02	20·94
Light vans .		4·1	4·8	5·1	5·4	5·6	5·8	6·1	6·2	6·3	7·2	8·4	9·08	9·80	9·84	10·37
Other commercial vehicles .		7·8	6·9	7·3	7·0	7·2	7·6	8·2	8·1	7·8	8·5	9·2	9·58	9·99	10·18	10·57
All motor vehicles .	29·0	28·9	33·0	36·6	37·8	40·3	43·3	47·8	50·3	49·9	57·8	64·7	69·36	75·00	78·12	82·33
Pedal cycles .	17·1	14·7	12·4	12·9	14·2	12·9	11·7	11·3	10·1	10·0	8·8	8·5	7·47	6·69	5·69	4·95

TABLE 2.21

Indices of yearly vehicle-miles travelled on all roads except motorways

Vehicle-Miles (percentage of 1960)

Class of vehicle	1938	1949	1950	1951	1952	1953	1954	1955	1956	1957	1958	1959	1960	1961	1962	1963
All motorcycles	31	31	43	55	60	67	69	75	74	83	83	97	100	96	86	75
Solo motorcycles									96	101	95	105	100	93	79	69
Scooters									26	42	55	82	100	106	103	89
Mopeds									49	62	68	86	100	95	92	83
Motorcycle combinations									101	107	111	108	100	91	6	67
Cars and taxis	41	30	38	43	45	49	55	63	68	67	82	92	100	111	120	129
Buses, coaches, trolleybuses and trams	79	103	104	106	107	107	106	106	107	102	100	100	100	101	101	102
All commercial vehicles	42	63	63	66	66	69	72	76	77	76	84	94	100	106	107	112
Light vans		45	53	56	60	62	63	67	68	70	80	92	100	108	108	114
Other commercial vehicles		81	73	76	73	75	79	85	85	82	89	96	100	104	106	110
All motor vehicles	42	42	48	53	54	58	62	69	72	72	83	93	100	108	113	119
Pedal cycles	229	197	166	173	191	173	157	152	135	133	118	113	100	90	76	66

2.20. (A similar remark also applies to Table 2.22.) Working with unrounded figures, the mileages in Table 2.20 were expressed as percentages of the values in 1960. Table 2.21 records these values to the nearest 1 per cent.

Some idea of the amount of traffic on motorways can be formed from the available figures for M.1, M.10 and M.45 which together form part of what is known as the London-Birmingham motorway. This was opened in November 1959, and in the first three years of operation it carried 347, 428 and 459 million vehicle-miles respectively. The proportion of heavy commercial vehicles was well above the average for all roads, and the proportion of motorcycles was well below average. Various figures are now available for the other motorways as well. During November and December 1963, when 296 miles were in use, the vehicle-mileage travelled was rather less than 2 per cent of that travelled on ordinary roads.

Vehicles in use

The published licensing returns give a breakdown of numbers of vehicles with current licences; these are sufficiently detailed to obtain reasonably accurate estimates of the numbers of vehicles in use in the various classes distinguished in the manual censuses, (although no correction has been made to allow for vehicles licensed but not in use). Other sources provided estimates, where necessary, of government and armed forces vehicles of civilian type. For reasons given below, the returns for public-service vehicles were again preferred as the basis of estimating the numbers of buses etc., in use.

The types of vehicle comprising the various classes counted in the manual censuses are listed below.

Traffic counts	*Licensing returns, etc.*
Solo motorcycles and scooters	Motorcycles over 50 cc without trailers or sidecars
	Government and military motorcycles
Mopeds	Motorcycles not over 50 cc without trailers or sidecars
Motorcycle combinations	Motorcycles with trailers or sidecars
Cars and taxis	Cars
	Hackney vehicles with not more than eight seats
	Government and military cars
	Motor tricycles
	Invalid carriages
Buses etc.	Vehicles licensed as public-service vehicles (from public-service vehicle returns) plus 4 per cent to account for government, military, and works buses.

Traffic counts	*Licensing returns, etc.*
Light vans	Farmers and general commercial vehicles not over 30 cwt
	Government and military vehicles not over 30 cwt
	Pedestrian-controlled vehicles
Other commercial vehicles	Farmers and general commercial vehicles over 30 cwt
	Government and military vehicles over 30 cwt
	Non-agricultural tractors
	Ambulances.

This classification has been chosen to correspond as closely as possible to that used in the 50-point census (see pp. 28–50).

Agricultural tractors, fire appliances, trench diggers, road rollers, etc., are not included. Solo motorcycles and scooters are combined into one group because their relative proportions cannot be decided from the licensing returns.

With the exception of buses, etc., for 1938, the numbers of vehicles in use, given in Table 2.22, are based on the above classification; the 1938 figure for buses was obtained from the licensing returns and is the sum of the number of trams and hackney vehicles with more than eight seats. Government and armed forces buses and coaches are included in this figure; it is assumed that the number of works buses in 1938 was negligible. In the post-war period the forces' vehicles have not figured in licensing returns, and a change in registration procedure for government vehicles was made in 1951. Before 1952 no separate details of government buses are given in the returns, and it is not known if these are included in the returns for 1949 and 1950. For these reasons, and to achieve maximum consistency with the figures of mileage of buses, etc., the estimates of numbers of buses, etc., in use from 1949 to 1961 are based on the returns for public-service vehicles. The numbers of vehicles licensed as public-service vehicles on 31st December are given in these returns, and the average of two successive values estimates the number of public-service vehicles in use during the intervening year. These numbers were increased by 4 per cent to account for the buses used by works (2 per cent), government (1 per cent), and armed forces (1 per cent). The figure for government buses and coaches is known to be accurate, and certain sources of information support the view that the number of forces buses is comparable. The 2 per cent allowance (roughly 1600) for works buses is a guess based on some indirect information, but is thought to be sufficiently accurate for present purposes, and this number has, in fact, been deducted from the totals of cars and taxis from 1949 to 1963. This 4 per cent addition differs in composition from that between the mileages of buses, etc., in Table 2.20 and the return mileages for public-service vehicles. This latter difference includes the mileage that public-service vehicles travel empty (which certain sources suggest is about 2 per cent).

Miles per vehicle per year

Using the unrounded figures from which the figures in Tables 2.20 and 2.22 were obtained, the average mileages per vehicle per year on all roads

TABLE 2.22
Vehicles in use

Thousands of vehicles (in September quarter)

Class of vehicle	1938	1949	1950	1951	1952	1953	1954	1955	1956	1957	1958	1959	1960	1961	1962	1963
All motorcycles	446	42	737	831	931	1019	1117	1230	1299	1439	1482	1686	1803	1798	1787	1762
Solo motorcycles and scooters	340	546	600	631	681	724	774	842	894	995	1052	1183	1270	1264	1256	1208
Mopeds			29	79	120	154	192	227	246	284	273	347	388	396	397	435
Motorcycle combinations	106	97	106	120	130	141	152	161	158	160	158	155	145	138	134	120
Cars and taxis	2006	2227	2356	2482	2608	2846	3178	3603	3964	4265	4629	5053	5624	6094	6680	7508
Buses, coaches, trolleybuses and trams	62	79	83	85	86	86	84	84	83	83	82	81	80	79	80	83
All commercial vehicles	523	918	970	1015	1048	1085	1120	1197	1274	1305	1354	1411	1483	1539	1559	1619
Light vans	225	393	423	449	480	515	543	599	665	696	740	784	830	868	886	920
Other commercial vehicles	298	525	547	566	568	569	577	598	609	608	614	628	652	671	672	699
All motor vehicles	3037	3866	4144	4414	4674	5035	5499	6114	6620	7092	7547	8231	8990	9510	10106	10972

except motorways, were found. These, rounded off to the nearest 500 for buses, etc., and to the nearest hundred for other vehicles, are given in Table 2.23 and are plotted in Fig. 2.12.

Because 4 per cent has been added both to the number of public-service vehicles and to their vehicle-mileage, to allow for buses not in public-service, the mileage per bus, etc., is the same as the passenger-carrying mileage per public-service vehicle. This is consistent with works, government, and armed forces buses having a lower overall mileage than public-service vehicles.

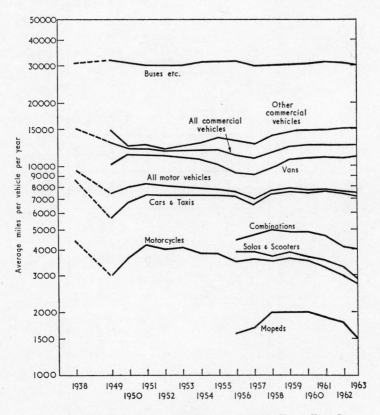

Fig. 2.12. Average miles per vehicle per year 1938–63 on all roads except motorways

No adjustment to the mileage per car and per motorcycle has been made for vehicles visiting this country or visiting other countries. The mileages in Table 2.20 are those driven on roads in Great Britain, while the numbers of vehicles are the numbers licensed in Great Britain. Figures supplied by the A.A. and the R.A.C. indicate that in 1963 about 80 000 vehicles visited Great Britain, and 300 000 visited other countries. This is an annual movement which has increased considerably in recent years.

TABLE 2.23

Average miles per vehicle per year on all roads except motorways

Class of vehicle	Annual miles per vehicle (hundreds)															
	1938	1949	1950	1951	1952	1953	1954	1955	1956	1957	1958	1959	1960	1961	1962	1963
All motorcycles	44	30	37	42	40	41	38	38	35	36	35	36	35	33	30	27
Solo motorcycles and scooters									39	39	37	39	37	36	33	29
Mopeds									16	17	20	20	20	19	18	15
Motorcycle combinations									45	47	50	49	49	47	41	40
Cars and taxis	86	57	68	73	73	73	73	73	72	66	74	76	75	77	75	72
Buses, coaches, trolleybuses and trams	310	320	310	305	305	305	310	310	315	300	300	305	305	310	310	300
All commercial vehicles	151	129	122	122	118	118	119	119	112	109	116	124	126	129	128	129
Light vans		103	114	113	113	109	106	101	93	91	98	107	109	113	111	113
Other commercial vehicles		148	127	129	123	126	132	137	133	129	139	146	147	149	151	151
All motor vehicles	96	75	80	83	81	80	79	78	76	70	77	79	77	79	77	75

Results

The most obvious feature of the results in Tables 2.20 and 2.21 is the persistent post-war increase in the total miles run by motor vehicles, and especially by cars. Total motor vehicle-miles have more than doubled in the eleven years from 1952 to 1963, and car mileage increased by 185 per cent in the same period. Commercial vehicles have shared in the increase, but to a smaller extent than cars. Commercial vehicle-mileage increased by 69 per cent in the eleven years from 1952 to 1963, light van-mileage increasing more rapidly than heavy commercial vehicle-mileage. Motorcycle-mileage showed a steady increase up to 1960, mainly due to the increase in scooters and mopeds, but since 1960 motorcycle-mileage has decreased quite sharply. Pedal-cycle mileages have decreased, but mileages of buses, etc., remained about constant from 1950 to 1956, and, after a 6 per cent fall, remained constant from 1957 to 1963. This fall is confirmed by the results of the 50-point census. The figures provide an estimate of the effect of the Suez crisis in 1956–7. Motor-vehicle-mileage would have been about 2 per cent higher in 1956 and 6 per cent higher in 1957 if fuel had not been rationed for parts of these years.

Trends in the numbers of vehicles in use in the various classes are similar to those of vehicle-mileages, resulting in a relatively small variation in mileage per vehicle. The persistent decline in miles per motorcycle between 1951 and 1956 is probably due to the increasing proportions of scooters and mopeds, which tend to have lower mileages.

Although heavy commercial vehicles have not increased as rapidly in numbers as light vans, the heavy commercial vehicles appear to be performing greater annual mileages per vehicle than in the early 1950's, and it is thought that this may to some extent reflect the raising of their speed limit and the increasing use of mechanical loading methods.

DISTRIBUTION OF TRAFFIC OVER THE ROAD SYSTEM

Reference was made above to a sample survey carried out in 1960 at more than 1000 sites representative of all classes of road and of all parts of Great Britain. This survey was concerned partly with the physical characteristics of the road system and partly with the distribution of traffic on the road system. A brief description of the second aspect is given here, full details of the complete survey being given in Road Research Technical Paper No. 62.[4]

Nature of Sampling Procedure

If the points had been distributed evenly over all classes of road, then the majority would have been on roads of little importance. To overcome this difficulty a stratified random sample was used, the roads being divided by an urban/rural classification (according to local authority areas), a qualitative classification ("trunk", "class I", "class II", "class III" and "unclassified"), and a geographical classification into ten areas (the nine Ministry of Transport Engineering Divisions and Scotland). In each of the 80 strata so defined, the number of sample points selected was at least five, the selection being made by a method involving the intersections of roads with lines randomly drawn on a map. In addition, the 50 points of the 50-point census referred to above (see p. 28) were themselves included in the 1000-point census. The selection of sample points was based on the road system as it existed in 1956, and consequently any roads (including motorways) built since 1956 were not represented.

Normally the counts were made at the request of the Laboratory by highway authorities during the months of May, June, September and October, 1960, these months being chosen to avoid extreme summer and winter flows. In general, two, three or four counts were made at each point, depending on the class of road, the counts at any one point being carried out on different days of the week. At least one count at every point was made on a Saturday or Sunday. All the counts were made manually and each covered an 8-hour period, either 6 a.m.–2 p.m. or 2 p.m.–10 p.m. The classification of vehicles was the same as that adopted for the 50-point census, as described above (see p. 33). The results of each 8-hour count were scaled up to represent the whole 24 hours of the same day, on the basis of 24-hour manual counts made at the census points of the 50-point census. These 24-hour totals were further scaled up to give estimates of the total flow at each point during the period November 1959 to October 1960, and hence average daily flows for that period were calculated.

Results

Estimates of vehicle-miles per day run by each class of vehicle on each class of road in urban and rural areas are shown in Table 2.24. Boroughs and urban districts are counted as "urban" and rural districts are counted as "rural". Over Great Britain as a whole, 54 per cent of the motor-vehicle-miles were run in urban areas, an amount less than proportionate to the population of these areas. Altogether trunk roads carried nearly one-quarter of the motor-vehicle-miles, class I more than one-third, class II and class III roads one eighth each, and unclassified roads about one sixth.

By combining all the returns it was possible to estimate the overall distribution of flow, i.e. the proportions of miles of road that carry any

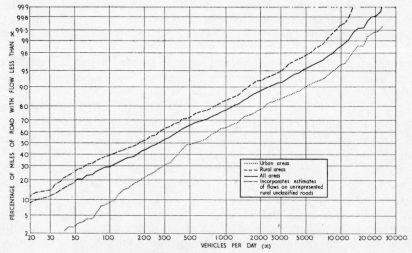

Fig. 2.13. Cumulative distribution of flow, motor vehicles

TABLE 2.24

Thousands of vehicle-miles per day, all roads in Great Britain, 1959–60

| | Urban | | | | | | Rural | | | | | | Urban and Rural |
	Trunk	Class I	Class II	Class III	Unclassified	All roads	Trunk	Class I	Class II	Class III	Unclassified	All roads	Total
Pedal cycles . . .	1057	3391	1790	1548	7104	14 891	624	1094	1007	2105	1248	6077	20 968
Motorcycles													
Mopeds . . .	126	532	217	209	495	1579	84	148	120	178	69	599	2178
Scooters . . .	302	1127	358	292	819	2897	331	489	223	310	131	1483	4380
Solo motorcycles .	620	1843	677	452	1493	5085	855	1202	603	1040	473	4173	9258
Motorcycle combinations	152	482	151	122	335	1243	186	233	116	144	52	731	1973
All motorcycles	1200	3984	1402	1076	3142	10 803	1456	2072	1061	1672	725	6986	17 789
Cars and taxis . .	9288	20 436	7399	4880	15 042	60 645	16 074	18 131	7013	8985	3496	53 700	114 344
Public-service vehicles .	490	2260	647	124	781	4302	686	931	340	343	166	2466	6768
Commercial vehicles													
Light vans . .	1713	4613	1688	1043	4254	13 312	2384	3199	1590	2468	1087	10 728	24 040
Other—2 axles .	2068	4388	1087	529	2180	10 253	4018	3110	1284	1530	737	10 677	20 930
3 axles or more .	363	548	88	46	109	1155	831	358	98	191	66	1544	2698
Articulated or with trailer	282	348	48	27	70	776	533	238	58	87	38	954	1730
All commercial vehicles .	4427	9898	2912	1645	6613	25 495	7765	6904	3030	4275	1927	23 903	49 398
All motor vehicles .	15 405	40 178	12 360	7725	25 577	101 246	25 981	28 038	11 445	15 275	6315	87 054	188 300

given amount of traffic. Figure 2.13 shows this distribution plotted on a cumulative basis, the horizontal scale indicating the numbers of vehicles per day and the vertical scale indicating the percentage of the road mileage estimated to carry less than this number of vehicles per day. The horizontal scale is logarithmic and the vertical scale is based on normal probability.

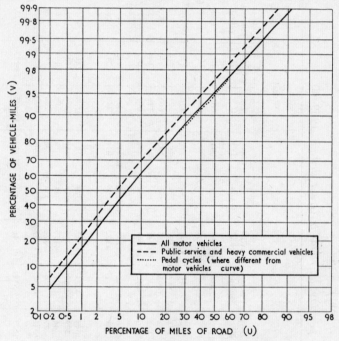

Fig. 2.14. Percentage of vehicle-miles, V, carried by the busiest U per cent of the road miles, all days

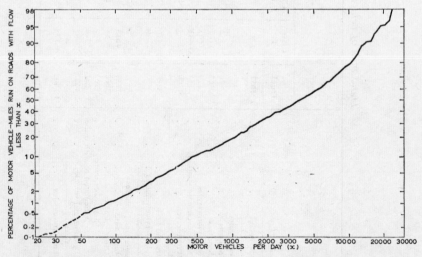

Fig. 2.15. Distribution of vehicle-miles among roads of different levels of flow

The fact that the cumulative curves are approximately straight lines shows that in urban and rural areas the traffic flow has a distribution known as the "log-normal" distribution.

This same information may be conveyed in two other ways, as shown in Fig. 2.14 and 2.15. Fig. 2.14 shows the extent to which the vehicle-miles are concentrated on the busiest roads. It shows, for example, that just over 95 per cent of all vehicle-miles are travelled on the busiest 50 per cent of the road mileage. Figure 2.15 shows the amount of travel on roads with different levels of flow. It shows, for example, that only 19 per cent of all motor-vehicle-miles are travelled on roads carrying less than the average flow of 1000 vehicles per day.

FORECASTS OF FUTURE NUMBERS OF VEHICLES

Estimates are given in this section of the numbers of motor vehicles that will be licensed in Great Britain during the next 50 years, broadly classified into four classes of vehicle. Economic forecasting of this type is a notoriously perilous undertaking, and the standards of rigour that can be applied fall far short of those usually demanded in scientific research. However, the value of such forecasts is such that the attempt is worth making; for example, trends over the next 20 years or so are obviously important in relation to proposed road improvements, while trends over 50 years or so are necessary in considering the provision of garage space in new housing areas.

Considerable use is made of data for the United States of America, since growth in the number of motor vehicles has proceeded much further there than in Great Britain.

Data

For the most part, this section is concerned with two quantities, the number of vehicles per head of population, and the rate of increase of this. For Great Britain the number of vehicles means the number of motor vehicles licensed at any time in the three months ending September. Four classes of vehicle are distinguished:

Cars (classified by c.c. or by h.p.)

Motor cycles (including mopeds, scooters, combinations and tricycles)

Agricultural tractors (£2-licence class)

Other vehicles (including commercial vehicles, public-service vehicles, taxis, pedestrian-controlled vehicles, other tractors, and exempt vehicles)

Vehicles operated under the Crown Vehicles Scheme and military vehicles are excluded. The former constitute under 1 per cent of the total number of vehicles.

The population figures used are the mid-year estimates of the *de facto* population made by the Registrars General for England and Wales and for Scotland, and include persons of all ages, including children.

For the United States, vehicles are usually classified as cars and others, and the figures were obtained from the annual return "Highway Statistics", issued by the U.S. Department of Commerce, Bureau of Public Roads. Motorcycles, of which there are a negligible number, are excluded. Population figures are normally those for July 1, and are taken from the annual "Statistical Abstract" of the United States Department of Commerce.[13]

Preliminary Discussion

The basic quantity to be studied is vehicles per head of population, for four classes of vehicle. Forecasts are made for the 50 years from 1960 for each of these classes and, by using projections of the population made by the Government Actuary, corresponding estimates of the numbers of vehicles are derived. The forecasts for vehicles per head in this chapter were published[14] in 1962 and used 1960 as a base; those for population were issued by the Government Actuary in 1963. It is intended to keep the former figures under review. The forecasts apply to Great Britain as a whole, but it is suggested below how they may be adapted to particular parts of the country.

For each class of vehicle, therefore, a curve is required stretching from 1960 to 2010. It will be postulated firstly that this will be a smooth curve: no doubt within 50 years there will be major social or economic events which will cause sharp changes in the development of the numbers of vehicles per head, but the dates of these are, it is supposed, unforeseeable. The forecasts are in any case only applicable if there are no catastrophic events such as world wars; if the reader believes that there will be such a catastrophe within ten years from now, his own estimates of numbers of vehicles in 15 years time may be very different from those presented here. It is also assumed in making the forecasts that there will be no substantial substitution by other means of transport (e.g. helicopter, hovercraft) for purposes for which motor vehicles are used at the present time. No explicit mention is made of the use of railways; it is believed that, in general, changes in railway usage will be dependent on changes in road usage, rather than the reverse. It is further assumed that the lack of road capacity will not be a major retarding influence on the growth of vehicle numbers. If no further construction or improvement were allowed, then the increases would clearly be much less than if road provision was reasonably closely related to the demand.

It seems reasonable to suppose that as well as being smooth the growth curve should continue the curve of growth experienced in the immediate past. This means that in 1960 the forecast curve should take the actual value, and that the percentage rate of growth per year should be close to that experienced in the few years up to 1960.

The algebraic form of the forecast curves is largely open to choice. It must have at least three constants that can be fitted, for if there were only two the whole curve would be determined by the current number of vehicles per head and its rate of growth. On the other hand, it is improbable that the the reliability of any forecasts would be such as to justify more than three constants. A type of curve often used to represent growth, in both social and biological phenomena, is the logistic curve, described mathematically in Appendix 1. It has three constants, and tends upwards

Manual roadside traffic count
PLATE 2.1

Single and multiple hand tallies for counting vehicles
PLATE 2.2

SYX-RRL vehicle counter and detector
PLATE 2.3

Interior of Streeter Amet RCH recording counter
PLATE 2.4

Fischer and Porter counter recording on punched tape
PLATE 2.5

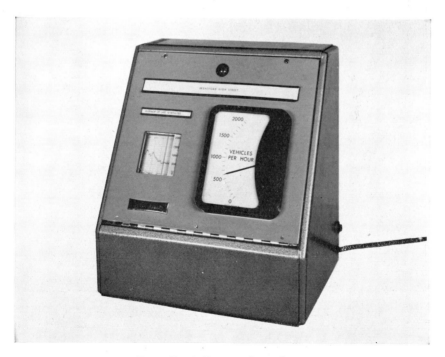

Decca flow indicator and recorder
PLATE 2.6

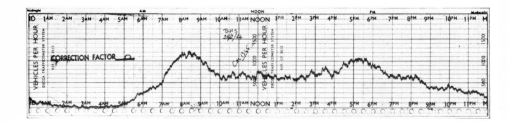

Record from Decca flow measuring equipment

PLATE 2.7

Fixings used for fastening traffic counter detectors

PLATE 2.8

Team inspecting automatic traffic counter
PLATE 2.9

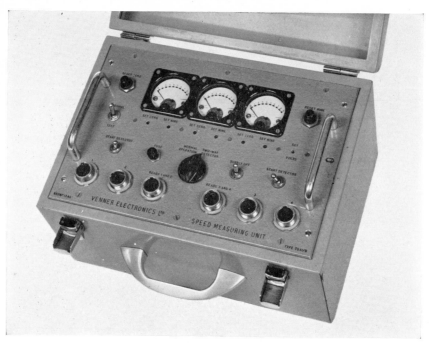

A transistorized speedmeter

PLATE 3.1

Detector layout used with transistorized speedmeter. The photograph shows
the layout using two pairs of detectors, one pair for each half of the road. The
third tube carries the signal from the detectors on the far side of the road to the
mobile laboratory

PLATE 3.2

**Version of transistorized speedmeter which
records on punched paper tape**

PLATE 3.3

Remote speed indicator and recorder (Decca trafficometry equipment)

PLATE 3.4

Radar speedmeter in use (Electro-matic model S2)

PLATE 3.5

Radar speedmeter (Electro-matic model S5)

PLATE 3.6

towards a limit with the passage of time. The percentage rate of growth decreases steadily as the upper limit is approached. This curve is used in this section for the forecasts of the number of vehicles per head. Forecasts of the number of vehicles follow a slightly less regular curve, since the predicted population growth is not quite uniform.

To find the third constant required to determine the forecast curve, it is necessary to estimate the upper limit, i.e. the maximum number of vehicles per head that will ever be demanded. The largest part of this section is devoted to considering what values of these "saturation levels" are reasonable.

Table 2.25 shows the number of vehicles per head in 1960, the percentage rates of growth per year in two recent periods, and the percentage rate of growth in 1960 used in fitting the forecast curve.

The forecast for motor vehicles as a whole is made by adding the four component forecasts; it is therefore not strictly a logistic curve.

TABLE 2.25

Vehicles per head and rates of growth Great Britain

Class of Vehicle	Vehicles per head, 1960	Percentage rate of growth per year		
		1955–58	1958–60	Assumed for 1960
Cars . . .	0·108	8·3	9·5	9·0
Motorcycles .	0·036	6·1	10·1	9·0
Agricultural tractors .	0·009	3·5	2·8	3·0
Other vehicles . .	0·031	3·5	3·8	4·0
All motor vehicles .	0·184	6·7	8·2	—

Some analyses of past and current data

EFFECT OF POPULATION DENSITY ON VEHICLES PER HEAD

It is known that the number of motor vehicles per head is greater in less densely populated areas. Figure 2.16 illustrates this for Great Britain and the United States in 1960. Great Britain has been divided into three parts (South of England, Wales and North of England, Scotland) and counties have been grouped to give at least 200 000 population in each group (see Appendix 2). Population density is plotted on a logarithmic scale.

It is clear that the number of vehicles per head for each of the four groups of points tends to fall as population density increases. Within each group much of the scatter of the points about the general tendency for that group can be attributed to variations in income or some related factor; American states with a high average income per head tend to lie towards the top of the cluster of points, and those with a low average income at the bottom, while in Great Britain the same is true of counties with high and low porportions of their population in a high social class, as defined by the Registrar-General for the 1951 Census of Population.

4

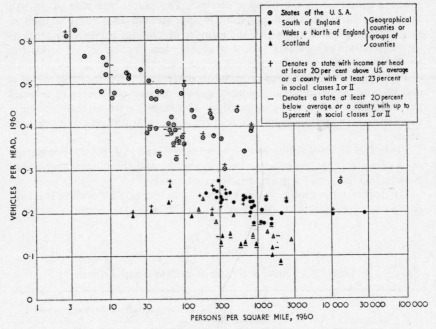

Fig. 2.16. Vehicles per head and population density, Great Britain and the United States, 1960

A further result shown by Fig. 2.16 is that while part of the difference between the numbers of vehicles per head in the two countries arises from the difference in population density, most of it must be attributed to other factors, such as differences in income levels. Table 2.26 gives the approximate number of vehicles per head in Great Britain as a proportion of that in the United States, both for the countries as a whole and for parts of it with similar population densities. While the overall vehicle ownership per head in Great Britain in 1960 was only 45 per cent of that in the United States, in areas with similar population densities the proportion was about 56 per cent. This largely refutes the argument that vehicle ownership in

TABLE 2.26

Vehicles per head in Great Britain as a proportion of vehicles per head in the United States, 1960

	Relative vehicles per head	
	Overall	Areas with 300 persons per square mile
United States	1·00	1·00
South of England	0·51	0·62
Wales and North of England . . .	0·37	0·48
Scotland	0·32	0·38
Whole of Great Britain . . .	0·45	0·56

Great Britain can never reach the levels found in the United States because Britain is a small crowded island while the United States has large open spaces; there seems to be no reason why the number of vehicles per head should not in the long run at least double, thus reaching the current United States level in areas of similar population density.

The percentage rates of growth in Great Britain and the United States have tended to decline over the course of the last 50 years, but this decline has not been at all closely related to the current number of vehicles per head, nor has it been uniform over the years. Thus the general trends over the course of the last 50 years provide little indication of what may be expected in the future, at least as regards the ultimate "ceiling" number of vehicles per head.

One reason for this is not hard to find: the rate of growth of vehicle numbers is closely related to the rate of economic expansion (as expressed, for example, by real income per head), and this expansion has not proceeded smoothly over the years. The most obvious example of this relation is the influence of the depression of the early thirties, when, especially in the United States, there was a fall in the number of vehicles per head. The relation between incomes and vehicle ownership is discussed further below.

EFFECT OF INCOMES ON VEHICLES PER HEAD

The relation between incomes and vehicle ownership can be looked at in at least three ways. In the first place there are several sets of data (Dawson,[15] some data collected by Smeed, and data supplied by the Ministry of Labour), which show at a given date the proportion of persons or of households owning cars and motorcycles at different levels of income. For cars this proportion varies from near zero for households in the lowest income group to 70 to 80 per cent for those in the highest income group; for motorcycles it increases with increase in income from zero to 14 per cent of households, and then in the highest income group (over £2000 per year per household, 1959) it falls to 10 per cent, according to the most recent data. From these data it is possible to predict the increase in total ownership likely to result from a uniform percentage increase of incomes. It is found that a 1 per cent increase in all incomes corresponds to between 1·0 and 1·6 per cent more cars, and to between 0·4 and 0·5 per cent more motorcycles. Larger increases in incomes would lead to nearly proportional increases in cars, up to about double the present incomes, but the maximum increase in motorcycles would be about 50 per cent. An increase of 100 per cent in incomes would give 20–25 per cent more motorcycles.

The second way of looking at the relation between vehicle ownership and income is to plot the number of vehicles per head for the whole of Great Britain for different years against an index of real income in those years. The method shows that, broadly speaking, for every 1 per cent by which real incomes rise the ownership of cars and motorcycles rises by 2 or 3 per cent. The figure of 2–3 per cent given by this method is about double the corresponding figure given by the first method. This implies that only about one half of the actual historical increase in the number of cars and motorcycles can be attributed directly to increasing prosperity; the remainder must be due to other factors, such as changes in social attitudes to motor vehicles and changes in the real cost of motoring.

Figure 2.17 show the total numbers of motor vehicles per head in relation to incomes between 1929 and 1960 both for Great Britain and for the United States. The horizontal scale refers to personal incomes after deduction of direct taxation and national insurance contributions, corrected to allow for the changing value of money. An exchange rate of 2·8 dollars to the pound has been assumed as a basis for comparing the values for the two countries. The data were mainly obtained from "National Income and Expenditure"[16] and the "Statistical Abstract of the United States"[13] for 1961; the early Great Britain income data were taken from the unpublished

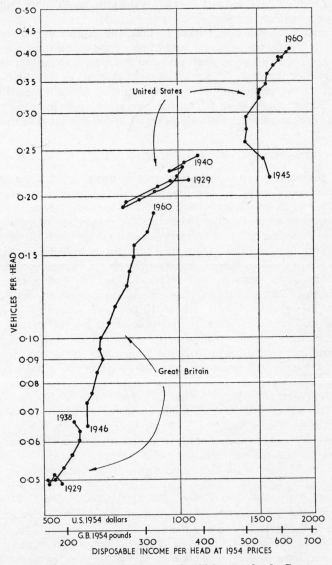

Fig. 2.17. Historical growth of vehicles per head, Great Britain and the United States, 1929–60, in relation to incomes

paper by Smeed. In Great Britain since the war, each 1 per cent increase in incomes has been accompanied by an increase of about 2·75 per cent in vehicles per head; in the United States, on the other hand, the corresponding increase in vehicles per head has recently dropped to about 1 per cent. This may indicate an approach towards saturation, but it is not clear whether a similar fall may be expected in Great Britain.

In the early post-war period a rapid increase in vehicles per head was experienced in the United States, without any corresponding increase in income; this can be attributed to a recovery from the artificially low number of vehicles at the end of the war in relation to the income levels at the time. This probably also explains to a great extent why the post-war rates of growth in the U.S.A. have been tending to decease; Fig. 2.17 does not give any grounds for supposing that this decrease means that saturation has practically been reached. Further evidence is provided by the fact that ownership was in 1960 substantially lower in the poorer states than in those with above-average incomes, as shown by Fig. 2.16.

The comparison in Fig. 2.17 of the vehicle ownership rates in the two countries is of interest. The current level in Great Britain is only slightly below the level in the United States for the same income. This perhaps tends to support the view that past trends in the United States may be helpful in forecasting future values for Great Britain.

The third method of relating vehicle ownership to income is by means of international comparisons, as shown, for example, by Maizels et al[17] and Dicks-Mireaux et al[18] For cars, this method gives much the same ownership elasticity (increase in ownership per unit increase in income) as comparisons between income-groups, but for motorcycles the situation is less clear and is discussed further in the section on estimates of saturation level.

A general conclusion from the above discussion is that while a knowledge of future levels of real income would give some indication of future levels of vehicle ownership, it would not by itself form a reliable basis for predicting far into the future; further, it is by no means clear whether predictions that can be made of future incomes are sufficiently reliable; if they are little more than extrapolation from past trends, then it would seem preferable to predict future vehicle ownership by extrapolating past trends in vehicle ownership.

GROWTH RATES IN COUNTIES AND STATES

It has been seen that while the national vehicle totals suggest that there is a growth process that is proceeding for the most part in a single direction but at a variable rate, these figures provide little or no indication of how much farther the process will go before reaching a "ceiling", the maximum number of vehicles per head that will ever be reached. The growth rates for individual counties of Great Britain and states of the United States will now be considered at some length; something can be learnt from these because the growth process is much more advanced in some of them than in others.

The data for the post-war periods 1956–60 (G.B.) and 1955–60 (U.S.A.) for cars are shown in Figs. 2.18 and 21.9. If y is the average percentage rate of increase per year of cars per head, and x is the average number of cars per head, and if the number of cars per head at the beginning of the

5-year period is denoted by u, and that at the end of the period by v, then

$$y = (v/u)^{1/5}$$
$$x = (uv)^{1/2}$$

In the case of Great Britain, each point (x,y) represents one or more geographical counties; neighbouring counties have where necessary been grouped (as in Appendix 2) so as to give at least 200 000 population per group. English counties have been distinguished from Welsh and Scottish ones, but none have been omitted for any reason; the group consisting of Cheshire and Flintshire is regarded as being in England. In the United

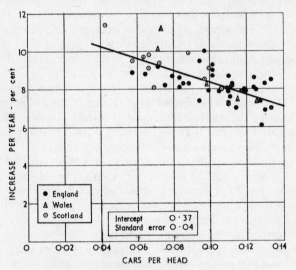

Fig. 2.18. Growth rates of cars per head, Great
Britain, 1956–1960

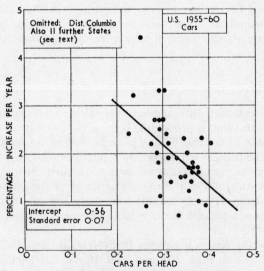

Fig. 2.19. Growth rates of cars per head,
United States, 1955–60

States each point represents a single state. The figures for the District of Columbia (largely Washington D.C.) tended to be erratic and have been omitted throughout. In 1955–60 the percentage increases tended to be lower, and more care was therefore necessary in removing the influence of extraneous factors; apart from the District of Columbia, eleven states were omitted. These consisted of the four with the largest population increases, two with the smallest increase in incomes, one with the largest increase in incomes, and four where the data suggested that there was a change in the basis of classification of vehicles.

Without enquiring at this stage into the underlying logic of the process, it may be noted that the diagrams show a tendency for the greatest percentage increases in cars per head to occur in those areas where the number of cars per head is least. Similar results were obtained when data for the two five-year periods prior to those in Figs. 2.18 and 2.19 were plotted. Straight lines have been fitted to the points in the diagrams so that the "intercept" of these lines on the x-axis can be read off; the values are given on the diagrams. The simplest interpretation to be put on any of these intercepts is that, during the period used in calculating it, any area with cars per head less than the value of the intercept would still be showing an increase. Although the areas studied in this section all have levels of cars per head appreciably less than the corresponding intercept, one may imagine that there are smaller areas, e.g. high class residential areas, in which car ownership would be much nearer the intercept and would still be increasing, though relatively less slowly.

The standard errors of the intercepts, given on the diagrams, are based on the usual statistical assumptions of linearity, randomness and independence; it should be noted that these assumptions may not be strictly true for the present data, for a variety of reasons. In particular, the assumption of linearity may not be valid, though there is practically no evidence of non-linearity in the diagrams and there seems to be no obvious reason why the relationships should not be reasonably straight over a limited extension of the observed range. It seems probable, therefore, that the standard errors quoted are too low, but they are perhaps not so low as to be valueless.

In Fig. 2.20 the intercepts for both countries have been plotted against year. It will be seen that while in Great Britain the intercept is increasing fairly rapidly and was in 1962 about 0·4 that for the United States has not increased much over the post-war period, and was about 0·55.

The other classes of vehicle show, during the most recent period, little consistent behaviour. In the United States, vehicles other than cars show a tendency markedly the reverse of that of cars; i.e. areas with the greatest number of "other vehicles" per head are experiencing the greatest rates of increase. The reason for this is not known.

In Great Britain, motorcycles show some tendency for rates of increase to be low where the level of ownership is high, but only if areas of low population density are excluded. Agricultural tractors and "other vehicles" show no useful correlation.

Consideration must now be given to the use, if any, that can be made of the intercepts that have been calculated, particularly those for cars. To take the most important case, the intercept of 0·37 for cars for the period 1956–60 in Great Britain (Fig. 2.18) means, as noted above, that in conditions obtaining during that period any area with fewer than 0·37 cars

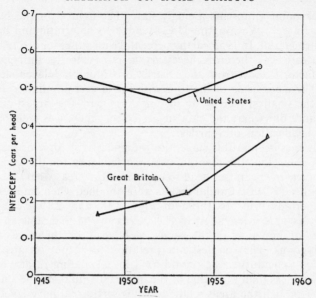

Fig. 2.20. Variations of intercept for cars per head

per head was tending to show an increase in cars per head. It is now convenient to introduce the idea of a current target level applicable to a particular area at a particular date. This is the level of car ownership for which there is at that date a potential demand; the actual level is less than this target level because of economic influences and the effects of congestion and other aspects of urban living. The current target level represents the current desire of the people in the area for car ownership; it therefore seems reasonable to suppose that only in exceptional circumstances, for example if a more desirable means of travel became readily available, would it decrease with the passage of time. It will be assumed that this current target level at a given date is the same for all areas within Great Britain; this is discussed below. On this assumption, the common value for it must be the intercept $0 \cdot 37$, since this is the level at which it is supposed that no further growth would occur. It follows, therefore, that in Great Britain in the period 1956–60 the current target level was $0 \cdot 37$ in all areas, and that growth in each area would proceed at least until that level was actually achieved. If, as a result of an increase in the potentialities of the motor car, or in the appreciation of its potentialities, the current target level were to rise, then growth would continue beyond $0 \cdot 37$ cars per head.

It is now of interest to consider the validity of the assumption stated above, that the current target level at a given date is the same in all areas. This assumption implies, for example, that shortage of road space in large towns serves to prevent the realization of the ultimate demand rather than to modify the demand itself. Fig. 2.21 throws some light on this assumption; here the diagrams for car increases for 1956–60 in Great Britain (Fig. 2.18) and for 1955–60 in the United States (Fig. 2.19) are shown with areas of high, middle and low population densities distinguished. While the data are insufficient to determine separate intercepts for each group of points, there is little evidence in the case of Great Britain that the regression lines

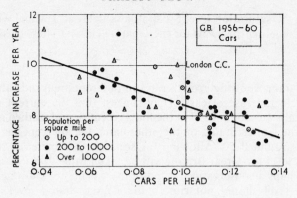

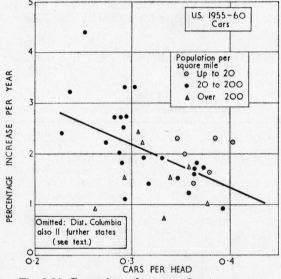

Fig. 2.21. Comparison of car growth rates on areas
of different population densities

differ. In the United States, however, there appears to be a slight tendency
for the rates of increase to be lower in the more densely populated states,
though this might be due to other factors. Thus the effect of congestion may
perhaps be thought of as similar to that of economic limitations; both tend
to restrict the number of vehicles, but neither puts an absolute upper limit
to the number, except an absurdly high one. Apart from population density,
the only other major factor that one might expect to give rise to different
target levels in different areas is the economic and social variation between
areas. However, the social differences are largely economic in origin; since
the target level refers to ownership free of economic limitations, this factor
would not therefore be important.

Estimates of saturation level

Because the data that have been examined for the four classes of vehicle
behave in different ways, and in order to achieve a self-consistent set of

4*

estimates, the saturation level for motor vehicles as a whole will be found by adding together the levels for the separate classes. These classes will now be considered in turn.

CARS

The diagrams showing growth rates in different areas indicate consistent behaviour in the case of cars. They suggest that the current intercept in Great Britain was about $0 \cdot 37$ in the most recent period studied and was still rising. In the United States, on the other hand, the intercept has maintained a level of around $0 \cdot 50$. Allowing for some further increase, the ultimate saturation level for Great Britain will be taken to be $0 \cdot 40$ cars per person. This is perhaps a conservative estimate; there is no obvious reason why the saturation level should not rise to the United States' level. Alternative forecasts using $0 \cdot 50$ instead of $0 \cdot 40$ have therefore been made. In 1960 seven of the states of the United States of America had more than $0 \cdot 40$ cars per head. The highest figure for any state was $0 \cdot 47$.

MOTORCYCLES

The study of growth rates in different areas does not show any marked evidence of a saturation level.

TABLE 2.27

Motorcycle ownership in various countries

Country	1950			1959 or 1960		
	Motorcycles as percentage of all motor vehicles	Motorcycles per head	Other motor vehicles per head	Motorcycles as percentage of all motor vehicles	Motorcycles per head	Other motor vehicles per head
Australia .	9	0·016	0·153	4	0·012	0·250
Austria .	48	0·020	0·021	61	0·094	0·059
Belgium .	27	0·017	0·048	41	0·066	0·096
Canada .	2	0·003	0·185	1	0·003	0·265
Denmark .	21	0·012	0·044	19	0·026	0·111
Eire* . .	4	0·002	0·044	9	0·008	0·079
Finland . .	13	0·002	0·015	30	0·022	0·051
Franch .	23	0·017	0·058	47	0·129	0·148
Germany .	48	0·019	0·021	49	0·078	0·080
Great Britain* .	17	0·015	0·074	19	0·036	0·148
India . .	—	—	—	14	0·000	0·001
Italy . .	57	0·016	0·012	61	0·071	0·045
Japan . .	—	—	—	41	0·010	0·015
Luxemburg .	25	0·016	0·046	20	0·031	0·128
Netherlands .	41	0·015	0·021	66	0·102	0·053
New Zealand	5	0·011	0·208	18	0·054	0·253
N. Ireland* .	10	0·007	0·068	15	0·023	0·137
Norway .	18	0·008	0·035	33	0·043	0·087
Poland .	—	—	—	67	0·021	0·011
Portugal .	6	0·001	0·011	11	0·003	0·023
Spain . .	8	0·000	0·006	55	0·016	0·013
Sweden .	38	0·030	0·049	15	0·028	0·160
Switzerland .	28	0·016	0·040	35	0·054	0·098
South Africa	4	0·002	0·052	6	0·004	0·070
United States*	1	0·003	0·322	1	0·003	0·410

*1960 for these countries; 1959 for the remainder.

Consideration of the trends in various countries (see Table 2.27) does not lead to any clear cut indication. It is thought that the main cause of any substantial increase in ownership will be technical developments in motorcycles, together with any change in social attitudes arising from such development or from other sources. Ultimately, a decrease in motorcycle numbers may be expected, but this is likely to be in the fairly distant future, and is too uncertain to be included in the prediction curve.

Taking the above considerations into account, a saturation level of $0 \cdot 06$ has been assumed.

AGRICULTURAL TRACTORS

No useful result was found or could have been expected by comparing different areas, and it has been assumed that the saturation level will be $0 \cdot 01$, about 10 per cent above the present level.

OTHER VEHICLES

The estimation of the saturation level for "other vehicles", mainly commercial vehicles, presents particular difficulties. Comparisons of growth rates in different areas lead to no useful conclusions, and over the last ten years there has been a rise rather than a fall in the rate of increase of the number per head over Great Britain as a whole.

In the United States the ownership rate of "other vehicles" was $0 \cdot 07$ in 1960 (including agricultural vehicles) and this figure is increasing. In one state the figure was 0.20. According to Glover[19] and the "Monthly Digest of Statistics of the Central Statistical Office", in 1960 about 58 per cent of the ton-miles of goods transport in Great Britain were carried by road, and this percentage is increasing, but it is not at present clear how far it can rise; nor is it clear how much the ton-mileage to be transported will rise.

A saturation level of $0 \cdot 08$ "other vehicles" per head has been assumed, but without any great confidence that the figure is reliable.

ALL MOTOR VEHICLES

Adding the saturation levels for the four separate classes of vehicle gives $0 \cdot 55$ motor vehicles per person. It may be remarked that this level was exceeded in 1960 in four states in the United States.

The forecast

BASIC CALCULATIONS

The ownership per head in 1960 and the assumed rate of increase of ownership for each of the four classes of vehicle were given in Table 2.25. The estimates of saturation level were discussed above. The use of the logistic curve has been discussed earlier in the section, and the curve is described in more detail in Appendix 1; inserting the numerical values into the equation (5) for the logistic curve gives the estimates of future vehicles per head shown in Figs. 2.22 and 2.23. These diagrams are all on the same scale. The forecasts for all motor vehicles, Fig. 2.24, are obtained by adding the corresponding forecasts for the four separate classes. The diagrams also show the actual levels of ownership for 1950 to 1960 (except for

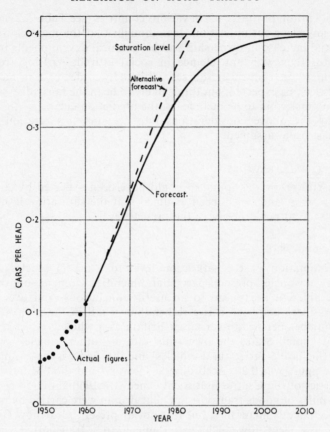

Fig. 2.22. Actual numbers of cars per head, Great
Britain 1950–60, and forecasts for 1961–2010

agricultural tractors and other vehicles in 1950, when definitions were
slightly different). Fig. 2.22 shows the alternative forecasts for cars based
on a saturation level of 0·50 as well as the main forecast based on 0·40.
The alternative is only 0·01 higher in 1970 and 0·04 higher in 1980.

Table 2.28 shows the forecasts for each class of vehicle at ten-yearly
intervals, based on Figs. 2.22, 2.23 and 2.24. Table 2.29 shows the corresponding numbers of vehicles, based on forecasts[20] made by the Government Actuary and the Registrars General that the population will rise from
about 51 million in 1960 to about 76 million by the year 2010.

APPLICATION TO PARTICULAR AREAS

The estimates in Figs. 2.22, 2.23 and 2.24 and in Tables 2.28 and 2.29
refer to Great Britain as a whole. Clearly, they are not applicable to
particular areas, but procedures are suggested below to enable them to be
extended in this way.

In the case of cars there is no evidence that the ultimate level will vary
substantially from area to area. It is therefore suggested that for the curve
in Fig. 2.22, or the cars per head column in Table 2.28, the time-scale is
moved along so as to give the correct current number of cars per head for

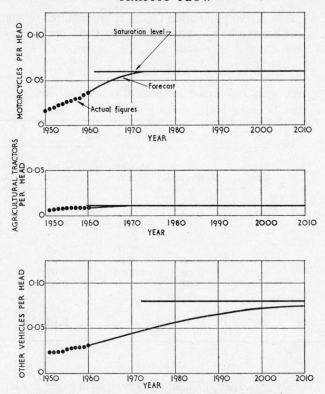

Fig. 2.23. Actual number of motor cycles, agricultural tractors and other vehicles per head, Great Britain 1959–60, and forecasts for 1961–2010

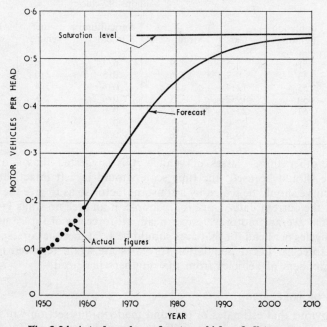

Fig. 2.24. Actual numbers of motor vehicles of all types per head, 1950–60, and forecasts for 1961–2010

the particular area. Local population forecasts are required to enable forecasts of cars per head to be converted into forecasts of the total number of cars.

TABLE 2.28

Summary of forecasts of numbers of vehicles per head in Great Britain, 1960–2010

| Year | Vehicles per head | | | | |
	Cars	Motorcycles	Agricultural tractors	Other vehicles	All motor vehicles
1960 (actual)	0·11	0·04	0·01	0·03	0·18
1965	0·16	0·05	0·01	0·04	0·26
1970	0·22	0·06	0·01	0·04	0·33
1980	0·33	0·06	0·01	0·06	0·45
1990	0·38	0·06	0·01	0·07	0·51
2000	0·39	0·06	0·01	0·07	0·53
2010	0·40	0·06	0·01	0·08	0·54
Saturation level	0·40	0·06	0·01	0·08	0·55

TABLE 2.29

Summary of forecasts of numbers of vehicles in Great Britain, 1965–2010

| Year | Population millions | Millions of vehicles | | | | |
		Cars	Motorcycles	Agricultural tractors	Other Vehicles	All motor vehicles
1960	51	5·5	1·9	0·4	1·6	9·4
1965	53	8·7	2·6	0·5	2·0	13·8
1970	55	12·4	3·1	0·6	2·4	18·5
1980	59	19·2	3·5	0·6	3·3	26·6
1990	63	23·7	3·8	0·6	4·1	32·2
2000	69	27·0	4·1	0·7	5·0	36·8
2010	76	30·4	4·6	0·8	5·7	41·5

For the other three classes of vehicle it is suggested that a different procedure should be used: the time scale should be left intact, but each forecast curve should be scaled by a constant factor so as to give the correct figure for the current date. Thus, for example, if an area now has 1·5 times the national average motorcycles per head, all forecasts of future numbers of motorcycles per head for that area should be 1·5 times the corresponding national forecast. Local population forecasts are again required for estimating numbers of vehicles from the numbers per head.

REVISION OF FORECASTS

It is obvious that estimates of the kind made in this section will need to be kept under review. Not only will the actual figures for a future date differ to a greater or lesser extent from the forecasts but methods may become available that are either inherently better or else are better suited for use in conditions obtaining at the future date. Until the estimates are formally revised, it is suggested that the forecasts may be provisionally revised by methods similar to those suggested for dealing with particular areas.

It may be of interest to speculate on some of the ways in which the forecasts made here may fail to correspond to future events. In the first place there are the relatively minor fluctuations in the general economy that will almost certainly cause the growth curves to deviate from smooth curves. More important are systematic departures from the forecasts. In the case of cars it has already been remarked that the saturation level may well rise further than predicted, at least to about 0.5, and this would tend to increase the number of cars to a higher level than the forecast. The saturation levels for motorcycles and "other vehicles" are largely based on judgment, which may turn out to have been faulty or based on an incomplete appreciation of the relevant factors. The number of motorcycles seems to be as much subject to fashion as to economics, and it may well be that there will be sharp changes either up or down. Commercial vehicles and public-service vehicles are both dependent to some extent on the transport policy of future governments, and this is hardly open to prediction.

MILEAGE PER VEHICLE

So far this section has been concerned only with numbers of vehicles, not with how far they will travel. It has been suggested that if there is a large increase in the number of vehicles, then on the average each one will perform a lower annual mileage. The trends in recent years in Great Britain[21] and the United States[13] are of interest in this connexion and are shown in Table 2.30.

There are several points of interest in Table 2.30. In the first place, the average number of miles per car year is higher in the United States than in Great Britain, in spite of the far larger number of cars per head. Secondly, over the last ten years mileage per car has tended to rise in both countries, in spite of increasing numbers of cars per head; the pre-war figure for Great Britain is higher than any of the post-war ones, but this is not true for the United States. Commercial vehicles have shown no clear trend in miles per vehicle over the last ten years, nor since 1940 in the United States. The decreasing mileage per motorcycle in Great Britain is attributable largely if not wholly to the increasing proportion of lightweight machines, particularly mopeds; this decrease may continue if the proportion of light motorcycles continues to increase. The decreasing overall mileage per motor vehicle in Great Britain is largely due to the greater rates of increase of the classes of vehicle that perform lower annual mileages, i.e. cars and motorcycles. It is worth noting here that although the average mileage per commercial vehicle is not changing at the present time, there is a tendency for the average unladen weight to increase. The rate of increase over the period 1957–1961 averaged $1\frac{1}{2}$ per cent per year.

The general conclusion to be drawn from these figures is that there is no real evidence that increasing numbers of vehicles tend to be accompanied by a decreasing mileage per vehicle. In fact, there is some indication that the opposite may sometimes be the case. Thus it seems reasonable to conclude that changes in numbers of vehicles of a given class will be accompanied by approximately the same proportional change in the amount of traffic on the road. In particular areas, such as central London, much less growth can be expected, owing to the shortage of road space but with increasing expenditure on the road system it seems likely that over the greater part of the country the amount of traffic will follow very much the same growth curve as the number of vehicles.

TABLE 2.30

Trends in miles per vehicle

	Miles per vehicle per year			
Great Britain	*1938*	*1951*	*1955*	*1960*
Cars	8600	7300	7300	7500
Motorcycles . . .	4400	4200	3800	3500
Commercial vehicles . .	15 100	12 200	11 900	12 600
Public-service vehicles .	31 000	30 500	31 000	30 500
All motor vehicles . .	9600	8300	7800	7700
United States	*1940*	*1950*	*1955*	*1959*
Passenger cars . . .	9100	9000	9400	9500
Commercial buses . .	36 000	36 500	34 000	38 000
School buses, etc. . .	8000	7800	7800	7700
Trucks and combinations .	10 600	10 800	10 700	10 600
All motor vehicles . .	9300	9300	9600	9800

RELIABILITY OF FORECASTS

There are three things that can usefully be said about the reliability of the forecasts that have been made, apart from the obvious one that forecasts of this kind cannot be reliable. The first is that it is not possible to put any quantitative measure to the range of error likely to be present; this is because of the subjective nature of much of the reasoning. In particular, with the trivial exception of that for agricultural tractors, the saturation levels finally assumed have not been arrived at as the results of calculation, but by judgment based on calculations.

Secondly, the forecasts for cars and for all motor vehicles are believed to be more reliable than those for the other classes of vehicle. In the case of cars there would seem to be fewer imponderables than in the case of motorcycles or of commercial vehicles.

Thirdly, the forecasts for the more distant future are far less reliable than those for the near future. Up to about ten years ahead the forecasts, particularly for cars, are fairly insensitive to the assumed saturation level, so any forecast which is essentially a statistical extrapolation of past trends is likely to be similar to that put forward here. For periods more than 20 years ahead, on the other hand, different people might well produce substantially different forecasts.

Comparison of actual and predicted figures for 1961, 1962 and 1963

The calculations and forecasts described above were published in 1962, and were made as from the base year 1960. As stated earlier, they will be subject to review, but it is of interest to compare them with the actual figures, available at the time of writing this section of this book, for the years 1961, 1962 and 1963.

The following are the comparisons:

TABLE 2.31

*Comparison of actual and predicted figures for 1961, 1962 and 1963
Vehicles per head, Great Britain*

	Actual					Predicted				
	Cars	M/c	Ag. Tr.	Others	Total	Cars	M/c	Ag. Tr.	Others	Total
1960	0·108	0·036	0·009	0·031	0·184	—	—	—	—	—
1961	0·116	0·036	0·009	0·031	0·193	0·119	0·040	0·009	0·032	0·199
1962	0·126	0·035	0·009	0·032	0·203	0·129	0·043	0·009	0·033	0·214
1963	0·141	0·035	0·009	0·032	0·217	0·140	0·045	0·009	0·034	0·226

Table 2.31 shows that the predicted 1963 figure for cars was a small amount (0·001) below the actual value, and that this was very similar to the error in the opposite direction among "other vehicles" (i.e. buses and commercial vehicles). The greatest error was in motorcycles, which have been decreasing instead of increasing.

From the point of view of planning for future road and garage requirements, the errors in motorcycle numbers are of less importance, and it is of course possible that the decrease may be of a temporary nature. While it should be emphasized that three years is from this point of view a very short period, the comparison is a satisfactory one except for motorcycles.

REFERENCES TO CHAPTER 2

1. TROTT, J. J., and P. J. WILLIAMSON. Measuring, classifying and counting wheel loads of moving vehicles. *Engineer, Lond.*, 1959, **208** (5422), 859–62.

2. TANNER, J. C., and J. R. SCOTT. 50-point traffic census—the first 5 years. *Department of Scientific and Industrial Research, Road Research Technical Paper* No. 63. London, 1962 (H.M. Stationery Office).

3. TANNER, J. C. The sampling of road traffic. *Appl. Statist.*, 1957, **6** (3), 161–70.

4. TANNER, J. C., H. D. JOHNSON and J. R. SCOTT. Sample survey of the roads and traffic of Great Britain. *Department of Scientific and Industrial Research, Road Research Technical Paper* No. 62. London, 1962 (H.M. Stationery Office).

5. MINISTRY OF TRANSPORT. Passenger transport in Great Britain, 1962. London, 1963 (H.M. Stationery Office).

6. CENTRAL STATISTICAL OFFICE. Monthly digest of statistics. London, (H.M. Stationery Office).

7. MACNAUGHTON-SMITH, P., and J. C. TANNER. Trends in traffic flow in Great Britain from 1938 to 1955. *Surveyor, Lond.*, 1956, **115** (3374), 1029.

8. DEPARTMENT OF SCIENTIFIC AND INDUSTRIAL RESEARCH. Road research 1958. The report of the Road Research Board with the report of the Director of Road Research. London, 1959 (H.M. Stationery Office).

9. MINISTRY OF TRANSPORT. Road motor vehicles. London (H.M. Stationery Office). (Published annually).

10. MINISTRY OF TRANSPORT. Public road passenger transport statistics. London (H.M. Stationery Office). (Published annually for years up to 1961.)

11. GLOVER, K. F. and D. N. MILLER. The outlines of the road goods transport industry. *J. roy. statist. Soc., Series A (General)*, 1954, **117** (3), 297–323; Discussion, 324–30.

12. MINISTRY OF TRANSPORT. The transport of goods by road. Report of a sample survey made in April 1958. London, 1959 (H.M. Stationery Office).

13. U.S. DEPARTMENT OF COMMERCE. Statistical abstract of the United States, 1961. Washington, D.C., 1961 (U.S. Government Printing Office).

14. TANNER, J. C. Forecasts of future numbers of vehicles in Great Britain. *Rds & Rd Constr.*, 1962, **40** (477), 263–74.

15. DAWSON, R.F.F. Ownership of cars and certain durable household goods *Bull. Oxf. Univ. Inst. Statist.*, 1953, **15** (5), 177–91.

16. CENTRAL STATISTICAL OFFICE. National income and expenditure, 1961. London, 1961 (H.M. Stationery Office).

17. MAIZELS, A., R. W. THOMAS and L. BOROSS. Trends in world trade in durable consumer goods. *Econ. Rev.*, 1959, (6), 14–36.

18. DICKS-MIREAUX, L. A., C. ST. J. O'HERLIHY, R. L. MAJOR, F. T. BLACABY and C. FREEMAN. Prospects for the British car industry. *Econ. Rev.*, 1961, (17), 15–46.

19. GLOVER, K. F. Statistics of the transport of goods by road. *J. roy. statist. Soc., Series A (General)*, 1960, **123** (2), 107–31; Discussion, 131–9.

20. CENTRAL STATISTICAL OFFICE. Annual abstract of statistics, No. 100, 1963. London, 1963 (H.M. Stationery Office).

21. SCOTT, J. R., and J. C. TANNER. Traffic trends in vehicle-miles in Great Britain, 1938–60. *Surveyor, Lond.*, 1962, **121** (3649), 645–8.

APPENDIX 1

The Logistic Curve

Denote time by t ($= 0$ in 1960) and vehicles per head by x ($= X$ in 1960). The most general logistic growth formula satisfies the differential equation.

$$\frac{dx}{dt} = cx(a-x) \ . \qquad \qquad \qquad \qquad \qquad \qquad \qquad (1)$$

where c and a are constants. The solution to (1) is

$$x = \frac{a}{1+be^{-act}} \ . \qquad \qquad \qquad \qquad \qquad \qquad (2)$$

This is an S-shaped curve, asymptotic to $x = O$ as t approaches $-\infty$, and to $x = a$ as t approaches $+\infty$. Equation (1) shows that the percentage rate of increase of x is $100\ c(a-x)$, i.e. it is proportional to the difference between x and its asymptotic value a.

If (2) is to give $x = X$ when $t = 0$, then

$$X(1+b) = a. \qquad \qquad \qquad \qquad \qquad \qquad (3)$$

If, further, the percentage rate of growth at $t = 0$ is known to be $100\ r$ per cent per year, then

$$c(a-X) = r. \qquad \qquad \qquad \qquad \qquad \qquad (4)$$

Formula (2) may thus put into the form

$$x = \frac{aX}{X+(a-X)e^{-art/(a-x)}} \ . \qquad \qquad \qquad \qquad (5)$$

in which the only unknown is the asymptotic level a.

Thus a logistic curve can be found to correspond with the current actual level of vehicles per head and with the current actual percentage rate of increase of vehicles per head. The curve is uniquely determined by fixing the asymptotic level a.

It may be remarked that the results in the last section of this chapter suggest that instead of using a logistic curve to provide a forecast for the country as a whole, it would have been more consistent to have used a logistic curve for each area, and then to have added the results over all the areas. For cars these logistic curves would all satisfy the same differential equation (1), and so would all have been the same curve but with time scales displaced by a variable amount depending on the current level of owner-ship. For other classes of vehicle, the saturation levels might be different in different areas. If this procedure had been followed, the curves for the whole country would not have been strictly logistic, but it is clear that they would not have departed substantially from a logistic form.

APPENDIX 2

Grouping of geographical counties used in Figures 2.16, 2.18 and 2.21 (counties not listed were kept separate)

Cambridge	Lincoln	Brecon	Argyll	Berwick
Isle of Ely	Rutland	Cardigan	Bute	Dumfries
Huntingdon		Merioneth	Kinross	Kirkcudbright
	Northampton	Montgomery	Perth	Peebles
Cheshire	Soke of Peterborough	Radnor		Roxburgh
Flint	E. Suffolk	Carmarthen	Aberdeen Banff	Selkirk Wigtown
Cumberland	W. Suffolk	Pembroke	Kincardine	
Westmorland			Moray	
	West Riding (inc. York C.B.)	Caithness	Nairn	
Hampshire		Inverness		
Isle of Wight		Orkney		
	Anglesey	Ross & Cromarty	Clackmannan	E. Lothian
Hereford	Caernarvon	Sutherland	Dumbarton	Midlothian
Shropshire	Denbigh	Zetland	Stirling	W. Lothian

Chapter 3

Speeds

SYNOPSIS

Measuring speed and journey time: methods using a long base; short base speedmeters; radar speedmeters; recording speed data. Speed, flow and delay surveys: moving-observer method; one-way streets; trailing vehicles with test car. Results of speed studies: speed distributions; precision of results; time mean speed and space mean speed; speed versus journey time speeds on different types of road; speeds of different classes of vehicle; trends in speeds. Speed/flow relations in Great Britain.

INTRODUCTION

Many traffic studies require the speed or journey time of traffic along a road to be measured or estimated. In economic studies, for example, the cost of a journey depends a great deal on the speed at which it is made. When new roads are being designed it is important to have a realistic estimate of the speeds at which vehicles will travel along them. The size of the lettering on signs and the layout of double white lines also need to be related to the speed of the traffic. Journey time measurement on a network of roads in a town can be used to indicate where road improvements are desirable.

If possible, speeds or journey times should be measured rather than estimated. Measurement of speed can be made from the roadside with a speedmeter; both speeds and journey times can be measured from a moving car in the traffic stream. Generalized results obtained from speed studies elsewhere can be used where it is necessary to estimate speeds or speed distribution.

A knowledge of the relationship between the speed and flow of traffic on a road enables the capacity of the road to be estimated. These relations are also of importance in the assessment of the effect of large-scale road improvements.

Methods of measuring speeds and journey times and the results of speed studies are given in this chapter together with speed/flow relations for urban and rural roads.

MEASURING SPEED AND JOURNEY TIME

Measurement of journey time involves timing vehicles between two points. The accuracy of the measurement depends on:

(*a*) The accuracy with which the time is measured.

Generally speaking the more accurate the results the more complicated are the methods.

(*b*) The accuracy with which the exact position of the vehicle is determined.

Speeds of vehicles are frequently obtained by timing vehicles over a known distance. In this case the accuracy of the measurements depends also on:

(*c*) The accuracy with which the distance travelled by the vehicle is determined.

The exception to this method is the use of the radar speedmeter which measures vehicle speed directly.

In general, methods of timing vehicles fall into two groups:

(1) Those in which vehicles are timed over a long distance (long-base), and

(2) those in which vehicles are timed over a short distance (short-base).

Generally speaking a short-base method (which requires more elaborate equipment) will only be used when speeds rather than journey times are required.

Methods using a long-base

The simplest method of timing vehicles is by means of stopwatches over a known distance of several hundred feet. This method is very simple to use, but the number of observations which can be made is limited to about 150 per hour. Skilled observers can read a stopwatch to 1/5th of a second. This gives an error of approximately ± 1 mile/h at 40 mile/h over 500 ft. A modification of the method, which permits more accurate determination of the position of the vehicle, incorporates the use of the Enoscope. This device consists of a mirror set at 45° to the road and so arranged that the observer who is stationed at one end of the marked section can look into the mirror and see the exact time at which the selected vehicle passes the end of the marked length. In congested traffic conditions the Enoscope cannot be used with any degree of efficiency, but a method has been reported from the Continent of Europe in which several operators using a number of stopwatches can deal with one-way volumes up to about 600 vehicles per hour.

As a modification of the method, detectors (say, pneumatic tubes) can be used to indicate when the vehicle enters and leaves the measured section. The detectors can be used to operate an electromagnetically controlled stopwatch and in this way it is possible to eliminate some of the human errors which occur when an ordinary stopwatch and the Enoscope are used. However, it is necessary to ensure that the identification of vehicles is such that it is clear that the same vehicle starts and stops the watch. These methods are cheap and can be operated by relatively unskilled staff, but they can only be used where both ends of the measured section can be seen.

REGISTRATION NUMBER METHOD OF MEASURING SPEEDS AND JOURNEY TIMES

The registration number method is suitable for measuring the journey times of vehicles over a distance of, say, half a mile or more. Two observers equipped with synchronized watches are stationed at the ends of the section along which journey times are being measured, and note down the registration numbers of vehicles and the times at which the vehicles pass them.

Subsequent comparison of the records obtained by the two observers enables the journey times of individual vehicles to be determined.

Although this method can be used successfully when the two timing points of the section under observation are situated at a great distance from each other, it is unsuitable where many vehicles enter, leave or stop within the section. In general, the greater the length of the section under observation the greater the likelihood that vehicles will not pass directly between the two timing points.

Traffic can be sampled if the flow is too great for the observer to record the time and arrival of every vehicle. One method of sampling often used is to record only those registration numbers which end in specified digits (see below). Observers can record times to an accuracy of about $\pm 0 \cdot 01$ minutes. Consequently, for journey times of about one minute, the accuracy of an individual measurement is between 1 and 2 per cent.

The following technique has been devised and used by the Laboratory for recording registration numbers.

FIELD TECHNIQUE. Before work begins two observers start their watches simultaneously, they then separate and take up their positions at opposite ends of the section of road. The observers usually note the vehicle classification and the registration number before the vehicle reaches the timing point and enter the watch reading as soon as possible after the passage of the vehicle. To facilitate the field work, only the figures of the registration number are noted; if letters only are recorded it is difficult to match vehicles in areas where one registration number predominates. A space on the form is used for each vehicle even if all or part of the information is missed. Besides facilitating the analysis, this ensures that a complete count of vehicles or of the sample of vehicles is obtained.

WATCHES. Although stopwatches are used for the timings, it is an essential part of the method that the watches must not be stopped during the period of observation. When the observers come together at the end of the work, the watches are then stopped simultaneously and any discrepancy noted so that the timings may be adjusted accordingly. The data sheets are usually supported on a board which is provided with a padded mounting for the watch in the top left-hand corner; the mounting should be designed to hold the watch securely without obscuring the dial. The watches should have a split second hand. This is an additional hand which normally rotates with the main hand but can be stopped independently and brought up to the main hand again later. A further refinement is to obtain watches engraved in tenths and hundredths of a minute instead of in seconds; the adoption of the decimal system simplifies the analysis, particularly if mechanical methods are employed.

SAMPLING. Observations are limited to traffic in only one direction at a time unless traffic is very light. Competent observers can cope with flows of up to 300 veh/h in one direction, with only a small proportion of missed vehicles. At higher flows sampling is adopted by recording vehicles with registration numbers ending in specified digits. For example, a 50 per cent sample may be obtained by selecting 'odd numbers only: a 30 per cent sample would be obtained by observing registration numbers ending in, for instance, 2, 4 and 7.

DURATION. It has been found that it is not usually economical to work for less than one hour at a time but periods of more than two hours are likely to cause undue strain on the observers. It is not uncommon to change the direction of working half-way through each period of observation. The total duration of the periods of observation is of course determined by the accuracy required. If both observers stop work simultaneously the results will be biased in favour of the faster vehicles. The bias may be avoided by arranging for the observer at the exit point to finish work later in order to allow time for all the vehicles recorded at the point of entry to reach him. If, however, the journey time along the section is small in relation to the duration of the work, the bias will be small and the use of staggered working will be unnecessary.

ANALYSIS. Comparison of the record sheets for the two ends enables the journey times to be obtained by subtraction. The following method of matching the two records has proved satisfactory. The vehicles recorded in a given period at the point of entry are numbered serially in the order in which they arrived. The record sheet for the exit point is then examined and, using each registration number in turn, as many vehicles as possible are identified. As each vehicle is matched, the serial number is entered on the exit record sheet. A list is then prepared showing the serial number, class of vehicle, entry time, exit time and journey time for each vehicle. It will not usually be possible to match the records completely due to vehicles turning off or stopping along the section, apart from the effect of omissions by the observers. Long journey times which it is suspected are due to a vehicle stopping for a short time should be eliminated. The list may then be used to prepare distributions of journey times and speeds and to calculate averages.

PEN RECORDER

Another method employs a chart recorder connected to pneumatic detectors on the road. One detector is placed at each end of, say, an 80-ft section of road, and a third detector is placed equidistant between these two. Each detector is connected to a separate pen of an operations recorder in which a paper chart is pulled at a uniform rate past the pens and on which also another pen produces a time trace, say, every quarter-second. The passage of a vehicle over any detector causes the appropriate pen to move and consequently the movement of a vehicle through the set of detectors produces a distinctive pattern on the chart. It is possible by this method to determine the time taken for the vehicle to travel between the two ends of the measured section and to determine in which direction it was travelling. Because wheel bases vary in length it is possible to use this method to study the speeds of all vehicles.

The greatest disadvantage of the pen recorder method of determining speeds is that the analysis is extremely laborious. Experience has shown that the rate at which the paper passes the pens varies slightly and consequently it is necessary to check the time scale quite frequently; this involves several measurements from the chart before each speed can be determined. When this method of recording speeds was used some years ago, it was found that it took two people six months to analyse completely the data obtained from one week's observations. To overcome this limitation, a special-purpose computer was designed in which a rack and pinion cursor was placed on the records and the resulting speed of the vehicle was indicated directly in miles per hour on a meter. Even so, analysis is more laborious than with other methods and this particular technique is only used when it is necessary to know the speed of all the vehicles passing a point during a given period of time.

Short-base speedmeters

Speedmeters with accurate methods of timing have been devised which can operate on bases of about six feet. In this way it is much more likely that the vehicle which first hits the "start" detectors will be the vehicle which first hits the "stop" detectors.

A transistorized speedmeter has been contructed by Venner Electronics to the Laboratory's specifications (see Plate 3.1). In this speedmeter the timing source is crystal-controlled and primary pulses are produced at the rate of 10 kc/s. These pulses are counted down twice by two and the resultant pulses, one every 0·4 millisecond, are fed into a counter consisting of three electronic decade units, the gate to which is opened when the vehicle arrives at the first detector and closed when the vehicle arrives at the second detector. The position of each decade, i.e. the number of pulses which have been counted, is indicated by a pointer on a simple meter. An alternative version, recently devised, projects illuminated figures just over an inch high on to a screen. If the detectors are placed across the road at a distance 70·4 inches apart (see Plate 3.2), the reading can be converted to a speed in mile/h by dividing into 10 000. The whole unit is portable and runs from two 6-volt lantern cells. The gate circuit has been so arranged that the meter is inoperative until a press-button is pushed; it will then record the speed of one vehicle and one only, holding that reading until the press-button is released. The machine remains inoperative until the press-button is pushed again. This feature permits accurate sampling, which is important when the flows exceed 300 vehicles per hour in one direction. The normal method of sampling in this case is to take every second vehicle, or for very high flows every third or fourth vehicle.

A further development of this instrument is an automatic recording speedmeter in which the time taken by each vehicle to pass across the distance base in punched on a 5-hole paper tape, together with a code describing the category of the vehicle (see Plate 3.3). The machine is operated by an observer who samples and classifies the vehicles: the equipment can record vehicles at a maximum rate of one every half-second. In practice, to avoid bias, since vehicles overtaking near the detector are liable to be missed, it is usual to sample vehicles when flows exceed about 400 vehicles per hour. The results are produced in blocks of four lines along the paper tape for each vehicle. A typical length of tape is shown in Fig. 3.1. This paper tape can then be read directly into an electronic computer.

The speedmeters described so far time vehicles across a known distance and present the answer in terms of time. A number of similar devices, of which the Ametron made by the Streeter Amet Company of Illinois is an example, present the result of a speed measurement directly in terms of miles per hour on a voltmeter. The instrument usually consists of a condenser which is initially charged to a known voltage and which is allowed to leak through a resistance during the time that the vehicle passes between the detectors. The voltage decay is exponential and the scale of miles per hour displayed on the meter is very nearly linear. The accuracy of the instrument depends on the quality of the components and the atmospheric conditions and is not therefore as high as can be achieved with crystal controlled counter methods.

An instrument designed by the Statens Väginstitut of Sweden employs wire dectors placed on the road a very short distance apart and when a moving vehicle is between the detectors a signal of a known frequency is

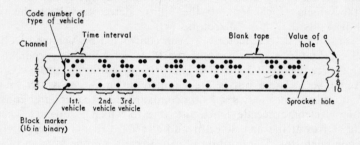

The first vehicle (on extreme left) was of type 5 and recorded a time interval of 251 (0·4 millisec units). Since the distance between the tubes is 70·4 in. this represents a vehicle travelling at 39·8 mile/h.

Fig. 3.1. A typical length of speedmeter tape

recorded on magnetic tape. The frequency is recorded for the time taken by one wheel to pass between the detectors, and analysis is by means of an electronic device that counts the number of cycles of the applied frequency which have been recorded in that time. Different frequencies can be used for different types of vehicle. Since automatic methods of analysis are available, this machine is both highly accurate and capable of recording in very dense traffic. The wire detectors which have been devised for this machine have crystal capsules embodied in them to convert the shock wave in the wire into an electric impulse to operate the equipment. There is some doubt whether wire detectors would be acceptable for use in Great Britain with the present state of the law.

The Decca Trafficometry equipment (see Plate 3.4) mentioned in Chapter 2 also includes devices for recording speed graphically. Vehicles are timed over two detectors normally 13 inches apart. The times for the last few vehicles are exponentially weighted to give an averaged time which is converted on a paper chart to speed in mile/h. It should be noted that the resulting speed is in fact a space-mean speed (see page 107).

Radar speedmeters

The only type of device which does not employ some form of timing to measure the speed of vehicles is the radar speedmeter. Different types of radar speedmeter are now available.

An American instrument, Model S2, made by Eastern Industries Incorporated has a low-powered radio transmitter operating on a frequency of

2455 megacycles per second. This speedmeter has been used extensively in Great Britain for both research and enforcement purposes. The output from the transmitter is fed to an array of eight dipoles so arranged that the majority of the power is projected forward in the form of a beam about 40° in width, which can be directed down the road. The radio waves are reflected from all objects within the field of the transmitter and if they are reflected from a moving object then the reflected wave has a frequency shift that is proportional to the speed of the object.

If F_r is the received signal frequency

$$F_r = \frac{c+v}{c-v} F_t$$

Where F_t is the transmitted frequency,
$\quad c$ is the velocity of light,
$\quad v$ is the velocity of the object.

The radar speedmeter receiver measures the Doppler or difference frequency (F_d) between the transmitted and received frequencies. This can be expressed as

$$F_d = \frac{2v}{c-v} F_t$$

Since the velocity of the object relative to that of light is very small, the formula can be simplified to the following:

$$F_d = \frac{2v}{c} F_t$$

or

$$F_d = \frac{2v}{\lambda}$$

where

$$\lambda = \frac{c}{F_t}$$

is the wave length of the transmitted radio wave.

The frequency difference is converted directly into a voltage reading which is therefore proportional to the speed of the object within the field. The speed is shown by a pointer on an indicator. The speed measured is the relative velocity between the moving object and the radar meter, i.e. the instrument responds to the component of the velocity of the vehicle along the line joining the vehicle and instrument. Since the equipment is placed at the side of the road (see Plate 3.5) there is thus a reduction in the apparent speed of the vehicle owing to the cosine effect. This effect, is however, very small under practical conditions. If two different reflected frequencies are received (as from two vehicles travelling at different speeds) the meter will select the higher frequency if the two signals are about the same strength. If one signal is more than twice the strength of the other the meter will select the stronger.

The range of Model S2 depends on the mounting height of the meter and the size of the reflecting surface. With the meter 3 ft from the ground the range varies from about 200 ft for large pantechnicons and buses to about 130 ft for small cars. Vehicles travelling either towards the instrument or away from it will still give a direct reading in miles per hour. The radar speedmeter is a valuable engineering tool with an accuracy claimed by the manufacturers of at least ± 2 mile/h. In practice it is generally nearer ± 1 mile/h. The indicator shows speeds up to 100 mile/h, though the speedmeter tends to underestimate speeds at the top of the range. There is a very convenient check for the accuracy of operation of part of the equipment. If a tuning fork is vibrated in front of the transmitter, it produces an effect equivalent to that of a vehicle which would produce a frequency shift equivalent to that of the tuning fork. It is thus possible to make a set of special tuning forks which will show on the meter the speeds 20, 30, 40, 50 and 60 mile/h, and the instrument can be checked whilst *in situ* using the tuning forks. The transmitted frequency should be checked in the laboratory every six months or so: this does not vary in use, normally.

A new radar speedmeter, Model S5 (see Plate 3.6), has recently been brought out by Eastern Industries Incorporated. This instrument, which replaces the speedmeter described above, has been designed very compactly and can be mounted on a vehicle window: the transmitting head is an inconspicuous unit about five inches in diameter. The beam width is 16°. A three position Range Switch is provided to enable the speedmeter to be set up to suit different locations and conditions of traffic; the approximate ranges corresponding to the three positions of the switch are 150 ft, 300 ft, and 500 ft. The speedmeter operates within a range of 0 to 100 mile/h with an accuracy of ± 2 mile/h. The transmitting frequency is in the range 10 510 to 10 525 megacycles/s and the power consumption is two amps at 12 volts.

In Britain, a radar speedmeter has been produced by Marconi Wireless Telegraph Company Ltd. An aerial array is used in which the main energy from the transmitter is beamed at an angle of 20° to the main axis of the instrument, so that if the intrument is aimed straight down the road then the beam of radio waves crosses the path of the vehicle at an angle of approximately 20°. The angled beam makes it easy to discriminate between vehicles; the speed indicated by the instrument is corrected to allow for the standard cosine correction. The beam is, however, so narrow that when a vehicle passes through it the recording needle often does not register long enough for an observer to take a reading of the vehicle's speed. An electronic hold circuit has therefore been incorporated into the instrument which, when in use, causes the needle to remain at its indicated position for a pre-determined short period to enable the observer to take his reading. The speedmeter will measure speeds up to 80 mile/h and the accuracy is ± 2 mile/h throughout the range. The transmitting frequency is in the band 10 675 to 10 699 Mc/s and the power consumption is $3\frac{1}{2}$ amps at 12 volts.

A French instrument MESTA 102 is available in Great Britain from S.F.I.M. (Great Britain) Ltd., but at the time of writing this speedmeter has not been used very much in Britain. Additional features include an indicator on which a limiting speed may be pre-set. When this speed is exceeded an audible signal is given. This limiting speed may be any speed up to 90 mile/h, the highest speed recorded by the instrument. A further control enables the equipment to operate on vehicles travelling in both directions or one only.

Recording speed data

It is possible to speed up field work and reduce the time spent in analysing data if some attention is paid to the methods of recording speed data. For most practical purposes, speeds are grouped during analysis either into 2-mile/h groups or 5-mile/h groups. A distribution with the 5-mile/h groups has the advantage that less calculation is necessary when carrying out statistical tests, and distributions with this size group are adequate to show any important difference between sets of observations. Such a distribution will also show immediately the number of vehicles exceeding 35, 40, 45 mile/h, etc. When an accurate determination of the mean speed is required it is better to use 2-mile/h groups.

SHEET FOR MANUAL RECORDING

A form has been devised (see Fig. 3.2) on which it is possible to record and group the speeds of vehicles as they are observed. It is possible with this form to obtain both the 2-mile/h speed groupings or the 5-mile/h speed groupings as required, since groups at the 10 mile/h points are sub-divided. The form can be used to record speeds obtained either with the radar speedmeter (and any similar direct reading speedmeter) or with the Venner transistor speedmeter. If the form is also sub-divided so that each category of vehicle can be entered up in a different column, then at the end of the series of observations a speed distribution for each category is directly available. The only remaining analysis in the laboratory consists in calculating the mean speeds, standard deviation and any combined distributions required.

When speeds are being measured with an instrument which presents the readings on a dial-type instrument, it has been found most satisfactory to group the observations to the nearest line shown on the scale. For example, the American radar speedmeter scale is calibrated in 2 mile/h divisions and, by associating each observation with the nearest line, the speeds are divided into 2 mile/h groups each having as its mean speed the value indicated by the appropriate line. If any attempt is made to read more accurately than this it is found that the results show a very marked bias towards those groups which are associated with the dial markings. In addition the attempt to read the scale in greater detail leads to eye strain and less rapid observations.

When using the Venner speedmeter the method of recording the results is rather different. The form lists the readings which define the upper limits of the speed groups. The method of coding the form is to scan down the list to find the first group which contains a printed figure equal to or larger than the observed reading. This is the group in which that particular observation must be placed. A similar form can of course be drawn up for any speedmeter giving time of transit. In the case of the Venner speedmeter used, the readings are converted into mile/h by dividing into 10 000. Thus, for example, for the speed group 55–57, denoted on the sheet by 56, 55 divided into 10 000 gives 181·8, so that the highest reading in the group is 181. It will be noted that this value is obtained by unrounded division.

RADAR AND TRANSISTOR SPEEDMETER RECORD

SITE:-   DIRECTION:-

SAMPLE:-   WEATHER:-

DAY & DATE:-   PERIOD:-

M.P.H.	Highest Reading in group		
70-	141		
68	149		
66	153		
64	158		
62	163		
+ -60- -	166 169		
58	175		
56	181 .		
54	188		
52	196		
+ -50- -	200 204		
48	212		
46	222		
44	232		
42	243		
+ -40- -	249 256		
38	270		
36	285		
34	303		
32	322		
+ -30- -	333 344		
28	370		
26	400		
24	434		
22	476		
+ -20- -	499 526		
18	588		
16	666		
14	769		
12	909		
0 - 10			

(left margin, rotated: READING IS HIGHEST IN GROUP - SPEED IS MEAN OF GROUP (Group 60+ is 60-61 m.p.h. and Group 60- is 59-60 etc.))

(right margin, rotated: TRANSISTOR BASE 70.4 inches.)

Fig. 3.2. Form for recording speedmeter data

PERFORATED PAPER TAPE

As mentioned earlier, a recording speedmeter is now available which will produce speed data in blocks on a perforated paper tape. The tape can be analysed automatically on an electronic computer and a typical print-out from the computer is shown in Fig. 3.3. This print-out presents the results which are normally required on a convenient foolscap form which can be easily filed.

SPEED DISTRIBUTION

WIGTON SITE 21
7/9/60 10.30AM, 11.30AM, 2.00PM, 3.00PM, 5.00PM

NO. OF PERIODS - 5
PERIOD LENGTH (MIN) - 60

TYPE	P	L	M	H	B	M/C	TOTAL
PERIODS USED	5	5	5	5	5.	5	5
SPEEDS USED	628	107	182	31	34	28	1010
FLOW - VEH/H	128	22	39	6	7	6	207
PERCENTAGE AT - (MILE/H)*							
10-15	-	-	1.2	3.4	-	-	0.3
15-	0.3	-	2.1	2.5	-	-	0.7
20-	2.1	2.5	9.1	14.3	2.9	-	3.9
25-	12.0	16.9	33.7	20.7	11.7	14.8	16.6
30-	25.0	27.3	33.3	46.3	32.1	24.8	27.6
35-	30.6	32.4	13.4	12.8	38.4	24.5	27.3
40-	20.9	13.7	6.7	-	14.9	21.4	16.6
45-	7.0	5.7	0.5	-	-	3.4	5.1
50-	1.7	0.9	-	-	-	7.3	1.4
55-	0.5	0.7	-	-	-	3.8	0.5
60-	-	-	-	-	-	-	-
65-	-	-	-	-	-	-	-
70-	-	-	-	-	-	-	-
75-	-	-	-	-	-	-	-
80-	-	-	-	-	-	-	-
85-	-	-	-	-	-	-	-
90-	-	-	-	-	-	-	-
95-	-	-	-	-	-	-	-
100-	-	-	-	-	-	-	-
105-	-	-	-	-	-	-	-
110-	-	-	-	-	-	-	-
115-120	-	-	-	-	-	-	-
MEAN - MILE/H	36.8	35.7	30.6	29.5	35.4	37.6	35.3
S.D.	6.3	6.2	5.9	6.2	4.7	7.8	6.7
S.E. OF MEAN	0.3	0.6	0.4	1.2	0.8	1.6	0.2
ERRORS > 120	1	0	1	0	0	0	2

DIGITS > 10   0
ODD DIGITS   0
TYPES   0

*CRITICAL SPEEDS IN FASTER GROUP

Fig. 3.3. Typical computor print out of results from the recording speedmeter

SURVEYS OF SPEED, FLOW AND DELAY

To make a survey of traffic conditions in an area or to investigate traffic schemes, it is usually necessary to measure traffic speeds and flow; measurements are also required of such quantities as stopped time at intersections and the concentration of standing vehicles. This type of information can be obtained by making observations from a moving vehicle in the traffic.

Yates[1] mentions the use of the moving-observer technique for counting pedestrians, and the Traffic Engineering Handbook[2] describes the use of a test vehicle for measuring traffic speeds; some experiments in the U.S.A. with this means of measuring speed are described by Berry and Green,[3] who also discuss the accuracy of the method. In all the above examples speed or flow are measured. In the succeeding paragraphs a method is described which was devised at the Road Research Laboratory[4] in which speed and flow are measured simultaneously; it has been used by Mortimer[5, 6] and Blensly,[7] to determine its suitability for application to American road and traffic conditions.

Moving-observer method

THEORY

Consider a stream of vehicles moving along a section of road in one direction so that, on the average, the number passing through the section per unit time is constant. The number of vehicles passing an observer per unit time depends on whether the observer is stationary or not. In fact, the net rate at which vehicles pass the observer is proportional to his speed relative to that of the stream. If, therefore, the observer makes runs with and against the stream at known speeds and counts the flows relative to himself, then it is possible to evaluate the number of vehicles passing through the section per unit time and also the mean speed of the traffic. This is considered in more detail in Appendix I where the following results, in terms of journey times through the section, are derived.

Flow,

$$q = \frac{(x+y)}{(t_a + t_w)}$$

Mean journey time,

$$\bar{t} = t_w - \frac{y}{q}$$

where x denotes number of vehicles met in the section when travelling against the stream,

y denotes number of vehicles that overtake the observer minus the number that he overtakes in the section,

t_a denotes journey time of the observer when travelling against the stream, and

t_w; denotes journey time of the observer when travelling with the stream.

Consequently, by counting x and y and measuring t_a and t_w, it is possible to evaluate q and $\bar{t}$. If n runs are made in each direction, then x, y, t_a, and t_w may be replaced by the average values for n runs.

It is seen that if $y = 0$, the journey time of the observer is equal to the mean journey time* of the traffic. The flows of different classes of traffic in a stream and their mean journey times can be obtained if x and y are counted for the separate classes.

In a one-way street no journeys against the stream would be possible, but by making two sets of runs with the stream, one at a low speed and the other at a higher speed, thereby obtaining two values of t_w and y, it would be possible to evaluate both t and q. To reduce errors, the two different speeds should be well separated from one another. In practice however where there are several one-way streets the flow is usually obtained by a stationary census, journey times only being estimated by the moving-observer method (see below).

EXPERIMENTAL TECHNIQUE

EQUIPMENT. A small, preferably even, number of test cars is required—usually two—each car carrying a driver and three observers.

One observer in the car counts opposing traffic, using hand tallies. Another observer carries a recording board on which is mounted a watch, preferably graduated in hundredths of a minute to simplify subsequent analysis. Attached to the recording board is a journey log, prepared in advance, on which the second observer records totals from the hand tallies and times at predetermined points *en route* together with the times of stopping and starting at intersections. A third observer can record the number of overtaking and overtaken vehicles and, if required, the number of parked vehicles.

If a tally of overtakings is not kept, the driver of the test vehicle is instructed to overtake as many vehicles as overtake him. The results obtained will not be as accurate (see below) but only two observers will be required.

ROUTES. Time will be wasted in practice if one section of road at a time is studied, and therefore the area under survey is mapped out into routes. It is convenient, although not essential, for the routes to be closed circuits so that the test cars can start at various points and make complete journeys in either direction. The route is then divided into sections; lengths of $\frac{1}{2}$ to 1 mile are convenient although a wide range of variation in section length can be accepted. The ends of sections should, so far as possible, include all the major intersections on the route so that large discontinuities in speed and flow do not occur inside the sections. Timing points are always placed at the entry and exit of any one-way system, but these systems are usually excluded from the analysis since they require special treatment, as has been mentioned.

JOURNEY LOG. Before experiments are started, a survey of the route is made and the journey log is prepared. An example of a typical log is shown in Fig. 3.4; in this case counts of vehicles in four different classifications were made with no tally count. Ends of sections are shown in large type and an

---

* For $y = 0$, the "Traffic Engineering Handbook"[2] wrongly states that the speed of the observer would be the modal route speed. Overtakings depend on relative speed, and the numbers of overtaking and overtaken vehicles will be equal for a vehicle travelling at a speed such that the total of the deviations from that speed is zero—that is, for a vehicle travelling at the mean speed.

LONDON TRAFFIC SURVEY NO. 9   ROUTE X DIRECTION 'RED'   SHEET 1

Date........................... Car No............................. Recorder.............................
Start time........................ Driver................................. Observer...........................

Timing Point or Intersection		S.T.	J.T.	P	C	O	B	
ELEPHANT (NEWINGTON CSWAY EXIT)		–	–	COUNT				
Borough Rd.	P				DRY / WET / RAIN			
Gt. Suffolk St. Trinity St.	L							
Marshalsea Rd. Long Lane	L							
Union St. Newcomen St.	P							
Southwark St. Boro' High St.	P							
Bedale St. St. Thomas St.	P							
London Bridge St.	P							
LONDON BRIDGE (SOUTH SIDE)	P							1
Arthur St. Monument St.	L							
CANNON ST. GRACECHURCH ST.	L							2
ST. SWITHIN'S LANE BANK	L							3
Poultry Threadneedle St.	L							
EXIT TO PRINCES ST.	–	–		COUNT				0
Gresham St. Lothbury	L							
London Wall	L							
Fore St.	L							
Chiswell St. Finsbury Sq. S	L							
OLD STREET	L							4
East Rd.	P							
Bath St. Shepherdess Wlk	L							
Goswell Rd. Angel Stn	L							
ST. JOHN ST. ISLINGTON HIGH ST.	L							5
Claremont Sq. Penton St.	L							
Penton Rise Rodney St.	L							
KINGS X BRIDGE CALEDONIAN ROAD	P							6

Fig. 3.4. A typical journey log

indication of the form of control at all intersections is given. Counter totals and journey times are entered at all section ends and the stopped times at all intersections are recorded.

VEHICLE CLASSIFICATION. Classes of vehicle should be clearly defined so that observers counting vehicles have no uncertainty about border-line cases. Vehicles that are held up temporarily (for example, at traffic signals) should be included with moving vehicles, though it is sometimes difficult to distinguish such vehicles from those standing or waiting on the road which are not included because they are not part of the flow.

NUMBER OF RUNS. Twelve to sixteen runs in each direction along the routes are usually sufficient to give reasonably consistent estimates of speed and flow.

QUEUEING-TIME INDICATOR. Apparatus has been devised[8] which greatly assists the observations of journey time in particular of stopped time. A vehicle may stop and start several times in the queue at an intersection, and as the time spent between intermediate stops and starts varies considerably between drivers, the stopped time is normally taken as the time from the first stop to the last start. The observer presses push buttons at each stop and start of the vehicle while queueing, and a change-over switch is operated as each new section of the route is entered. The required stopped time and the journey times are indicated by electrical digital registers and can be copied directly on to log sheets, the registers being then reset to zero.

PUNCHED PAPER TAPE. Analysis of the results of a moving-observer survey can be greatly speeded up by recording the observations directly on to standard 5-hole teleprinter paper tape which can then be read into an electronic computer. A paper tape unit has been devised which produces tape at the rate of one line every quarter second. Thus, the position of a hole punched in the tape to mark an event indicates the time of that event relative to the start of the tape. When using the paper tape in moving-observer surveys, tape is produced continuously during each run and "events" are punched on the tape as they occur. Times of starting and stopping and passing intersections are punched in code in one channel of the tape by one observer. By the use of press button units one or two other observers can record observations in the other four channels in the following different ways:

(1) Simple counts in four categories, one in each channel,
(2) Simple counts in three categories, with one total tally count,
(3) Simple count in two categories, with a tally count for each.

A computer programme is available for analyzing the results obtained in case 3 above. Survey tapes are read into the computer at approximately 25 times the speed at which the survey was carried out. This means, for example, that the results of a normal 5-hour survey will be analyzed in approximately 15 minutes. The programme averages the data from a number of survey tapes and produces journey time and flow on each road section in each direction for two classes of vehicles. The mean and standard deviation of the stopped time at each intersection in each direction, and the mean and standard deviation of the journey time of the observer along each section in each direction are also calculated.

ACCURACY OF METHOD. To check the accuracy of the method, the flows determined have been compared with those measured by a stationary observer at the roadside. A series of runs in each direction was made using the method, and a census of vehicles was taken. The results are shown graphically in Figs. 3.5(a) and (b), which show that for cars and commercial vehicles the opposing-vehicle count, without the tally correction, gives unbiased estimates with a fairly small random error. The standard errors are 14 per cent for cars and 3 per cent for commercial vehicles. The estimated values for other vehicles (buses, taxis, etc.) are, however, too high, the systematic error being + 25 per cent. This can easily be accounted for on the assumption that the average speed of this class is appreciably less than that of the test vehicle. Experience has shown that in heavy traffic even when told to drive at "about the speed of the surrounding vehicles" a driver will in fact travel at a faster speed than the average for all vehicles.

When the tally is included, as in Fig. 3.5(b), these errors disappear, as they should. The remaining errors appear to be quite random and the standard errors are 8 per cent for "other" vehicles and 4 per cent for all vehicles.

PRECISION OF THE METHOD. It has been shown that the full method gives an unbiased estimate of the flow. Random errors will occur, however, both from observers' errors and from random fluctuations in the flow. Observers' errors tend to increase with the magnitude of the flow being counted and with the number of classes of vehicle used, but experience shows that under normal conditions this is not a serious factor.

Errors arising from non-uniformity of flow always occur when a count over a sample period is used as an estimate of the mean flow throughout a longer period. This applies equally to a stationary census, when, for example, a few hourly counts during selected hours on one or two days may be used to estimate the total flow throughout a week or a month. The moving observer counts both the traffic that enters the section during his run and the traffic that was in the section when he started. The numbers are usually about equal, so that in terms of vehicles counted his observations are approximately equivalent to a stationary count over twice the single journey time or over the time for a complete return journey. Results of observations indicate that an estimate of the mean flow based on moving-vehicle counts will have about the same precision as that based on a sample census covering the same period.

ADVANTAGE OF THE METHOD. The main advantage of the moving-observer method is that it enables a large and varied amount of information to be collected quickly. It is economical in manpower; a small team of observers with one or two cars can collect reliable traffic data on a considerable mileage of streets. Additional information on parked vehicles, causes of exceptional delay etc., can be recorded if required.

One-way streets

The "moving-observer" method has been used by the Laboratory in traffic surveys in London and in other cities. A different method was, however, used in the 1962 London Traffic Survey carried out jointly by the London Traffic Management Unit of the Ministry of Transport and the

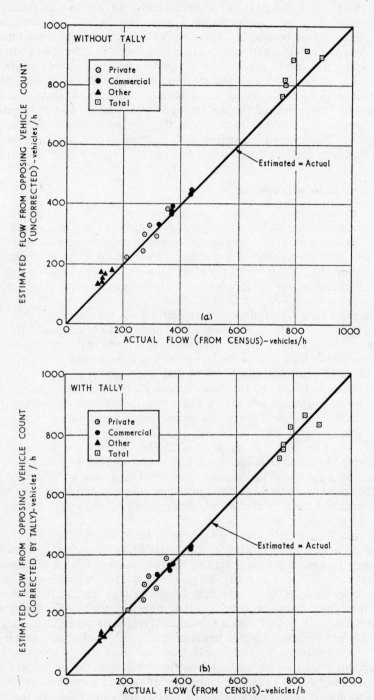

Fig. 3.5. Comparison between flow estimated by "moving-observer" method and actual flows

Road Research Laboratory, as a large number of one-way systems had then recently been put into operation. The journey times and stopped times were measured as before, but the flow was obtained from three-minute stationary counts at 1000 points spread out over the area. The counting programme was spread evenly over all the days of the survey, counts being made at each point once in the morning and once in the afternoon on different days of the week at times corresponding to car journeys. The method had been devised for the survey in 1961 and used in conjunction with the moving-observer method, so that the measurements, could be compared. The results suggest that both methods gave a good estimate of total flow over the whole network.

Trailing vehicles with test car

The moving-observer method cannot be easily applied in practice on rural roads because of the difficulty of travelling at the average speed of traffic on account of the lighter flows and freer driving conditions. A modified form of the method was therefore adopted in a survey of journey times on nearly 2000 miles of the road network between London and the Midlands, carried out in 1955 as part of an investigation into the London-Birmingham motorway (see Chapter 4).

The procedure is to follow a particular vehicle for about two miles, to stop in a layby or other convenient place and then to commence following another vehicle; the procedure is repeated indefinitely in the same direction until the whole route is covered. An observer in the car notes down mileages and times of passing through towns and important road junctions. The watch used should be of the "accumulating" type, i.e. one that can be switched off for the period during which the car is stationary, without the hand returning to zero. The reading on the watch at any instant is therefore the average journey time of the vehicles followed up to that point; this greatly simplifies analysis of the results. The observer is responsible for correcting, as far as possible, for errors due to the slowing down of the test car to a stop, and to the subsequent restarting; one system used is to switch off the watch halfway through the deceleration period and to switch it on when the speed of the test car has reached one-half of the estimated speed of the vehicle to be followed.

Personal bias in selecting the vehicles to be followed is avoided by the following technique. While the test car is stationary the observer makes any necessary entries on the log sheet and refers to a map to check his position on the route. When he is ready, he gives a signal to the driver who thereupon turns his attention to the first vehicle to pass, and starts to follow it. If the vehicle happens to be in a long bunch of traffic, it is sometimes not possible to follow it and a subsequent vehicle is taken instead. This probably introduces some bias towards the faster vehicles. In following a vehicle it is unnecessary—and inadvisable—to follow closely behind it and other vehicles can be allowed to come between the followed vehicle and test car. The following distance should be allowed to vary throughout the run, although it is necessary to ensure that at the end of the run the time interval between the two vehicles is roughly the same as that at the start. The adoption of this procedure is desirable in the interests of safety as well as to avoid influencing the driver of the vehicle being followed.

For most of the roads included in the above survey, only cars were followed, the results for commercial vehicles being estimated from those of cars by means of relations between the speeds of commercial vehicles and those of cars of the type described elsewhere (see p. 105). Since, in general, the work was limited to one run in each direction, the estimated journey times on short segments of road were not very reliable. However, the investigation was mainly concerned with long journeys and here the reliability of the estimates was quite satisfactory. For example, the data obtained on road A.1 suggested that in a journey of 100 minutes the error was unlikely to be more than 5 per cent; longer journeys were correspondingly more accurate.

The main disadvantage of the method is that it may require the test car to follow vehicles travelling at high speeds. It may therefore be desirable in the interests of safety to apply the method only in the case of less important roads where very high speeds are unlikely to be encountered.

RESULTS OF SPEED STUDIES

Speed distributions

The speeds of vehicles are affected by road layout, amount and composition of traffic, weather, state of the road and by various other factors which vary according to place and time. Even when the speeds of vehicles of a particular class at a given location at a given time are considered, the values show a considerable amount of scatter, primarily because of variations in vehicle and driver characteristics. The example, in Fig. 3.6, which refers to the speeds of cars at a point on a section of dual-carriageway road in a rural area, shows different methods of illustrating the variability in the speeds of individual vehicles. The histogram in Fig. 3.6(a) is a block diagram showing the percentage of individual vehicles in specified speed groups (in this case 5 mile/h groups). This diagram shows that the speeds of individual vehicles tend to cluster about the mean value, and that the frequency decreases as the departure from the mean increases. Fig. 3.6(b) is a cumulative frequency diagram which shows the percentage of speeds exceeding any specified value. The cumulative frequency diagram is the most common method of illustrating speed distributions and is particularly useful when two or more distributions are being compared.

As would be expected, the scatter of vehicle speeds is greatest when speeds are limited only by the capabilities of vehicles and by the wishes of their drivers and not by the road layout, amount of traffic etc., e.g. on lightly-trafficked motorways; on the other hand, when driving conditions are unfavourable, e.g. in built-up areas, drivers of vehicles capable of high speeds are forced to travel at much the same speeds as drivers of other vehicles and the scatter of speeds is greatly reduced. This is illustrated in Fig. 3.7 which shows cumulative frequency diagrams of speed distributions on five roads with varying degrees of driving conditions; on the motorway the speeds of individual vehicles covered a range of about 70 mile/h (from less than 30 mile/h to over 90 mile/h), while at the other extreme the speeds in the high street covered a range of only about 20 mile/h (from just less than 10 mile/h to just over 25 mile/h).

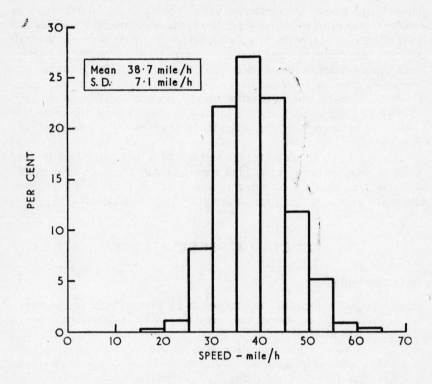

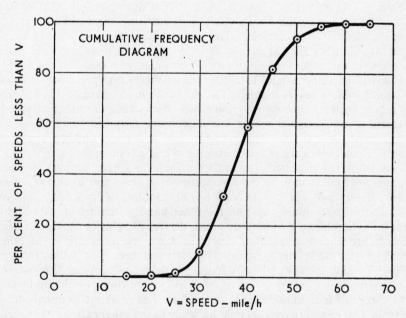

Fig. 3.6. Methods of illustrating a speed distribution

For statistical purposes, there are certain objections to the use of the range of a variable as measure of scatter but the concept of "standard deviation" is generally acceptable; this is defined as the square root of the average value of the squares of the differences between individual values and the mean. For many statistical distributions, including speed distributions, it is found that 95 per cent of individual values lie within about two standard deviations on each side of the mean. Fig. 3.7 shows the values of standard deviation calculated for the five speed distributions illustrated; the values range from 3·4 to 13·0 mile/h.

It is apparent from Fig. 3.7 that the standard deviation of a speed distribution is a function of the mean speed and it has been found that for speeds measured at a point, the "coefficient of variation", i.e. the standard deviation divided by the mean, is roughly one fifth.

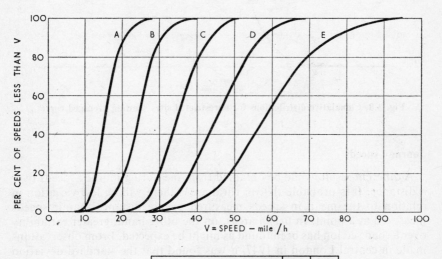

Site	Mean (mile/h)	S.D. (mile/h)
A – High street, 1952	16·1	3·4
B – Inner suburban road, 1958	24·3	4·9
C – Outer suburban road, 1958	35·2	6·0
D – Rural road 1958	45·6	8·4
E – Motorway, 1960	59·2	13·0

Fig. 3.7. Distributions of speeds on five different roads

Speed measurements were made at the rural 50 point sites (see Chapter 2) in 1960 and a "standard" distribution for each of the busiest sites was obtained by dividing the measured speeds of cars by the mean speed of cars for that site. The cumulative distributions obtained in such a way for the twelve sites considered are shown plotted in Fig. 3.8. The curve shown was obtained by grouping the results. It would appear that the "standardized" speeds obtained by dividing by the mean have approximately the same distribution at all the sites considered. The curve is similar to that of a "normal" distribution with standard devaition of 0·19 times the mean.

5*

This relation between the standard deviation and the mean refers to the speed distribution of cars or of light, medium or heavy commercial vehicles (as defined later, p. 111). For composite classes of vehicle (e.g. all clases of vehicle combined or all classes of commercial vehicle combined) the standard deviation in relation to the mean would be greater than indicated above.

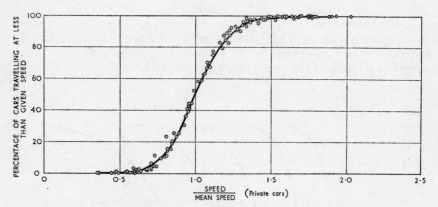

Fig. 3.8. Cumulative distributions for unrestricted sites showing averaged curve

Journey speeds

A different result would be obtained from measuring journey speeds over a distance. It is probable that in rural areas there will be less variation in relation to the mean in speeds measured over a distance than in speeds measured at a point. In urban areas, on the other hand, greater variability over a road section has been found as might be expected. From observations made in central London in 1947, it was found that the standard deviation of the reciprocal of the journey time varied with the mean according to the formula

$$S_u = 0.37\,(\bar{u})^{1.29}$$

where $\bar{u}$ is the mean reciprocal journey time in min^{-1}, and S_u is the standard deviation also in min^{-1}. The reciprocal u of a journey time t is of course proportional to the journey speed for a given road section. Over the range of times measured the expression above is approximately equivalent to the standard deviation of the reciprocal of the journey time being equal to one third of the mean.

Despite the variability in the speeds of individual vehicles, the mean is however, for many purposes, a satisfactory measure of vehicle speeds.

Precision of results

As described above even the speeds of a particular class at a given location at a given time show a considerable amount of scatter, giving rise to a speed distribution with its associated standard deviation. An estimate of the "standard error" of the calculated mean speed of this distribution is obtained by dividing the standard deviation by the square root of the number of speeds measured. Thus, for example, if measurements of speeds of 100 cars gave a mean speed of 40 mile/h, since the standard deviation is about one fifth of the mean, the standard error of the mean would be about 0·8 mile/h. This shows that the mean speed under particular conditions can be estimated fairly precisely. It should be noted however that the mean speed often depends critically on the location and conditions at the time of the measurements.

A statistical test to determine whether two mean speeds differ "significantly", i.e. the difference between them is greater than would be expected to occur by chance, is described by Leeming.[9]

Time-mean speed and space-mean speed

Most of the speed distributions described above refer to distribution of vehicle speeds over a period of time at a point in space: it is also possible to consider the distribution in space at a given instant. The mean speeds obtained from the two types of distribution are distinct and are called the "time-mean speed" and "space-mean speed" respectively.[10]

If a speed distribution in time is obtained the time-mean speed is given by

$$\bar{v}_t = \frac{\sum vt}{n}$$

and the space-mean speed is given by

$$\bar{v}_s = \frac{n}{\sum \dfrac{1}{v_t}}$$

where the v_t are the individual speeds in time and n is the number of observations.

If the speed distribution in space is obtained the space-mean speed is given by

$$\bar{v}_s = \frac{\sum v_s}{n}$$

and the time-mean speed by

$$\bar{v}_t = \bar{v}_s + \frac{\sigma_s^2}{v_s}$$

where the v_s are the individual speeds in space, σ_s; is the standard deviation of the v_s. These relations are derived in Appendix 2. The last equation shows that the time-mean speed is never less than the space-mean speed.

Speed measurements from aerial photographs can be used to derive speed distributions in space directly; radar speedmeters and timing devices give time-mean speed. It should be noted that in the latter case if the times are averaged and used to produce a mean speed, the space mean is obtained.

The general relations between the distributions of speed in space and time has been derived by Haight and Mosher.[11]

If $f(v)\delta v$ is the probability that a speed in time is in the range $v + \delta v$, then the corresponding density $F(v)$ in space is given by:

$$F(v) = \frac{\bar{v}_s}{v} f(v).$$

In a particular investigation it may not be very important which of the two means is used, but it is most important that the same mean should be used throughout any investigation, so that all the comparisons are fair. There is danger that a comparison of mean speeds measured some years apart or by different investigators will be invalid because they are not of the same kind.

Speed versus journey time

The choice between time- and space-mean speeds is really one between speed and journey time. Now time is a directly measurable physical quantity. On any route or section of road, the length is a fixed quantity while the duration of the journey varies. Times on successive sections are additives whereas speeds are not. The delay caused by two intersections is equal to the sum of the delays caused by each one, provided that they are sufficiently far apart. In planning a journey it is desirable to know how long it will take rather than what the average speed will be. Journey time is also used in economic asssessments. There is therefore much to be said for using average times in preference to average speeds when assessing the effect of a change.

On the other hand it is quite often the direct measurement of speed that is required, as for example for enforcement purposes. In addition speed measurements are frequently more consistent. It has been found that journey times often have very skew distributions with a long "tail" consisting of very slow journeys, whereas the corresponding distributions of speed tend to be more symmetrical. It was found from data of journey time and journey speed for roads in central London that the coefficient of variation (i.e. the standard deviation devided by the mean) was 20 to 25 per cent less in the case of speeds. This is an important result, since it means that only about 60 per cent of the number of runs are needed to give the same proportional accuracy in the mean speed as in the mean journey time.

Speeds on different types of road

Since cars usually constitute the majority of vehicles in the traffic and since they travel faster than other types of vehicle and are therefore more susceptible to changes in driving conditions, it is useful to consider how the mean speed of cars varies on different types of road. Typical values for the mean speed of cars obtained in measurements in recent years on roads in Great Britain are as follows:

TYPICAL SPEEDS OF CARS

RURAL	Motorway	Mean speed (mile/h)
	3 lane	60
	2 lane	58
	Dual carriageway	
	2 lane	40–55
	Single Carriageway	
	3 lane	35–40
	2 lane	25–40
	1 lane	10–35
URBAN	Suburban	
	Dual Carriageway	30–40
	Single Carriageway	20–35
	Central	10

The above values refer to mean speeds on straight and level sections of road or to journey speeds over long sections of road which may include curves, gradients, intersections, etc. They are not applicable to individual curves, gradients or at intersections, particularly roundabouts or signal-controlled junctions, where speeds would, of course, be lower.

SPEEDS ON MOTORWAYS

The excellent layout of motorways, in the form of wide dual carriage-ways, easy alignment, gentle gradients, controlled access, flyover junctions etc., probably enables motorists to travel as fast as they wish, subject to the limitations of their vehicles, so that speeds are much higher than on all-purpose roads. A further factor is that motorways probably attract vehicles capable of higher speeds and that slower or older vehicles may remain on ordinary roads. Table 3.1 gives typical mean speeds measured by radar speedmeter on the Preston by-pass motorway and on the London-Birmingham motorway together with the results of similar measurements by the Laboratory on motorways in certain other countries in Western Europe.

Table 3.1 shows that the mean speeds of cars on all the motorways were between 50 and 60 mile/h and that there were marked differences between the different classes of vehicle, particularly on the British motorways. Some of the speed differences between different motorways are probably partly attributable to the fact that the measurements were taken in different years and that comparison is affected by a long-term increase in vehicle speeds. However, the higher speeds on the London-Birmingham motor-way, particularly those of cars and light commercial vehicles, are probably partly explained by the greater width of carriageway on this road; most of the London-Birmigham motorway, including the sites where the measure-ments were taken, has dual three-lane carriageways while the other motor-ways studied had dual two-lane carriageways. As would be expected, speeds on the dual three-lane carriageways are highest in the offside lane and lowest in the nearside lane, for example in June 1960 the mean speeds of cars in the three lanes were, from left to right 52, 61 and 69 mile/h respectively.

TABLE 3.1

Speeds on straight, level sections of motorways

| Class of Vehicle | London-Birmingham Motorway (May, 1960) (2 × 3 lanes) | Preston By-pass (May, 1959) (2 × 2 lanes) | Mean speed (mile/h) European motorways (June, 1957) | | | |
			Germany (2 × 2 lanes)	Netherlands (2 × 2 lanes)	Belgium (2 × 2 lanes)	France (2 × 2 lanes)
Cars	59	53	54	53	52	52
Light commercial	49	46	46	45	40	43
Medium ,,	41	37	40	41	38	36
Heavy ,,	37	33	38	40	35	35

Speeds of different classes of vehicle

Commercial vehicles travel more slowly than cars, particularly on the faster roads. On roads where, because of traffic conditions, the average speed of cars is low, the speed of commercial vehicles is much the same as that of cars. As conditions improve so the mean speeds differ to an increasing extent. The results of observations made at the rural 50 point sites in 1960 are shown in Fig. 3.9.

The clasifications used in Fig. 3.9 are as follows:

Cars (including taxis and dual purpose vehicles).

Light commercial vehicles (up to 30 cwt unladen weight, i.e. built on a car chassis).

Medium commercial vehicles (over 30 cwt unladen weight, with two axles only).

Heavy commercial vehicles (more than two axles; including articulated vehicles and all commercial vehicles towing trailers).

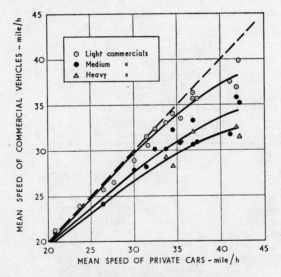

Fig. 3.9. Comparison of mean speeds of cars
and mean speeds of commercial vehicles

Similar relations between the speeds of cars and speeds of various classes of commercial vehicles were found from earlier observations,[12] but commercial vehicles, particularly heavy vehicles, the legal limit of which was raised from 20 to 30 mile/h on 1st May 1957, are now travelling faster relative to cars. It has been found that the relations hold approximately for the journey speeds of vehicles on roads with a considerable amount of rise and fall as well as on level roads. Fig. 3.9 emphasizes the need for distinguishing between cars and the different types of commercial vehicle in speed studies on rural roads. If all classes of vehicle are combined speed differences will be harder to detect and they may be liable to misinterpretation if the composition of traffic varies. These relations have an important application in some speed investigations. For many purposes it is necessary only to measure the speeds of cars, which are most sensitive to changing conditions and to estimate the mean speeds of other vehicles from relations of this type.

Trends in speeds

Technical advances in vehicle design would be expected to cause the speed of traffic to rise over the years in places where driving conditions are favourable. On the other hand, the general increase in the amount of traffic on the roads would be expected to cause a reduction in the speed of traffic, particularly on roads which are already congested. There is evidence of the existence of both types of trend and that, broadly speaking, speeds are increasing in rural areas and decreasing in urban areas. There has been a slight tendency for the mean speeds in central London and other cities to drop (see Chapter 7). On the other hand the results of speed measurements on a few main roads near London, (shown in Table 3.2) suggest that the average speed of cars increased by about 1 mile/h (about $2\frac{1}{2}$ per cent) per annum between 1947 and 1955.

TABLE 3.2

Speeds of cars at four sites
on rural or suburban roads (1947–1955)

Site	Date	Mean speed (mile/h)	Increase in mean speed per year (mile/h)
A40 Western Avenue . .	November, 1947	37·0	1·4
	November, 1954	47·0	
A.4 Great West Road . .	June, 1950	39·4	0·6
	June, 1955	42·4	
A.10 Great Cambridge Road	July, 1952	32·9	1·4
	September, 1955	37·0	
A.40 near West Wycombe .	October, 1953	43·9	0·5
	October, 1955	44·8	
	Average . .		1·0

The proportions of vehicles using the centre and offside lanes on the London-Birmingham motorway tended to increase over the year after the motorway was opened. The trends in speeds of cars and commercial vehicles on the motorway are shown in Fig. 3.10. There was a slight but steady increase in speed of both cars and commercial vehicles up to the end of 1962.

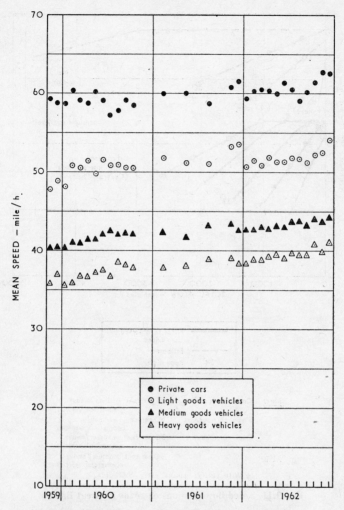

Fig. 3.10. Trends in speeds on the London–Birmingham motorway. Mean speeds on straight, level sections

SPEED/FLOW RELATIONS IN GREAT BRITAIN

The results of measurements of speed and flow on roads of different width in central London and in rural areas are shown in Fig. 3.11. The following formula can be fitted to the central London results:

$$v = 31 - \frac{q+430}{3(w-6)} \quad \text{or 24 mile/h whichever is the lower,}$$

where v = running speed is mile/h,

$\quad\quad q$ = total flow (both sides of the road together) in veh/h,

$\quad\quad w$ = carriageway width in feet,

provided the width is at least 20 ft and the resulting value of speed is not less than about 10 mile/h.

The running speed is defined as the speed obtained by excluding delays at intersections controlled by traffic signals or police.

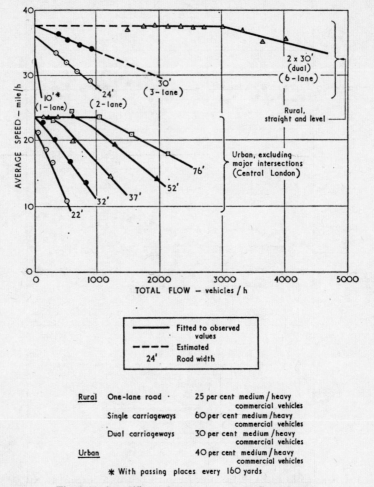

Fig. 3.11. Speed/flow relations on roads in Great Britain

It must be emphasized that this particular formula is only applicable to the ranges of flow covered by the observations and in traffic conditions similar to those obtaining on the roads studied. These roads were somewhat variable in width (w refers to the average width of a section $\frac{1}{2}$ to 1 mile long) and parking was permitted on most of them.

Evidence on the effects of parking on the speed of traffic under various conditions (see Chapter 10) has been used to estimate the speed/flow relation in the absence of parking. It appears that at all levels of flow the average effect of parking was to reduce the effective width by about six feet. This means that the speed/flow relation for a road with no parking would be expected to be

$$v = 31 - \frac{q+430}{3w} \qquad \text{or 24 mile/h, whichever is the lower}$$

where the symbols have the same meaning as above.

The observations on rural roads of different width are rather limited, but similar results appear to hold, as shown in Fig. 3.11. Before fitting a formula to the rural results it is necessary to make an adjustment for the effects of the particular compositions of traffic. For instance, the high proportion of commercial vehicles on the 24-ft and 30-ft wide carriageways would have the effect of lowering the average speeds. The appropriate adjustments were made using separate speed/flow relations for cars, light commercial, medium commercial and heavy commercial vehicles which are given in Table 3.3, based on those given on p. 233 (for A.5) and the appropriate passenger car unit equivalents on p. 234. (For an explanation of passenger car units see p. 200).

TABLE 3.3

*Speed/flow relations for different
types of vehicles on rural roads*

Road	Vehicle Type	Speed (mile/h) at flow Q passenger car units/hour
2 lanes	Car	$41 \cdot 9 - 0 \cdot 0084 Q$
	Light commercial	$38 \cdot 3 - 0 \cdot 0068 Q$
	Medium ,,	$34 \cdot 1 - 0 \cdot 0048 Q$
	Heavy ,,	$29 \cdot 2 - 0 \cdot 0023 Q$
3 lanes	Car	$47 \cdot 7 - 0 \cdot 0062 Q$
	Light commercial	$40 \cdot 5 - 0 \cdot 0037 Q$
	Medium ,,	$33 \cdot 9 - 0 \cdot 0012 Q$
	Heavy ,,	$27 \cdot 4 - 0 \cdot 0002 Q$

The following result was obtained for the average composition for rural roads:

$$v = 51 - \frac{q + 1400}{6w} \quad \text{or 43 mile/h whichever is the lower}$$

where v = average speed of traffic in mile/h,

q = total flow in veh/h,

and w = the carriageway width in feet.

This formula can probably be applied to roads with between two and six lanes. The composition of the traffic is assumed to be the average for rural roads (25 per cent medium and heavy commercial vehicles).

When considering the economic capacity of a road (see Chapter 6) it is necessary to know separately the relations between the speeds of different classes of vehicle and the flows of each class. This can be simplified by the use of Fig. 3.9, which shows that under a wide variety of conditions the average speeds of other classes of vehicle can be predicted with reasonable accuracy if the average speed of cars is given. Allowance can be made for changes in traffic composition by using the passenger car unit equivalents given in Chapter 6.

The speed observations on two- and three-lane roads have been analysed to give a set of speed/flow relations, as shown in Table 3.3.

International comparison of speed/flow relations on two-lane roads

Figure 3.12 compares the results of speed/flow measurements made on the continent of Europe, in the U.S.A. and in Great Britain. It will be seen that there is good agreement between the European and American results but the figures for Great Britain, even where corrected for the percentage of commercial vehicles, are low. This could be accounted for by the 20

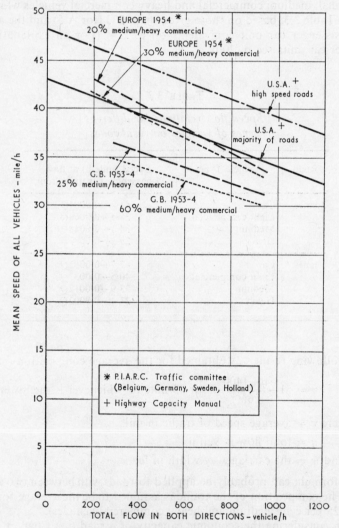

Fig. 3.12. Speed/flow relations on two-lane roads

mile/h speed limit on heavy commercial vehicles, which was in operation when the measurements were made in Great Britain, and by differences in the performance of commercial vehicles in different countries. There is good general agreement between the slopes of the curves and the reduction in speed produced by a given increase in flow can therefore be predicted with reasonal precision.

REFERENCES TO CHAPTER 3

1. YATES, F. Sampling methods for censuses and surveys. London, 1949 (Charles Griffin & Company Limited).
2. EVANS, H. K. (Editor.) Traffic engineering handbook. New Haven, Conn., 1950 (Institute of Traffic Engineers), 2nd edition.
3. BERRY, D. S., and F. H. GREEN. Techniques for measuring over-all speeds in urban areas. *Proc. Highw. Res. Bd, Wash.*, 1949, **29**, 311–18.
4. WARDROP, J. G., and G. CHARLESWORTH. A method of estimating speed and flow of traffic from a moving vehicle. *J. Instn civ. Engrs Part II*, 1954, **3** (1), 158–71.
5. MORTIMER, W. J. Moving vehicle method of estimating traffic volumes and speeds. *Traff. Engng*, 1956, **28**, (12), 539–44.
6. MORTIMER, W. J. Moving vehicle method of estimating traffic volumes and speeds. *Bull. Highw. Res. Bd, Wash.*, 1956 (156), 14–26.
7. BLENSLY, R. C. Moving vehicle method of estimating traffic volumes. *Traff. Engng*, 1956, **27** (3), 127–29, 147.
8. ELLSON, P. B. Queueing-time indicator for use in a moving vehicle. *Instrum. Prac.*, 1959, **13** (7), 736–41.
9. LEEMING, J. J. Statistical methods for engineers. London, 1963 (Blackie), chapter 8.
10. WARDROP, J. G. Some theoretical aspects of road traffic research. *Proc. Instn civ. Engrs Part II*, 1952, **1**, (2), 325–62; Discussion, 362–78.
11. HAIGHT, F. A. and W. W. MOSHER. A practical method for improving the accuracy of vehicular speed distribution measurements. *Bull. Highw. Res. Bd, Wash.*, 1962 (341), 92–96.
12. CHARLESWORTH, G. and T. M. COBURN. The influence of road layout on speeds and accidents in rural areas. *J. Instn munic. Engrs*, 1957, **83** (7), 221–40.

APPENDIX 1

The evaluation of the flow and mean speed of a stream of traffic by a moving observer

Consider a stream of vehicles moving along a section of road, of length l, in such a way that the average number q passing through the section per unit time is constant. The stream can be regarded as consisting of flows q_1 moving with speed v_1, q_2 with speed v_2, etc.

Suppose an observer travels with the stream at speed v_w and against the stream at speed v_a. Then the flows relative to him of vehicles with flow q_1 and speed v_1 are

$$\frac{q_1(v_1 - v_w)}{v_1}$$

and

$$\frac{q_1(v_1 + v_a)}{v_1}$$

respectively.

If t_w denotes the journey time l/v_w corresponding to speed v_w,

t_a „ the journey time l/v_a corresponding to speed v_a,

x_1 „ the number of vehicles with speed v_1 met by the observer when travelling against the stream,

y_1 „ the number of vehicles with speed v_1 which overtake the observer when travelling with the stream (or minus the number he overtakes).

then

$$q_1(t_a + t_1) = x_1$$
$$q_1(t_w - t_1) = y_1$$

Similar results hold for all the other speeds, so that if

q denotes flow of all vehicles in the stream $= q_1 + q_2 + \ldots$

x „ total number of vehicles met in the section when travelling against the stream,

y „ number of vehicles overtaking the observer minus the number he overtakes when travelling with the stream,

t „ mean journey time of all vehicles in the stream, that is,

$$\frac{(q_1 t_1 + q_2 t_2 + \ldots)}{q}$$

then summing over all speeds gives

$$q(t_a + \bar{t}) = x$$
$$q(t_w - \bar{t}) = y$$

or

$$q = \frac{(x+y)}{t_a + t_w}$$

$$\bar{t} = t_w - \frac{y}{q}$$

The mean speed is given by $l/\bar{t}$, which is the space-mean speed, see p. 107.

APPENDIX 2

Relation between time-mean and space-mean speeds

Suppose there are subsidiary streams of traffic with flows q_1, q_2, q_c and speeds v_1, $v_2 \ldots v_c$, let the total flow be given by

$$Q = q_1 + q_2 \ldots + q_c$$

$$= \sum_{i=1}^{c} q_i$$

Consider the subsidiary stream with flow q_i and speed v_i. The average time-interval between its vehicles is evidently $1/q_i$ and the distance travelled in this time is v_i/q_i. It follows that the density of this stream in space, i.e. the number of vehicles per unit length of road at any instant (the concentration) is given by

$$k_i = q_i/v_i, \quad i = 1, 2 \ldots c \quad . \qquad . \qquad . \qquad . \qquad . \qquad . \qquad (1)$$

The total concentration is given by

$$K = \sum_{i=1}^{c} k_i$$

Putting $f_i' = k_i/K$ gives the frequency f_i' of v_i in space. The time-mean speed is defined as

$$\bar{v}t = \sum_{i=1}^{c} q_i v_i / Q \quad . \qquad . \qquad . \qquad . \qquad . \qquad . \qquad . \qquad (2)$$

and the space-mean speed is defined as

$$\bar{v}_s = \sum_{i=1}^{c} k_i v_i / K \qquad . \qquad . \qquad . \qquad . \qquad . \qquad . \qquad (3)$$

But from equation (1)

$$k_i v_i = q_i \qquad . \qquad . \qquad . \qquad . \qquad . \qquad . \qquad . \qquad (4)$$

and therefore

$$\bar{v}_s = \sum_{i=1}^{c} q_i / k = QK \qquad . \qquad . \qquad . \qquad . \qquad . \qquad . \qquad (5)$$

From (5)

$$\bar{v}_s = \frac{Q}{\sum k_i}$$

$$= \frac{Q}{\sum \frac{q_i}{v_i}}$$

from (2) and (4)

$$\bar{v}t = \sum_{i=1}^{c} k_i v_i^2 / Q$$

$$= K \sum_{i=1}^{c} f_i' v_i^2 / Q$$

$$= \sum_{i=1}^{c} f_i' v_i^2 / \bar{v}_s \text{ from (5)}$$

$$= \sum_{i=1}^{c} f_i' \{\bar{v}_s + (v_i - \bar{v}_s)\}^2 / \bar{v}_s$$

$$= \{(\sum_{i=1}^{c} f_i') \bar{v}_s^2 + \sum_{i=1}^{c} f_i' (v_i - \bar{v}_s)^2\} / \bar{v}_s$$

$$(\text{since } \sum_{i=1}^{c} f_i' (v_i - \bar{v}_s) = 0)$$

$$= \bar{v}_s + \frac{\sigma_s^2}{\bar{v}_s}$$

where

$$\sigma_s = \sqrt{\{\sum_{i=1}^{c} f_i' (v_i - \bar{v}_s)^2\}}$$

is the standard deviation of the space distribution of speed.

Chapter 4

Traffic Surveys

SYNOPSIS

Methods of making traffic surveys: methods of obtaining information on the origins and destinations of existing movements; estimation of future traffic movements; selection of future road network; traffic assignment; justification of the construction of new roads. Examples of traffic studies; London-Birmingham motorway origin-and-destination survey; Oxford traffic survey; London travel survey.

INTRODUCTION

Traffic congestion in towns and on the main roads between them is a serious problem in many places. Minor road improvements often provide worthwhile alleviation of congestion but when these measures become ineffective owing to increases in traffic the construction of new roads needs to be considered. Before these are constructed it is desirable to answer the following questions:

(*a*) How many miles of new road are needed and where should they be situated?

(*b*) How many traffic lanes and what type of intersections will each new road require?

(*c*) Can the construction of the new roads be justified?

There are various methods of answering these questions but usually they include the following steps:

(i) Information is collected on the origins and destinations of traffic in the area.

(ii) This information together with planning information and data on traffic trends is used to estimate the origins and destinations of traffic in the area at some future date appropriate to the expected life of the new road system.

(iii) A layout of new roads is selected which will apparently suit the future origin-destination pattern.

(iv) The estimated traffic movements are assigned to the complete network of new and old roads.

The estimated traffic flow on each road obtained from (iv) provides the basic data needed to answer questions (*b*) and (*c*) for the selected layout of new roads. Question (*a*) is difficult to answer directly but by assigning the traffic movements to several different networks of roads it is possible to decide which of the schemes is most suitable. This method of selecting a road network is not as inefficient as it might appear since planning and other considerations usually place a limit on the number of acceptable road layouts.

120

This chapter describes the different methods of carrying out steps (i) to (iv). Details of three surveys in which the Laboratory has taken part are included.

METHODS OF MAKING TRAFFIC SURVEYS

Methods of obtaining information on the origins and destinations of existing movements

There are five main methods of carrying out origin-and-destination surveys: by roadside interview; by giving postcards to drivers; by noting registration numbers; by placing tags on vehicles; and by home interview.

ROADSIDE INTERVIEW

Vehicles are stopped at a number of points and drivers are questioned about their journeys. The survey stations are usually situated at points where the road system intersects one or more cordons; these are chosen to intercept all important movements in the area under consideration. One arrangement uses two sets of cordons at right-angles to form a rectangular grid as shown in Fig. 4.1.(*a*). An alternative arrangement, particularly suited to a single town, has a series of cordons round the city centre combined with radial cordons as shown in Fig. 4.1(*b*). If the movements being studied are predominantly in one direction at each point in the area one set of cordons may suffice, e.g. radial cordons may not be needed in towns and cordons at right-angles to the line of travel may be suitable for studying a proposed road between towns. Short cordons that divide the area into irregular zones as shown in Fig. 4.1(*c*) can be used but it is more difficult to make efficient use of the interview data. Both directions of traffic at a survey station should be interviewed but not simultaneously except possibly at special sites, e.g. dual-carriageways or roads with very little traffic. If, however, the survey covers most of the day it may be sufficient to interview traffic in one direction only and to assume that the journeys in the opposite direction are the reverse of those in the direction interviewed.

The questions asked depend on the purpose of the survey and are usually designed to determine the last point that the vehicle needed to be at and the next point to which it needs to go. This information may be obtained by direct questioning or a series of questions may be asked; for example, the origin may be found by asking questions of the type:

Where did you start this journey?
Have you made any calls since you left there?
(If answer is yes) Where was the last place at which you called?

If the origin or destination of a journey is a considerable distance from the area being considered it may be decided that the point of entry to or exit from the area will be unchanged by any modification to the road layout. If so, the questions should be designed to determine the point of entry or exit. The questions put to drivers of commercial vehicles are sometimes different from those put to drivers of cars so that each is most likely to give the correct answers.

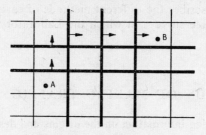

(a) Rectangular grid of cordons

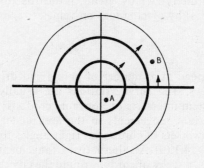

(b) Ring and radial cordons

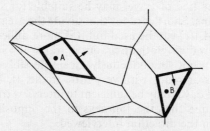

(c) Irregular network of cordons

In each of the diagrams the algebraic sum of the flows from A to B that cross any one of the thickened cordons in the direction shown is an estimate of the total flow from A to B. The best estimate is the average of the estimates obtained at each cordon.

Fig. 4.1. Layout of cordons for roadside-interview and postcard origin-destination surveys

To avoid bias the question must be framed with care and interviewers should be instructed to keep to a consistent wording of them. The answers must be obtained in sufficient detail for the origins and destinations to be coded accurately afterwards, and each answer should be written down before the next question is asked so that mistakes in the records are minimized. The answers are usually written on pre-printed forms and it is well worthwhile spending considerable care over their design. The forms may conveniently include the questions to be asked; adequate space for recording replies should be provided, preferably using a "box" for each; additional "boxes" for subsequent coding of the data should also be included.

Other questions may be asked, e.g. purpose of journey, and the interviewer can record directly other information such as type of vehicle, number of occupants, etc.

Interviewers have no statutory powers to stop and question drivers and therefore it is necessary to have police control. Usually a very good response to the interviewing is obtained but regular drivers may get irritated.

Although roadside-interview surveys are often carried out simultaneously at all points, it is possible to deal with different survey points and different directions of travel on different days using a small number of interviewers.

The main disadvantage of the roadside-interview method is that drivers are delayed while being interviewed. Queueing can and should be avoided by taking a sample of the vehicles passing the interview point. The most suitable method of selecting the sample is for the policeman at the site to stop the next vehicle that passes a predetermined sampling line after receiving a signal from the interviewer that the previous interview is complete. The policeman is available to control traffic round the stationary vehicle while the interview is taking place. The sampling line should be placed sufficiently far away for the policeman to be able to stop the next vehicle crossing it when required; bias is introduced if he lets the faster vehicles go by before stopping a slower one. A variation of this "variable-sampling" method selects two vehicles at a time: the vehicles are interviewed simultaneously by two interviewers.

The variable-sampling method requires a classified count of all vehicles that pass in the direction being studied while interviewing is in progress so that the proportion of each type of vehicle being sampled during each period can be obtained. The proportion being sampled will vary with the time of day and, to some extent, from one type of vehicle to another.

Sampling appears businesslike to the public and regular drivers appreciate the possibility of getting through without being stopped.

The variable-sampling method of carrying out roadside-interview surveys is very flexible and can be adapted to suit many different types of investigation. Finding suitable sites for interview stations is usually not difficult: on roads with three or more lanes a separate interviewing bay is laid out with rubber cones; on lightly-trafficked two-lane roads one lane can be used for interviewing and the other used for two-way working under the direction of the policeman. At all interviewing sites suitable signs are needed to give adequate warning of the obstruction to drivers in both directions.

POSTCARDS

This method involves asking each driver to complete and return a prepaid postcard given to him as he passes one of a number of selected points. The method is basically similar to the roadside-interview method and the sites for distribution are selected in the same way as roadside-interview stations. Vehicle delay is negligible and the method is simpler and cheaper than most.

The questions asked on the card are similar to those asked in the roadside interview method. They must be very carefully worded as the driver is very unlikely to seek advice if he does not understand them. The method has the serious disadvantage that a substantial proportion of cards are not returned. If drivers who do not return their cards have a pattern of traffic movements which is different from that of the drivers who do, the results of the survey will be biased. A comparison in Manchester[1] between the roadside-interview and postcard methods showed no such bias however, Well planned and publicized surveys have yielded returns of 50 per cent or more.

REGISTRATION NUMBERS

Observers, stationed at points forming a cordon, record registration numbers of vehicles entering and leaving an area. The results are analysed by comparing the two lists of registration numbers; one for vehicles entering the area and the other for vehicles leaving it. Each registration number that occurs in both lists corresponds to a vehicle movement between the two points where the number was observed. Registration numbers that occur in one list only are assumed to represent journeys which originate or finish inside the area. It is usually advantageous to note the times of entry and exit also; this information facilitates matching the records and can be used to determine journey times. By setting an upper limit to the journey time, through traffic, which stops in the area for an appreciable time, can be distinguished from the remaining through journeys. It is customary to classify vehicles according to type and to record the full registration mark (letters as well as figures). Sampling is achieved by recording only those numbers which end in one or more specified digits. It is most important that numbers are recorded accurately and the rate of sampling should be low enough for this to be done. Allowance can be made for registration numbers that are known to be incorrect or incomplete. If the travel time through the area is appreciable it may be desirable to stagger the observations at entry and exit points.

The advantages of this method are that traffic is not normally delayed and that police control is not normally necessary; it is usually considered suitable for urban areas. However, since recording must be done at all points simultaneously, a larger number of observers is required. The method has the disadvantage that the information about each journey is limited to the point of entry and exit from the area being studied; neither the origin nor the destination is obtained. Any through journeys past a loophole in the ring of survey points will be classified as terminating journeys. Mistakes in recording are an even more serious source of bias; a through journey which has one of its registration numbers recorded incorrectly will be recorded as two terminating journeys instead of one through journey. If attempts are made to simplify the task of recording by noting part of the registration number only, through journeys will tend to be over estimated as there is the possibility of falsely matching two terminating journeys to give a through journey.

TAGS ON VEHICLES

Coded tags are placed on vehicles as they enter an area and are taken off when they leave it. Times of entering and leaving may be marked on the tags so that the journey times can be determined. The method is similar to the registration-number method but errors are less likely and analysis is easier. A disadvantage is that drivers may object to the tags and they may remove them.

HOME INTERVIEWS

A sample of the population is interviewed at their homes. The proportion of households that are interviewed normally lies between 1 and 10 per cent and it is customary to obtain information on the journeys of all members of the households. Methods of choosing the sample vary but their aim is to select a known and unbiased proportion of the households in each district in the area. The questions asked depend on the object of the study but it is usual to obtain details of journeys made by persons or vehicles on the previous day or days. Information should not be asked about journeys made more than a few days before the interview as people forget journeys, particularly casual ones, quite quickly. In one survey it was estimated that less than half the casual journeys made a week before the interview were remembered.

The method is particularly suitable for studying traffic demands in large urban areas. Unlike the other methods described so far it enables information to be obtained on journeys by public transport and on foot as well as by car. The possibility of bias is small and errors and omissions are unlikely since interviews can be carried out unhurriedly. The method is expensive and requires detailed planning and trained interviewers; several visits may be needed before an interview can be carried out.

In some studies the amount of time spent in interviewing has been reduced by making two short visits to each household sampled instead of one long one: on the first visit the interviewer collects basic details of the household and leaves a form for each member of the household on which he or she can record details of journeys made on a specified day; the completed forms are collected on the second visit. It was found that interviewers could cope with 50 households per week by this method; satisfactory returns were obtained from 90 per cent of the households visited by the interviewers.

Another method of obtaining the required information is to send to each of the selected households a letter asking the members of the household to enter on forms enclosed with the letter details of all journeys made on a particular day. The forms are returned in prepaid envelopes. To avoid bias in the results it is desirable that attempts should be made to obtain completed forms from households that do not reply; this can be done by sending postal reminders or by visiting the houses concerned.

The information obtained in a home-interview survey is limited to journeys made by persons resident in the area. Additional interview surveys at commercial premises are made to obtain the movements of commercial vehicles; journeys into the area by non-residents are obtained by a roadside interview or postcard survey on the roads crossing the perimeter of the areas. Details of public-transport journeys across the perimeter by non-residents are usually collected by asking a sample of passengers to fill in and return a prepaid postcard.

The accuracy of home-interview surveys is often checked by determining from the interviews the journeys that should cross one or more screen lines;

the results are compared with those obtained by a roadside-interview survey on all roads intersected by the screen lines.

PERIOD COVERED BY SURVEY

To conform to Ministry of Transport censuses, surveys should cover the period 6 a.m. to 10 p.m. However, for various reasons, it may be necessary to reduce the working day to twelve hours or less and to apply expansion factors derived from volumetric census data. In urban areas surveys are sometimes confined to peak hours.

Information should be obtained on days of the week when the traffic situation is a problem. The five days Monday to Friday usually have very similar traffic patterns and it is rarely essential to cover each of the days. Week-ends are usually unimportant in large urban areas but may be the biggest problem in towns on holiday routes. Saturdays are often a difficulty in market towns.

Except where holiday traffic is heavy the time of year of the survey is not very important. Surveys are often made in the summer to correspond roughly with the Ministry of Transport censuses in August; additional reasons for summer working are that the weather is better, the hours of daylight are longer and that casual labour is easier to find.

DURATION OF SURVEY

Surveys are often concentrated into the shortest possible period of time using large numbers of staff who are often on site for long periods at a time. This method may cause the least inconvenience to the local authority's office but is rarely the most accurate way of obtaining the data. The results will be more representative and less likely to be affected by abnormal weather conditions or special events if the effort is spread over a longer period. This procedure can lead to economy in the amount of equipment and the number of staff required at any time (although not in total effort). Extending the period of a home-interview survey is a simple matter. With the other methods the effort can be spread (and errors due to fatigue reduced) by working for part of the day only; one way is to divide the day into periods of about two hours each and to work alternate periods on one day and the remaining periods on another. The work in the roadside-interview and post-card methods can be further spread by manning a limited number of points at a time.

The amount of data that needs to be collected will depend on the accuracy desired from the results. If the number of vehicles sampled at each site in a roadside-interview or postcard survey is proportional to the flow at the site the estimate of the flow making a given movement will be expected to have an accuracy given by:

$$V \simeq \frac{1}{\sqrt{qkm}}$$

where

V is the coefficient of variation of the estimated flow (the coefficient of variation is the ratio of the standard deviation to the mean),

q is the estimated flow in vehicles per hour,

k is the sampling factor expressed as the ratio of the total number of vehicles interviewed at a site to the flow in vehicles per hour at the site,

m is the number of cordons intersected by the particular movement.

The formula also applies where q is the sum of a number of flows with the same m. If flows with different values of m are combined and if k varies to some extent from site to site it is more difficult to estimate the accuracy, but it is unlikely that the coefficient of variation is seriously underestimated if the formula is used with m equal to unity. If this is done the formula can be rearranged as follows to determine the value of k required:

$$k \simeq \frac{1}{qV^2}$$

It should be noted that it is not necessary to estimate small movements accurately as the various movements will usually be combined to assess the flow on a road; the smallest flow that will be important and the accuracy desired of it should be used to calculate the sampling factor that is necessary. As an example, if a flow of 400 vehicles per hour is required to have a co-efficient of variation not greater than 5 per cent the sampling factor is unity, i.e. the number of interviews has to equal the flow in an hour. The last formula may also be used to assess the sampling factor required for surveys by the registration-number or tags-on-vehicles methods.

Using the results of a large number of origin-destination surveys in Great Britain, Duff and Bellamy[2] have established a relationship between the percentage of through traffic and population. The results shown in Fig. 4.2, are of value in assessing sampling factors for by-pass investigations.

In home-interview surveys the corresponding theoretical formula for calculating the sample of households required is:

$$p \simeq \frac{1}{hqV^2}$$

where

p is the proportion of households interviewed,

h is the period in hours, to which the journey data from each household refers,

q is the estimated flow in vehicles per hour making any movement or sum of movements,

V is the coefficient of variation of q.

Using the values of q and V which were used in the previous example the proportion interviewed should be $\frac{1}{12}$ if data on journeys covering a period of 12 hours are collected. Analysis of data obtained in Phoenix City[3] suggests that the actual accuracy is only half the theoretical figure; this corresponds to a four-fold increase in the size of sample required.

ANALYSIS

The amount of data collected in a survey by any of the methods described usually justifies mechanical analysis. The form of the data for mechanical analysis and the results required should be agreed at an early stage with the person responsible for the analysis, preferably before the commencement of the survey. Data should be thoroughly checked before they are sent

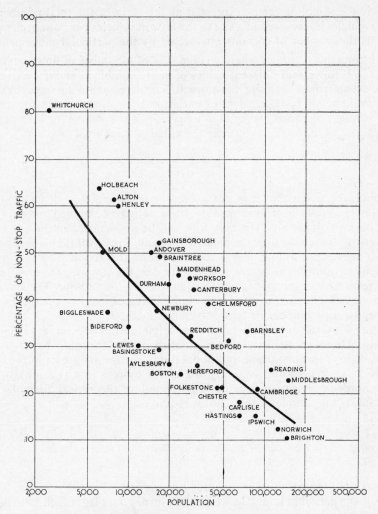

Fig. 4.2. Percentage of through non-stop traffic related to size of town (Duff and Bellamy)

for processing and as far as possible the method of analysis should verify that the results are reasonable.

In the registration-number method, analysis commences with registration number matching to obtain the journeys; the other methods give the journeys directly.

The first stage in the analysis of the journeys is to code the origins and destinations in some way. Usually the area under consideration is divided into a number of zones and each origin and destination is coded by the designation of the zone containing it. The zones should divide the area into sections with uniform land use and should be just small enough to define the origins and destinations satisfactorily; they need not be of uniform area. Zones that define the "catchment area" associated with a section of main road are more useful for subsequent traffic assignment than zones that have main roads as their boundary. If possible the zones used in the roadside-interview and postcard methods should not be intersected by the cordons.

It is necessary to associate with each journey an "expansion factor" to allow for the probability that such a journey will be intercepted. These expansion factors are then summed for each possible origin-destination combination to give a table of flows making each movement. Depending on the particular journeys used it may be for a particular type of vehicle, mode of travel, time of day, etc. If the table is for the whole day, the flows in each direction between the origin-destination pairs are often replaced by the mean of the two observed flows on the grounds that over a 24-hour period each movement is balanced by an opposite one.

The method of calculating the expansion factors depends on the type of survey; the following examples show how factors for producing hourly flows of vehicles are derived:

ROADSIDE-INTERVIEW AND POSTCARD METHODS. A journey from a given origin to a given destination will generally cross a number of cordons as shown in Fig. 4.1. By inspection these cordons can be divided into two groups, those that must be crossed by the movement and those that do not need to be crossed.

If a cordon must be crossed, an estimate of the total flow making a particular movement is given by the sum of the flows making that movement at each of the survey stations on the cordon. As there is the possibility that a journey may cross the cordon three times, twice in the forward direction and once in the reverse direction, the algebraic sum of the flows should be taken, i.e. any flow in the reverse direction should be subtracted from the forward flow. The algebraic sum also allows for crossing the cordon more than three times. If more than one cordon must be crossed by a movement then the average of the flows at each cordon is taken. When allowance is made for the number of cordons crossed the expansion factor is given by:

Expansion factor $= u/[phm(1-r)]$ at cordons that must be crossed and zero at cordons that need not be crossed

where

u is the p.c.u. (passenger car unit) factor of the vehicle making the journey (this term is not required if flows are to be in vehicles per hour).

p is the ratio, for the appropriate direction, period of work and class of vehicle, of the number of vehicles interviewed (or for which postcards were returned) to the number of vehicles passing.

h is the number of hours during which journey data for the appropriate direction were collected at the site,

m is the number of cordons which must be crossed by the movement; m is positive for movements in the forward direction and negative for movements in the reverse direction,

r is the proportion of vehicles not represented by interviews or postcards i.e. the ratio for the appropriate direction and class of vehicle, of the number of vehicles passing in periods when no journeys of vehicles of this type were recorded to the total number passing in all periods.

When a survey is being carried out using ring cordons only, all through movements pass into and out of at least one ring cordon. Technically, this

6

cordon need not be crossed. The best estimate of the flow making a through movement will be the mean of the flows crossing this cordon in the two directions not the algebraic sum. The formula quoted above should, therefore, be used with m equal to plus two for this cordon: the expansion factor is zero for the remaining cordons.

It should be remembered that for the purpose of these calculations all cordons other than ring cordons must be considered extending to infinity at each end when deciding whether any given movement will cross them.

Although each journey has a single expansion factor it may be convenient to deal with the different parts of the factor at different stages in the computation, e.g. the effect of m might be left until the rest of the expansion factor has been summed for a particular movement.

REGISTRATION-NUMBER AND TAGS-ON-VEHICLES METHODS.

$$\text{Expansion factor} = u/ph$$

where

p is the proportion of vehicles passing that have their registration numbers recorded (or to which tags are attached),

u,h have the same meaning as in the roadside-interview method.

HOME-INTERVIEW METHOD. The expansion factor for each vehicle journey is given by:

$$\text{Expansion factor} = u/ph$$

where

u is the p.c.u. factor of the vehicle making the journey (if required),

p is the proportion of households interviewed,

h is the period, in hours, to which the journey data from each household refer.

Similar expansion factors are used if it is desired to produce the flow of persons, instead of vehicles, by any mode of travel.

Estimation of future traffic movements

Since any new road will need to cater for traffic for some time ahead it is desirable to estimate the traffic pattern on a proposed road layout for some future date not for the present. This estimation has been carried out in a number of ways[4,5] which may be reduced to the following three basic methods:

(a) The existing origin-destination table is expanded to give future movements; these movements are then assigned to the proposed road system.

(b) A mathematical model which represents the existing traffic movements is produced and is used to predict future traffic movements; the future movements are then assigned to the proposed road system.

(c) The existing movements are assigned to the proposed road system; an estimate is then made of the increase in traffic that will be generated by the construction of the new roads and this increase is added to the original assignment.

It should be noted that, although method (*a*) does not allow directly for traffic increases generated by the construction of the new roads, these increases can be estimated after assignment as in method (*c*). The mathematical model in (*b*) can include the effect the new roads will have on the traffic movements. Method (*c*) can be extended to allow for increases in flow with time as well as increases generated by the new roads.

FUTURE TRAFFIC ORIGINATING AND TERMINATING IN EACH ZONE

Some methods of calculating future traffic movements require estimates of the total number of future journeys originating and terminating in each zone. One method[6] of obtaining these estimates assesses the future number of journeys that will be made by each household and the purpose of the journeys, and uses these figures to calculate the expected number of journeys originating and terminating in the various zones. More detailed methods use origin-destination surveys to derive formulae which relate the present traffic terminating in a zone or originated by its population to other characteristics of the zone, e.g. population, population density, vehicle ownership, family income, type of land use, purpose of journey etc. As an example it was found in the Chicago Area Transportation Study[7] that the number of journeys per dwelling unit per annum could be approximated by the formula:

$$y = 682 \cdot 84 + 3 \cdot 8109 \, x_1 + 0 \cdot 1939 \, x_2$$

where

y is the estimated journeys per dwelling unit per annum.
x_1 is the number of cars per 100 dwelling units,
x_2 is the number of dwelling units per 10 acres.

After forecasts of the future characteristics of each zone have been prepared the formulae are used to calculate the future traffic terminating in each zone. The possibility of future changes in the constants of the formulae has to be considered.

Any method of estimating future journeys must ensure that there is no contradiction between the total numbers of journeys originating and terminating in the whole area.

DIRECT EXPANSION OF EXISTING MOVEMENTS

CONSTANT-FACTOR METHOD. The origin-destination table is expanded by multiplying each entry by a constant factor derived from the expected life of the road system and past rates of growth of vehicle mileage in the area being considered, or some comparable area. In Great Britain as a whole the average vehicle-mileage has been increasing at about 8 per cent per annum compound; in Central London the figure is about 5 per cent per annum compound. The rate of increase of traffic in terms of passenger car units is rather less; about $6\frac{1}{2}$ per cent per annum compound for England and Wales as a whole.

Changes in land use can be allowed for to some extent by local adjustments to the table; differing rates of growth between the movements can be dealt with by using different factors for different sets of movements, e.g. movements to or from the centre of a city might be given a smaller factor than the rest.

AVERAGE-FACTOR METHOD.[5]   An estimate is made of the future traffic originating and terminating in each zone using the method outlined above, the flow making each movement is then calculated using the formula:

$$T_{ij} = \tfrac{1}{2}t_{ij}\left[\frac{T_i}{t_i} + \frac{T_j}{t_j}\right]$$

where

T_{ij} is the future flow from zone i to zone j,

t_{ij} is the present flow from zone i to zone j,

T_i, T_j are, respectively, the total future traffic originating at zone i and terminating at zone j,

t_i, t_j are, respectively, the total present traffic originating at zone i and terminating at zone j.

In general, the calculated values will not give total flows originating or terminating in a zone which agree with the future estimates. This discrepancy can be reduced by calculating a second set of estimates with the formula using the first estimates in place of the present flows, i.e. by the substitution:

$$t_{ij} = T_{ij}; \qquad t_i = \sum_j T_{ij}; t_j = \sum_i T_{ij}$$

By repeated use of this procedure the discrepancy between the total flows originating or terminating in a zone and the future estimates can be reduced to an insignificant amount.

FRATAR METHOD.[5]   This method also requires estimates of the future traffic originating and terminating in each zone. Using the notation of the previous paragraph the flow making each movement is given by the formula:

$$T_{ij} = t_{ij} \cdot \frac{T_i}{t_i} \cdot \frac{T_j}{t_j} \cdot \frac{\sum_k t_{ik}}{\sum_k (T_k/t_k)t_{ik}}$$

An iterative process similar to that described in the previous paragraph is used to obtain agreement between the total flows originating and terminating in each zone and the future estimates; at each step new estimates are calculated with the formula using the previous estimates in place of the present flows. The method is normally used where the flow making each movement is equal to the flow making the reverse movement: in these cases it is usual to mean the calculated values for each pair of movements before proceeding to the next iteration.

FURNESS METHOD.[8]   Estimates of the future traffic originating and terminating in each zone are also required by this method. An iterative process is used in which the movements are made to agree alternately with the estimated future traffic originating in each zone and the estimated future traffic terminating in each zone until both conditions are approximately satisfied. The successive estimates are given by the formulae:

$$T_{ij} = t_{ij} \cdot \frac{T_i}{t_i}$$

$$T'_{ij} = T_{ij} \cdot \frac{T_j}{\sum_i T_{ij}}$$

$$T''_{ij} = T'_{ij} \cdot \frac{T_i}{\sum_j T'_{ij}} \text{etc.}$$

This method gives the same solution as the Fratar method and requires less computation. Both methods are equivalent to multiplying each movement by two constants, one determined by the origin and the other by the destination of the movement: the product of the constants is uniquely determined by the estimated future flows originating and terminating at each origin.

SYNTHESIS OF MOVEMENTS

The most common mathematical model for synthesizing traffic movements assumes that the flow from one zone to another is given by the formula:

$$t_{ij} = kA_iA_jf(z_{ij})$$

where

    t_{ij} is the flow from zone i to zone j,
    k is a constant,
    A_i, A_j are measures of the size or attractiveness of zones i and j,
    $f(z_{ij})$ is a function of z_{ij}, the distance from zone i to zone j, or the time or cost of travelling between them.

The function $f(z_{ij})$ has been referred to as the "deterrence function". If it is taken to be the inverse square of z_{ij}, the formula is similar to the law of gravitation and for this reason the model is often called a gravity model.

The factors are usually fitted so that present movements are predicted as accurately as possible; a small origin-and-destination survey is normally sufficient for this purpose. The model can then be used to calculate future movements using the estimated future values of A_i, A_j and z_{ij}, It should be noted that the z_{ij} will be affected to some extent by the type of future road network: this point is referred to later.

Deterrence functions are often inverse powers of the time or distance between zones but Tanner[9] has pointed out that this type of function cannot give valid estimates at both very small and very large distances or times. He has suggested as an alternative a function of the form $e^{-\lambda z_{ij}} z_{ij}^{-n}$ where λ and n are constants. For many purposes n may be put equal to unity; for journeys to work a typical value of λ was then found to be $0\cdot2$ if z_{ij} is measured in miles (range 2-25). In small towns the deterrence function is sometimes taken as unity.

Journeys starting at home usually have A_i proportional to the population of zone i. For journeys to work A_j is usually proportional to the amount of employment in zone j; for shopping journeys it is often proportional to the amount of retail employment; for social journeys it is proportional to the population. Journeys to home are obtained by assuming that they are the reverse of journeys from home.

Three main variations of the formula exist: the formula may be used as it stands; the A_i may be adjusted so that the number of journeys originating in a zone agrees with a predetermined total; lastly, both the A_i and the A_j may be adjusted so that the flows originating and terminating in each zone agree with predetermined totals.

If the flow originating in each zone has to equal a predetermined figure t_i then the formula for calculating the flow from zone i to zone j becomes:

$$t_{ij} = \frac{t_iA_jf(z_{ij})}{\sum_j A_jf(z_{ij})}$$

Tanner[9] has shown that the amount spent per head on travel is roughly independent of the length of the journeys. If the deterrence function is in terms of cost and the total amount spent on travel in zone i is L_i then the formula becomes:

$$t_{ij} = \frac{L_i A_j f(z_{ij})}{\sum_j A_j z_{ij} f(z_{ij})}$$

If both the flow originating and the flow terminating in each zone must equal predetermined values then an iterative procedure has to be used, and it can be shown that the final result is independent of the value assumed initially for A_i and A_j. The solution can be obtained by the Fratar or by the Furness method described above using the values of the deterrence function in place of the present movements. This variation of the formula is particularly applicable to home-to-work journeys since the total number terminating in any zone must equal the number of jobs in that zone. If the deterrence function is taken to be unity, i.e. distance has no effect on the distribution of journeys, then iteration is not required, the flow making each movement being given by:

$$t_{ij} = \frac{t_i t_j}{\Sigma t_i} \left(= \frac{t_i t_j}{\Sigma t_j} \right)$$

A different type of mathematical model has been used in the Chicago Area Transportation Study.[7] This is called an "opportunity" model and states that the number of journeys making a particular movement is proportional to the product of the number of possible destinations in the terminating zone and the proportion of journeys from the same origin which do not terminate at zones nearer the origin. If the number of zones is fairly large, the flow making each movement is given approximately by the formula:

$$t_{ij} = t_i [e^{-mt_s} - e^{-m(t_s + t_j)}]$$

where

t_{ij}, t_i and t_j have the meanings used earlier,
t_s is the total number of destinations nearer to zone i than zone j,
m is a constant.

In the study referred to, nearness was measured in units of journey time.

GENERATED TRAFFIC

The mathematical model described earlier gave the following formula for the flow from one zone to another:

$$t_{ij} = k A_i A_j f(z_{ij})$$

If z_{ij} is reduced by an amount Δz_{ij} the flow will be increased by an amount:

$$\Delta t_{ij} = k A_i A_j [f(z_{ij} - \Delta z_{ij}) - f(z_{ij})]$$

$$= \frac{t_{ij}}{f(z_{ij})} [f(z_{ij} - \Delta z_{ij}) - f(z_{ij})]$$

If Δz_{ij} is small relative to z_{ij} then:

$$\Delta t_{ij} \simeq -\frac{t_{ij}\Delta z_{ij}}{f(z_{ij})} \cdot \frac{d}{dz_{ij}}f(z_{ij})$$

If the deterrence function is z_{ij}^{-n} this becomes:

$$\Delta t_{ij} \simeq t_{ij}\frac{n\Delta z_{ij}}{z_{ij}}$$

Providing that a suitable deterrence function can be selected, the full formula or its approximation can be used to estimate the increase in traffic between a pair of zones that will be generated by a given reduction in the journey time between the zones. Empirical studies of flows between towns have usually shown that if the deterrence factor is assumed to be z_{ij}^{-n} then n lies between 2 and 3·5. Applying this figure to the approximate formula suggests that the percentage increase in traffic is 2 to 3·5 times the percentage decrease in journey time.

MODE OF TRAVEL

The complete pattern of movements can be obtained by estimating car and commercial vehicle journeys by the methods outlined above and adding to them separate estimates of journeys by public transport. It is probable, however, that methods described earlier which estimate the number of journeys made by each household can predict the total future journeys more accurately then the future journeys by car, commercial vehicle or public transport separately. If total journeys are obtained an estimate is needed of the proportion that will be by car or commercial vehicle, public transport or on foot.

Methods of finding the different proportions usually depend on such factors as the length of the journey, or the time taken, by different forms of transport and the availability of cars. For example, the Cumbernauld Development Corporation[6] has assumed that work journeys shorter than half-a-mile would be made by walking; where cars were available for longer journeys it was assumed that a proportion of them would be used for the journeys and that half the cars would have a passenger; all other journeys would be by public transport.

If the method of deciding the mode of travel uses journey times or distances the distribution of journeys between different forms of transport will depend on the future transport network.

Selection of future road network

A desire-line diagram, a graphical method of illustrating the future origin-destination pattern, is often used to assist in the selection of a suitable road network. The diagram is prepared by marking the zone centres on a suitable map; each pair of zone centres is then joined with a line whose width represents the flow making that movement. To reduce the number of lines on the diagram, minor movements are often omitted. Further clarity is achieved by grouping the lines according to their direction (e.g. one group might be $22\frac{1}{2}$ degrees either side of north-south); a diagram is then produced for each group. By comparing the desire-lines with the present road network an indication of desirable positions for new roads can be obtained.

Theoretical work has been done on the most desirable layout of streets in a town,[10] see Chapter 7, and the optimum spacing of arterial roads[11] and this work can be used to assist in the design of a new road layout.

In most cases planning and civil engineering considerations will reduce to a small number the road networks that need to have their traffic consequences assessed.

Traffic assignment

To assess the efficiency of a proposed road system and to determine the number of lanes on the new roads and the types of junction required, it is necessary to know the distribution of the future traffic movements on the road network. When small networks are considered it may be sufficient to judge which route each movement will follow; the flow on each road can then be calculated. The assumption that a by-pass to a town will carry the through traffic between its ends is an example of this method of route selection.

The following paragraphs describe the more systematic methods of selecting routes and assigning traffic to them that are required when large networks of roads are being considered.

FACTORS AFFECTING CHOICE OF ROUTE

Many factors affect the choice by a traveller of the route and type of transport he will use to reach his destination. One important factor is journey time: this is to be expected since journeys are rarely an end in themselves; their object is usually to get the traveller to his destination in the minimum possible time. The money expended on the journey is probable also an important factor but its effect on the choice of route tends to be concealed by the fact that the quickest route is often the cheapest. Its effect is more likely to be noticed when journeys by different types of transport are compared. Distance is probably not important except in so far as it affects the cost of a journey.

Journey time is the factor that is most commonly used for traffic assignment and studies in Great Britain and America that have used this factor have given results that agree closely with observed conditions.

METHODS OF ASSIGNMENT

The simplest method of assigning traffic using one of the factors is to assume that each movement will travel by the route which minimizes this factor. If this method is used with a network in which traffic travels between the centroids of a few large zones, there is a tendency for a great deal of traffic to use some roads and none to use alternative routes which may only be a little longer. This effect can be reduced by increasing the number of points where traffic can start or finish a journey. For example, in the Oxford Traffic Survey described later, (see pp. 160-9), the centre of each section of road in the network was made a starting and finishing point for journeys.

Several methods have been used to reduce the all or nothing effect of the minimum path method. One method that has been used extensively in the U.S.A.[12] depends on the selection of two minimum routes, one using existing roads only and the other including new roads. The percentage of journeys that will be made by using the new-road route is derived from the ratio of the time via the new-road route to the time on the other route with the help of an "assignment curve" of the type shown in Fig. 4.3: the use of the new road decreases gradually from about 100 per cent for drivers who would halve their journey by using the new road to 0 per cent for drivers whose journeys would take twice as long. Some assignment curves use other factors such as distance ratio, time difference or distance difference; combinations of factors have also been used.

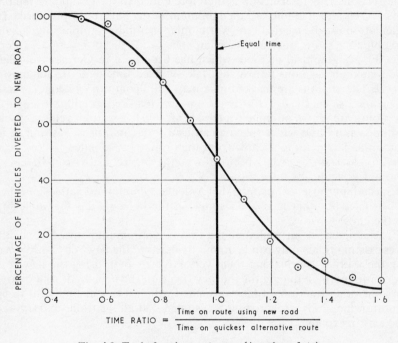

Fig. 4.3. Typical assignment curve (American data)

Another method, which has been used in Manchester,[13] assigns traffic equally between all routes with a journey time not greater than 1·15 times the minimum value.

A third method assumes that there are different classes of driver, each influenced by the various factors in a different way and each travelling by his own minimum path. In the Oxford Traffic Survey it was assumed that there were two groups of driver: those who were prepared to use any available road and those who would only use main roads because they disliked, or were ignorant of, the side streets.

SELECTION OF ROUTES

The methods of assignment outlined above require a means of selecting the route between a given origin and destination that minimizes the journey time or other factor used. It is often a simple matter to select some likely routes and to determine which of these is the minimum but there is no guarantee that a better route has not been overlooked. Systematic procedures for finding the minimum path have been published and one by Moore[14] is most frequently used: this method gives the minimum path from a single origin to all destinations. The Laboratory uses an alternative procedure[15] that also gives the minimum path to all destinations. The paths are found in increasing order of length. At each stage in the process there is a group of intersections on the road network whose minimum paths are known, and these are used to calculate the lengths of paths to intersections that are connected by a direct road to an intersection in the group. The minimum of the calculated paths is the minimum path to the appropriate intersection. This intersection is therefore added to the group and the process is then repeated until all the minimum paths have been obtained. The calculation can be carried out by a tabular method or graphically[16] and is suitable for use on an electronic computer.

A simple graphical method, which has been used in Germany[17] divides the roads into sections on which it takes a fixed time, e.g. $0 \cdot 2$ minutes, to travel. The sections are marked on a map and "contours" of equal journey time are drawn by eye starting from the required origin (see Fig. 4.4). Contours are drawn at regular intervals of, say, five sections; closer spacing is unnecessary and wider spacing can lead to errors in the position of the contours. The minimum paths from the origin are extended to reach each contour as soon as it has been drawn; the correct paths can be chosen without difficulty by inspection.

Special purpose computers that calculate minimum paths have been constructed but none have had a simple method of assigning the traffic flows to the chosen routes.

The assignment curve method requires two minimum paths. The one that uses existing roads only can be found by deleting the new roads or by making the journey times along them very large. A path using the new roads can be found by reducing the journey times on the new roads to a quarter, or some other fraction, of their estimated value: if this method fails to find a route which uses a new road it is assumed that all the traffic will travel on the existing roads.

ASSIGNMENT OF TRAFFIC MOVEMENTS TO ROUTES

If each movement is assigned to the minimum path separately it is a straightforward matter to sum the individual flows on each section of road. Where the minimum paths from one origin to all destinations are calculated simultaneously time can be saved by assigning all the movements from the one origin at the same time by using the following procedure.

Suppose that all the destinations and any junctions on the minimum routes that are not destinations are labelled $D_1, D_2, \ldots, D_i, \ldots, D_n$ in order of increasing length of their minimum paths from the origin. Suppose also that the previous destination or junction on the minimum path to D_i is P_i (P_i is the origin if no destination or junction intervenes). The first step of the process takes the traffic terminating at D_n, assigns it to the road from P_n to D_n and adds it to the traffic terminating at P_n to give the flow that arrives at P_n. The next step takes the traffic arriving at D_{n-1}, assigns it to the road from P_{n-1} to D_{n-1} and adds it to the traffic approaching P_{n-1}.

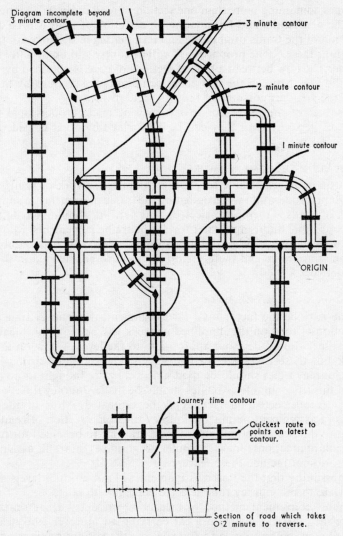

Fig. 4.4. Graphical method of finding quickest routes

By continuing the process of taking the destinations and junctions in decreasing order of minimum path until the origin is reached, the process ensures that a destination or junction is not dealt with until the total traffic approaching it is known. The process of assignment can be checked by verifying that the assigned flow leaving the origin is equal to the sum of the flows from the origin to all destinations.

If two equal routes to a single point are found it is normally assumed that traffic travelling to or beyond that point will travel equally by the two routes.

EXPANSION OF ORIGIN-DESTINATION DATA

Mention has been made of a method of assignment in which each section of road has originating and terminating traffic. If this method is used with zones containing more than one section of road it can be assumed that the traffic originating and terminating on a section of road will be a fixed proportion of the traffic originating and terminating in the zone containing the section; these "zone proportions" will of course add up to unity in any one zone. The flow between a pair of sections of road is obtained by multiplying the flow between the two zones containing the sections by the product of the zone proportions of the two sections.

The values of the zone proportions may be made proportional to the lengths of the sections or they can be determined by other considerations such as land use.

SIMPLIFICATION OF ROAD NETWORK

It is usually impracticable to use the complete network of roads in the area under consideration when assigning the traffic movements: a simplified network of roads is therefore selected. This network should include as few roads as possible but it must cater for all the traffic movements. Many side roads duplicate one another in terms of service to traffic or are only used by terminating traffic and therefore do not need to be included in the simplified network.

COLLECTION OF NETWORK DATA

If time is to be the factor used for assignment, the journey time along each section of road on the simplified network will be required. Ideally the journey times should be those appropriate to the level of flow on the new network but these times are, of course, not known. For existing streets present journey times should be used unless they are thought to be unrealistic; in this case suitable estimates should be made. Journey times on new roads or reconstructed ones can only be estimated. Most of the basic methods of assignment permit the journey time on a section of road to be different in the two directions and allow extra time to be added for turning movements at junctions; some computer programmes for traffic assignment, however, do not include these features.

The possibility that the traffic assignment will not produce levels of flow appropriate to the journey time selected is dealt with later.

The most convenient method of measuring present journey times is to infiltrate into the traffic stream a car carrying an observer who measures the time taken by the vehicle to travel along the various sections of road. The flows on the roads can also be obtained by this method which is described in Chapter 3. The runs in the test car should be spread over the hours chosen for the survey and it is important to spread the observations over several days to avoid chance effects on any given day. A programme of journeys should be planned beforehand with runs commencing at regular intervals, e.g. one every hour, and each journey time should be weighted by the flow during the period it represents.

If distance is the factor used for assignment the preparation of the network data is much simpler: distances can be obtained from a map and they are, of course, independent of the future level of flow on the network. The use of cost as a factor for assignment requires a suitable method of estimating the cost of travel along each section of road; motor vehicle costs are often expressed as a function of time and distance but other factors such as parking can be included.

ACCURACY OF METHOD OF ASSIGNMENT

Before a method of assignment is used to predict the pattern of traffic on a new road system it is desirable to check the accuracy of the method. A simple way of doing this is to assign the present traffic movements to the existing road system and to compare the results with the actual pattern of flows. The differences can be attributed partly to the method of assignment and partly to sampling errors in the origin-destination data; in general, the method of assignment will account for the major part of the discrepancies.

Results from the study in Oxford have led to the conclusion that errors due to the method of assignment were of the order of 10 per cent on roads carrying 400 vehicles per hour and about 5 per cent on roads carrying 1200 vehicles per hour. These results indicate the order of accuracy that can be obtained; it is unwise to assume that the figures are applicable to other sites and methods.

Estimated future traffic flows on a proposed road network also include inaccuracies due to the unknown errors in the estimated future traffic movements.

ELECTRONIC COMPUTER PROGRAMMES

The methods of assignment that have been described involve the processing of larger amounts of data and are therefore suitable for use with an electronic digital computer. A number of programmes have been written, mainly in America, and a useful review of them is given by Mertz.[18]

Two complementary programmes[19] have been written at the Laboratory for a Ferranti Pegasus II computer. The results of the assignment consist of turning movements at each intersection and the flows along each section of road between intersections.

Flow information can be provided in the form of movements between sections or alternatively in the form of movements between zones containing several sections together with a list giving the zone proportions for each section. This information is punched on to a paper tape which, together with another tape defining the road network, forms the data for the first programme.

The first programme calculates the quickest route between each pair of sections and assigns the traffic flow between them to the roads forming the quickest route. The output gives the turning movements at each junction. The second programme is used to combine in any desired proportions the assignments produced by the first programme for different types of driver. The output from the programme gives the flows and turning movements, both being converted from the units used in the computation to vehicles per hour or other convenient units before being printed out.

The network is limited by the programme to a maximum of 255 sections and the units of journey time must be chosen so that the total journey time by the quickest route from one section to any other is less than 1023. The maximum number of zones that can be considered is 44 if zone proportions are used, (255 if the computer has a magnetic tape unit).

Using this programme, a traffic assignment for a network of 140 sections required about $1\frac{1}{2}$ man weeks for data tape preparation and two hours of computer time; the average time for a similar assignment by hand was about 50 man weeks.

MODE OF TRAVEL

If the number of journeys by each form of transport is determined without reference to the proposed road network then each type of movement can be assigned separately by the method described above. If it is assumed that each traveller minimizes his journey time or cost or some other factor, it is possible to assign the total number of journeys making a movement to a network that includes both roads and public transport routes. Since the route of a traveller will depend to a large extent on the availability of private transport, this method is reasonable only if each traveller is assigned to a network appropriate to his car ownership, e.g. the network might be public-transport routes only for a traveller without a car whereas a car owner might be assigned to a network in which the effective "cost" of public transport was high.

JOURNEY-TIME/FLOW RELATIONS

A difficulty with using journey time as the factor for assigning traffic is that the journey time along a section of road depends upon the level of flow. If the assignment is to be reliable it is therefore necessary that the journey times used for assigning the traffic movements should be those appropriate to the level of flow produced by the assignment.

The Road Research Laboratory has used a method of obtaining this correspondence between journey time and flow that depends on successive assignments by quickest route. The first assignment uses present journey times and gives a first set of flow estimates. This set of flow estimates is used to calculate journey times for a second assignment and the results from this are combined in a fixed ratio with the first set of flow estimates to give a second set. The second set is used to calculate journey times for a third assignment and the results from it are combined in the same fixed ratio with the second set of estimates to give a third set of flow estimates and so on. This method has been tried on three networks with about 140 sections and with speed/flow relations applied to about 25 of them. When each estimate was obtained by combining the flow from each assignment with the previous estimate in equal proportions, the flows on two of the networks, settled down without serious oscillation after five or six assignments. On the third network the flows continued to oscillate and did not converge until the weight given to the new assignment at each stage was greatly reduced; about 15 assignments were required before the flows converged satisfactorily.

Efforts are being made to reduce the number of assignments required for this method by selecting the optimum proportions for combining the successive estimates and assignments.

Several types of journey-speed/flow relations for urban roads have been tried; the most suitable appears to be one which assumes that:

(a) The journey speed and the running speed in a given direction depend only on the flow in that direction.

(b) The journey-speed/flow and running-speed/flow relations are linear, intersect at zero flow, and fit observed values at one other level of flow.

(c) The slope of the running-speed/flow relations is twice the slope of the running-speed/total-flow relations quoted in Chapter 3.

(d) There is a maximum speed of 24 mile/h.

(*e*) There is a minimum speed of 4 mile/h. (This value has been chosen to deter through traffic from using the link without preventing its use by terminating traffic.)

The following formula was derived from these assumptions:

$$j = R + \frac{2Q}{3(w-6)} - q\left[\frac{R-J}{Q} + \frac{2}{3(w-6)}\right] \text{ subject to } 4 \leqslant j \leqslant 24$$

where

j is the journey speed in the appropriate direction (mile/h),
q is the flow in the appropriate direction (veh/h),
w is the average total width of the carriageway (feet),
Q is the observed flow level (veh/h),
J is the corresponding observed journey speed at a flow level of Q (mile/h),
R is the observed running speed at a flow level of Q (mile/h).

A similar formula for rural roads can be obtained from the speed/flow relations for rural roads shown in Chapter 3. Journey speeds on rural roads can be assumed to be the same as running speeds for the purpose of calculating the formula.

One advantage of allowing for a speed/flow relation in the way described is that two parallel routes tend to have the traffic distributed between them in such a way that the journey time by either route is the same: without the relation the quickest route would take all the traffic however small the difference between the two journey times.

A very detailed model for predicting traffic flows has been developed in Toronto.[20] As a first step the model calculates the number of journeys originating in each zone; it then distributes the destinations of the journeys among the other zones according to the journey time for the movement and the attractiveness of the destination zone; the movements are then assigned to their quickest routes. The flows obtained from the assignment are used to adjust the journey times for another assignment and so on; in addition, the journey times obtained as a result of the assignments are used at intervals to redistribute the journeys from each origin to the various destinations. Each road has one of ten different journey-time per-mile flow per-lane relations depending on the speed limit and the number of signalized intersections per mile.

The type of speed/flow relation that has been used by the Laboratory is an improvement on the use of fixed journey times, but it does not allow for changes in the traffic flows crossing the street at the various junctions nor for changes in the design of junctions or their method of control. A more realistic method of successive assignments could allow for these effects and for changes in road layout and land use that seem desirable as a result of previous assignments. An outline of such a method might be as follows:

(*a*) A tentative development plan is prepared for the area being studied.
(*b*) The future traffic movements are estimated from the proposed road network and land use.
(*c*) A suitable journey-time/flow relation is estimated for each section of the proposed road network.

(*d*) The traffic movements are assigned to the road network using the journey-time/flow relations.

(*e*) If the road network appears generally satisfactory its detailed design is modified to suit the assigned flows and the journey-time/flow relations are modified accordingly. The sequence is continued from (*d*).

(*f*) If the road network is unsatisfactory it is amended and the sequence is continued from (*b*).

(*g*) If a satisfactory road network for the proposed land use cannot be achieved the development plan is modified and the sequence is re-started at (*b*).

The process terminates when a satisfactory road network has been produced.

Justification of the construction of new roads

Before new roads are constructed it is necessary to weigh the advantages of the new network against the cost of its construction and the loss of amenity involved. Although it is difficult to give a monetary value to some of the factors in such a comparison it is possible to estimate the economic benefits of the new network and to compare them with the construction costs. The corresponding rate of return on the capital expenditure provides a measure of the justification for the new network. Details of the method of calculating the economic benefits are given in Chapter 15.

EXAMPLES OF TRAFFIC STUDIES

The Road Research Laboratory has taken a large part in several traffic studies and in the remainder of this chapter three that are of general interest are described. In one study an assessment was made of the economic effects of the construction of the London-Birmingham motorway, in the second the traffic benefits of various relief road proposals for the City of Oxford were assessed and in the third information was obtained on travel in London.

London-Birmingham motorway origin-and-destination survey

In 1955, the Laboratory in collaboration with the University of Birmingham made an assessment of the economic effects of the London-Birmingham motorway. For this purpose, estimates were required of the amount of traffic that would transfer from existing roads and of the consequent savings in vehicle times. The basic data used in making these estimates were obtained by carrying out a survey of the origins and destinations of traffic and by measuring journey times on the existing road network.

Details of the London-Birmingham motorway, which was completed in 1959 at a cost of £22·6 million, are given in Fig. 4.5. Apart from the end points, access from other roads is limited to nine points along the motorway (Fig. 4.6). Information about the origins and destinations of traffic on roads in the area likely to be affected was obtained by intercepting vehicles at the

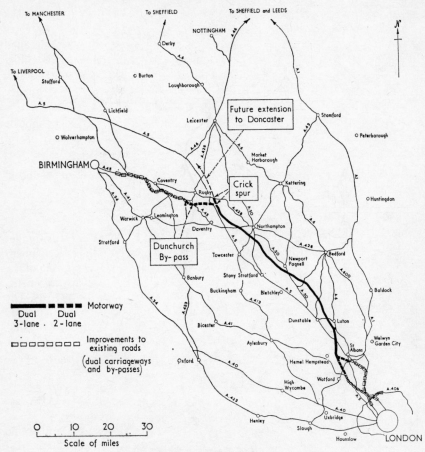

Fig. 4.5. The London–Birmingham motorway

23 points shown in Fig. 4.7 and inviting a sample of drivers to provide the necessary information, which was noted on a questionnaire. Traffic in one direction only was sampled on a given day.

FIELD PROCEDURE

Wherever possible a lay-by was used for interviewing, but where no suitable lay-by was available, the nearside lane of a three-lane carriageway or one of the lanes of a dual carriageway was separated off by means of barriers. A typical layout of a survey station is shown in Fig. 4.8. Temporary traffic signs in advance of the station asked drivers to proceed slowly and to stop if requested. Particular attention was given to the design and siting of the signs because it was essential in the interests of safety, as well as to facilitate the sampling technique, that the approaching traffic should be travelling more slowly than usual and that there should be no overtaking. Signs, with lettering eight inches high, were placed on the offside verge as well as on the nearside verge, as shown in Fig. 4.9. As a further precaution, barriers were used in many instances to funnel traffic into a single line as it approached the survey station.

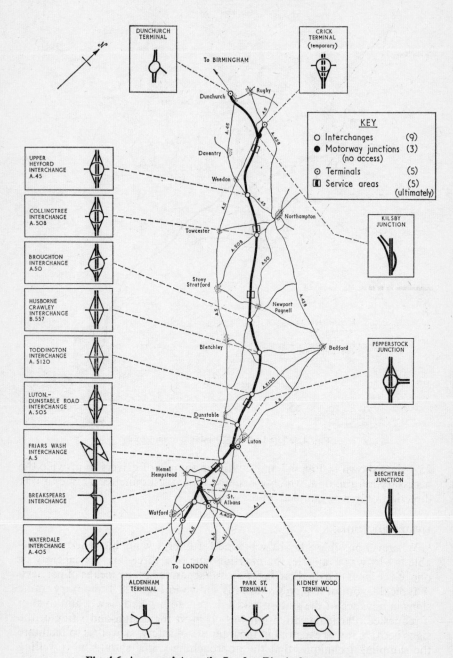

Fig. 4.6. Access points on the London-Birmingham motorway

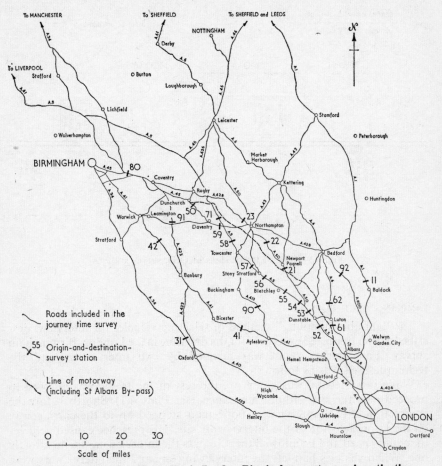

Fig. 4.7. Extent of traffic studies in London–Birmingham motorway investigation

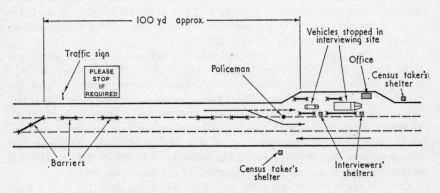

Not to scale

Fig. 4.8. Typical layout of O.D. survey station

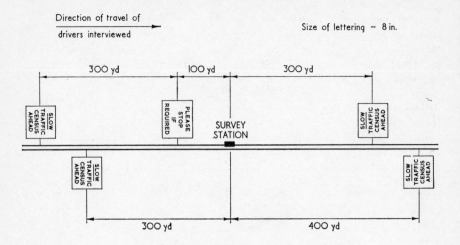

Fig. 4.9 Siting of traffic signs at O.D. survey stations

SAMPLING TECHNIQUE

The "variable-sampling" method of selecting vehicles for interview, described earlier (see p.123), was used for the first time in the London-Birmingham
survey. Each survey point was manned by two interviewers and the
technique used was as follows:

While interviewing was going on, the rest of the traffic was allowed to
proceed past the site without hindrance, (see Plate 4.1). Shortly before the
completion of each interview, a policeman stepped on to the carriageway
on the approach side of the interviewing site. His presence caused vehicles
to reduce speed and he allowed them to pass the interviewing site in a single
line. When vehicles had left the interviewing site and the interviewers were
ready to start fresh interviews, a signal was given to the policeman by the
supervisor or by one of the interviewers. The policeman then directed the
first two vehicles which reached him into the interviewing site and allowed
the rest of the traffic to carry on; he then usually left the carriageway until
the interviews were almost complete and the procedure was repeated. On
occasions, however, conditions were such that he considered it advisable to
remain on the carriageway throughout.

On some occasions it was found that the policeman did not wait for a
signal before drawing the two vehicles out of the traffic stream; this was
often prompted by the failure of the supervisor or interviewer to give the
signal on previous occasions. The usual consequence was that the interviewers were overworked and that the forms were not properly completed.
Alternatively, it meant that vehicles had to wait until the interviewers were
ready. The most serious objection to this departure from the prescribed
technique was that it empowered the policeman to select the vehicles for
interview, thus violating the requirement of a random sample.

Another fault, which occurred on a few occasions, was that at the time
the signal was expected vehicles were being permitted to pass the site at too
great a speed. This meant that after receiving the signal the policeman was

unable to direct to the interviewing site the first two vehicles that reached him. Instead, he allowed the faster vehicles to pass before making his selection and the sample was biased in favour of slow-moving commercial vehicles. Most of the error arising from this fault was removed in the analysis by introducing the complication of using separate sampling factors for the different classes of vehicle.

Because of departures from the recommended sampling technique, the drivers interviewed were sometimes not a random sample of all drivers travelling in the particular direction, and the two interviewers working continuously were sometimes overworked, but vehicle delay was normally kept to a minimum. The vehicles required for interview were not forced to queue up beforehand while the delay to other vehicles was almost negligible. The form of questioning was rather more elaborate than usual, mainly because additional information was required in the investigation of the economic value of the motorway; in general, interviewing lasted about 50 or 60 seconds. Although this may seem excessive, the interviewers reported that this delay did not seem to irritate drivers and that very good co-operation was obtained. The experience gained in this investigation stresses the importance of distinguishing between delay caused by queueing and the time spent in interviewing.

LOCATION OF SURVEY STATIONS

The positions of the 23 survey stations are shown on the map in Fig. 4.7. The points were highly concentrated on road A.5 and on other roads near the line of the proposed motorway, so as to intercept short-distance as well as long-distance traffic which might use the motorway. On the outlying roads the stations were infrequent since only long-distance traffic on these roads needed to be considered as potential motorway traffic. This method of arranging the interception points was a departure from the usual method of locating the points on a number of screen lines drawn at right angles to the direction of travel. The "screen-line" method produces the same concentration of interception points on the different routes irrespective of their importance, but has the advantage of being simple to analyse. The method used in this investigation allocates the points roughly in proportion to the estimated importance of the various routes but requires a special method of analysis (see p.155).

DURATION OF SURVEY

At each station, the survey lasted for 16 hours (6 a.m. to 10 p.m.) on each of two weekdays, one day for interviewing in each direction. At station 11 on A.1 in Hertfordshire and station 31 on A.34 in Oxfordshire an extra two days' work was carried out to obtain more reliable information about long-distance traffic on these routes. Because of the high flow of commercial traffic at night on A.5 and A.1, interviewing was carried out on two nights from 10 p.m. to 6 a.m. at stations 56 and 11. This required the erection of special flood-lighting equipment powered by mobile generators (see Plate 4.2).

The schedule of work was arranged so that each county authority had to work at only one site on a given day. Another requirement was that no vehicle would be stopped more than once on a single journey; vehicles making return trips and regular users of the roads were of course liable to be stopped more than once on different occasions.

The survey was limited to weekdays but in the analysis allowance was made for Saturday and Sunday traffic by using factors derived from traffic-census data. It would not have been possible, with the resources available, to investigate week-end journeys with the same degree of accuracy as could be done for week-day journeys because of the wide fluctuations, due to season and weather, in the amounts and character of week-end traffic.

INFORMATION OBTAINED IN INTERVIEWS

Two types of form were used by interviewers to record the details given by drivers, one for cars and coaches, and the other for commercial vehicles; these are reproduced in Figs. 4.10 and 4.11 respectively. Before the interview was begun the interviewer formally obtained the assent of the driver to co-operate and told him briefly of the purpose of the survey; the recommended form of the preamble is given in section (D) on the form.

The relevant place-names were entered in sections (E) and (F) as follows:

Section (E)	(i) origin of journey
	(ii) last "essential stop" (if any)
Section (F)	(i) destination of journey
	(ii) next "essential stop" (if any)

The term "essential stop" is here used to denote a stop at a place for a purpose that could be realized only at that particular place. It was considered to be very important to obtain this information since many drivers are not concerned merely with travelling from one place to another; businessmen, for example, sometimes combine several business calls on a single trip and commercial vehicles often stop to make collections or deliveries *en route*. In assessing the amount of travel between different centres it was considered that a journey segmented by a number of "essential" stops should be regarded, not as a single journey, but as a number of separate journeys. Hence, in interpreting the record of interview of a driver who had made one or more "essential stops" before being interviewed, the place of the last "essential stop" in part (ii) of section (E) is treated as the origin of the journey and the entry in part (i) is ignored. Likewise the place of the next "essential stop" proposed, if any, in part (ii) of section (F) is treated as the destination of the journey, instead of the entry in part (i). It is not necessary to put the information about the other segments of the journey on record; if these segments have a bearing on the investigation then the driver would be liable to be stopped for interview at other stations and the information about the other segments obtained independently. The term "essential stop" does not, of course, refer to incidental stops for the purpose of obtaining petrol, refreshments, etc., since such stops do not contribute to a driver's purpose in travelling and could be made at a variety of points *en route*; such stops would be transferred to points on the motorway.

The expression "essential stop" is only used for convenience in describing the concept and it was not used in questioning drivers. As shown in Figs. 4.10 and 4.11 the style of questioning varied with the class of vehicle, and interviewers were given instructions on the method of dealing with cases in

(A) Hour commencing
(24 hour clock)

(B) Station and Direction
Code Number

(C) Class of Vehicle
(Underline)

1. Private Car

2. Coach

Enter
Code No.
of Class

(D) Introductory Remark:— "WOULD YOU MIND ANSWERING A FEW QUESTIONS
ABOUT THE JOURNEY YOU ARE MAKING? THE
INFORMATION IS REQUIRED IN CONNECTION WITH
THE NEW ROAD PROGRAMME."

(E)   "WHERE DID YOU START OUT FROM ON THIS JOURNEY?"

(i)

"HAVE YOU MADE ANY STOPS SINCE YOU LEFT THERE?"
If NO, omit next question and cancel rectangle (ii).

Private Car: "WHERE WAS THE LAST PLACE
THAT YOU STOPPED AT FOR A PURPOSE
SPECIALLY CONNECTED WITH THE PLACE?
THAT IS, APART FROM STOPS FOR PETROL,
MEALS, REFRESHMENTS AND SIMILAR
PURPOSES."

Coach "WHERE WAS THE
LAST PLACE THAT THIS
COACH STOPPED TO PICK
UP OR SET DOWN
PASSENGERS?"

(ii)

Nat. Grid Ref.

(F)   "WHERE ARE YOU TRAVELLING TO?"

(i)

"WILL YOU BE MAKING ANY STOPS BEFORE YOU GET THERE?"
If NO, omit next question and cancel rectangle (ii).

Private Car: "WHERE IS THE NEXT PLACE
THAT YOU INTEND TO STOP FOR A
PURPOSE SPECIALLY CONNECTED WITH THE
PLACE? THAT IS, APART FROM STOPS
FOR PETROL, MEALS, REFRESHMENTS
AND SIMILAR PURPOSES."

Coach: "WHERE IS THE
NEXT PLACE THAT THIS
COACH STOPS TO PICK UP
OR SET DOWN
PASSENGERS?"

(ii)

Nat. Grid Ref.

(G) Category of
Journey

Enter
Code
No.

Private Car: Show the card
to the driver and ask:

"WHICH OF THESE
CATEGORIES DOES
YOUR JOURNEY COME
UNDER?"

Enter code no. in box.
In case of refusal to reply
enter Y.

Coach: Underline one of
the following and enter
code no. in box

7. Privately hired or
Tour

8. On a regular
service

9. Other

(H) Number of
Occupants

(including
driver)

Private Car:

Men   Women

Children
under 16

Coach: Total number
of occupants

NOTE: Do not make entries in the following sections unless specially instructed

(J) Alternative Routes
Enter 1, 2 or 0

(K) Registration
Letters

Fig. 4.10. Record-of-interview form—car or coach

which the prescribed form of questions did not seem applicable. In the case of multi-axle commercial vehicles, only one question was asked in Section (E), and one in Section (F). It referred to the load rather than to the driver, because it is common practice for the driver of a long-distance heavy commmercial vehicle to be changed *en route* but for the load and the vehicle to carry on. The use of the impersonal form of question avoids underestimation of the length of journey.

COMMERCIAL VEHICLE

(A) Hour commencing (24 hour clock)	**(B)** Station and Direction Code Number
(C) Class of vehicle (Underline) 3. Light commercial van 4. Lorry or heavy van: 2 axles, no '20' plate 5. " " " " 2 axles, with '20' plate 6. " " " " 3 or more axles	Enter Code No. of Class

(D) Introductory Remark:- "WOULD YOU MIND ANSWERING A FEW QUESTIONS ABOUT THE JOURNEY YOU ARE MAKING? THE INFORMATION IS REQUIRED IN CONNECTION WITH THE NEW ROAD PROGRAMME."

2 axles (classes 3, 4 and 5) "WHERE DID YOU START OUT FROM ON THIS JOURNEY?"	3 or more axles (class 6) "WHERE WAS THE LAST PLACE THAT ANY LOAD WAS PUT ON OR TAKEN OFF THIS VEHICLE?"
(i)	
"WHERE WAS THE LAST PLACE THAT YOU STOPPED TO MAKE A COLLECTION OR DELIVERY?"	Enter place name in rectangle (ii)
(ii)	

Nat. Grid Ref.

(F) 2 axles (classes 3, 4 and 5) "WHERE ARE YOU TRAVELLING TO?"	3 or more axles (class 6) "WHERE IS THE NEXT PLACE THAT ANY LOAD WILL BE PUT ON OR TAKEN OFF THIS VEHICLE?"
(i)	
"WHERE IS THE NEXT PLACE THAT YOU STOP TO MAKE A COLLECTION OR DELIVERY?"	Enter place name in rectangle (ii)
(ii)	

Nat. Grid Ref.

(H) Number of Occupants (including driver)   Men   Women   Children under 16

NOTE: Do not make entries in the following sections unless specially instructed.

(J) Alternative Routes Enter 1, 2 or 0   **(K)** Registration Letters

(L) Unladen Weight (not required in the case of Light Goods Van)   TONS   CWT

Refers to whole vehicle/Excludes one or more trailers   (Underline appropriately)

(M) Total number of axles ....   **(N)** Total number of tyres .....

Fig. 4.11. Record-of-interview form—commercial vehicles

The six squares at the bottom of Section (E) were used in the office to enter the national grid reference of the place-name. As explained above, if there was an entry in part (ii), this was used instead of the entry in part (i). The six squares at the bottom of Section (F) were used in a similar way.

The category of journey of cars in section (G) was obtained by showing the driver a card bearing the inscription:

*Please state the number of the category into which your
journey falls*

1. Travelling for private reasons.

2. Expenses of this vehicle on this journey paid by my
    employer or by my own business concern (wholly or part-
    ly).

3. Travelling on business. Expenses of this vehicle on this
    journey paid by myself.

4. Travelling to or from my place of work at my own expense.

5. Not included in any of the above.

This information was required in assessing the economic value of the savings in running costs and in the time of occupants of vehicles transferring
to the motorway. Interviewers were instructed to ask only for the number of
the category of journey and not to discuss the subject with the driver.

The information about occupancy in section (H) was obtained by inspection.

Sections (J), (K), (L), (M) and (N) were used to provide special information at a few of the stations. Section (J) was completed in two cases in which
traffic from the London area had the choice of two important routes before
arriving at the station; the answer was obtained by displaying a card bearing two lists of towns. Unladen weights of commercial vehicles were noted
in section (L) at one station on each of the major routes; classification
according to unladen weight is the method used in licensing vehicles and it
has been employed in previous economic studies. The details about numbers
of axles and tyres in sections (M) and (N) are used in conjunction with the
information in section (L) to correlate different methods of classifying
commercial vehicles.

TRAFFIC CENSUSES

While the survey was in progress, a census was taken of the number of
vehicles passing in the direction of interviewing to determine the proportions of the different classes of vehicle sampled by the interviewers in each
hour. In addition, a separate census was taken of vehicles travelling in the
opposite direction to complete the census information required for general
purposes.

CODING OF PLACE-NAMES

Some system of coding the places of origin and destination was necessary
to permit analysis by punched-card techniques and rather than devise a
special system, the Ordnance Survey national grid reference system was
used. In this, a place-name is denoted by the six-figure reference number of
the 10-km square in which it lies. Most of the references required were obtained from the Ordnance Survey Gazetteer but special lists had to be com-
piled for localities and postal districts in the London and Birmingham areas.
In analysing the results of the survey, journey terminations must be grouped

into areas, and although the national grid system lends itself more readily to the use of rectangular areas than irregular ones, such as administrative areas, the latter may be used if required.

STAFF REQUIREMENTS

The field-work was carried out in 8 hour shifts, the staff required per shift being:

One station supervisor (who also acted as relief interviewer)
Two interviewers
Three census-takers (including one relief census-taker)
Two policemen.

The number of policemen employed varied considerably according to the amount of traffic and the figure of two was an average rather than a standard requirement. In some cases it was sufficient to have only one man, relieved at intervals, to carry out the essential function of directing vehicles into the interviewing site. When traffic was heavy, however, an extra man was required to control the traffic and, in particular, to direct vehicles emerging from the interviewing site.

The total number of 8 hour shifts in the survey was 104, employing an average of eight men per shift, so that the total labour used in the field amounted to 832 man-days (using "day" in this context to denote an 8 hour shift). In addition, the subsequent coding of place-names is estimated to have taken about $1\frac{1}{2}$ man-days for each 8 hour shift of field work, bringing the total basic labour to 988 man-days. The field work was carried out by the six county authorities concerned, with the exception of the four nights' work which was done by the Laboratory. In most cases the stations were manned by engineering or clerical staff from the local authorities but in a few instances casual labour was engaged. The coding of place-names was also carried out by the county authorities.

The total number of interviews used in the analysis was 40 900, after the rejection of 471 forms on account of incompleteness, illegibility, etc. These figures exclude 92 drivers who had refused to supply information, i.e. only about 0·2 per cent of all drivers approached.

JOURNEY-TIME SURVEY

Journey times on 1800 miles of road (see Fig. 4.7) were measured by the "following car" method described in Chapter 3. In addition to the various main routes between the London area and the Midlands, many feeder roads were included and runs were also made as far north as Liverpool, Manchester, Sheffield and Leeds. The total distance travelled by the test cars was about 5000 miles.

The results for the runs in the two directions were combined to give the average journey times on each segment of road. The values were then marked on a large-scale map to show the times between towns and important junctions, in the same way as distances are shown on motoring maps. It was then comparatively simple to find the time between any two towns and this was done for a large number of possible journeys.

METHOD OF ANALYSIS

The information on the interview forms, being already in code, was transferred directly on to punched cards, one card for each interview. Subsequently the following additional information was gang-punched on to the cards, after sorting into the appropriate groups:

"Sampling factor".
"Interception factor".
Saving (or loss) in journey time by transferring to motorway.
Additional mileage incurred by transferring to motorway.
Motorway access points used.

"Sampling factors" and "Interception factors" were required because of the special methods employed in the origin-and-destination survey.

SAMPLING FACTORS. The "variable sampling" technique used in the origin-and-destination survey meant that the proportion of vehicles sampled was not constant but varied according to the flow of traffic and the rate at which the interviewers worked. Therefore separate sampling factors had to be calculated for each of the six classes of vehicle for each hour at each survey point. A sampling factor was found by dividing the number of vehicles of the particular class in the census by the number in the sample. Separate values for different hours of the day were necessary to avoid bias due, for example, to the variation in the proportion of potential motorway traffic at different times of day. Separate factors for different classes of vehicle were desirable to eliminate the effect of possible bias in the classes of vehicle selected for interview.

The overall average sampling factor throughout the survey was $3 \cdot 3$ but individual values varied considerably, being high when the flow was high. For example, at the point on A.45 between Coventry and Birmingham carrying about 6000 vehicles per day in one direction, the average factor was $7 \cdot 2$.

In using the results, each journey intercepted had to be treated not as one journey but as "x" journeys, where x denotes the sampling factor. Thus the number of journeys of a particular type at a survey point was found, not by counting the cards in the appropriate group but, by summing the sampling factors.

INTERCEPTION FACTORS. The use of interception factors was a device to enable the data on the punched cards, from the various survey stations, to be combined to give the best estimate obtainable from the data of the number of journeys per day, between any particular origin and any particular destination. The method also obviated the need for carrying out large amounts of manual computation.

Because of the variation in the concentration of survey points on different routes, the chance of a particular journey being intercepted depended upon the route taken. For example, journeys from London to Birmingham were liable to interception at ten points on route A.5/A.45, two points on route A.41 and one on route A.40/A.34 (Fig. 4.7). If these three routes were the only possible routes from London to Birmingham, the best estimate of the total number of journeys per day between London and Birmingham would be obtained by finding the average number of such journeys intercepted per station on each of the three routes separately, and summing the three values obtained. This calculation is arithmetically equivalent to allocating a weight of 1/10 to journeys intercepted at each of the 10 points on A.5/A.45, a weight of 1/2 to journeys intercepted at each of the two points on A.41 and a weight of 1 to the single point on route A.40/A.34. These weights are here described as "interception factors".

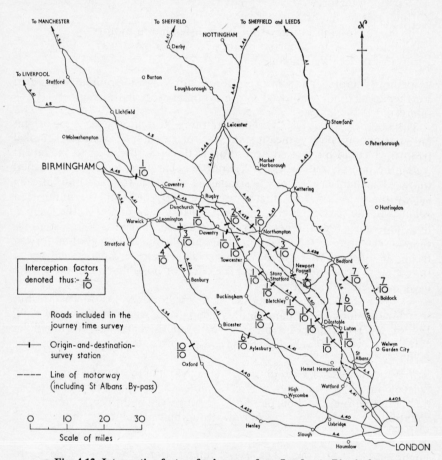

Fig. 4.12. Interception factors for journeys from London to Birmingham

Apart from the three routes mentioned above, there are of course many other possible routes from London to Birmingham, consisting mainly of parts of the three main routes in conjunction with other roads. The use of interception factors must therefore be extended to take account of such routes. For example, a journey from London to Birmingham may be made via Aylesbury, joining A.5 at Towcester. This journey would miss the first six points of interception on A.5 but it would be liable to interception at survey station 90 between Aylesbury and Buckingham (Fig. 4.7). The interception factor for this point must therefore be 6/10. By similar reasoning, interception factors were allocated to all of the survey points as shown in Fig. 4.12. It will be noted that the values satisfy the condition that for all reasonable routes between London and Birmingham the sum of the interception factors is unity. Some allowance is made for circuitous routes, e.g. for vehicles starting out from London along A.1 to get to Birmingham.

The interception factors in Fig. 4.12 apply not only to London-Birmingham traffic but also to journeys with southern terminations in an area south and east of London and with northern terminations in the North-West Midlands, North Wales and Lancashire. For journeys with northern terminations in the North-East Midlands, Yorkshire and further north different factors had to be used. Separate sets of factors had also to be derived for journeys originating or terminating within the interception area, e.g. London/Northampton, Coventry/Luton, Dunstable/Daventry. A total of 147 sets of interception factors was found to be necessary and for each set a sorting of the cards according to journey terminations was required. Further sorting was then required according to survey station before the interception factors could be gang-punched on to the cards.

The main advantage of using interception factors was that, after they had been entered on the cards, it was no longer necessary to consider the results from the different survey stations separately. For example, if it was required to find the number of journeys per day between a particular pair of journey terminations, the cards for all survey stations combined were sorted according to the entries in the journey termination columns and the appropriate groups of cards were selected. Since in one sense each card represented x journeys, where x is the sampling factor, and in another sense each card represented y journeys, where y is the interception factor, the total number of journeys was given by Σxy where Σ denotes summation over all cards in the group. This computation could be carried out automatically by punched card machines.

SAVING IN JOURNEY TIME. For each of a large number of combinations of origin and destination the mean journey time of cars on existing routes was derived from the journey-time map, the results for commercial vehicles being estimated from those for cars. Similarly the journey time for the quickest notional route including all or part of the motorway was obtained, and the difference in time was entered on the appropriate group of cards. This procedure was carried out not only for journeys which would show an estimated saving in time by transferring, but also for a large number of journeys with an estimated increase in journey time if they transferred to the motorway. The main reason for including such journeys was that they might be required in assessing the effect of assuming higher speeds on the motorway, which might convert a time loss into a saving, so that the journey qualified for inclusion in the traffic assigned to the motorway.

In the analysis, the total savings in vehicle time to, say, all traffic assigned to the motorway, or to any other particular set of journeys, was determined by computing Σxyz, where x denotes the sampling factor entered on an individual card, y the interception factor and z the time saving, while Σ denotes summation over all the cards in the group.

ADDITIONAL MILEAGE INCURRED. Journey distances were measured in the journey-time survey and were included in the analysis in the same way as journey times. For many journeys the distance by the route including the motorway was longer than by the ordinary route in spite of the saving in time. Information about the changes in vehicle mileage was necessary in the economic assessment and accordingly the changes were entered on the punched cards.

MOTORWAY ACCESS POINTS USED. In estimating the saving in time if a journey transferred to a route including the motorway, it was necessary to determine the points of entry to and exit from the motorway, and this information was entered on the cards. The information was used to predict the degree of usage of the various access points and the traffic flow on individual sections of motorway. This information also provided a convenient means of calculating the time savings for the higher assumed speeds on the motorway, without the necessity of repeating the whole analysis.

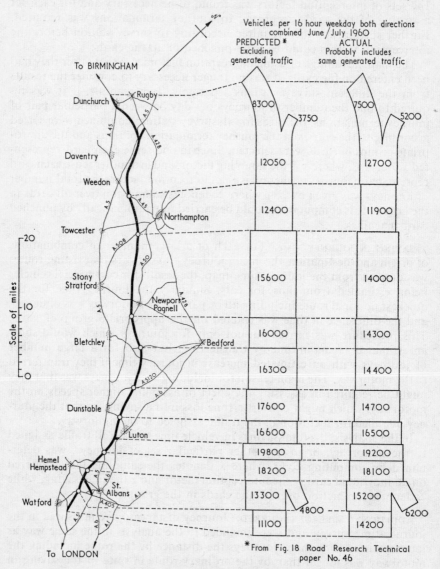

Fig. 4.13. Comparison of actual with predicted flow on the motorway

Since the distance between each pair of access points was known, the incremental time savings could be calculated and added to the time savings produced by the first set of assumed speeds, to give the time savings for the second and third sets of assumed speeds. As already mentioned, there are 13 access points on the motorway including the four end points (Fig. 4.6) permitting 76 possible combinations of entry and exit points.

TRAFFIC ASSIGNMENT

Assignment was based largely on the assumption that journeys which would save time by transferring would in fact do so and that journeys which would lose time would not transfer. However, special consideration was given to journeys for which the estimated saving or loss in time was not appreciably different from zero. It would not have been logical to assign all journeys with an estimated saving of a minute or two and to reject all journeys with an estimated loss of a minute or two; in these cases it was assumed that 50 per cent of journeys would transfer and that 50 per cent would remain on existing roads.

The process of traffic assignment was carried out for each of three sets of assumed motorway speeds, which were checked against speed measurements made by the Laboratory on motorways and ordinary roads in Belgium, France, Germany and the Netherlands (see Table 4.1).

RESULTS

Although estimates of flow, time savings, etc., were obtained for three sets of assumed motorway speeds, the results given below refer to the traffic assignment based on the lowest set of assumed speeds. This set appeared at the time to be the most realistic and subsequent measurements after the motorway opened in 1959 confirmed that this was so.

Figure 4.13 gives the predicted and actual variation in traffic along the length of the motorway and shows that there is quite good agreement between the two. Averaged over the whole of the motorway the traffic in June/July, 1960 was 4 per cent less than the prediction for diverted traffic only; since actual traffic flows probably include some traffic generated by the construction of the motorway it may be concluded that diverted traffic in 1960 fell short of predictions by rather more than 4 per cent. However, there is evidence that the degree of diversion from other roads has increased since 1960; traffic flow on the motorway during the second year of operation (1960-61) was 23 per cent higher than during the first year (1959-60) while traffic on the main alternative route (A.5) declined. In the predictions it was assumed that generated traffic would eventually amount to 30 per cent of diverted traffic and if present trends continue it seems likely that the predicted level of traffic, including the generated traffic, will be attained within the next few years.

An economic assessment showed that in 1960 the motorway would yield a rate of return of about 10 per cent of the capital cost.

Further details of the traffic estimates and the economic assessment are given in Technical Paper No. 46.[21]

TABLE 4.1

Mean speeds on straight level sections of motorway:
observed values in different European countries and
assumed values on London–Birmingham motorway
(mile/h)

EUROPEAN MOTORWAYS

Country	Car	Light commercial vehicles (up to 1½ tons unladen)	Medium commercial vehicles (2-axled)	Heavy commercial vehicles (multi-axled)
Belgium*	52	40	38	35
France*	52	43	36	35
Germany†	54	46	40	38
The Netherlands†	53	45	41	40
Belgium and France combined	52	42	37	35
Germany and the Netherlands combined	54	45	41	38
Average for 4 countries	53	44	39	37

ASSUMED ON LONDON-BIRMINGHAM MOTORWAY‡

Assignment No.	Car	Light commercial vehicles (up to 1½ tons unladen)	Medium§ commercial vehicles (1½-3 tons unladen)	Heavy§ commercial vehicles (over 3 tons unladen)
1	53	42	37	32
2	53	47	42	37
3	53	52	47	42

* Low mileage of motorway in these countries
† High mileage of motorway in these countries
‡ Mean speeds on straight level sections of motorway corresponding to assumed mean journey speeds
§ The method of classifying medium and heavy commercial vehicles in the London-Birmingham motorway investigation was somewhat different from that used in the European speed measurements but other information suggests that this will have a negligible effect on the comparison.

Oxford traffic survey

A traffic survey of Oxford was carried out during August and September 1957 under the direction of a Committee made up of representatives from the Oxford City Council, the Ministry of Transport and Civil Aviation, the

Ministry of Housing and Local Government, and the Road Research Laboratory. Subsequently the results of the survey were used by the Laboratory to assess the effects on traffic of a number of relief road proposals for Oxford. A map of the Oxford area showing the streets referred to in this account is given in Fig. 4.14.

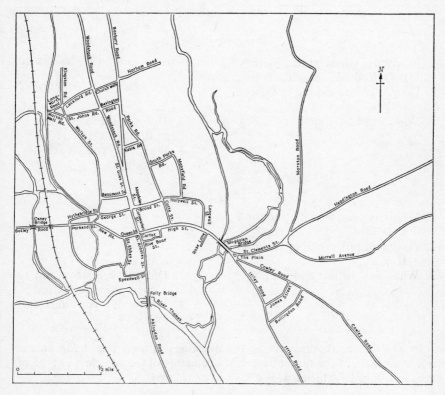

Fig. 4.14. Map of central area of Oxford

ORIGIN-AND-DESTINATION SURVEY

The origin-and-destination survey was carried out by the roadside-interview method at eight sites on roads approaching the centre of the city. The data collected covered the period 8.00 a.m. to 8.00 p.m. on each of the six days Monday to Saturday, interviewing time being equally divided between traffic entering and leaving Oxford. On any one day, six hours of interviewing was undertaken in staggered periods which lasted for one hour or 1½ hours. In this way the complete 12 hours were covered in two interlocking shifts on separate days. Two survey points were manned each day. Each point was manned for a total of 12 shifts; one in each direction on each of of the six weekdays.

Interviewing was undertaken in rotation by four survey teams; two manned the two survey points while one coded the records of its previous two days' work and one checked the coding of the other team.

Each survey team consisted of two persons. One person made a simple

7

volumetric count of all the vehicles passing the survey point, while the other questioned the sample of drivers selected for interview. A policeman controlled traffic at the survey points and directed the selected vehicles into the correct lane for questioning. The variable-sampling method of selecting drivers for interview was used.

The questions asked differed slightly for incoming and outgoing traffic and according to the replies received as follows:

Incoming traffic

1. Where did you start this journey?
   If Oxford—What address?
2. Do you intend calling in Oxford?
   If *Yes*   If *No*
3. What will be the first address?   3. Do you specially want to go through Oxford?
                                          4. Where is your next destination?

Outgoing traffic

1. Where is your next destination?
   If Oxford—What address?
2. Have you just called in Oxford?
   If *Yes*   If *No*
3. What was the last address?   3. Did you specially want to come through Oxford?
                                          4. Where did you start this journey?

In addition to the answers to the questions, a note was made on the interview form of the total number of occupants of the vehicle and type of vehicle stopped. Vehicles were classified as follows:

  (i) Scooter and solo motor-cycles.
 (ii) Cars, taxis and motor-cycle combinations.
(iii) Private coaches and buses.
 (iv) Service buses.
  (v) Light commercial vehicles.
 (vi) Medium commercial vehicles.
(vii) Heavy commercial vehicles.

The volumetric enumerator recorded the totals of all vehicles (except service buses) passing in each of the above classes. Service bus data (Class iv) obtained from time-tables were added later.

The survey was preceded by a test run at one survey point about a week before the starting date.

A comparison of 24-hour automatic traffic counter records during August and September 1957 with those for the year August 1957 to July 1958 showed that the flow in the survey months was about equal to that in the average month. August and September therefore were suitable months to carry out a survey of the city.

ANALYSIS

The city and surrounding fringe areas were divided into zones having boundaries which roughly formed concentric rings and radials, with Carfax Crossroads as an approximate centre. Thus central, inner, intermediate and outer groups of zones were defined, the boundaries being dictated by geographical features and the nature of the urban development. The outer zones covered the whole of England and Wales, and were divided by extensions of the radials so that each zone formed a reasonable natural reception or supply area for traffic originating in or destined for Oxford. Fig. 4.15 illustrates the zoning; the numbers were selected in a logical sequence to suit the mechanical sorting.

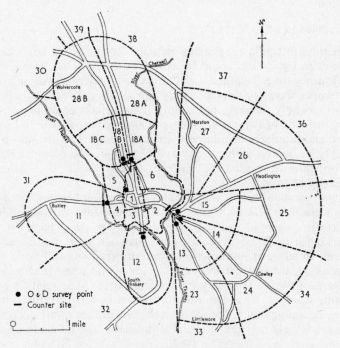

Fig. 4.15. Map of zones, survey points and counter sites used in traffic survey

The method of recording the information obtained on the questionnaires depended on the subsequent method of sorting. With about 40 000 interviews to handle, it was decided that mechanical sorting by punched cards was desirable. The questionnaires were brought into an operations room and the information was coded by the enumerator teams in rotation every third day. The operations room was arranged in the form of cubicles on a central table with complete sets of reference books, gazetteers and maps. The coding was done direct on to Hollerith "mark-sensing" cards by marking appropriate column numbers with a soft pencil. The information common to every card on a particular day was gang-punched on to the groups of cards which were then passed through a mark-sensing reproducer to translate the pencil marks into holes in the appropriate columns. In the next stage the cards were sorted into order and gang-punched with the expansion factor appropriate to the type of vehicle, site, direction and period of day. After the cards had been sorted by origin and destination, the expansion factors were summed for the cards in each group to give the flow making each movement.

JOURNEY-TIME SURVEY

A journey-time survey of Oxford was conducted in two parts, one covering about 4·7 miles of road in the central area and the other covering about 28 miles in the outer districts. Observers in a test vehicle recorded journey times along the sections of road and the duration of stops at the various intersections.

TRAFFIC ASSIGNMENT

The method of traffic assignment assumed that as a first approximation traffic between two points could be assigned entirely to the route with the shortest journey time. To allow for differences in driver behaviour two basic road networks were considered, firstly the whole network including side roads and secondly the main roads only. Thus drivers could be considered as falling into one of two groups, those who were prepared to use any road in Oxford and those who would only use main roads. The first group would presumably be familar with the city and be prepared to do more elaborate navigation; those who used the main roads only might do so either from unfamiliarity or from choice.

In the present road layout, limited as it is by the river bridges, there is only one major example of a main road route "competing" with an alternative route through side roads, namely where the route along High Street and Cornmarket for traffic between east and north can be by-passed via Long- wall Street. In terms of journey time the route via Longwall Street is, gen- erally speaking, the quicker but it was evident that some vehicles making this movement did, in fact, stay on the main roads. The relation between the existing flows on these two alternative routes was therefore used as a basis for calculating in what proportion the two groups of drivers (the users of main roads only and the users of all available roads) made up Oxford traffic.

It was clear that although the number of zones used in the origin-destina- tion survey was limited by practical aspects of coding and analysis to about 30, this was too coarse a division to give sufficient detail for assignment purposes. It was therefore decided that each section of road between inter- sections on the networks should be regarded as a separate source of traffic. On the assumption that traffic generation was approximately uniform over the road system in any given zone the traffic to that zone was distributed among the sections of road passing through it in proportion to their lengths and it was assumed, for the purpose of the calculations, that the traffic was generated at the midpoint of the road sections.

The traffic movements between road sections were assigned to both the "main roads only" network and the "all roads" network representing the existing layout. The quickest routes were obtained graphically by the method developed at the Laboratory and described on page 138 using a large diagram for each origin.

A study of these assignments to the two networks showed that, as expected, the flow along High Street and Cornmarket was too high when the main road network alone was used and too low when all drivers were assumed to be familiar with the side streets as well. The flows on the Longwall Street route exhibited the opposite effect. An approximation to traffic along these roads at the time of the survey could therefore be obtained by combining the main road and all road assignments in the appropriate proportions.

It was anticipated that there would be some journeys started and completed entirely within the central area which would not have been recorded at the interview points. The flow measurements obtained during the journey time survey included both this traffic and that passing the survey points. On the other hand the traffic assigned to the networks was only that which passed the survey points so in any case a difference would be expected between observed and assigned flows.

This difference was assumed to be constant over all the roads in the central area. The two groups of assigned traffic were therefore combined in the proportions $K: 1-K$, where K was chosen to make the ratios of observed to assigned flows equal on the effectively parallel sections of the main road route and the Longwall Street route. In this case K was found to be $0 \cdot 8$, which meant that approximately 80 per cent of the traffic appeared to be familiar with the side roads.

Inspection of the combined assignment showed that although it was satisfactory in many respects when compared with data from the automatic counters and other sources, there appeared to be an excess of eastbound traffic on High Street, coupled with a deficiency of similar traffic on Broad Street. Reference to the "quickest route" maps showed that, for eastbound traffic, the journey time between the Broad Street/Cornmarket intersection and the High Street/Longwall Street intersection was the same via Broad Street or via Cornmarket and consequently the eastbound traffic passing between these points had been divided equally between the two routes.

It will be recalled that journey time was assumed to be the major factor influencing choice of route. However, when journey times are very similar other considerations may become important. In this instance the two routes were equally quick but the observed distribution of existing traffic was strong evidence that drivers used the side street route, perhaps because they found it quicker in the opposite direction or possibly because of the reputation of Carfax.

The assignment to the "all roads" network was therefore modified so as to transfer all this particular movement to the side street route and then K was recalculated. This time it was found to be $0 \cdot 7$ and so the two groups of traffic were combined in the ratio 7:3.

COMPARISON OF ASSIGNED AND OBSERVED TRAFFIC ON THE EXISTING NETWORK

At Carfax the assigned traffic was compared with flows observed during the journey-time survey and also with observations made in connexion with studies of the traffic signals. The mean hourly flow through Carfax, as estimated by the three methods, was as follows:

Assignment from O.D. survey   1730 veh/h between 8 a.m. and 8
p.m.

Observations of flow through signals (observations on 2 part-days)   1670 veh/h between 7.30 a.m. and 6.30 p.m.

Flows from journey-time survey   1770 veh/h between 8 a.m. and 8 p.m.

The flows from the journey-time survey included traffic circulating inside the central area but did not include motorcycles. The study of the signals included all traffic but covered a slightly different period on two days only.

Assigned traffic was also compared with results from automatic traffic counters which recorded inbound traffic on the five main approaches to Oxford during the survey period.

Site	Mean flow between 8 a.m. and 8 p.m. (veh/h)	
	Assignment	Automatic counter
Magdalen Bridge	1010	1090
Folly Bridge	320	360
Osney Bridge	450	490
Woodstock Road	340	330
Banbury Road	470	470

At Magdalen Bridge and at Folly Bridge the automatic counter was sited approximately on the boundary of the central area, whereas the interview points were some little distance outside it. Traffic to the city centre from the region between the interview points and the central area boundary would thus be counted by the counter but not interviewed in the origin-destination survey.

There is no simple explanation of the difference in flows recorded at Osney Bridge, where the counter and interview sites were close together, but it is believed that it was caused to some extent by the assignment to the wrong entry route of some through traffic interviewed as it left Oxford on other roads. For example, an outbound vehicle from the west interviewed at Cowley Road might have had an origin in zone 30 and therefore have been allocated to Woodstock Road although in fact it came in via Botley Road.

Figure 4.16 shows that the assigned traffic agreed well with actual traffic on the existing network. There are, however, a few points which merit comment.

It is likely that the flow up Catte Street was underestimated, the movement being assigned to Longwall Street and Holywell Street. The decision to use Catte Street is probably not made until the queue at Carfax has been seen by the driver, so here average journey time was obviously not the only criterion used in route selection.

The assigned flow along High Street into Carfax included the left turn movement known to use Blue Boar Street and was consequently higher than the observed flow.

The flows in Magdalen Street given by the journey time survey were almost certainly too low: this was attributed to the short length and complexity of the section which made observations very difficult.

The flows assigned to Broad Street and George Street were low compared with the observed flows. One of the assumptions made in the preparation of the detailed origin-destination table was that the traffic from the original survey zones was equally generated along each unit length of road lying within that zone. This was clearly not so in some cases, particularly where car parks are sited, and it was believed that the presence of car parks in or near Broad Street and George Street led to this difference between observed and assigned traffic.

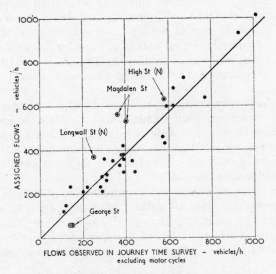

Fig. 4.16. Comparison of assigned and observed flows on sections in the central area—existing network

There was also a substantial difference on the western approach from Parkend Street to Queen Street for which there is no obvious reason. It is possible that internal generation from, say, the station and errors in observation of existing flows may be in part responsible but otherwise it is difficult to explain.

The correlation between assigned and observed traffic shown in Fig. 4.16 was good, in view of the comments made above, with a mean ratio between assigned and observed flows of $0 \cdot 95 : 1$. When allowance had been made for the absence of motorcycles in the observed flows, the ratio became $0 \cdot 85 : 1$. This implies that 15 per cent of the traffic in the central area was made up of movements which started and finished inside this area. The figures support the original belief of the Committee carrying out the survey that a separate study of this internal traffic would not be justified in view of the labour which would have been required to obtain a limited amount of information.

It was concluded that the overall agreement between assigned and observed traffic was good, bearing in mind that the original survey was based on very large zones in comparison with the road network finally considered, which itself did not include all roads known to carry traffic. As a result it was considered that the division of drivers into only two groups and the use of journey time as the sole index by which routes were selected in each group was justified, and that the method could be used to estimate the traffic distribution on proposed new layouts. If anything, the method possibly tended to underestimate the traffic using new roads since no weight is given to the general attractiveness of a new road.

THE TRAFFIC CONSEQUENCES OF THE PROPOSED NEW ROADS

Traffic movements were assigned by the graphical method to the proposed complete outer ring of by-passes and three relief road proposals and the results were reported to the City Council in 1959. The computer programmes described earlier were used to assign the traffic movements to a further six relief road proposals so that details of their traffic consequences could be made available for a Public Inquiry, held in December 1960 at Oxford, to decide on alterations and additions to the City of Oxford Development Plan.

In each of the proposed schemes it was assumed that the new roads would be built to a sufficiently high standard to accommodate any amount of diverted traffic without appreciable increase in the journey time along them, that traffic on them would travel at speeds appropriate to urban dual carriageways, and that the junctions would have sufficient capacity to carry the traffic without increasing the delay.

Included in all the schemes was the complete ring of outer by-passes, both present and proposed. Since all traffic being assigned had been interviewed at the boundary to the central area (and was therefore obviously not by-passing Oxford), it was not assigned to either of the existing northeastern or southwestern by-passes unless on its journey it also used part of the new outer by-passes.

The total traffic was assigned to the complete network and the "main road only" network for each scheme, the resulting distributions being combined in the ratio 7:3. Where routes of equal journey time existed between two points and there was no other evidence as to how the traffic would distribute itself, it was assigned equally between them; there were, however, no important instances of this in the new networks.

No allowance was made for traffic generated by the new roads nor for the effect of any changes in land use.

ECONOMIC ASSESSMENT OF THE PROPOSALS

It has been shown by Charlesworth, Reynolds and Wardrop[22] that the relation between total costs per vehicle mile and the mean speed of vehicles on a road for "normal" traffic composition and for speeds up to 45 mile/h could be closely approximated by:

$C_m = 4 \cdot 0 + 100/V$ (up to 35 mile/h)
$C_m = 4 \cdot 6 + 80/V$ (between 35 and 45 mile/h)

where

C_m = total average cost per vehicle mile in pence (net of tax),
V = average running speed of traffic in mile/h.

On this basis an assessment was made of the rate of return which would be expected from the different schemes. It did not take into account the value of savings on Sundays or during the "night" hours 8 p.m. to 8 a.m. nor any changes in accidents. It also gave no value to non-working time.

Further details of the survey and the results from four assignments are given in a publication by the City Council.[23] Unpublished reports[24,25,26] by the Laboratory describe the other assignments made for the Public Inquiry.

London travel survey

A survey of travel in Greater London was undertaken in 1954 by the Social Survey Division of the Central Office of Information on behalf of the Road Research Laboratory, the British Transport Commission and the London Transport Executive. The succeeding paragraphs are based on reports issued by the London Transport Executive[27] and the Road Research Laboratory.[28]

From the Laboratory's point of view the main purpose of the survey was to collect information about people travelling by road. Information about vehicles was already available from studies of traffic flow, but nothing was known of the occupants of the vehicles, why they were travelling, the details of their journeys, or whether they were travelling during working hours or in their own time.

AREA COVERED

The main survey area (see Fig. 4.17) was that defined by the London Transport Executive as Central London (the "red bus" area) and was slightly larger than the Registrar General's definition of the Greater London Conurbation. To meet the requirements of the London Transport Executive the 1954 survey also included six towns (Dartford, Grays, Hemel Hempstead, Reigate, St. Albans, and Watford) and some of the countryside immediately adjacent to them.

HOME-INTERVIEW SURVEY

Information about travel in the area was collected by interviewing in their own homes a sample of all persons living in the area.

The field work was carried out between 26th January and 14th April, 1954, in the main survey area, with an extension after Easter to 5th June in the country towns. The information obtained, therefore, relates mainly to the winter period and almost entirely to travel during school-term time. A staff of 64 interviewers was employed.

SAMPLING PROCEDURE

Households, and not individuals, were chosen as sampling units for the survey to facilitate assessment of differences in travel habit according to income, ownership of cars, etc. All polling districts in the main survey area were grouped into 15 zones and the number of addresses allocated to each zone was in proportion to size of population; this ensured a strictly proportional representation of the population in all parts of Greater London. The main survey sample was selected in two stages to reduce interviewing costs. In the first stage, 209 polling districts were selected from a total of about 600; in the second stage approximately 25 addresses were selected from the electoral registers of each sample of 209 polling districts. The procedure adopted

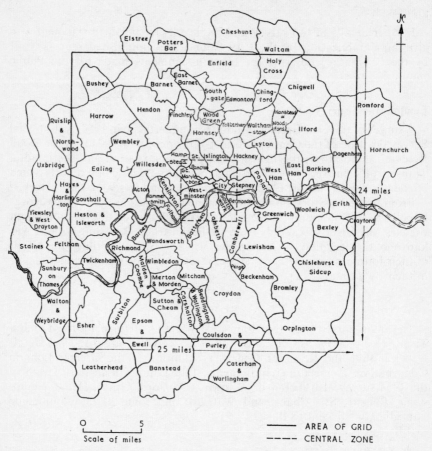

Fig. 4.17. Area covered by the London Travel Survey

for selecting the sample of 209 polling districts ensured that the chance of selection varied in proportion to size, whereas the 25 addresses were selected systematically at equal intervals from the electoral registers.

The sample of addresses in the six neighbouring towns was selected in one stage at equal intervals from the electoral registers. In Hemel Hempstead, rating lists were used and rateable units selected instead, because the rapid expansion due to the growth of the new town rendered the electoral registers out of date. In Reigate, however, the wards comprising Reigate M.B. were separated from the remainder, and the sampling fraction increased in the outer area to five times the proportion in the town proper. The number of households interviewed in the area was then sufficient to permit separate analysis of the results.

In mid-1954, the population of the main survey area was 8 640 000 and the number of households approximately 2 740 000; the corresponding figures for the country towns were 380 000 and 120 000 respectively. The field staff interviewed 3885 households in the main area and 1530 in the country towns. This corresponds to a response rate of 79 per cent of all addresses issued, the balance being non-contacts and refusals. About 90 per cent of persons in the households interviewed provided full details about their travel, and adjustments were made where necessary for the remaining 10 per cent during the analysis.

The resulting sampling fraction for the main survey area was approximately 1 in 700, while for the country towns as a whole it was about 1 in 80; but, in fact, the sampling fraction varied considerably between one town and another on account of the decision to interview an equal number of households in each country town.

TRAINING OF INTERVIEWERS

The abnormally large staff, which included a high proportion of new interviewers, was given a thorough training and briefing. This consisted of instruction in the purpose and scope of the enquiry, sampling procedure, detailed definitions and coding together with scripted interviews. Detailed examination of the schedules completed was followed by further mock interviews and four days' interviewing in the field.

INFORMATION OBTAINED IN INTERVIEWS

There was considerable discussion about the form and content of the questionnaires the position being somewhat complicated because of the need to satisfy the requirements of both the Laboratory and the London Transport Executive. Two pilot surveys were therefore carried out, as a result of which it was decided to use two questionnaires, a household schedule and a travel log, both to be filled in by the interviewer.

The household schedule was designed to obtain information about the composition of the household and also about each of its members—occupation, income group, place and hours of work, etc.

A travel log was completed for each member of the household over three years of age who had travelled in the previous seven days. On it were recorded details of all the journeys made except those made on foot or by persons employed as drivers of commercial vehicles, public-service vehicles, and taxis, while driving in the course of their work. Journeys made by commercial travellers were included in the survey.

Copies of the two questionnaires are shown in Figs. 4.18 and 4.19.

A journey was defined as a movement to a particular destination for a particular purpose. Journeys could consist of several stages, or rides, a ride being defined as a movement between two points without a change of vehicle. If a journey was broken for a subsidiary reason (e.g. shopping during the journey to work), and the break was for less than 10 minutes, then it was considered to be one journey consisting of two rides, but if the break was for more than 10 minutes then it was considered that there were two journeys, made for different purposes.

The form of transport used and the time of starting and finishing each ride were recorded.

For the recording of journeys each interviewer was supplied with a copy of Bartholomew's Reference Atlas of Greater London, which covered an area 25 miles east-west by 24 miles north-south and included most of the sample area (see Fig. 4.17); it was divided into half-mile squares coded on a grid system. This atlas was used as a grid reference. The starting and finishing point of each ride was recorded by the interviewer and coded according to its position on the grid. Origins and destinations outside the grid area

Classification

(i) Interviewer...............................,   (v) Sampling Area Code   (xi) Type of Dwelling

(ii) Authorisation No.

(iii) District   (vi) Household Serial No.

     Central Area   1

     Outer Catchment

     Area: Watford   3   (vii) Head of Household's
         St. Albans   4   (Letter)
         Dartford   5
         Reigate   6
         Grays   7   (viii) Total No. in Household
         Hemel Hempstead   8

(iv) Name of Sampling Area

     L.A.A.................................

     ....   (ix) Date of first interview

     Ward or Parish........................   (x) No. of calls to complete
     ....   first interview..............

Type of Dwelling:
Bungalow (in. Prefab.)............1
Detached House......................2
Semi-detached House............3
Terraced House.....................4
Part of House........................5
S/c Flat.................................6
Others (specify)....................7

(xii)   Back Garden......Yes..............8
                   No..............9

(xiii) No one in Household interviewed
     Reason.................................
     ....
     ....

Q.1   HOUSEHOLD COMPOSITION

Household composition			Income group	Occupation				
(1) Relationship to Housewife	(2) Sex M F	(3) Age	(4) NIL / £3 and under / Over £3–£5 / Over £5–£7 10 / Over £7 10–£10 / Over £10–£20 / Over £20 / D.K. / Ref. unmasked	(5) Worker Housewife Scholar Other	(6) Was Worker at work in last 7 days — Yes No	(7) Travel Information obtained — Yes No	(8) If no Travel Information — Why not?	(9) Total calls to interview this person
A	Y X	0 1 2 3 4 5 6 7 8	Y X 0 1	2 3	4 5		
B	Y X	0 1 2 3 4 5 6 7 8	Y X 0 1	2 3	4 5		
C	Y X	0 1 2 3 4 5 6 7 8	Y X 0 1	2 3	4 5		
D	Y X	0 1 2 3 4 5 6 7 8	Y X 0 1	2 3	4 5		
E	Y X	0 1 2 3 4 5 6 7 8	Y X 0 1	2 3	4 5		
F	Y X	0 1 2 3 4 5 6 7 8	Y X 0 1	2 3	4 5		
G	Y X	0 1 2 3 4 5 6 7 8	Y X 0 1	2 3	4 5		
H	Y X	0 1 2 3 4 5 6 7 8	Y X 0 1	2 3	4 5		

Q.2   WORKING HOURS AND PLACE OR WORK

ADDRESS OF WORKPLACE/SCHOOL STREET, BOROUGH/POSTAL DISTRICT (1)	OFF. USE (2)	WORKING/SCHOOL HOURS 24 hour clock		Return for Mid-day meal Yes No (5)	HOURS OF FINISHING WORK ON HALF DAY TIME 24 hour clock (6)
		Commencing Hours (3)	Ending Hours (4)		
A				3 4	
B				3 4	
C				3 4	
D				3 4	
E				3 4	
F				3 4	
G				3 4	
H				3 4	

FULL ADDRESS OF INFORMANT..

Fig. 4.18. London Travel Survey household schedule

were recorded by means of a special code, and a separate code was used for all rides to and from railway stations.

All journeys were classified as being "regular" or "casual"; a "regular" journey was defined as one made at the same time every day (to within an hour), for the same purpose, by the same means of transport, and between

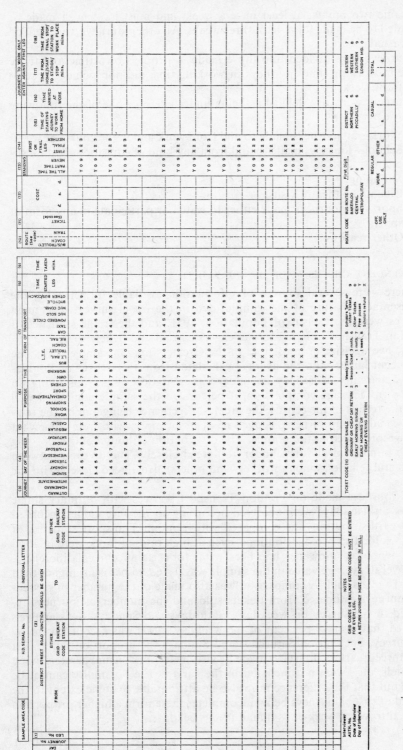

Fig. 4.19. London Travel Survey log

the same two points, at least once a week, and must have been made or intended to be made for at least three weeks. All other journeys were defined as "casual".

Journeys were divided into those made in people's own time and those made in working time; journeys in working time did not include those to and from work.

Journeys were also defined as being undertaken for one of the following purposes:

  (i) Work—all journeys made to and from work and in the course of work.
 (ii) School—journeys made to and from any kind of educational establishment.
(iii) Shopping.
(iv) Cinema or theatre visits.
 (v) Sport—all journeys made either to watch or participate in any form of sport.
(vi) Other reasons.

INDEPENDENT CHECKS MADE OF THE SAMPLE

There were several sources of information available for checking the representative nature of the sample used in the travel survey. The main sources were the Census of Population, 1951, and the traffic statistics of London Transport relating to passengers carried and tickets sold.

The average size of household in the Greater London sample was some 2 per cent larger than the average calculated from the Census of Population, apparently caused by an under-representation of persons living on their own. The age composition of persons in the sample compared well with the results of the census, the greatest divergence being among the relatively small group of persons aged 65 years or more, who were somewhat under-represented in the sample. The distribution of households according to the number of children under 16 agreed closely. The division between males and females, among workers and others, also agreed closely with the census.

All journeys made on London Transport services with ordinary single tickets on Tuesdays were analysed according to the fare values recorded and this distribution was compared with London Transport statistics of tickets sold. The two distributions, even at high rates of fares, were in good agreement after allowance had been made for certain technical differences. The overall average value in the sample was $0 \cdot 16d.$ (5 per cent) higher than that of tickets sold. A comparison was also made of the number of passenger journeys estimated from tickets sold and the number of journeys recorded in the survey on weekdays, Saturdays and Sundays. This analysis showed that over 90 per cent of the weekday traffic was accounted for by the survey, but that on Saturdays and Sundays the proportion fell to just over three-quarters. Journeys made by visitors to London and persons living in hotels, etc., were not included in the survey. The possibility cannot be ruled out that the difference may also be attributable to some extent to the record of casual journeys being incomplete; these form a higher proportion of total travel at week-ends than during weekdays.

One of the uncertainties of a home-interview survey is the effect of memory on the accuracy of information about activities which took place several days previously. This applies particularly to casual journeys and before any analysis of casual travel was begun the figures were examined to see if any corrections for this factor were necessary. Table 4.2 shows the number of casual rides reported for each of the seven days covered by the survey and the interval between the interview and the rides reported. The weighted average for the whole week shows a progressive decline from 0·44 to 0·18, suggesting that approximately 60 per cent [(44 − 18)/44] of casual journeys were forgotten after seven days. On the crude assumption that all the differences are due to the effect of memory, i.e. that the same number of casual journeys were made every day, then it appears that only 70 per cent of all casual journeys were recollected, i.e.

$$\frac{\text{average for whole week}}{7 \times \text{average number of rides on day before interview}} = \frac{2\cdot16}{7 \times 0\cdot44} = 70 \text{ per cent.}$$

TABLE 4.2

Effect of interval between travel and interview on number of casual rides reported

Number of days between travel and interview	Total number of casual rides reported	Weighted average number of casual rides per person interviewed*
1	6875	0·44
2	6031	0·38
3	5185	0·33
4	5067	0·32
5	4342	0·28
6	3669	0·23
7	2744	0·18
TOTAL	33 913	2·16

* 15 668 persons interviewed in Greater London and the country towns.

Further analysis showed that 70 per cent is a slight overestimate of the percentage of casual journeys which were remembered and that the proportion of casual journeys remembered was higher for weekend than for weekday journeys. Also, the proportion of journeys that were casual varied considerably on different forms of transport. The results were therefore adjusted by dividing the number of casual rides on each form of transport by the proportion of the total number of casual rides remembered, this operation being carried out separately for weekday, Saturday and Sunday journeys. This method implicitly assumes that the same proportion of casual journeys was forgotten irrespective of the form of transport used and that the forgotten casual rides were distributed in the same way as reported rides, both regular and casual.

REFERENCES TO CHAPTER 4

1. SOUTH-EAST LANCASHIRE AND NORTH-EAST CHESHIRE AREA HIGHWAY ENGINEERING COMMITTEE. A highway plan 1962. Manchester, 1962 (South-East Lanchashire and North-East Cheshire Area Highway Engineering Committee).

2. DUFF, J. T., and D. A. de C. BELLAMY. Surveys to determine the origin and destination of traffic. *Department of Scientific and Industrial Research, Road Research Laboratory Research Note No.* RN/2364/JTD.DAB. Harmondsworth, 1955 (Unpublished).

3. SOSSLAU, A. B., and G. E. BROOKE. Appraisal of sample size based on Phoenix O-D survey data. *Bull. Highw. Res. Bd, Wash.*, 1960, (253), 114-27.

4. SCHMIDT, R. E., and M. E. CAMPBELL. Highway traffic estimation. Saugatuck, Conn., 1956 (Eno Foundation for Highway Traffic Control).

5. MARTIN, B. V., F. W. MEMMOTT and A. J. BONE. Principles and techniques of predicting future demand for urban area transportation. Cambridge, Mass., 1961 (Massachusetts Institute of Technology).

6. CUMBERNAULD DEVELOPMENT CORPORATION. Cumbernauld New Town. Traffic analysis report. Cumbernauld, 1958 (Cumbernauld Development Corporation).

7. CHICAGO AREA TRANSPORTATION STUDY. Final report in three parts. Volume II. Data projections. Chicago, Ill., 1960 (Chicago Area Transportation Study).

8. FURNESS, K. P. Trip forecasting. Paper presented at a seminar on the use of electronic computers in traffic planning, London, 1962 (Unpublished).

9. TANNER, J. C. Factors affecting the amount of travel. *Department of Scientific and Industrial Research, Road Research Technical Paper* No. 51. London, 1961 (H.M. Stationery Office).

10. SMEED, R. J., and E. M. HOLROYD. Some factors affecting congestion in towns: the area required for roads in the central areas of towns for journeys to and from work by car. *Engineering for Traffic Conference*, London, 1963 (Printerhall Ltd.).

11. CREIGHTON, R. L., I. HOCH and M. SCHNEIDER. The optimum spacing of arterials and of expressways. *Traff. Quart.*, 1959, 13 (4), 447-94.

12. HIGHWAY RESEARCH BOARD. Traffic assignment. *Bull. Highw. Res. Bd, Wash.*, 1952, (61).

13. SHAW, A. E., and R. A. MARSH. Computer analysis of traffic census. *Local Govt. Finance*,1962, 66 (7), 155-6.

14. MOORE, E. F. The shortest path through a maze. Paper presented at the International Symposium on the Theory of Switching, Harvard University 1957.

15. WHITING, P. D., and J. A. HILLIER. A method for finding the shortest route through a road network. *Operat. Res. Quart.*, 1960, 11 (1/2), 37-40.

16. CRAIG, D. M. Wrexham's traffic study. *Traff. Engng & Control*, 1961, 3 (3), 163-8.

17. MINARTZ. Traffic planning by graphical methods. *Strasse u. Verkehr*, 1960, 46 (7), 352-60.

18. MERTZ, W. L. Review and evaluation of electronic computer traffic assignment programs. *Bull. Highw. Res. Bd, Wash.*, 1961, (297), 94-105.

19. WHITING, P. D. Computer programmes for allocating traffic by the quickest route method. *Department of Scientific and Industrial Research, Road Research Laboratory Research Note* No. RN/3829/PDW. Harmondsworth, 1960 (Unpublished).

20. IRWIN, N. A., N. DODD, and H. G. VON CUBE. Capacity restraint in assignment programmes. *Bull. Highw. Res. Bd, Wash.*, 1961, (297), 109-27.

21. COBURN, T. M., M. E. BEESLEY and D. J. REYNOLDS. The London-Birmingham motorway. Traffic and economics. *Department of Scientific and Industrial Research, Road Research Technical Paper* No. 46. London, 1960 (H.M. Stationery Office).

22. CHARLESWORTH, G., D. J. REYNOLDS and J. G. WARDROP. Road improvements: choosing priorities by a new formula. *Engineering*, 1959, **188** (4873), 185-8.

23. CITY OF OXFORD. Oxford traffic survey 1957. Oxford, 1959 (University Press).

24. HILLIER, J. A., and P. D. WHITING. Oxford traffic survey: an assessment of the traffic consequences of some further proposed road layouts. *Department of Scientific and Industrial Research, Road Research Laboratory Research Note* No. RN/3876/JAH.PDW. Harmondsworth, 1960 (Unpublished).

25. HILLIER, J. A. and P. D. WHITING. Oxford traffic survey: an assessment of the traffic consequences of a modified intermediate ring road. *Department of Scientific and Industrial Research, Road Research Laboratory Research Note* No. RN/3889/JAH.PDW. Harmondsworth, 1960 (Unpublished).

26. HILLIER, J. A., and P. D. WHITING. Oxford traffic survey: an assessment of the traffic consequences of the Oxford Preservation Trust proposals. *Department of Scientific and Industrial Research, Road Research Laboratory Research Note* No. RN/3968/JAH.PDW. Harmondsworth, 1961 (Unpublished).

27. LONDON TRANSPORT EXECUTIVE. London travel survey 1954. London, 1956 (London Transport Executive).

28. DAWSON, R. F. F., and J. G. WARDROP. Passenger-mileage by road in Greater London. *Department of Scientific and Industrial Research, Road Research Technical Paper* No. 59. London, 1962 (H.M. Stationery Office).

Chapter 5

Theoretical Models of Traffic

SYNOPSIS

Theoretical studies of traffic; statistical models; Lighthill–Whitham theory of traffic flow; use of computers in traffic flow studies; capacity of a road, a simple model. Single-lane experiments.

INTRODUCTION

A traffic model is any system whether physical or abstract whose behaviour can be observed or calculated and is related to the behaviour of traffic in some useful way. Physical models have been proposed, but they have not been used as far as is known. What has been done is (1) to regard certain aspects of traffic behaviour as examples of random phenomena and to treat them by the methods of statistics, and (2) to consider the flow of vehicles as analogous to a flow of liquid in a channel whose behaviour is then the consequence of certain laws of flow. The statistical approach has been more useful in treating such problems as delay at traffic signals, the formation of queues, and indeed any problems where average values and probabilities are the main concern. It is also the more developed. The study of traffic as a more or less deterministic flow has been of more immediate application to the study of flow and capacity. It has however applications to the traffic signal situation. It has also enriched the subject with certain picturesque conceptions such as wave propagation, shock waves, bottlenecks, etc., which may prove to be of value in future developments of the subject. A combination of the statistical and deterministic points of view or methods of treatment may be necessary.

THEORETICAL STUDIES OF TRAFFIC

The earliest theoretical work on road traffic problems was concerned with the capacity of roads, and several papers were published in 1924–26. This work, which was based on somewhat artificial assumptions about uniformity of speed and spacing between vehicles, is summarized by Normann in the *Highway Capacity Manual*.[1]

An important advance was made in 1934 by Kinzer,[2] who assumed, without verification, that vehicles were distributed at random along a two-lane road with a known speed distribution and calculated the probability that a particular vehicle would travel a given distance before it was interfered with by another vehicle. Adams[3] showed in 1936 that an assumption that vehicle arrival times at a point on the road are randomly distributed is justified on most occasions, although not when traffic is heavy. This result was the foundation of most of the later theoretical work.

The problem of delay at traffic signals was an obvious choice for study. Clayton[4] assumed uniform arrivals at fixed-time signals, but Garwood[5] found the distribution of delay to the first arrival during the red period at vehicle-actuated signals in the presence of random traffic. This work was extended by Greenshields,[6] Raff,[7] Wardrop,[8] and Tanner,[9] whose solution included the problem of delay to pedestrians crossing the road (further studied by Mayne[10]). Tanner[11] also investigated the problem of an uncontrolled crossing of two streams.

So far a complete theoretical solution has not been obtained even for the case of fixed-time signals. However, this problem has been solved successfully by the Road Research Laboratory by simulation methods, first using a special purpose delay computer[12] and later a general purpose electronic computer (see Chapter 9 and Webster[13]). Vehicle-actuated traffic signals, which are considerably more complex, have also been simulated by this method, and it is very probable that the important problem of linked systems of signals will be dealt with in the same way.

A number of statistical investigations into the movement of random traffic along the road, including the overtaking of vehicles, have been made in recent years, and include those by Newell,[14] Kometani,[15] Tanner,[16] Beckmann, McGuire and Winsten,[17] and Miller.[18] An alternative approach, which is limited to vehicles confined to a single lane and does not allow for statistical fluctuations, has been followed by Pipes[19] and others. A striking innovation was the wave theory of Lighthill and Whitham,[20] who treated traffic as a special kind of fluid with its own law of motion. This theory also omits probability considerations, but has a wide field of application.

There is scope for a general theory of traffic flow which combines the wave theory with statistical ideas. Meanwhile, there is a place for simulation using an electronic computer in all phases of traffic movement. This has been tried on a limited scale by Gerlough[21] for the ease of movement on a freeway.

Traffic distribution on a network has been discussed by Wardrop[8] and by Prager.[22] This problem arises in connexion with the design of relief roads.

A systematic method of determining the most economical route through a network was devised by Whiting and Hillier.[23] This is a necessary preliminary to most methods of assigning traffic to new routes for design purposes.

Recently a considerable number of theoretical papers on traffic have been published, covering car following, fluid flow, delays at intersections, distribution on networks, economic problems and other topics. A useful selected bibliography has been isued by the Highway Research Board[24] and a review of the literature has been made by Haight.[25]

The First Symposium on the Theory of Road Traffic Flow was organized by General Motors Research Laboratories in Detroit in December 1959, and the Proceedings, edited by R. Herman were published in 1961.[26] The Second Symposium was held in London in June 1963, and was arranged by the Road Research Laboratory with the active assistance of General Motors Research Laboratories and the Organization for Economic Co-operation and Development. A summary of the 35 papers has been given by Buckley.[27]

Some theoretical work does not have immediate practical applications, either because it is not sufficiently close to the real problems facing traffic engineers and planners or because the work of observation or experiment necessary to relate the theory to practice has not been carried out.

A brief outline is given below of the main theories, i.e. the statistical and the fluid flow theories.

Statistical models

If the passage of vehicles past a fixed point is noted the number arriving in a given interval is variable. To a large extent arrivals are found to be random, that is, any given element of time is as likely to contain an arrival as any other equal element. The distribution of arrivals in a given interval is known as the Poisson distribution. If the average rate of arrival of vehicles is m per unit time (any arbitrary unit), then if the time is divided up into successive units the proportion of these units during which no vehicle arrives, one vehicle arrives, and so on, are the terms of the series

$$0 \quad 1 \quad 2 \quad 3$$
$$e^{-m}\left(1+m+\frac{m^2}{2!}\times\frac{m^3}{3!}\ldots\right) \quad\ldots\quad\ldots\quad\ldots\quad\ldots\quad (1)$$

Since the expression within the bracket is e^m, the sum of all the proportions, i.e. probabilities, is clearly unity as it should be.

If we consider the time intervals between vehicles it may be deduced that the probability of an interval t exceeding t_0 is given by

$$p(t > t_0) = e^{-mt_0} \quad\ldots\quad\ldots\quad\ldots\quad\ldots\quad (2)$$

We may regard the Poisson distribution as a model for discussing problems which depend on the arrival of vehicles at a point. A specially obvious case is that of finding the best time cycle for a set of traffic signals at a junction. It may be required to find the arrangement which will result in the least average delay to the vehicles using the junction. The flow on each road fixes the value of m for that road. The random arrival of the vehicles takes place in accordance with the Poisson formulae (1) and (2), and such things as the average delay, the average length of queue and any other statistical entity can then be evaluated either mathematically or on a computer by Monte Carlo methods of feeding in the random intervals between vehicles.

It might be noted that the computer can deal equally well with times of arrival actually recorded at the junction or a similar one. The original special purpose computer was used to calculate delays for recorded traffic over a period of several hours and also for the same traffic artificially increased by fixed percentages to cover future conditions. The use of the Poisson distribution frees one however from dependence on such observations and enables one to consider rates of flow and combinations of flows which may not have been observed in practice. All that is necessary is to have made sure by earlier observation that the arrival of vehicles is sufficiently near to random for the Poisson distribution to form an adequate model. The problem of traffic signals had been earlier considered using the less realistic model of uniform traffic flow. The Poisson distribution is much closer to the truth, but is not of course exactly correct. The distribution of vehicles along the length of a road may also in certain circumstances be treated as random (see Wardrop[8]).

The assumption of the Poisson distribution implies that the behaviour of one vehicle is not influenced by others. If, for example, vehicles cannot overtake one another because the road is too narrow or too crowded then a deviation from the Poisson distribution may be expected. Since a driver will allow a certain distance between himself and the vehicle in front, (a distance which increases with the general speed of the traffic), there will be fewer short distances than would be expected from the Poisson distribution and distances less than a certain amount will not occur at all. It has been shown that a distribution that fits the observations can be obtained by assuming that the observed distribution is a combination of Poissonian chance effects with a distribution of following distances known from observations of driver behaviour in controlled following tests. The use of such a modified Poisson distribution might be necessary in certain problems where the simple Poisson would lead to insufficiently accurate results. A distribution of this type, in which the following distances are fixed, has been discussed by Tanner.[11]

Traffic does not consist of identical vehicles moving randomly. Individual vehicles and drivers differ in many respects. From the point of view of traffic flow important differences are the speeds at which the drivers desire to drive their vehicles, their capacity for overtaking others, their size as affecting overtaking by others, the type of motion employed (e.g. buses make more frequent stops than other vehicles) and so on. When traffic observations are made, these differences are noted. They contribute to the spread about the mean which is characteristic of almost any observed quantity, vehicle speed for instance. The distributions of these differences in normal traffic must be taken into account where necessary in order to arrive at appropriate results. The calculations are normally made in these cases on the observed distributions, the various characteristics being assumed to occur at random in the traffic.

An example of this, which is considered later from the point of view of a fluid theory of traffic flow, concerns the flow of traffic along a stretch of road with little gain from or leakage to side roads. Given the distribution of vehicles on the road at time t_0, suppose we wish to find the distribution at time t. The method adopted from the statistical point of view is to assume that each vehicle would travel at its own chosen speed independently of the others. The distribution of vehicle speeds for that road is known from observation but the speeds appropriate to the vehicles in the traffic situation whose future progress is to be predicted is not known. The curve of vehicle concentration* or density along the road at $t = t_0$ is drawn as a continuous smoothed curve. Each element of this curve is then regarded as composed of a mixture of vehicles of different speeds as shown by the observations on the actual traffic. The elements of concentration are then propagated along the road at the appropriate speeds becoming spread out in the process owing to the speed range. When this is done for each element of the original curve and the results summed together the predicted concentration curve for the chosen time t is obtained.

* The concentration of traffic is the number of vehicles per unit distance along the road, usually vehicles per mile.

It may seem odd that the concentration at any one point is assumed to spread out with the whole range of velocities of which the traffic is capable but this is largely a matter of scale. It one can regard the traffic as divided into groups of vehicles, each large enough to contain enough vehicles to form a representative selection of the speed distribution, and yet small enough to contain only a small fraction of the vehicles being studied and over which the concentration does not greatly change, then the treatment may be expected to give reasonably good results. One difficulty is that it is assumed that, in the initial state of the traffic, vehicles are distributed at random so far as speed characteristics are concerned, yet at time t there will be a tendency for the faster vehicles to be in front and slower ones at the rear. Thus if one worked out from the initial state the distribution at t_1 and again for a later time t_2 one would not expect to get the same result if one attempted to calculate the state at t_2 from that at t_1. For complete generality therefore one needs to know the speed characteristic of each car in the initial state and the calculation of later states would be done not statistically but by considering each individual vehicle in turn.

Problems of flow of this kind have been tackled from the point of view of liquids in channels as will now be discussed. Here the flow of traffic along a long road is the primary problem, rather than a secondary one as it is in the case of the statistical treatments.

The Lighthill-Whitham theory of traffic flow[20]

It is an observed fact that speed and flow are not generally independent of one another. At very light flows speeds are more or less independent of the flow. As the flow increases up to the maximum which the road allows the speed diminishes as the flow increases. Circumstances may arise, as will be explained later, in which flow and speed decrease together until the traffic is brought to rest.

The relationship between speed and concentration is simpler than that between speed and flow; at low concentrations where vehicles move independently of one another the speed is constant, and at higher concentrations the velocity falls continuously as concentration increases.

Some examples of this relation are shown in Figs. 5.7, 5.8, 5.9, 5.10 and 5.11 (see pages 190–2). If observations of flow and concentration are made on a length of road it will be found that various flows are found at any particular concentration but there will certainly be an average flow appropriate to that concentration. If q represents flow and k represents concentration the relation may be written

$$q = q_x(k) \quad . \qquad . \qquad . \qquad . \qquad . \qquad . \qquad . \qquad . \qquad . \qquad . \qquad (3)$$

in which the function will generally depend on the position on the road which is being studied, i.e. on x, representing the distance along the road.

The flow at any point is related to the space mean speed v of vehicles (see p. 107, Ch. 3) near that point by the relation

$$q = kv \quad . \qquad . \qquad . \qquad . \qquad . \qquad . \qquad . \qquad . \qquad . \qquad . \qquad (4)$$

and it follows that v is also a function of the concentration. If we consider the flow in and out of a short length of road dx we get the usual equation of continuity which expressed the fact that if the concentration of vehicles has increased it must have been due to a difference in the amounts flowing in at one end and out at the other:

$$\frac{\partial q}{\partial x} + \frac{\partial k}{\partial t} = 0, \qquad \qquad \qquad (5)$$

flow being measured in the direction of increasing x.

Since from (3) q_x is a function of k and x but not of t, we have

$$\frac{\partial q}{\partial x} = \frac{\partial q_x}{\partial x} + \frac{\partial q_x}{\partial k} . \frac{\partial k}{\partial x} \quad \text{and} \qquad \qquad (6)$$

$$\frac{\partial q}{\partial t} = \frac{\partial q_x}{\partial k} . \frac{\partial k}{\partial t} \qquad \qquad \qquad (7)$$

Inserting from (7) into (5) we get

$$\frac{\partial q}{\partial x} + \frac{1}{\dfrac{\partial q_x}{\partial k}} . \frac{\partial q}{\partial t} = 0 \qquad \qquad \qquad (8)$$

or

$$\frac{\partial q}{\partial t} + \frac{\partial q_x}{\partial k} . \frac{\partial q}{\partial x} = 0 \qquad \qquad \qquad (9)$$

Since the rate of change of any quantity f with time at a point moving with velocity u along the road is

$$\frac{\partial f}{\partial t} + u . \frac{\partial f}{\partial x}$$

it is clear that (9) means that for a point moving with velocity $\partial q_x/\partial k$ the value of q remains constant. Thus the motion of the vehicles along the road can be represented by the propagation of the flow-space curve, each point moving at a speed $\partial q_x/\partial k$, which depends only on the flow and on the changing characteristics of the road. If the flow is the same function of concentration at all points the velocity does not change and each value of flow is propagated at the appropriate constant speed $\partial q_x/\partial k$, derived from (3). Such a motion is that found in waves of finite amplitude in which the velocity of propagation is a function of amplitude.

Though there is a wave flow of this kind in terms of flow there is not a similar wave in terms of density. Using (6) with (5) we get

$$\frac{\partial q_x}{\partial x} + \frac{\partial q_x}{\partial k} . \frac{\partial k}{\partial x} + \frac{\partial k}{\partial t} = 0 \qquad \qquad \qquad (10)$$

or

$$\frac{\partial k}{\partial t} + \frac{\partial q_x}{\partial k} . \frac{\partial k}{\partial x} = -\frac{\partial q_x}{\partial x} \qquad \qquad \qquad (11)$$

which means that for a point moving with velocity $\partial q_x/\partial k$, the concentration increases if $\partial q_x/\partial x$, is negative and diminishes if $\partial q_x/\partial x$ is positive. Now

$\partial q_x/\partial x$ negative means that the wave is travelling into a part of the road in which for a given concentration the flow is decreasing, i.e. flow is becoming more difficult. In such a road the concentration increases as the traffic proceeds, as might be expected.

It is a well known feature of most waves of finite amplitude that they change their shapes as they proceed since the different parts move at different speeds. In the case of traffic waves the relationship (3) has a form something like that shown in Fig. 5.1. We assume that the flow does not depend on x so that instead of $\partial q_x/\partial k$ we may now write dq/dk.

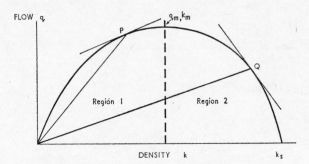

Fig. 5.1. Relation between flow and concentration

There is a maximum flow q_m at some concentration k_m. For concentrations less than k_m the wave velocity dq/dk is positive, for concentrations greater than k_m it is negative and for the maximum flow q_m it is zero.

Consider the propagation of a wave of flow as illustrated in Fig. 5.2 along a uniform road. Let it be assumed that the values of k correspond to values less than k_m in Fig. 5.1. As the wave progresses the low values of q travel

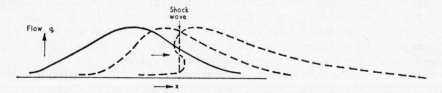

Fig. 5.2. Successive stages of wave moving to the right and developing a shock

with higher velocities than the larger values. The curve tends to become flatter in its forward slope and steeper in its rear slope. There will come a time when the slope behind becomes vertical and further deformation of the curve would lead to an S-shaped section of curve giving three values of the flow at each point. This is impossible and before this happens the smooth wave is replaced by a shock wave. i.e. a sudden discontinuity, as in Fig. 5.3 where the flow changes discontinuously from q_1 to q_2. By considering the continuity of vehicles during the passage of the shock wave one finds that it has a velocity U given by

$$U = (q_2-q_1)/(k_2-k_1) \qquad . \qquad . \qquad . \qquad . \qquad . \qquad . \qquad (12)$$

where k_2 and k_1 are the concentrations corresponding to q_2 and q_1. This is the slope of the chord joining the points k_1, q_1 and k_2 and q_2 in the q, k diagram. Shock waves can have positive or negative velocities. A shock wave in a rising part of a traffic wave, i.e. one in which $q_2 < q_1$, would immediately begin to flatten out. It was also shown by Lighthill and Witham that the position of the shock in Fig. 5.2 is such that it cuts off equal areas of the S-shaped part on the right and left of it.

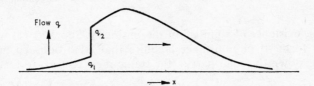

Fig. 5.3. Form of the wave after the shock has developed

We have seen that waves can be of two kinds: those having normal propagation $v = dq/dk$ and shock waves. There is a particular type of shock wave which is caused by a change from conditions represented by $k < k_m$ and $k > k_m$ in Fig. 5.1. In traffic represented by points on the left, where $k < k_m$, waves are propagated forward; in the other kind they are propagated backwards. Consider traffic approaching traffic signals or some other obstruction which brings the vehicles successively to a halt. In the region of halted vehicles the flow is zero and the concentration is the greatest possible, k_s in Fig. 5.1. The region of k_s will be propagated backwards down the road by means of a shock transition as illustrated in Fig. 5.4. In the case

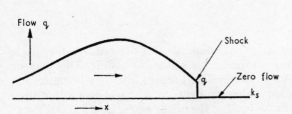

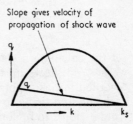

Slope gives velocity of propagation of shock wave

Fig. 5.4. Shock moving left in traffic moving right and halted by fixed obstacle

Velocity of shock derived from flow-concentration diagram

of vehicles piling up behind a slow moving lorry the flow immediately behind the lorry would not be zero, it might in fact equal the flow of vehicles before they were held up. In that case we should not have a discontinuity of flow but one of concentration and a transition from $k < k_m$ to $k > k_m$ as illustrated in Fig. 5.5. The velocity of the discontinuity is zero. A transition from region 1 to region 2 may occur if the flow rises to q_m, the maximum of which the road is capable, as for example when flow enters a bottleneck not large enough to take it. In such a case the transition from region 1 to region 2 may begin without any discontinuity in flow and

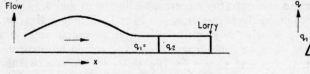
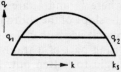

Fig. 5.5. Sudden change of concentration without change of flow in traffic accumulating behind slow-moving vehicles

Line joining points q_1 and q_2 is horizontal so velocity of discontinuity is zero

without the existence of a finite flow discontinuity. Shock waves will almost inevitably form. If circumstances require that conditions be propagated backwards down the road part of the traffic must convert to region 2.

RELEASE OF A QUEUE AT A TRAFFIC SIGNAL

The flow representing a queue of vehicles waiting to move when the signals go green may be shown as in Fig. 5.6. There is no flow anywhere, but to

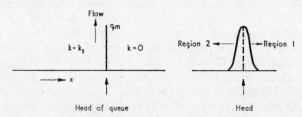

Fig. 5.6. Idealized wave for queue at instant of release. All possible flows at head of queue

Wave soon after instant of release. Idealized form is limit of this at instant of release

get the calculation started we may assume that at the head of the queue we have all flows up to the maximum q_m which is possible. This may be regarded not as a point but as a very small region, the flow being zero at each end and rising to q_m somewhere in between. There is also a transition from region 2 to region 1 at the head of the queue where flow is q_m. We may follow the flow as it proceeds further. The front portion of the wave under the conditions of region 1 flattens out, the low flows being in the lead. The rear portion is propagated backwards also flattening out. Since the flow at the point of the original head of the queue is q_m its speed of propagation is zero and the flow there remains at the maximum value q_m. It also remains a point of transition from region 1 to region 2. It is interesting to note that this result shows that the rate of flow past the original head of the queue should be the maximum of which the road is capable. The complete process of the passage of a finite queue after a hold up can be examined in this way. The flow through a bottleneck has also been considered in detail. Shock waves and transitions from region 1 to region 2 are formed.

The Lighthill-Whitham wave theory has been applied to see whether the formation of a shock wave could occur as predicted at the rear of a group of vehicles. For one such group the observed results seemed to fit the Lighthill calculation better than the statistical one already described. For another road the shock wave was not observed to form and the results seemed in better agreement with the statistical calculation (see Smeed[28]).

Some comments may be made on the description of the Lighthill–Whitham theory given here. It is recognized by the authors that the wave equation (9) is only the simplest form that the system can take. More elaborate equations containing terms of higher derivatives would be arrived at if certain additional aspects of flow were taken into account, for instance that drivers drive not merely in relation to the vehicle ahead but to traffic conditions further along the road and that their reactions are gradual and not instantaneous. These features introduce something analogous to diffusion into the wave process. Again a driver cannot instantaneously change his speed; this introduces an inertia effect.

It may be pointed out that the Lighthill–Whitham theory as defined is able to deal with traffic in which overtaking is occurring. The speed of traffic which appears in the formulae is the space mean speed, and the q, k curve adopted is that found from the average of a number of observations of flows for each concentration. In these flows overtaking of vehicles will generally be occurring. Some of the diffusion and inertia effects have also been brought into the equations via these averagings. It is possible however to regard the theory as applying to individual vehicles which follow one another without overtaking. The discrete nature of the actual traffic is converted into a continuous nature by regarding each vehicle as occupying the space between it and the one ahead. If the velocity of a vehicle is completely determined by the distance from the one ahead and perhaps by the position along the road we shall then arrive at the wave equation once again. This type of flow in which overtaking does not take place may occur by regulation, as in most tunnels or on bridges, or may be forced by concentration of traffic. The initial stage of the flow when vehicles start from a queue at rest also has rather few overtakings. It seems probable that the q, k curve that applies to these non-overtaking states of flow may not apply to more confused traffic. One would expect that the flow for a given concentration would be higher if for whatever reason overtaking were not occurring. If this is so it would be important to use the curve appropriate to the circumstances. Finally it may be pointed out that the Lighthill–Whitham theory applies to the flow of traffic in one direction without interference from traffic in the opposite direction. If it could be shown that the flow in one direction was a function not only of the concentration of that flow but also of the opposing flow we should have the situation in which q would have to be regarded as a function of k, x and t, the variation with x and t deriving partly from permanent or time dependent features of the road and also from the nature of the opposing traffic flow. Such a situation would lead to the propagation of waves of varying amplitude which would not have the simplicity of the waves already discussed but which it should certainly be possible to treat by step by step methods.

The use of computers in traffic flow studies

If the laws which govern the behaviour of a car in traffic are known or assumed, the behaviour of a large group of vehicles can be evaluated by step by step calculations. These are done most appropriately on a large computer. Some work of this kind has already been carried out, mainly for traffic flow through intersections, rather than for the propagation of traffic along lengths or systems of roads. A sufficiently large and fast computer, if supplied with the rates at which vehicles were entering and leaving a road system and their probable routes within it, could simulate the movements of the traffic and evaluate the probabilities of jams, hold-ups and delays within the system. Such a simulation for a network of any size would however tax the largest computers now available.

Capacity of a road: a simple model

The distance at which one vehicle follows behind another as a function of speed determines an upper limit to the number of vehicles which a road can carry. Many formulae for this distance have been derived from assumptions regarding the behaviour of the driver and his natural desire to drive so that at all times he will be able to avoid a collision with the vehicle ahead. Most of the proposed formulae would be derivable from the following assumptions by taking various special cases.

(1) The vehicle ahead can be stopped in an emergency with average deceleration a_1 ft/sec.^{2}
(2) The following driver will not wish to stop or cannot stop with a deceleration greater than a_2, where a_2 is less than a_1.
(3) There will be a delay of T sec (reaction time) before the following driver can respond to the slowing down of the vehicle ahead.
(4) The following driver will desire a separation of s_0 ft between his vehicle and the one ahead when they come to rest.

To fulfil these conditions the following driver must allow a separation s between the two vehicles given by

$$s = vT + \frac{v^2}{2}\left(\frac{1}{a_2} - \frac{1}{a_1}\right) + s_0 \text{ ft} \quad . \quad . \quad . \quad . \quad . \quad (13)$$

where v is the velocity in ft per sec. If l is the length of the vehicle ahead in test the headway between the vehicles is $s+l$, and the rate of flow is one vehicle in $(s+l)/v$ sec or $v/(s+l)$ per sec. This then gives the maximum flow of which traffic would be capable at the given speed. The maximum flow of all speeds is given by

$$q_m = \frac{1}{T + \sqrt{2}\sqrt{(l+s_0)(1/a_2 - 1/a_1)}} \text{ veh/sec} \quad . \quad . \quad . \quad (14)$$

The density at which this maximum flow occurs is

$$k_m = \frac{1}{2(l+s_0) + T\sqrt{\dfrac{2(l+s_0)}{(1/a_2 - 1/a_1)}}} \text{ veh/mile} \quad . \quad . \quad . \quad (15)$$

By choosing suitable values for the constants in these formulae a large range of observed values can be matched. If we assume that the following distance s is given by (13) even when the vehicle ahead is not moving at a uniform speed we get a relationship between q and k which may be used in the Lighthill–Witham theory when overtaking is not allowed or does not take place. Such formulae have been used in discussing the problem of vehicles starting up from stationary queues at traffic signals.

Chandler, Herman and Montroll[29] have considered how a disturbance is transmitted backwards along a line of vehicles, by assuming a wider form of relationship than that given by (14) for one vehicle following another at variable speed. The main object of the investigation was to see whether, as the disturbance was propagated it increased or died away; in more succinct terms, whether the motion was stable or unstable. It may be noted here that the fact that the disturbance is propagated backwards among the vehicles does not contradict the Lighthill–Whitham result that waves are normally propagated forward along the road. Relative to the vehicles even the forward waves are moving backwards. According to observations carried out by Chandler, Herman and Montroll the acceleration of a vehicle attempting to follow another is on average proportional to the difference of velocity of the two vehicles at about 1·5 sec earlier. Motion becomes unstable when the product of this time lag and the proportionality constant exceed one-half.

SINGLE-LANE EXPERIMENTS

Much of the theoretical work on "car following" needs to be tested under traffic conditions before it can be applied. It is difficult to make these tests, because of the variability of traffic and of layout, visibility etc., on the road itself. In an attempt to provide observational data the Laboratory conducted some experiments in 1962–3 in which a fixed number of vehicles travelled on a circular track one lane wide[30] (see Plate 5.1). The drivers were instructed to drive as fast as was comfortable and the average speed was measured with different numbers of vehicles present. Four circles were used, of inner kerb radii 50, 100, 200 and 415 ft. The radius of the average paths of the vehicles was about 6 ft greater than this in each case. Further tests were made on a straight track at a number of fixed speeds and also on some of the circles at fixed speeds.

By this means the relation between the speed and the average concentration (vehicles per mile) of the traffic could be found (see Figs. 5.7, 5.8, 5.9, 5.10 and 5.11).

Figure 5.7 shows that on a curve of radius 56 ft the average speed was fairly constant at about 17 mile/h over a range of concentration of 0 to 130 veh/mile. As the concentration increased above this level the speed fell, reaching 10 mile/h at 170 veh/mile, 5 mile/h at 200 veh/mile and about 1 mile/h at 250 veh/mile. Even at 300 veh/mile, i.e. with one vehicle every $17\frac{1}{2}$ ft, it was still possible for the vehicles to move, although the movements were very spasmodic and the average speed extremely low.

As Fig. 5.7 shows, in one test the traffic was "speeded up" to almost double its former speed, from $5\frac{1}{2}$ to $10\frac{1}{2}$ mile/h; this was done by waving the drivers on.

Fig. 5.8 shows that on a radius of 106 ft the appearance of the curve is similar, average speeds being about 21 mile/h up to a concentration of 100 veh/mile but falling thereafter as on the smaller radius. The diagram also shows the results of the tests made at a fixed speed. These did not agree

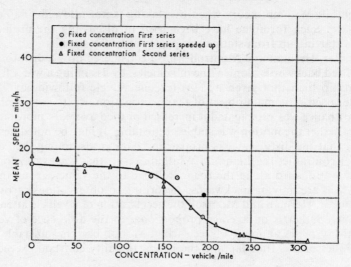

Fig. 5.7. Speed and concentration. Radius 56 ft

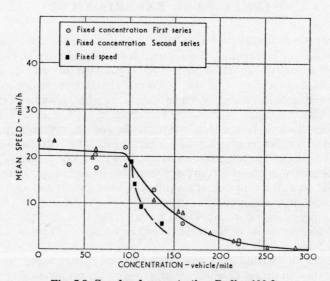

Fig. 5.8. Speed and concentration. Radius 100 ft

with those made at fixed concentration but the shape of the curve is similar.

Figs. 5.9 and 5.10 are also somewhat similar although there is a great deal of variation in the results on the radius of 206 ft. Results for fixed speeds in Fig. 5.10 seem to agree reasonably well with those for fixed concentration. Taking all the results on curved paths, the average speed remained at about the value giving a sideways acceleration of ½ g up to the critical level of concentration.

Fig. 5.11 shows the results obtained in straight runs and compares them with some observations made on a motorway when the traffic in one direction was restricted to a single lane. It will be seen that over the range

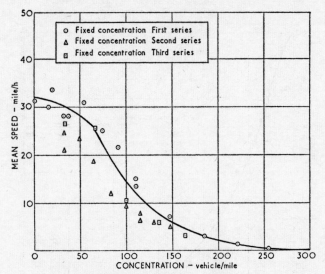

Fig. 5.9. Speed and concentration. Radius 206 ft

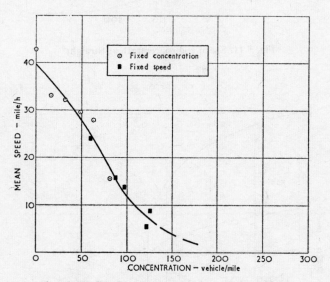

Fig. 5.10. Speed and concentration. Radius 421 ft

of concentrations observed, from about 40 to 160 veh/mile, the speed fell continuously and at a high rate as the concentration increased. The results obtained on the motorway agree very well with those obtained on the research track.

The curves in Figs. 5.7 to 5.11 can be put in a different form by plotting speed against flow, the flow being obtained simply by multiplying the concentration by the speed. Fig. 5.12 shows the results of doing this. The curves have been somewhat idealized and should not be assumed to be precise. The figure also shows a "headway" curve based on results given by

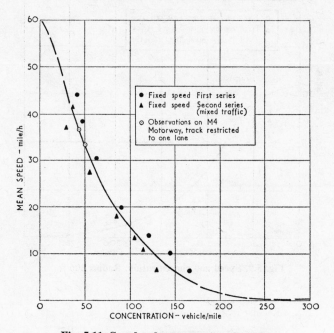

Fig. 5.11. Speed and concentration: Straight

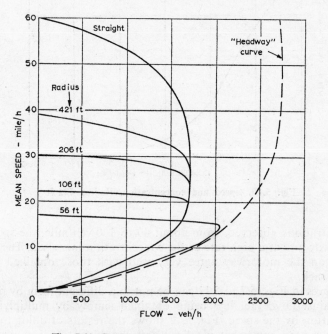

**Fig. 5.12. Speed and flow: Idealized curves based on
Figs. 5.7–5.11**

London–Birmingham motorway origin-and-destination survey. Roadside interview station by day

PLATE 4.1

London–Birmingham motorway origin-and-destination survey. Roadside interview by night

PLATE 4.2

Experiment on the capacity of a single lane using a circular track of 200-ft radius, on central area of Research Track, Crowthorne

PLATE 5.1

Reduction in capacity produced by a bottleneck,
Central London

PLATE 6.1

(a)
Controlled experiment on saturation flows at traffic signals: (a) light vehicles
only

PLATE 6.2

(b)

(c)

Controlled experiment on saturation flows at traffic signals: (b) heavy vehicles
only, (c) 60-ft wide approach

PLATE 6.2

(a)

(b)

Classification of traffic sites: (a) a typical "good" site, (b) a typical "average" site

PLATE 6.3

(c)

Classification of traffic sites: (c) a typical "poor" site

PLATE 6.3

Experiment to determine the capacity of a weaving section of a large roundabout

PLATE 6.4

(a)

(b)
Traffic and pedestrians: (a) London, (b) Glasgow
PLATE 7.1

(c)

Traffic and pedestrians: (c) Edinburgh

PLATE 7.1

Smeed and Bennett[31] in 1949, based on observations of pairs of following vehicles on the road and on some measurements of headways on an airfield. It will be seen that the maximum flow on the curves of radius greater than 100 ft was about 1700 veh/h but in the case of the 50 ft radius the maximum flow was about 2000 veh/h at a speed of 13 mile/h. The 'headway' curve agrees with the lower part of the 50 ft radius curve but shows higher flows at a given speed than was found in all the other cases.

The results of the straight tests are summarized in Table 5.1.

TABLE 5.1

Concentration, speed and flow on straight runs

Concentration (veh/mile)	Speed (mile/h)	Flow (veh/h)
25	50	1250
50	34	1700
75	23	1725
100	17	1700
125	11	1375
150	6·5	975
175	4	700
200	2	400

The effect of radius on the capacity of a lane is shown in Table 5.2.

TABLE 5.2

Curvature and lane capacity

Radius of inner kerb (ft)	Maximum flow (veh/h)	Corresponding speed (mile/h)
50	2000	13
100	1700	19
200	1700	25
400	1700	30
Straight	1700	17–35

These results show that

 (i) the capacities of curved lanes of 100 ft radius and upwards are virtually the same as those of a straight lane, and

 (ii) the capacity of the 50 ft radius curved lane used was apparently about 15 per cent greater than that of lanes of 100 ft radius or more, probably because drivers could see further ahead in the stream than on the curves of greater radius.

Some observations[32] on car following with visual cues have confirmed that better information about the behaviour of vehicles ahead in the stream reduces headways.

REFERENCES TO CHAPTER 5

1. HIGHWAY RESEARCH BOARD. *Highway Capacity Manual.* Washington, D.C., 1950 (U.S. Department of Commerce, Bureau of Public Roads).

2. KINZER, J.P. Applications of the theory of probability to problems of highway traffic. (Abstract.) *Proc. Inst. Traff. Engrs. 5th Annual Meeting,* 1934 (Institute of Traffic Engineers), p. 118.

3. ADAMS, W. F. Road traffic considered as a random series. *J. Instn civ. Engrs,* 1936, **4,** 121.

4. CLAYTON, A. J. H. Road traffic calculations. *J. Instn civ. Engrs,* 1941, **16,** 247.

5. GARWOOD F. An application of the theory of probability to the operation of vehicular-controlled traffic signals. *Suppl. J. Roy. Statist. Soc.,* 1940, **7,** 65.

6. GREENSHIELDS, B. D., D. SHAPIRO, and E. L. ERICKSEN. Traffic performance at urban street intersections. *Yale Bureau of Highway Traffic Technical Report No. 1.* New Haven, Conn. 1947 (Yale Bureau of Highway Traffic).

7. RAFF, M. S. The distribution of blocks in an uncongested stream of traffic. *J. Amer. Statist. Ass.,* 1951, **46,** 114–23.

8. WARDROP, J. G. Some theoretical aspects of road traffic research. *Proc. Instn civ. Engrs, Part II,* 1952, **1,** 325–78.

9. TANNER J. C. The delay to pedestrians crossing a road. *Biometrika,* 1951, **38,** 383.

10. MAYNE A. J. Some further results in the theory of pedestrians and road traffic. *Biometrika,* 1954, **41,** 375.

11. TANNER, J. C. A problem of interference between two queues. *Biometrika,* 1953, **40,** 58.

12. HILLIER, J. A., P. D. WHITING and J. G. WARDROP. The automatic delay computer. *Department of Scientific and Industrial Research, Road Research Laboratory Research Note No.* RN/2291/JAH.PDW.JGW. Harmondsworth, 1954 (Unpublished).

13. WEBSTER, F. V. Traffic signal settings. *Department of Scientific and Industrial Research, Road Research Technical Paper* No. 39. London, 1958 (H.M. Stationery Office). (Reprinted with minor amendments 1961.)

14. NEWELL, G. F. Mathematical models for freely-flowing highway traffic. *J. Operat. Res. Soc. Amer.,* 1955, **3,** 176–86.

15. KOMETANI, E. On the theoretical solution of highway traffic capacity under mixed traffic. *Mem. Fac. Engrs, Kyoto Univ.,* 1955, **17** (2), 79–98.

16. TANNER, J. C. A simplified model for delays in overtaking on a two-lane road. *J. roy. Statist. Soc. Series B,* 1958, **20** (2), 408–14.

17. BECKMANN, M., C. B. MCGUIRE and C. B. WINSTEN. Studies in the economics of transportation. New Haven, Conn., 1956 (Yale University Press).

18. MILLER, A. J. A mathematical model for the study of road traffic. *M.Sc. Thesis, Manchester University.* Manchester, 1958 (Unpublished).

19. PIPES, L. A. An operational analysis of traffic dynamics. *J. appl. Phys.,* 1953, **24,** 274–81.

20. LIGHTHILL M. J., and F. B. WHITHAM. On kinematic waves, II. A theory of traffic flow on long crowded roads. *Proc. roy. Soc. (Series A),* 1955, **229,** 317–45.

21. GERLOUGH, D. Simulation of freeway traffic on a general-purpose discrete-variable computer. *Ph.D. Dissertation, University of California,* 1955 (Unpublished).

22. PRAGER, W. Problems of traffic and transportation. *Symposium on Operating Research in Business and Industry. Midwest Research Institute.* Kansas City, Missouri, 1954 (Midwest Research Institute).

23. WHITING, P. D., and J. A. HILLIER. A method for finding the shortest route through a road network. *Department of Scientific and Industrial Research, Road Research Laboratory Research Note* No. RN/3337/PDW.JAH. Harmondsworth, 1958 (Unpublished).

24. HIGHWAY RESEARCH BOARD. References on theory of traffic flow and related subjects. *Circular* 438. Washington, D.C., 1961 (National Research Council, Division of Engineering and Industrial Research).

25. HAIGHT, F. A. Mathematical theories of traffic flow. New York and London, 1963 (Academic Press).

26. HERMAN R. (Editor.) *Theory of traffic flow.* Amsterdam, 1961 (Elsevier Publishing Co.).

27. BUCKLEY, D. J., Second international symposium on theory of traffic flow. *Traff. Engng & Control*, 1963, **5** (7), 425–7.

28. SMEED, R. J. Theoretical studies and operational research on traffic and traffic congestion. *Bull. Inst. int. statist.*, 1958, **36** (4), 347–75.

29. CHANDLER, R. E., R. HERMAN and E. W. MONTROLL. Traffic dynamics: studies in car following. *Operations Res.*, 1958, **6** (2), 165–84.

30. WARDROP, J. G. Experimental speed/flow relations in a single lane. *Second International Symposium on the Theory of Road Traffic Flow*, 1963. (To be published).

31. SMEED, R. J. and G. T. BENNETT. Research on road safety and traffic flow. *Institution of Civil Engineers Road Paper* No. 29. London, 1949 (Institution of Civil Engineers).

32. HERMAN, R. and R. ROTHERY. Car following and steady state flow. *Second International Symposium on the Theory of Road Traffic Flow*, 1963 (To be published).

Chapter 6

Traffic Capacity

SYNOPSIS

Methods of assessing the capacity of roads. Capacity of rural roads. Practical capacity of urban roads. Capacity of signal-controlled intersections. Capacity of roundabouts. Capacity of priority intersections. Comparison of different types of intersection.

INTRODUCTION

A knowledge of the traffic capacity of roads and streets is required by engineers and town planners who are concerned with making the best use of existing roads, planning new roads or the improvement of traffic routes.

Although the capacity of roads for traffic and the factors which affect it have been widely discussed for many years, there is still some confusion about the meaning of traffic capacity. Definitions, methods of assessment and values of capacity quoted for given conditions vary considerably, and the reasons are not always clear.

This chapter considers a number of alternative methods of assessing road capacity and discusses their advantages and disadvantages. In particular it considers "practical" measures of capacity, emphasizes the importance of the relation between traffic speed and flow in arriving at practical values and considers the important role which economics has to play. The method of dealing with variations in the types of vehicle composing the traffic stream and of using "passenger car units" is described. Standards of capacity which have been adopted by the Ministry of Transport for rural roads are given. Practical capacities based on observations are given for rural roads and for urban roads and also for intersections controlled by traffic signals, by roundabouts, and by "priority" signs.

METHODS OF ASSESSING THE CAPACITY OF ROADS

"Theoretical" capacity

Early attempts to estimate the capacity of a section of road free from intersections were based on headway, i.e. the distance between the fronts of two successive vehicles. For instance, the Laboratory measured headway between following vehicles at different speeds and found the following relation to hold in practice:

$$h = 17 \cdot 5 + 0 \cdot 8v + 0 \cdot 004v^2,$$

where h = average headway between following vehicles in feet,
v = speed in ft/s.

The relation between speed and minimum safe headway can be deduced theoretically as:

$$h = a + bv + \left(\frac{d' - d}{1936}\right)v^2$$

where a = headway between stationary vehicles (ft),
  b = reaction time (seconds),
  d' = braking distance of following vehicle from 30 mile/h (ft),
  d = braking distance of leading vehicle from 30 mile/h (ft).

This relation is of the same form as that determined experimentally and quoted above. If we take a as 17·5 ft, b as 0·8 s and v as 44 ft/s (30 mile/h), for observed minimum headway we find that $(d' - d)$ is 8 ft; in view of the fact that the braking distances of most cars range between 50 and 110 ft, it may be concluded that cars frequently travel too close together for safety.

If the headways between all vehicles are given by the above formula for h, then clearly the time interval between the passage of successive vehicles past a point on the road is h/v. That is to say, one vehicle passes in each period of h/v seconds. This is equivalent to a flow (or volume) of traffic of v/h vehicles per second or 3600 v/h vehicles per hour.

A number of calculations of maximum flow at a given speed, based on actual headways or calculated safe minimum headways, have been made, and the results show very large variations. The values are usually over 2000 vehicle/h/lane and sometimes as much as 3000 vehicle/h/lane (at the speed which corresponds to the maximum flow). In any case they are based on the assumption that vehicles follow one another at equal intervals and at the same speed. These conditions are very unrealistic and are seldom observed on the road. Under actual driving conditions, particularly with mixed traffic, severe congestion occurs at flows much lower than these. The problem has since been approached from the practical rather than the theoretical point of view.

Practical capacity

The term "practical capacity" was introduced in the U.S.A. in the Highway Capacity Manual,[1] where it is defined as "the maximum number of vehicles that can pass a given point on a roadway or in a designated lane during one hour without the traffic density being so great as to cause unreasonable delay, hazard, or restriction to the drivers' freedom to manoeuvre under the prevailing roadway and traffic conditions". This definition gives a reasonable method of approach, but in practice it is necessary to choose one or more arbitrary criteria of what constitutes restriction of traffic movement, or "congestion". Measures of congestion which have been studied are:

  (i) Mean speed of traffic.
 (ii) Mean difference in speed between successive vehicles.
(iii) Standard deviation of speeds.
 (iv) Actual speeds in relation to desired speeds.
  (v) Actual numbers of overtakings in relation to desired numbers.
 (vi) Estimates of the proportion of vehicles impeded, based on the distribution of time-intervals between successive vehicles.

Method (vi) depends on the distinction between "random" intervals between vehicles which do not influence one another, and intervals between vehicles where the first is impeding the second.

In the American studies all these measures were considered and emphasis was given to those concerned with speed. In their report on the capacity of straight level two-lane rural roads in various European contries, Hondermarcq, Elkouby and Lefevre[2] concluded that the proportion of impeded vehicles is the most useful measure of congestion and dismiss mean speeds as being too variable to be reliable.

At first sight the proportion of impeded vehicles is an excellent index of congestion, which has the advantage over all the others that it does not require speed measurements to be made. It is, of course, open to the objection that it is not obvious what is the maximum degree of congestion which can be tolerated, but a similar difficulty occurs with all the measures which have been mentioned. A more serious objection is that no account is taken of the amount by which the vehicles are impeded; and it is very desirable that this should be included.

Speed/flow relations

The Road Research Laboratory has concentrated almost exclusively on the relation between the average speed of vehicles and the flow as a guide to road capacity, particularly in towns. The chief reason for this preference is that loss of time is of direct concern to drivers and vehicle operators, and this can be calculated from the average speed. Also the average speed can be found without the need for very precise measurements, and the effects of delays at intersections or bottlenecks can be included without difficulty.

It has been argued that average speeds tend to vary in an inexplicable way, and therefore they do not provide a firm basis for capacity calculations. It is shown (see Chapter 3) that a large part of the variation in average speeds (particularly in towns) can be explained as the effect of a number of factors, and the relations found between speed and these factors can be interpreted in terms of capacity.

Economic capacity

Much of the arbitrariness involved in choosing the minimum acceptable speed can in principle be removed by relating the savings in time which could be achieved by improving the road in the most economical way to the cost of such an improvement. If the rate of return expressed in monetary terms compares favourably with that available for capital investments in general, widening is economically justified, and the road may be considered to be carrying a volume in excess of its "economic capacity". This concept of economic capacity, in which the traffic capacity of a road is related to the economics of transport and road improvement was introduced by Schuhl[3] and independently by Charlesworth[4] but was not defined precisely. The following definition is suggested:

The *Economic capacity* of a road is the total traffic passing along it in a year which, with the hourly distribution and composition by vehicle type throughout the year peculiar to that road, is just not sufficient to make the most economical improvement economically justifiable when the monetary benefits to road users are compared with the overall cost of the improvement, taking the normal return on capital investment as standard.

There are points in this definition that need amplifying. The problem of evaluating economic benefits from road improvements is discussed in Chapter 15, where it is shown that savings in working time and reductions in material losses due to accidents can be put in monetary terms, but that it is more difficult to treat non-working time and suffering caused by accidents in this way. This means that there are additional benefits from road improvements which may have to be left out of the economic account, and this must be remembered when such calculations are being considered.

The type of improvement considered is not specified. In the case of a reasonably straight and level rural road the only practicable improvement is by widening. Considerations of safety dictate that roads shall be either two-lane, three-lane, dual-carriageway two-lane, or dual-carriageway three-lane (unless more than six lanes are required). It would be expected that a road which just needs widening would need to move up one step in this progression, although strictly the widening should be that which gives the greatest rate of return on expenditure; in practice this is usually the same thing.

The method discussed above has one apparent disadvantage because the economic capacity of a road varies with the cost of the land through which it passes. This means, for example, that much more congestion will be accepted in cities where land is expensive than in rural areas where it is relatively cheap; but this is normal policy and the economic approach merely underlines the reasons for it.

Thirtieth highest hourly volume

In practice, traffic volume varies from hour to hour, and in discussing capacity it is useful to define a particular volume which is to be used for planning purposes. The concept of the "thirtieth highest hourly volume", or the volume which is equalled or exceeded in only 30 hours throughout the year, was given prominence in the American Highway Capacity Manual.[1] There has since been a fairly wide acceptance of this idea, both in the United States of America and in Europe. It is stated in the Manual that this volume tends to be very stable for a given road, and that it is the volume for which the ratio of benefit to expenditure is near the maximum. It is clearly uneconomic to attach too much importance to the exceptionally high peaks which occur on only a few occasions throughout the year. On the other hand, much of the benefit to a driver would be lost if reasonable provision were not made for normal peak traffic.

To obtain the thirtieth highest hourly volume for a given road requires a continuous count of traffic throughout each of the 8760 hours of the year. This can be done as regards the total number of vehicles of all kinds by means of automatic traffic counters, but it is quite impracticable to obtain this information in respect of the various classes of vehicles.

The "Busy Week"

An alternative approach which has been adopted by the Ministry of Transport in Great Britain is to base capacities on the conception of a "busy week". Carriageway capacities are expressed in terms of the volume which can be passed safely and without too great a reduction in speed during a 16-hour day (6 a.m. to 10 p.m.). By averaging the traffic over seven consecutive days during the summer (a busy week) a 16-hour volume is obtained which will only be exceeded on exceptional occasions. In determining the capacity, allowance must be made for the hourly variations which occur during the busy week. Generally, the traffic flow during the peak hour in the same week is about 10 per cent of the 16-hour daily average but, as will be seen later, there is a fairly big variation on individual roads.

Passenger car units

The capacity of a road or intersection is frequently specified in terms of "passenger car units". These are introduced to make an allowance for differences in the amount of interference to other traffic by the addition of one extra vehicle to the traffic, according to the type of vehicle. For example, a large lorry is longer, wider and slower than the average car, and therefore has a considerably greater effect on other vehicles by making it more difficult for them to overtake and by slowing down those which are forced to follow it.

On any particular section of road under particular traffic conditions the addition of one vehicle of a particular type per hour will reduce the average speed of the remaining vehicles by the same amount as the addition of, say, x cars of average size per hour. Under these conditions we say that one vehicle of this type is equivalent to x *passenger car units*.

In the case of a bottleneck, and in particular an intersection, one can arrive at a slightly different definition, which is, however, equivalent to applying the one given above to maximum flow conditions. This definition is that if a particular type of vehicle under saturated conditions requires x times as much time at the intersection as is required by an average car then that type is equivalent to x passenger car units.

One might expect this quantity x, the passenger unit equivalent of the type of vehicle in question, to vary with the flow of traffic as well as other factors such as the width of road and the kind of environment. Fortunately, however, observations have shown that passenger car unit equivalents are approximately the same for all flows and road widths, although they vary appreciably according to the kind of environment (e.g. rural road, urban street, roundabout, traffic signals).

Passenger car unit equivalents have in general been derived from observations. In the case of rural and urban roads the results of these observations are given on page 202. In the case of traffic signals and roundabouts the second method mentioned above was used, relations being found between the maximum flow through an intersection and the proportions of vehicles of different classes, under experimental conditions and (in the case of signals) under road conditions. Table 6.1 summarizes passenger car unit equivalents for various conditions. These will be given again under the appropriate headings.

BUSES

It was found that the passenger car unit equivalent for buses varied with the flow of buses. The results are shown in Fig. 6.1. It will be seen that for

TABLE 6.1

Passenger car unit equivalents

	Passenger car units			
	Rural roads* (Ministry of Transport)	Urban Streets	Round-abouts	Traffic Signals
Cars and light vans . .	1·0	1·0	1·0	1·0
Commercial vehicles medium	}3·0	1·75	}2·8	}1·75
Commercial vehicles heavy .		2·5		
Buses and coaches . .	3·0	3.0	2·8	2·25
Motorcycles . . .	1·0	0·75	0·75	0·33
Pedal cycles . . .	0·5	0·33	0·5	0·2

*With moderate amounts of gradient and curvature.

streets with bus flows equal to the average in Central London one bus is equivalent to 2.75 p.c.u's.

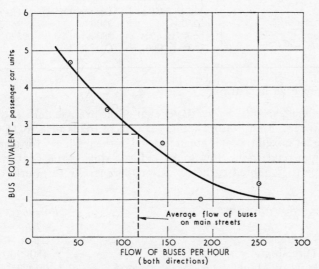

Fig. 6.1. Bus equivalents in terms of cars (Central London, 1956–58)

THE CAPACITY OF RURAL ROADS

Ministry of Transport standards

The standard carriageway capacities recommended by the Ministry of Transport[5] are expressed in passenger car units in a 16-hour day, for roads in which design features which affect capacity, such as lateral clearances, width of verges, curvature, sight distances and gradients, conform to certain minimum standards. The standard lane width now recommended is 12 ft on all important roads, except on three-lane roads where an overall carriage-way width of 33 ft is recommended.

The following figures have been recommended as the capacities of the various types of carriageway:

	Passenger car units per 16-hour day
Two-lane carriageways . . .	Up to 4500
Three-lane carriageways . . .	4500 to 9000
Dual two-lane carriageways . .	9000 to 25 000
Dual three-lane carriageways . .	Over 25 000

In terms of mixed traffic these capacities are equivalent to the following values:

	Capacity-vehicles per 16-hour day		
	Percentage of medium and heavy commercial vehicles, buses and coaches:		
	15%	22½%	30%
Two-lane	Up to 3250	Up to 2900	Up to 2600
Three-lane	3250–6500	2900–5800	2600–5200
Dual two-lane . . .	6500–19 000	5800–17 000	5200–15 000
Dual three-lane . . .	Over 19 000	Over 17 000	Over 15 000

Capacity for peak hour traffic

In passenger car units about 10 per cent of the average daily traffic passes during the peak hour, with a range for typical roads of 8 to 15 per cent. The range for mixed traffic is greater owing to the tendency for medium and heavy commercial traffic flow to be reduced during the peak hour. The design capacities quoted earlier correspond generally to hourly capacities as follows:

Carriageways	*Passenger cars per hour*
Two-lane	Up to 450
Three-lane	450–900
Dual two-lane	900–2500
Dual three-lane	Over 2500

The use of speed/flow relations

As already mentioned the Laboratory has up till now concentrated almost exclusively on the relation between the average speed of vehicles and the flow as a guide to road capacity. The results obtained for rural roads are summarized in Fig. 3.11 which shows the mean speed of traffic against the total flow on straight level roads of different widths. On the narrower roads the average speed falls linearly with increasing flow over the range studied. On the wider roads the average speed remains substanti-ally constant for moderate flows, but after a certain flow is reached the

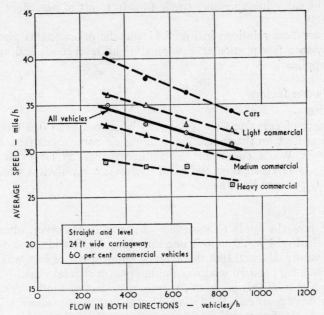

Fig. 6.2. Relation between average speeds of different classes of vehicle and traffic flow on a two-lane road

linear reduction of speed with increasing flow occurs. The slope of the line decreases as the carriageway width increases.

To arrive at a figure for "practical" capacity for rural roads it is necessary to decide what is the minimum acceptable average speed. If 35 mile/h is chosen then the maximum permissible flow on a 30-ft wide road is about 700 vehicle/h, on dual 25-ft wide carriageways 3000 vehicle/h, and so on.

Effect of commercial vehicles

It is shown (see Chapter 13) that the speeds of commercial vehicles are affected less than those of cars by changes in road layout (excluding gradients). The same holds for changes in traffic flow as illustrated in Fig. 6.2, which shows the mean speed of each of four classes of vehicle at different levels of total flow on the straight level 24-ft wide carriageway.

When considering commercial vehicles a further factor must be taken into account, namely, that the heavier and slower vehicles cause more interference to other vehicles than do the lighter and faster vehicles. This has been studied in the case of the 24-ft wide carriageway by using multiple regression analysis to relate the average speed of cars to the flows of vehicle subdivided according to both direction and type. It was found that the effect of medium commercial vehicles travelling in the same direction was about twice that of cars while the effect of heavy commercial vehicles was over three times that of cars. In terms of capacity, therefore, such a vehicles is equivalent to three cars. It was not possible to subdivide the effect of opposing traffic according to class of vehicle but the average effect was about equal to that of cars in the direction of travel. Results of this type are of value in expressing traffic flow in terms of passenger car units (see p. 200).

The speed/flow relations in Fig. 3.11 and the other results given above refer only to a few particular sites on straight, level roads and are not of general application.

Effect of other factors

CURVATURE

The effect of curvature on speeds has been measured (see Chapter 13) but not its effect on the speed/flow relation on rural roads (see, however, pp. 189–93). While curvature can reduce speeds by large amounts at relatively low levels of flow, the effect is almost certainly less when speeds are already reduced by congestion.

GRADIENT

Similar remarks apply to the effect of gradient. However, observations on a gradient of 1 in 20, about one mile long, 22 ft wide, and with only slight curvature, showed that the average uphill speed of cars was reduced by 1.1 mile/h for each 10 medium and heavy commercial vehicles per hour ascending the hill. This is about $5\frac{1}{2}$ times the effect of similar vehicles and 11 times that of a car on a level road. Thus the effect of commercial vehicles on the capacity of up-gradients is much greater than that on level roads.

Economic capacity of rural roads

The "economic capacity" of a road was defined on p. 198. Using this approach the economic capacities of some two- and three-lane rural roads have been calculated and the values obtained have been compared with the capacities recommended by the Ministry of Transport.[5]

In illustration of the method, the economic capacity of straight and level two- and three-lane roads in rural areas will now be considered. The relevant speed/flow relations are shown in Fig. 6.3. From these relations can be calculated the saving in vehicle-hours in any hour due to widening from two to three lanes, or three lanes to a two-lane dual carriageway. This has been done for each hour of the year to give the annual savings. A study of the variation in traffic flow throughout the year at two points has shown that an appropriate "typical" flow can be used for this purpose and, conveniently, this is approximately equal to the average hourly flow in a 16-hour day (6 a.m. to 10 p.m.) in August, which is the basis of the censuses carried out periodically by the Ministry of Transport at some 5000 points on main roads in Great Britain. The savings corresponding to this "average" flow have to be multiplied by a factor (about 6000) to convert them to annual savings, and costed in the way described in Chapter 15, excluding non-working time (e.g. leisure time, time spent travelling to and from work) in the first instance.

The total economic benefits from widening are affected by changes in accident rates, and an allowance has been made for this, based on accident rates on two-lane roads, three-lane roads and dual carriageways and on the estimated material costs of accidents (see Chapter 15). The total resulting benefits of widening from two to three lanes and from three lanes to dual carriageway are shown, in relation to flow, in Fig. 6.4. They are expressed as a capital sum per mile of road, assuming an interest rate of 5 per cent.

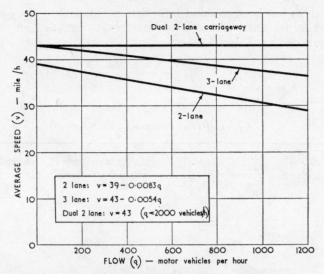

Fig. 6.3. Speed/flow relations on straight level roads with "normal" traffic composition (25 per cent medium/heavy vehicles)

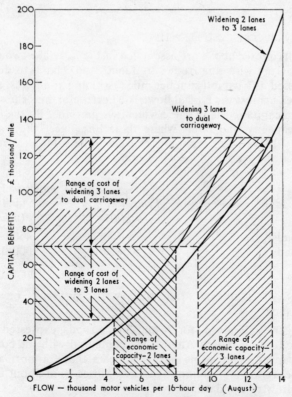

Fig. 6.4. Relation between capital benefits from widening and flow on straight level rural roads (including effect of estimated charges in accident rate but omitting non-working time)

An analysis has been made of information obtained by the Ministry of Transport on the costs of widening rural roads. Rounded off these costs are summarized in Table 6.2.

TABLE 6.2

Costs of road widening (1958 *values*)

	Cost per mile (£ thousand)	
	Normal range	Average
2 to 3 lanes	30–70	50
2 lanes to dual carriageway (2 × 2 lanes)	60–130	90
3 lanes to dual carriageway (2 × 2 lanes)	70–130	100

COMPARISON OF COSTS AND BENEFITS

The results quoted above are assembled in Fig. 6.4. The two curves show the benefits from widening from 2 to 3 lanes and 3 lanes to dual carriageway, expressed as a capital sum per mile (assuming an interest rate of 5 per cent), plotted against the typical flow. The horizontal lines show the normal limits of the capital costs of these widenings per mile. By the definition of economic capacity, the point where these lines meet the corresponding curves gives the value of economic capacity. The values are as follows:

	Typical flow *(veh/h)*	*Economic capacity Flows in* 16-*hour day in August (vehicles)*
2-lane roads . .	275–500	4500– 8000
3-lane roads . .	550–850	9000–13 500

COMPARISON OF ECONOMIC CAPACITY WITH MINISTRY OF TRANSPORT STANDARDS

The Ministry's standards for 2- and 3-lane roads, expressed in terms of vehicles per 16-hour day in August, are compared with the corresponding economic capacities in Table 6.3. It appears that for normal traffic on straight level roads the economic capacity varies from about two to three times the Ministry standard.

Comparison between the two values is complicated by the use for which the Ministry figures are intended. The procedure in Memorandum 780[5] is to add 150 per cent to the 1959 census flow to allow for future traffic. If

TABLE 6.3

| | Traffic per 16-hour day (7-day week in August) | | |
| | Economic capacity (vehicles) | Ministry standards | |
		Basic (p.c.u's)*	"Normal" traffic† (vehicles)
2-lane roads . .	4500–8000	4500	3000
3-lane road . .	9000–13 500	9000	6000

* Passenger car units.
† Assuming no pedal cycles.

this exceeds the standard value then widening of an existing road should be considered, although it may be desirable to postpone it for some years. In practice this will presumably mean that all existing roads should be widened well before they reach the standard flow, so that the difference in practice between the alternative standards is even greater than appears at first sight.

EFFECT OF INCLUDING NON-WORKING TIME

The economic capacities quoted above take no account of non-working time. It is shown in Chapter 15 that the average value of a vehicle-hour is substantially increased if non-working time is valued at the same rate as working time. Although there is considerable uncertainty on this point, it is perhaps useful to consider the effect on economic capacity. Using values appropriate to those used for the cost of widening, the values of economic capacity become:

2 lanes: 2250–4000 veh/16-hour day (M.O.T. Standard 3000 veh/16 hour day)

3 lanes: 5500–8500 veh/16-hour day (M.O.T. Standard 6000 veh/16 hour day).

EFFECT OF CHANGES IN TRAFFIC COMPOSITION

It is possible to calculate the effect of changes in traffic composition on the value of economic capacity using individual speed/flow relations and factors giving the relative effects of different classes of traffic on the average speed of a given class (see Appendix 1). The results are unexpected. If the proportion of medium and heavy vehicles (including buses and coaches) varies within the range 0 to 50 per cent, and the average value of a vehicle-hour is unchanged, the economic capacity expressed in vehicles per hour is virtually constant (within 6 per cent). If allowance is made for the increased value of the time of medium and heavy commercial traffic, the conclusion remains substantially the same. One would have expected that changes in composition would affect the economic capacity in vehicles per hour and that to adjust for this "economic passenger car units" would be needed; but this is apparently not the case.

This result suggests that, as far as the economic capacity of straight level roads is concerned, no weighting is required for "heavy" vehicles. On the other hand, it is known that the effects of these vehicles on gradients are much greater than those of "light" vehicles, and it is possible that even for a moderate gradient a detailed calculation of economic capacity would show that a substantially increased weighting for the heavier vehicle is justified. The Ministry standard gives these vehicles a weight three times that of light vehicles for normal roads (and it is understood that this refers to roads with gradients less than 1 in 25). This corresponds to a variation in capacity in vehicles of two to one in the range of composition of 0 to 50 per cent "heavy" vehicles. The weight of three seems rather high,[6] and it might be more reasonable to reduce this to a weight of two light vehicles (or passenger car units).

THE VALUE OF THE THREE-LANE ROAD

The results quoted above seem to show that there is a place for the three-lane road in the scheme of things, in conformity to the Ministry standards. They are based on the explicit assumption that the most economic widening at each stage is the next in the series: 2, 3, 2×2 lanes. This is true in terms of current returns only, and one marked advantage of the economic capacity concept is that the decision whether to widen a road depends only on the present traffic flow, not on future traffic, which is notoriously difficult to predict.

However, it is useful to consider the possibility that a two-lane road might be widened to a dual carriageway in a single step, omitting the stage of a three-lane road altogether. If this alternative is considered, the two programmes can be compared over the period which would be covered by the three-lane road, which would be about 12 years at the present rate of increase of traffic. It can be shown that in a typical case the benefits over this period are about 75 per cent greater in the single-stage case where the dual carriageway is introduced earlier.

The present cost of the two-stage process, on the other hand, would be about the same as that of a single-stage process. It follows that, at least in some instances, the omission of the three-lane road would appear to be justified. The result depends on the changes in accident rate which have been assumed and on the assumption that traffic will continue to increase (although not necessarily at the present rate) until widening from three lanes to dual carriageway would be justified. This means that the one-stage process is the more risky.

Discussion of results

These results appear to suggest that the capacity standards in Memorandum 780[5] are somewhat low. For instance, if, for the sake of simplicity, all the various values quoted for economic capacity are averaged (roughly equivalent to taking average costs of road widening and assuming that the value of non-working time is half that of working time), the economic capacities of two- and three-lane roads become 5000 and 13 000 vehicles per 16-hour day. However, there is some evidence[7] to show that accident rates per vehicle-mile on three-lane roads tend to increase when the flow is much above 9000 vehicles per day (see Chapter 13). For this reason it might be preferable to limit the capacity of a three-lane road to 10 000 vehicles per 16-hour day.

If these capacity figures are to be useful they need to be converted to passenger car units. If a revised equivalent of two passenger cars per medium or heavy commercial vehicle (or bus/coach) is accepted, the above capacities which refer essentially to traffic with about 25 per cent of medium and heavy vehicles can be converted to passenger car units. The results, rounded off, are as follows:

		Capacity in p.c.u.
		per 16-hour day (August)
2 lanes	. . . . .	6000
3 lanes	. . . . .	12 000

In applying these results to existing roads, it would be logical to allow them to reach this level of flow before widening the road. Since in practice a period of up to five years may elapse between the decision to widen a particular road and the completion of the work, the decision should be taken when present traffic plus 40 per cent equals the capacity. This assumes that the recent rate of increase of traffic, 7 to 8 per cent per annum, is maintained. If the rate of increase changes, the five-year allowance can be changed in proportion. At the present rate of traffic growth a road which has just been widened to three lanes at the appropriate capacity will last for about 13 years before it needs to be widened once again to a dual carriageway.

In the case of new building the decision as to the width of road required, given an estimate of the traffic which will use the road when it is opened, should strictly depend on a detailed calculation of the costs and benefits of alternative routes. In practice it may be simpler to plan for an ample increase in traffic to cover, say, 20 years (i.e. 150 per cent at the present rate, assuming only simple interest) without the need for further widening. This would generally mean building to dual-carriageway standard, which is desirable on accident grounds.

THE PRACTICAL CAPACITY OF URBAN ROADS

Observations of traffic flow and speed have been made on streets in Central London and the results for streets of different widths are summarized in Fig. 6.5. The running speed shown is the speed between intersections, excluding the time spent stopped at intersections. The following formula has been fitted to these results (see Chapter 3):

$$V = 31 - \frac{q + 430}{3(w - 6)}$$

where V = running speed (between intersections) in mile/h, q = total flow (both sides of the road) in veh/h, w = carriageway width in feet.

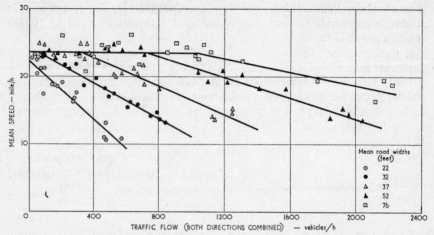

Fig. 6.5. Relation between mean speed and flow in Central London

From this formula the capacity of streets in traffic conditions comparable to those in Central London, i.e. with substantial amounts of parking, can be determined.

The principal factors which affect the capacity of individual roads or streets are width of carriageway, standing vehicles, composition of traffic, layout features such as gradient and sight distance, pedestrians crossing the road, weather and surface.

Effect of carriageway width on capacity

If 15 mile/h is taken as a minimum acceptable running speed, the capacities of streets of varying width are as follows (see Table 6.4):

TABLE 6.4

Capacity of Central London Streets when running speed is 15 mile/h

Carriageway width (ft)	Capacity (vehicles per hour)
20	250
30	700
40	1200
50	1700
60	2150

There is an increase of about 500 veh/h for each 10-ft increase in width, but the capacity is not directly proportional to the width. The capacity of a wide (two-way) street is greater than that of two narrow streets of the same total width. These results apply to a street which is of more or less uniform width. Where marked changes in width occur special allowance must be made for the bottlenecks which are produced. An example of such a bottleneck is shown in Plate 6.1.

Effect of parked vehicles

The effect of imposing restrictions on waiting has been investigated in a number of cases and the results are summarized in Table 6.5.

TABLE 6.5

Effect of parking on speed

Site	Average Street width (ft)	Parked vehicles per mile		Journey speed (mile/h)		Speed increase (mile/h) per decrease of 100 parked veh/mile
		Before	After	Before	After	
Central London (No waiting 1947)	40	44	16	8·0	8·7	2·5
London suburbs (No waiting 1949)	30	42	29	14·7	15·2	3·8
Central Glasgow (No waiting 1952)	39	171	53	6·9	7·9	0·8
Central London (Unilateral waiting 1953)	30	255	186	11·9	13·8	2·8
Three suburban high streets	32	Average 41		Average 16·8		4·8*

* Speed of light vehicles.

All the waiting restrictions resulted in the speeding up of traffic and, with the exception of Glasgow, it appears that the average increase is about 3 mile/h for each 100 parked vehicles removed. These results refer to changes in parked vehicles above the level of 10 per mile.

The effect on road capacity of parked vehicles is not proportional to the numbers parked. The following table, based on experiments with one or two vehicles parked on a ¼-mile stretch of 26-ft carriageway, as well as the experiments summarized in Table 6.5, gives an indication of the effective reduction in carriageway width produced by various numbers of parked vehicles per mile.

Parked vehicles per mile (both sides added together)	Effective loss of carriageway width (feet)	Loss of capacity at 15 mile/h (p.c.u./h)
5	3	200
10	4	275
50	7	475
100	8½	575
200	10	675
500	12	800

It will be seen that small numbers of parked vehicles have relatively large effects in reducing capacity and that the effect of a given increase in parking diminishes as the intensity increases.

Effect of pedestrians

The influence pedestrians have on speeds has not been examined in Central London but observations have been taken in the suburbs in streets 30 to 35 ft wide. It was found that the average speed of a car was reduced by $\frac{1}{4}$ mile/h for every 100 pedestrians per hour per mile of road, crossing on pedestrain crossings. Pedestrians crossing elsewhere had a negligible effect on car speeds. This is equivalent to a reduction in capacity on these streets of 20 veh/h for every 100 pedestrians per hour per mile on crossings.

Effect of the composition of traffic

A great deal of work on this subject has been done in the U.S.A. where Normann[1] has found that one heavy commercial vehicle has the same effect on speed on a multi-lane road as two cars, and on a two-lane carriageway as $2 \cdot 5$ cars. Several measurements of speed and flow have however been made in Great Britain from time to time during various strikes of buses, taxis, and commercial vehicles. The results of these investigations, which of course refer to central London under the prevailing conditions, show that:

(1) The average unit of mixed traffic in the study summarized in Fig. 6.5 is roughly equivalent to $1\frac{1}{2}$ light vehicles.

(2) One heavy commercial vehicle is equivalent to between two and three light vehicles and one bus to about two light vehicles.

(3) The average commercial vehicle is roughly equivalent to $1\frac{1}{2}$ light vehicles.

Some experiments on 30-ft roads through suburban shopping centres gave similar results.

Capacity in terms of passenger car units

Smeed[8] has shown that the speed/flow relations quoted on page 209 can be modified to take account of the traffic composition and can be put in the following form:

$$v = 31 - \frac{0 \cdot 70Q + 430}{3(w-6)}$$

where Q is measured in passenger car units. In this form the effects of parked vehicles are included. If the effects of parked vehicles are estimated on the basis of the results given earlier it appears that they had the effect of reducing the effective width of the carriageway by about six feet at all levels of flow. This means that in the absence of parked vehicles the speed/flow relation becomes

$$v = 31 - \frac{0 \cdot 70Q + 430}{3w}$$

In terms of capacity this gives

$$Q = 4 \cdot 3 \, (31 - v)w - 610 \text{ p.c.u./h.}$$

with no parked vehicles.

Tidal flow

On town streets 30–35 ft wide, tidal traffic with the flow in one direction up to three times that in the other direction had no appreciable effect on capacity. The heavier flow travelled slower than the lighter flow, but the average speed was hardly affected.

Effect of weather and road surface

Wet weather may reduce traffic speed. On wood blocks speeds were observed to be 14 per cent less when the road was wet than when it was dry, i.e. a loss of capacity of about the same proportion. On a rough surfacing no such reduction in speed in wet weather was observed.

The capacity of an urban route

This may be defined as follows: *the capacity of a route* is the flow which produces the minimum acceptable journey speed on the route as a whole. The relations between speed and flow on uninterrupted sections and between delay and flow at signal-controlled intersections are described in Chapter 9 and these can be combined to give the relation between journey speed and flow for a route with a given number of intersections. Observations have shown that a major intersection in London (i.e. an intersection of two main streets) on the average causes about five times as much delay as a minor intersection. Some values of delay plotted against flow for two groups of streets of different average width are shown in Fig. 6.6.

These values of delay at intersections have been used in conjunction with speed/flow relations given for streets 30-ft and 48-ft wide, to determine the speed/flow relation of such streets with various numbers of

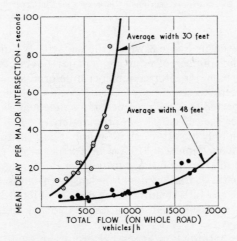

Fig. 6.6. Delay per major intersection on two groups of streets in Central London

equivalent major intersections per mile. The results of the calculation are shown graphically in Fig. 6.7 in which journey speed is plotted against flow. A great deal of discretion must be used in applying these results to other streets and other conditions of traffic, but they are indicative of the effect of intersections on capacity; linear interpolation should give reasonably accurate values for other street widths. An alternative method of

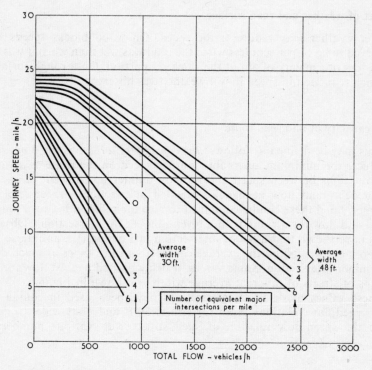

Fig. 6.7. Effect of intersections on journey speed in Central London

presentation is given in Fig. 6.8 where the capacity for different streets is plotted against the number of equivalent major intersections per mile. It will be seen that six major intersections per mile produce a loss of capacity of about 40 per cent.

It might be expected that the presence of a single major intersection on a road would reduce the capacity by approximately one half, on the grounds that the traffic can only pass through it for about half the time. On this view any additional intersection would have no further effect on capacity, and the curves of Fig. 6.8 would fall abruptly from their initial value to about half of it, and remain at that level as the density of intersections increases. However, the capacity falls steadily as the density of intersections increases, and is halved at relatively high densities of two per mile and upwards (see Fig. 6.8).

This apparent contradiction arises because the present view of capacity is based on the relation between journey speed and flow on the road as a

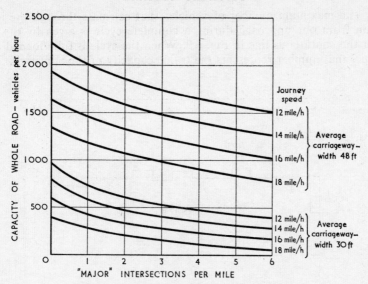

Fig. 6.8. Capacity of streets in Central London

whole, not on maximum flows. Consider a road of a given length and width. If it has no intersections, the flow producing an acceptable speed has a certain value. If one intersection is added, and the flow remains unchanged, the journey speed along the road is reduced by an amount depending on the length of the road. If the road is very long the effect of one intersection may be quite small. In order to bring the speed back to its original level, it is necessary to reduce the flow until the consequent increase of speed on the open section exactly balances the delay at the intersection. The change in flow required (i.e., the change in capacity) will also depend on the length of the road, and it will not have a fixed value such as one half.

THE CAPACITY OF SIGNAL-CONTROLLED INTERSECTIONS

The amount of traffic that can pass through a signal-contolled inter-section depends on the amount of "green" time available to the traffic and on the flow of vehicles past the "stop" line during the green period when the signals are "saturated", i.e. fully loaded. If the numbers of vehicles passing the stop line during successive short intervals of time are counted and the results averaged over a number of cycles, an estimate can be made of the way the average rate of discharge varies with time during the cycle. Fig. 6.9 shows values determined for one arm of an average busy inter-section in London working with the normal signal sequence, red, red with amber, green, and amber used in Great Britain. A characteristic of the diagram is the high and relatively constant rate of discharge reached shortly after the start of the green period;* this is termed the saturation

* According to Lighthill and Witham[9] the flow at the stop line is the maximum that can occur on a road controlled by signals.

flow. The maximum number of vehicles that can pass through the intersection from one approach during a complete cycle is given by the area under the continuous line in Fig. 6.9. When the cycle is fully loaded as in Fig. 6.9 that number represents the traffic capacity of the approach.

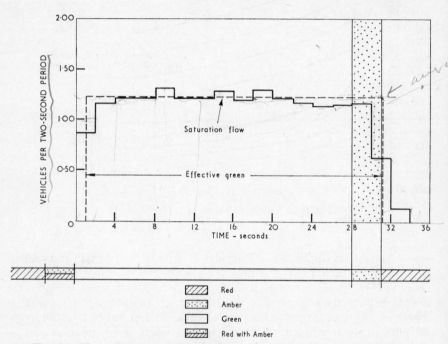

Fig. 6.9. The variation of saturation flow within the cycle in a typical case

Because of starting delays, traffic does not pass at the saturation flow during the whole of the green period, although the effect of this on capacity is more than offset by vehicles running on into the amber period. To a first approximation, the combined green and amber periods can be replaced by an "effective green time" during which vehicles are assumed to pass at the saturation flow and a "lost time" during which no vehicles pass, the value of effective green time being chosen so that the product of saturation flow and effective green time equals the number of vehicles passing during the combined green and amber periods, i.e. equals the area under the continuous line in Fig. 6.9.

In Chapter 9 a description is given of the way in which this approximation can be used in the calculation of delays, optimum cycle times, green times, etc., once the values of saturation flow and effective green time (or lost time) are known. To provide information about these quantities and their dependence on traffic conditions, carriageway width, etc., investigations have been made at a total of about 70 signal-controlled intersections, 60 in London and 10 in Glasgow. In addition a number of controlled traffic experiments have been made on a test track on the variation of saturation flow with width of carriageway, traffic composition and parking. The results of these investigations into saturation flow are described below.

Technique of saturation flow measurement

METHOD OF OBSERVATION

For each selected arm of an intersection observers recorded the numbers of vehicles which crossed the stop line during successive two-second periods after the start of the green period until the flow appeared to fall below saturation level. These numbers, together with information regarding the road layout, traffic composition and direction of traffic movement were recorded on Hollerith cards at the site using a portable machine specially built for this purpose.[10] This machine consisted essentially of a Hollerith hand punch modified to total, every two seconds, the number of vehicles recorded by the observers using push buttons and to punch these sub-totals in successive columns of the card. Information about traffic composition, right-turners and parked vehicles was stored in the machine until the red period commenced when it was automatically punched on to the card. One Hollerith card was used for each signal cycle and contained all the relevant information for that cycle. The cards could be sorted mechanically for any combination of traffic conditions using standard Hollerith equipment. By this procedure, data processing and analysis were simplified and speeded up.

Intersections were chosen which were reasonably busy at all times of the day and observations were made of 8000 signal cycles.

METHOD OF ANALYSIS

Saturation flows for each cycle were derived by averaging the two-second counts during the green period but excluding those in the first few periods after the start of the green.

With each traffic cycle were associated values of carriageway width, proportion of medium and heavy commercial traffic, proportion of trams (Glasgow only), proportion of right-turning traffic in the stream observed and the position of parked cars (if any). The dependence of saturation flow on these quantities was investigated by considering each variable in turn, at the same time making any necessary adjustments for changes in the mean values of the other variables.

The variation of saturation flow with carriageway width was found by relating the actual saturation flows of these groups to the carriageway width. However, in studying the effect of right-turners and commercial vehicles, it was found more satisfactory to use saturation flows relative to the value for some standard condition and to relate these relative saturation flows to the variable concerned. The standards used were 10 per cent of right-turners and 25 per cent of medium and heavy commercial vehicles.

CONTROLLED TRAFFIC EXPERIMENTS

To supplement the observations of actual traffic on the road and to extend the range of some of the variables, some controlled traffic experiments were carried out on a test track. Traffic signals were erected at points on the track and the approach to the signals was delineated by temporary kerbing, white lines and bollards. It was then a fairly simple matter to move these when it was desired to change the approach width of the carriageway. About 80 vehicles of various kinds were assembled for the tests and this traffic was circulated on a one-way circuit containing the signals, drivers being asked to drive in their usual manner (see Plate 6.2). The advantage of tests of this kind is that the variables can be controlled much more satisfactorily than on the road and consistent results can be obtained quite quickly. On the other hand, the tests suffer from the degree of artificiality inherent in them and in these particular tests there was no turning traffic or cross traffic, either vehicular or pedestrian, and there were no bicycles in the traffic.

As in the tests on the road, observations were made of saturation flow by counting the numbers of vehicles passing in successive two-second intervals. The analysis of these results was simpler, however, because it was possible to control the variables to a much greater extent.

Results

SHAPE OF THE SATURATION FLOW/TIME CURVE

Reference has already been made to Fig. 6.9, which shows the average number of vehicles per two seconds of the green period in a typical case. This curve was derived from fully saturated green periods only. Similar curves were drawn for groups of cycles representing several different traffic conditions and the effective green time was evaluated from the saturation flows and the numbers of vehicles passing in saturated cycles. From the effective green times the lost times were derived: the lost time for all the London sites was found to have a mean value of about two seconds; the standard deviation of lost time in a single cycle was about three seconds. Mean values at individual sites ranged from nought to seven seconds.

EFFECT OF APPROACH ROAD WIDTH

The results of the various experiments showed that under normal road conditions, saturation flow varies with the approach road width, the amount of turning traffic and the composition of traffic, and is affected by the presence of parked vehicles. In terms of passenger car units (p.c.u.) with no turning traffic, with no two-wheeled vehicles and with no parked vehicle present on the approach or exit, the peak hour saturation flow is given as follows:

w (ft):	10	11	12	13	14	15	16	17
s (p.c.u./h):	1850	1875	1900	1950	2075	2250	2475	2700

where w is the approach width (measured from kerb to inside of pedestrian refuge or to centre line, whichever is the smaller) and s is the saturation flow. For approach widths greater than 17 feet the peak hour saturation flow varies linearly and is given by

$$s = 160w \text{ p.c.u./h*} \text{ (In off-peak periods 6 per cent less).}$$

The experiment under controlled conditions has shown this relationship to be linear up to at least 60 feet.

These values compare with figures from the United States of America of 1250 passenger car units per hour of green time per 10-ft width with no turning traffic quoted in the Highway Capacity Manual,[1] but higher values

---

* It should be noted that previous saturation flow figures given by the Laboratory were about 10 per cent lower because they were not corrected for the effects of two-wheeled vehicles.

have been observed at particular intersections in the U.S.A. In 1940, Clayton[11] published values ranging from 1200 to 1800 vehicles/h per 10-ft width for streets in London.

EFFECTS OF COMPOSITION OF TRAFFIC

The effect of different types of vehicles on the saturation flow is given by the following equivalents (see pp. 200–1).

1 heavy or medium commercial vehicle:	$1\frac{3}{4}$ p.c.u.
1 bus:	$2\frac{1}{4}$ p.c.u.
1 tram:	$2\frac{1}{2}$ p.c.u.
1 light commercial vehicle:	1 p.c.u.
1 motorcycle:	$\frac{1}{3}$ p.c.u.
1 pedal cycle:	$\frac{1}{5}$ p.c.u.

RIGHT-TURNING VEHICLES. The effects of right-turning vehicles can also be expressed in terms of number of straight-ahead vehicles:

  1 right-turning vehicle: $1\frac{3}{4}$ straight-ahead vehicles (if crossing an opposing stream).

The last figure may tend to underestimate the effect of a right-turning vehicle because cases where right turners were given special phases or where they frequently blocked the intersection were omitted. In using this result it should be noted that this gives the effect of right-turning vehicles on their own stream (unless they are given special lanes). In addition to this effect they take extra time to discharge from the intersection. Some leave during the green time through gaps in the opposing traffic, and an estimate of these should be made. The others, which are waiting within the intersection itself when right of way is changed, will discharge at roughly one vehicle every $2\frac{1}{2}$ seconds. The delay to the cross traffic and the effect of the right turners on the capacity of the intersection can be calculated on this basis. See Reference 12 for more details.

EFFECT OF A PARKED VEHICLE. It has been found that the reduction in saturation flow caused by a parked vehicle is equivalent to a loss of carriageway width at the stop line. Allowing for the theoretical effect of changing the green period, this can be expressed approximately as follows:

$$\text{Effective loss of carriageway width} = 5\cdot5 - \frac{0\cdot9\,(z-25)}{k}\ \text{feet (if positive)}$$

where $z\ (\geqslant 25\text{ feet})$ = clear distance of parked car from stop line (feet). If $z < 25$ feet, take as 25 feet) and k = green time (seconds).

If the whole expression becomes negative the effective loss is taken as zero. The effective loss should be increased by 50 per cent for a parked lorry or wide van.

DEPENDENCE OF CAPACITY ON CYCLE TIME. If right turners do not cause difficulty the capacity becomes greater as the cycle time increases, because the ratio of lost time to useful time decreases, although the effect becomes negligible when the cycle is very long. In practice, it is usual to set an upper limit of 120 seconds for the cycle time (although in special cases this is increased). If the capacity were taken as the flow which could just be accommodated by such a cycle the delays would generally be excessively high (as with all types of intersections). As before, a practical capacity of

90 per cent of this maximum possible flow, which produces generally acceptably delays, is recommended.

In general, if the ratio of the flow to the saturation flow is calculated for each arm of an intersection and the highest ratio for each phase is denoted by y, then the cycle time, c_m which will just pass all the traffic, is given by

$$c_m = \frac{L}{1 - Y}$$

where Y is the sum of the selected y values over the phases and L is the total lost time in the cycle (consisting of periods when all signals show red or red/amber plus the "lost" time for the individual phases). If c_m is given, the maximum value of Y which can be accommodated is therefore given by

$$Y = 1 - \frac{L}{c_m}$$

If, for practical purposes, c_m is taken as 120 seconds and Y_{pract} is 90 per cent of its maximum possible value then

$$Y_{pract} = 0{\cdot}9 - 0{\cdot}0075L$$

EFFECT OF GRADIENT

Measurements at a number of sites have shown that a down gradient on the approach to traffic signals increases the saturation flow and an up gradient reduces it. Within the range of gradient between 5 per cent down and 10 per cent up, the saturation flow is increased (decreased) by 3 per cent for each 1 per cent of gradient down (up).

EFFECT OF SITE LOCATION

The saturation flows quoted on page 218 refer to average sites (see Plate 6.(3b)). At sites where there are no restrictions to visibility, alignment is good, there are no bottlenecks in the roads leaving the intersection and no pedestrians crossing (see Plate 6.3(a)), the saturation flow may be increased by 20 per cent. At poor sites, where visibility is severely restricted, alignment is bad, there are obstructions in the exit roads or there is much interference from pedestrians (see Plate 6.3(c)), the saturation flow may be reduced by 15 per cent. More details on capacity are given in Refs. 12 and 13. A method of measuring saturation flow at traffic signals is given in Ref. 14.

THE CAPACITY OF ROUNDABOUTS

When designing a roundabout for a road junction it is necessary to know the amount of traffic which a given design can handle, and how this capacity is affected by changes in the characteristics of the traffic.

In 1955 the Laboratory needed information on the capacity of roundabouts. The available information (see Clayton;[15,16] Highway Research Board;[1] Shrope[17] was conflicting and the effects of some important factors had not been measured. Wynn, Gourlay and Strickland[18] had obtained some useful data on weaving and merging traffic, but these had not been related to roundabout capacity. Friedrich[19] and Grabe[20] gave some semi-theoretical values for roundabout capacity, but their assumptions about behaviour in the weaving section were very arbitrary.

The Road Research Laboratory had begun the study of this problem in 1947 with tests on an artificial layout with 45 vehicles, running at predetermined speeds in two or three columns which weaved across one another. These preliminary experiments were restricted to a weaving section 250 feet long and 24 feet wide and were made under conditions which were rather artificial. In 1955, because the available information was limited, the Laboratory decided to make some experiments on a large scale to find the capacity of a single weaving section (see Fig. 6.10) using a method which had not, it is believed, been used before. In these experiments 130 vehicles took part, and they circulated continuously through the weaving section, so that equilibrium conditions could be achieved (see Plate 6.4).

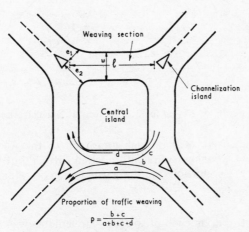

Fig. 6.10. Relevant dimensions of weaving section and proportion of weaving traffic for use in capacity formula at roundabout with square island

Description of Experiments

ARRANGEMENT OF TESTS

The tests were made on a large concrete apron at Northolt Airport and took four days in all. The type of layout used is shown in Fig. 6.11; the central part of the layout represented one weaving section. Up to 130 vehicles were assembled for the tests; they included a number of double-decker London Transport buses (present on only two days), medium and heavy commercial vehicles, light vans, cars and taxis. Two or three motorcyclists also took part in the tests, but their vehicles were not included in the traffic counted.

The vehicles were divided into ten groups, each group containing about the same proportion of cars, taxis, buses, etc. The vehicles in each group performed a particular manoeuvre in the weaving section. Some entered from the left and emerged to the left, some entered from and emerged to the right and others weaved from left to right or right to left. In almost all the tests the two weaving streams were equal in numbers. Each test lasted 10 to 12 minutes; during the first two minutes conditions settled down, and a queue

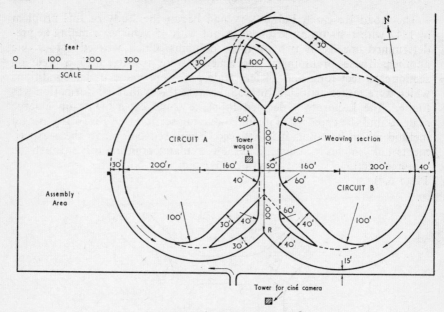

Fig. 6.11. Layout for weaving tests at Northolt Airport

of moving vehicles formed in each approach to the weaving section. In most cases the approaches were fully loaded throughout the remainder of the test and these conditions were regarded as giving "maximum" flow.

OBSERVATIONS

The flow of traffic on each of the four movements was recorded on teleprinter tape by observers stationed on a tower-wagon, using coloured labels for identification. The dimensions of the weaving section were varied over a considerable range of length and width, and the proportions of medium and heavy commercial vehicles (including buses) and of weaving traffic were also varied.

VARIABILITY OF THE DATA

As a measure of the inherent variability of the data, each test was subdivided into 36-second periods and the standard deviation of the flow between periods calculated. This was used to provide an estimate of the standard deviation of the mean flow; this was found to be about 120 veh/h, whatever the value of the mean flow.

Results

The results can be expressed by the following formula:

$$Q_m = \frac{108w\left(1+\dfrac{e}{w}\right)\left(1-\dfrac{p}{3}\right)}{\left(1+\dfrac{w}{l}\right)} \quad \text{p.c.u. per hour} \quad . \quad . \quad . \quad (1)$$

where Q_m = maximum flow through weaving section
(dry weather, no pedal cycles)
w = width of weaving section (ft)
e = average of entry widths (ft)
l = length of weaving section (ft)
p = proportion of weaving traffic to total traffic in weaving
section (see Fig. 6.10).

This formula is a modification of the one previously published,[21] which expresses the maximum flow in terms of passenger car units instead of vehicles and treats the ratio w/l in the more logical manner suggested by W. F. Adams.[22] It is based on variations in the parameters over the ranges of w of 20–60 feet; e/w of 0·4 to 1·0; w/l of 0·12 to 0·4; p of 0·4 to 1·0. In practice it is probably permissible to use this formula outside the ranges of these values although it is doubtful whether the ratio w/l should be greater than 0·4.

It was found that in wet weather the maximum flow through the weaving section was reduced by about 10 per cent.

A comparison between the formula and the results observed during the experiments is shown in Fig. 6.12. It will be seen that the agreement is good, being within the inherent variability of the data.

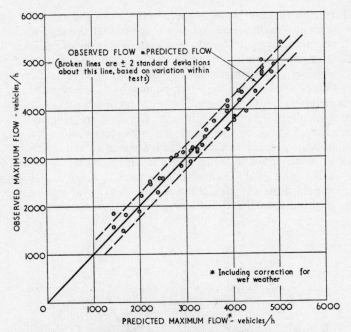

Fig. 6.12. Comparison of observed maximum flow with value
predicted by formula (1)

One difficulty that arises in using the above formula is that weaving sections rarely conform to the simple design used in the tests upon which the formula is based. Thus, it is often more realistic to use "effective" dimensions of the weaving section instead of the actual dimensions in certain cases, and Fig. 6.13 indicates how this may be done.

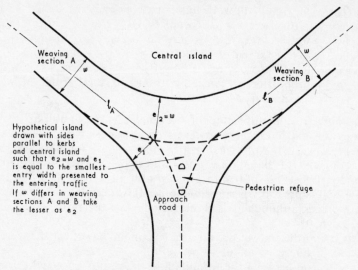

Fig. 6.13. Construction to be used for estimating the effective length and entry width of a weaving section in the absence of a channelization island

A further difference between the conditions of the controlled tests and those of most weaving sections in practice is that the sections in the tests were always "open ended" and there was no danger of vehicles "blocking back" from an adjoining weaving section and so limiting the flow. In practice most neighbouring weaving sections tend to suffer from some interaction effects between them, which may block the roundabout partially or completely Fig. 6.14 shows a delay/flow curve at a particular roundabout where a blockage was just beginning: the flow entering the roundabout became less as the delay increased. If the weaving section has a large area it can usually provide sufficient storage space to reduce the chances of blocking. With short weaving sections "interaction" is therefore much more likely to take place than with large weaving sections. Observations of the maximum flows through the weaving sections of a variety of roundabouts have indicated that the observed capacities of the smaller roundabouts

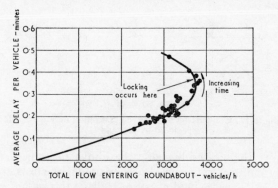

Fig. 6.14. Delay/flow curve for a particular roundabout showing the commencement of "locking"

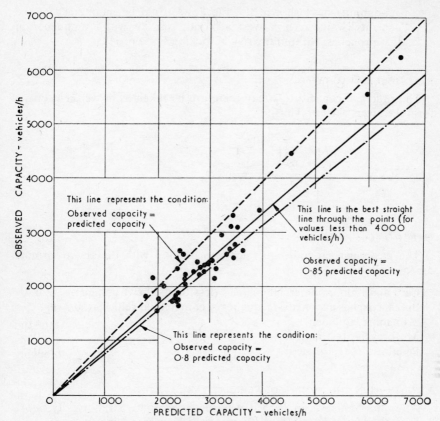

Fig. 6.15. Comparison of observed capacity of a weaving section with value predicted by the laboratory's formula

are on average about 85 per cent of the calculated values, whereas with weaving sections over 4000 veh/h even better agreement was obtained (see Fig. 6.15).

It is desirable to decide on some practical capacity for roundabouts in the same way as for traffic signals and priority intersections. The following points were borne in mind in determining such a value:

(1) Driving conditions under heavy flow in large weaving sections are difficult and are considered by some people to be undesirable. From a practical standpoint, therefore, all roundabouts should be treated similarly. Ninety per cent of the observed capacity would be 77 per cent of the capacity given by the formula in the average case.

(2) Because of the scatter of the results in Fig. 6.15 it would be unrealistic to claim too great an accuracy for this percentage, and 80 per cent may be taken as a practical value.

(3) All roundabouts are in danger of locking with the present "no priority" system at roundabouts in Great Britain when the flow reaches the observed capacities (i.e. 85 per cent of the calculated values on average). Experiments with priority signs on the approaches to

9

roundabouts have shown that the flows could be maintained at the "capacity" value even in overload conditions, i.e. with long queues on all approaches, without the risk of locking,[23] see p. 319.

PRACTICAL CAPACITY

The practical capacity Q_p may therefore be taken as 80 per cent of the formula given earlier. Thus,

$$Q_p = \frac{86w\left(1+\dfrac{e}{w}\right)\left(1-\dfrac{p}{3}\right)}{1+\dfrac{w}{l}} \text{ p.c.u./h} \quad . \quad \quad . \quad \quad . \quad (2)$$

EFFECT OF COMPOSITION

The passenger car unit equivalents to be used with the above formula are as follows:

Cars and light commercial vehicles (less than 30 cwt unladen):   1·0
Buses, coaches and medium and heavy commercial vehicles (30 cwt
    or more, unladen):   2·8
Motorcycles (estimated):   0·75
Pedal cycles (estimated):   0·5

VARIATIONS IN THE NUMBER OF VEHICLES TAKING PART

After the first tests in 1955 it was suggested that, paradoxically, more traffic might be able to weave if fewer vehicles were trying to do so. As a check on this suggestion, two tests were made in 1956 in which the numbers of vehicles taking part were progressively changed. One test was not very successful, as the number of cases was small. The results for another test are shown in Fig. 6.16. It will be seen that the maximum flow increased with the number of vehicles taking part up to a maximum of about 3250 veh/h and it appears that when all the vehicles took part the maximum flow was less—about 3100 veh/h. This result is not conclusive, because almost every point was based on a comparatively short period (4 to 5 minutes) while the final point (90 vehicles) was the result of a separate complete test. If we take this result at its face value the "maximum" flow as measured in the main series of tests may be about 5 per cent below the absolute maximum. However, the difference is not large, and in any case the ultimate capacity, when the weaving section is overloaded (without becoming jammed), is of more practical importance since it would be very difficult to prevent this condition occurring. This ultimate capacity is the quantity which we have called Q_m.

JOURNEY TIME AND FLOW

During the test described above, measurements were made of journey times from a point on each approach 200 feet before the beginning of the weaving section to the exit from the weaving section. The averages of these journey times are plotted against the flow of traffic in Fig. 6.17, which shows that the journey time increased rapidly when the flow exceeded 90 per cent of the "maximum" value. Very similar curves have been obtained on two weaving sections of an existing roundabout.

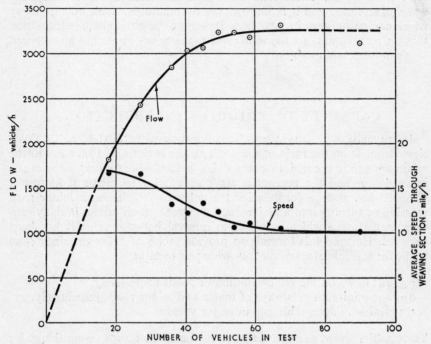

Fig. 6.16. Effect on maximum flow and on speed of number of vehicles in tests

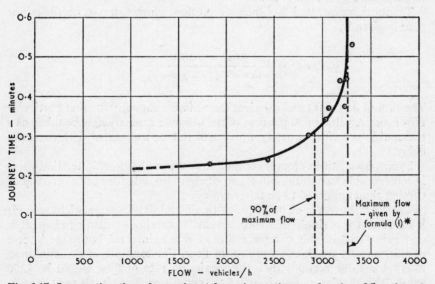

Fig. 6.17. Journey time through experimental weaving section as a function of flow through the section *See page 222.

The capacity of a roundabout

It is not necessarily safe to use the results of these experiments, which relate to an isolated weaving section, to determine the capacity of a complete roundabout. There may be mutual interference between adjacent weaving sections, and it is known that roundabouts "lock up" in a way which could not occur in these tests. It seems to be a reasonable assumption that the maximum flows found in these experiments would not be exceeded in a complete roundabout.

CAPACITY OF PRIORITY INTERSECTIONS

The capacity of priority intersections, e.g. those with "HALT" or "SLOW" signs depends on the ratio of the flows on the major and minor roads, the minimum gap in the major stream which is acceptable to merging or crossing vehicles, and the maximum acceptable delay to minor road traffic. Tanner[24] has given a formula for the delay to vehicles on a minor road crossing or turning into a major one-way street which carries initially random traffic upon which a minimum interval between vehicles has been imposed. He used this formula to provide tables of delay to minor road traffic for several values of the following parameters:

q_M, q_m: flows on the major and minor roads respectively.
β_M, β_m: minimum headways of major and minor roads respectively.
$\propto$: minimum acceptable gap in major stream.

These tables show, as expected, that, as the traffic builds up on the major road and fewer gaps become available, delays increase—theoretically to infinity (see Fig. 9.3 on p. 286).

Tanner demonstrated that the greatest flow which can pass on the minor road is given by

$$q_m(\text{max}) = \frac{q_M(1 - \beta_M q_M)}{e^{q_M(\alpha - \beta_M)} \left(1 - e^{-\beta_m q_M}\right)}$$

The sum of q_m (max) and q_M gives the ultimate capacity for that particular flow ratio. A value of 90 per cent of the ultimate capacity may be taken as a reasonable practical capacity which will not be associated with excessive delay.

Some observations of gaps acceptable to drivers have indicated that there is considerable variability but a gap of eight seconds for traffic crossing or turning right appeared to be fairly typical.

Table 6.6 shows the ultimate capacities if a minimum gap of eight seconds is assumed for a single minor-road vehicle entering or turning right. It is convenient in this table to refer, not to minimum interval, but to the inverse of this, namely the maximum rate of flow. For example, if the minimum interval is three seconds then the maximum rate of flow would be 1200 veh/h. This maximum flow is called the saturation flow; it is a very important quantity with signal control and was discussed earlier.

TABLE 6.6

Calculated capacities of intersection of major one-way road with minor road

(minimum acceptable gap in major stream for minor-road
vehicle is assumed to be eight seconds)

Saturation Flow (veh/h)		Ultimate Capacity (veh/h)			Practical Capacity (90% of ultimate— veh/h)		
Major Road	Minor Road	Major flow / Minor flow			Major flow / Minor flow		
		1	2·5	4	1	2·5	4
3600	1200	980	1050	1130	880	950	1020
1800	1200	980	1010	1060	880	910	950
1200	1200	920	950	980	830	860	880
3600	720	790	910	1000	710	820	900
1800	720	780	880	950	700	790	860
1200	720	760	830	890	680	750	800

The saturation flow on the side road is firstly taken to be 1200 veh/h (i.e. $\beta_m = 3$ seconds). This means that two vehicles need a gap of at least $8+3$ seconds, three vehicles a gap of at least $8+6$ seconds, etc. In practice this case would correspond roughly to a minor road with one lane for traffic entering the intersection and with visibility and regulations such that drivers need not stop if there is no traffic on the major road. The case of poor visibility on the minor road is covered by assuming an alternative value of saturation flow of 720 veh/h ($\beta_m = 5$ seconds), assuming that each driver has to stop and look before entering the main road even with little or no traffic on the main road. Three values of saturation flow on the major road (1200, 1800 and 3600 veh/h) are assumed, corresponding roughly to major road (one-way) approach widths of 30 ft, 15 ft, and 10 ft. Practical capacities for these cases, corresponding to 90 per cent of the ultimate capacities, are also given in Table 6.6.

COMPARISON OF DIFFERENT TYPES OF INTERSECTION

"Priority" intersections and traffic signals

A priority intersection can be made into a signal-controlled one merely by adding the necessary signal equipment—no change in layout is strictly necessary, though such a change often is made. Thus, the capacity of these two types of intersection with the same layout can easily be compared. Sometimes there is an intermediate stage when channelization of the

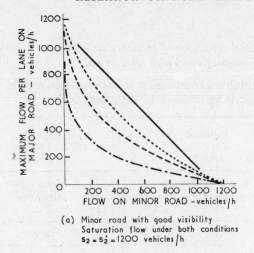

(a) Minor road with good visibility
Saturation flow under both conditions
$s_2 = s_2' = 1200$ vehicles/h

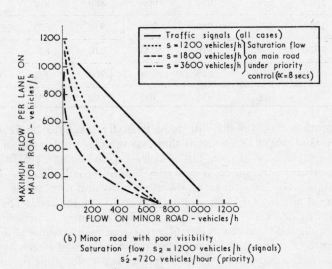

(b) Minor road with poor visibility
Saturation flow $s_2 = 1200$ vehicles/h (signals)
$s_2' = 720$ vehicles/hour (priority)

Fig. 6.18. Comparison of traffic signs capacity with that of
priority control

junction allows traffic from the minor road to negotiate the intersection in two parts. This simply makes the operation equivalent to two crossings of one-way streets, which can then be dealt with in the manner already described.

Comparisons have been made between signal control and priority in the following cases:

Major road (one-way) with saturation flow of 1200, 1800 and 3600 veh/h.

Minor road (one or two-way) with saturation flows of 720 veh/h (poor visibility) and 1200 veh/h (good visibility).

Minimum acceptable gap in major stream for one minor-road vehicle crossing or turning right: 8 seconds.

Fig. 6.18 shows curves of maximum flow per lane on the major roads for given flows on the minor road, in two cases, of good and poor visibility on the side road. The corresponding flows under signal control (with a cycle time of 120 seconds and a total lost time of 6 seconds per cycle) are also shown. The capacity of the intersection as a whole is, of course, equal to the sum of the two flows corresponding to a point on the appropriate curve. It can be seen that in all the cases given traffic signals offer more capacity. The extra capacity obtained expressed as a percentage of the capacity without traffic signals is given in Table 6.7.

TABLE 6.7
Extra capacity of traffic-signal control over priority control at some typical intersections

Saturation flow veh/h			Percentage increase in capacity produced by traffic signals—for ratio of flows (major to minor) of:		
	Minor Road				
Main Road	With traffic signals	Without traffic signals	1 : 1	2½ : 1	4 : 1
1200	1200	1200	24	20	16
1800	1200	1200	43	48	47
3600	1200	1200	75	107	115
1200	1200	720	50	37	28
1800	1200	720	79	70	64
3600	1200	720	117	139	143
1200	720	720	12	14	13
1800	720	720	26	36	39
3600	720	720	45	76	91

It can be seen that the benefits of installing traffic signals increase as:

(1) The saturation flow increases on the main road;
(2) The saturation flow (both with and without signals) increases on the minor road—this is because, without signals, minor road vehicles are looking for a relatively larger gap;
(3) The saturation flow on the minor road with signals increases relative to its value without signals.

Roundabouts and Traffic Signals

Comparisons of capacity between individual roundabouts and signals can usually be made with reasonable accuracy. It is more difficult to make general comparisons between these types of intersection because the amount of land used, the value of the land and the cost of construction are usually important, and it is difficult to estimate the minimum area necessary for the two types of control under comparable traffic situations. Because of of this a comparison has been made of the areas involved in conventional roundabouts and traffic-signal installations to provide a given capacity.*

* The results of more recent calculations are given in Ref. 72 using a more realistic intersection model but the general conclusions are substantially the same.

With the assumptions listed in Appendix 2 a comparison was made for a four-arm cross-roads under the following traffic conditions:

Capacity of whole intersection: 2000, 4000, 6000 veh/h
Ratio of flows on crossing roads: 1:1, $2\frac{1}{2}$:1, 4:1

Percentage turning right (= percentage turning left) 0, 10, 20, 30, 40. The results are shown in Table 6.8 where it can be seen that, with little

TABLE 6.8

Total extra area required to form the intersection
(see Fig. 6.19)

In units of 100 sq. yds

% right turners	Flow ratio	Capacity:					
		2000 veh/h		4000 veh/h		6000 veh/h	
		Traffic signals	Round-about	Traffic signals	Round-about	Traffic signals	Round-about
0	1 : 1	0	9	0	25	5	80
	$2\frac{1}{2}$: 1	0	9	2	35	0	70
	4 : 1	0	9	0	35	5	80
10	1 : 1	0	8	0	20	25	65
	$2\frac{1}{2}$: 1	1	9	7	30	10	60
	4 : 1	2	9	4	30	20	75
20	1 : 1	2	8	6	15	50*	55
	$2\frac{1}{2}$: 1	6	9	20	30	25*	60
	4 : 1	6	9	20	30	35*	70
30	1 : 1	10	7	15*	**15**	50*	**50**
	$2\frac{1}{2}$: 1	6	9	20*	25	35*†	55
	4 : 1	6	9	20*	30	55*	70
40	1 : 1	10	**6**	15*	**10**	70*	**45**
	$2\frac{1}{2}$: 1	6	9	25*	**25**	65*†	**50**
	4 : 1	6	8	20*	30	80*†	**80**

* Indicates that two lanes were allowed for right turns from major road.
† Indicates that two lanes were allowed for right turns from minor roads.
Note: Bold type indicates that roundabouts occupied the same or less area than traffic signals.

turning traffic and for low capacity, traffic signals do not require any extra space over and above the area occupied by the normal crossing or "feeder" roads (see Appendix 2 for assumptions regarding widths of feeder roads). Roundabouts on the other hand always need extra area but this does not increase as the amount of turning traffic increases as is the case with signals. In fact, owing to there being less weaving, the extra area required diminishes. The table shows that, under the assumptions made, traffic signals almost always give the highest capacity for a given area but there are cases when the capacity is high and there are appreciable numbers of turning traffic

when roundabouts take up the same or less area. These cases ??
by showing the extra area figures in bold type in Table 6.8.

It should be noted that the study described above referred o?
ventional types of intersection. Experiments have shown th?
signals to the approaches of existing roundabouts[25] has in so?
increased the capacity of the intersection and reduced the liability ??ck.
The increase in capacity has only been of the order of 10 per cent but was
in one case as much as 50 per cent over the value of flow which was found
to be the highest at which the chances of locking were negligible. However,
as has been mentioned, priority signs have been found to be effective in
eliminating locking. Locking can occur even with signals, and a presence
detector is now commercially available which can automatically adjust the
all-red clearance period to suit the traffic conditions and thus can virtually
eliminate the incidence of locking.

REFERENCES TO CHAPTER 6

1. HIGHWAY RESEARCH BOARD, COMMITTEE ON HIGHWAY CAPACITY. Highway capacity manual. Washington, D.C., 1950 (U.S. Department of Commerce, Bureau of Public Roads).

2. HONDERMARCQ, H., J. ELKOUBY and P. LEFEVRE. Report of Committee on Study of Traffic Flow and Road Characteristics in relation to Traffic. *Permanent International Association of Road Congresses, Xth Congress Istanbul*. Paris, 1955 (Permanent International Association of Road Congresses).

3. SCHUHL, A. Design width of roads in relation to traffic. *La Route*, 1949, No. 66 (bis), 33–7.

4. CHARLESWORTH, G. Research on town traffic. *Public Works and Municipal Services Congress*, 1952, *Final Report*. London, 1953 (Institution of Municipal Engineers), Discussion, p. 468.

5. MINISTRY OF TRANSPORT. Memorandum on the design of roads in rural areas. *Memorandum* 780. London, 1961 (H.M. Stationery Office).

6. WARDROP, J. G., and J. T. DUFF. Factors affecting road capacity. *International Study Week in Traffic Engineering, 1–6 October, 1956, Stresa, Italy*. London, 1956 (World Touring and Automobile Organisation).

7. RAFF, M. S. Interstate highway-accident study. *Bull. Highw. Res. Bd., Wash.*, 1953, (74), 18–45.

8. SMEED, R. J. The traffic problem in towns. Manchester, 1961 (Manchester Statistical Society).

9. LIGHTHILL, M. J., and G. B. WITHAM. On kinematic waves II. A theory of traffic flow on long crowded roads. *Proc. roy. Soc., Series A*, 1955, **229**, 317–45.

10. ELLSON, P. B. P.E.P. A portable electric punch for recording traffic data directly into punched cards. *Instrum. Pract.*, 1957, **11** (7), 714–24.

11. CLAYTON, A. J. H. Road traffic calculations. *J. Instn civ. Engrs.*, 1940–41, **16** (7), 247–64; Discussion, 264–84; (8), 568–94.

12. WEBSTER, F. V., and B. M. COBBE. Traffic signals. *Department of Scientific and Industrial Research, Road Research Technical Paper* No. 56.(In preparation.)

13. WEBSTER, F. V., and R. F. NEWBY. Research into the relative merits of round-abouts and traffic-signal-controlled intersections. *Proc. Instn civ. Engrs,* 1964, **27** (Jan.), 47–76.

14. ROAD RESEARCH LABORATORY. A method of measuring saturation flow at traffic signals. *Department of Scientific and Industrial Research Road Note* No. 34. London, 1963 (H.M. Stationery Office).

15. CLAYTON, A. J. H. Traffic capacity of roundabouts at road intersections. *J. Instn civ. Engrs,* 1945, **23** (3), 149–54.

16. CLAYTON, A. J. H. Working capacity of roads. *Proc. Instn civ. Engrs, Part II,* 1955, **4** (3), 665–70.

17. SHROPE, E. B. Testing a traffic circle for possible capacity. *Proc. Highw. Res. Bd, Wash.,* 1952, **31**, 415–24.

18. WYNN, F. H., S. M. GOURLAY and R. I. STRICKLAND. Studies of weaving and merging traffic. A symposium. *Yale University Bureau of Highway Traffic Technical Report* No. 4. New Haven, Conn., 1948 (Yale University Bureau of Highway Traffic).

19. FRIEDRICH, P. The capacity of roundabouts with continuous traffic. *Planen u. Bauer,* 1951, **5** (11), 251–5.

20. GRABE, W. Leistungsermittlung von nicht Lichtsignalangesteurerten Knotenpunkten des Strassenverkehrs. *Forschungsgesellschaft für des Strassenwesen, Forschungsarbeiten aus dem Strassenwesen, Neue Folge, Heft* 11. Bielefeld, 1954 (Kirschbaum Verlag).

21. WARDROP, J. G. The traffic capacity of weaving sections of roundabouts. *Proceedings of the First International Conference on Operational Research (Oxford 1957).* London, 1957 (English Universities Press Ltd)., pp. 266–80; Discussion, 180–1.

22. ADAMS, W. F. Discussion on working capacity of roads by A. J. H. CLAYTON *Proc. Instn. civ. Engrs,* 1955, **4** (2), 675–6.

23. BLACKMORE, F. C. Priority at roundabouts. *Traff. Engng & Control,* 1963, **5** (2), 104–6.

24. TANNER, J. C. A theoretical analysis of delays at an uncontrolled intersection. *Biometrika,* 1962, **49** (1/2), 163–70.

25. WEBSTER, F. V. Greenford roundabout experiment. *Traff. Engng & Control,* 1962, **2** (5), 266–71.

APPENDIX 1

Speed/flow relations for cars and for light, medium and heavy commercial vehicles on a two- and a three-lane straight level rural road

Space-mean speeds (see p.107, Ch.3) of four classes of vehicles at two sites on A.5 were related to the total flow by the following regression equations:

2 *lanes*

Cars:	$V_P = 41 \cdot 9 - 0 \cdot 0119q$
Light vans:	$V_L = 38 \cdot 3 - 0 \cdot 0096q$
Medium vehicles:	$V_M = 34 \cdot 1 - 0 \cdot 0067q$
Heavy vehicles:	$V_H = 29 \cdot 2 - 0 \cdot 0033q$

3 *lanes*

Cars:	$V_P = 47\cdot7 - 0\cdot0087q$
Light vans:	$V_L = 40\cdot5 - 0\cdot0052q$
Medium vehicles:	$V_M = 33\cdot9 - 0\cdot0017q$
Heavy vehicles:	$V_M = 27\cdot4 - 0\cdot0003q$

where V_P, V_L, V_M, V_H are the space-mean speeds in mile/h of the four classes of vehicles and q is the total flow in motor vehicles per hour.

The above speed/flow relations apply to the composition of traffic given in the first column of Table 6.I which shows the relative proportions of vehicles on A.5, the London to Holyhead Trunk Road, and normal composition. The composition of traffic on A.5 is very different from the "normal" composition shown in the second column of the same table, and the relations have therefore been corrected to refer to normal composition, using factors derived from those given by Wardrop and Duff,[6] as follows:

1 Light van   = 1 car
1 Medium vehicle = 1·41 cars
1 Heavy vehicle   = 2·19 cars

These factors have been combined in proportion to the classes of vehicle in both the A.5 and the normal composition, giving:

A.5   1 Average vehicle = 1·41 cars
Normal 1 Average vehicle = 1·16 cars

To allow for the change in composition, the coefficients of q in the speed/flow relations have been multiplied by $1\cdot16/1\cdot41$. The overall speed/flow relations shown in Fig. 6.3 were obtained by combining the relations for the various classes in the appropriate proportions. Although strictly the speed/flow relations should be converted to journey time/flow relations before being combined in this simple way, the error involved is likely to be small.

TABLE 6.I

	Percentage	
	A.5	Normal
Cars	32	65
Light vans	7	10
Medium vehicles†	41	17
Heavy vehicles	20	8

APPENDIX 2

Assumptions used in comparison of areas occupied by roundabouts and traffic-signal intersections

Abbreviations g = green time s = saturation flow
R.T. = right turning vehicle(s)
S.A. = straight-ahead vehicle(s)

† Includes buses and coaches.

(1) AREA. The area used for comparison is the total area of the round-about or traffic signal intersection (including approaches) less the original area of the intersecting feeder roads (see Fig. 6.19).

(2) WIDTH OF FEEDER ROADS

Flow approaching intersection (veh/h)	Type of carriageway	Width for approaching traffic (feet)
0–800	Single	12
800–1600	Dual (with 10 ft central reserve)	24
1600–2400	Dual (with 10 ft central reserve)	36

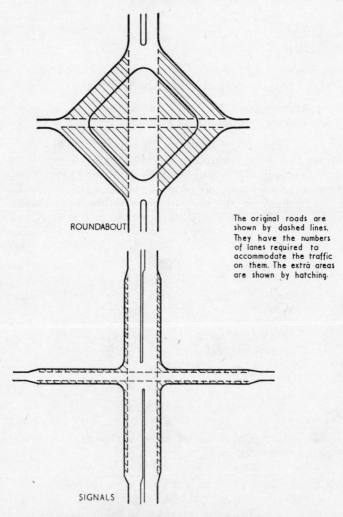

ROUNDABOUT

The original roads are shown by dashed lines. They have the numbers of lanes required to accommodate the traffic on them. The extra areas are shown by hatching.

SIGNALS

Fig. 6.19. Diagram showing extra area for roundabout and signals in a typical case (as tabulated in Table 6.8)

(3) TRAFFIC COMPOSITION. Twenty-five per cent medium and heavy commercial traffic, left turners equal in number to right turners.

(4) ROUNDABOUTS. Capacity according to formula given in this chapter. Conventional layouts with $l/w = 4$* where possible (never less) and $e/w = 0 \cdot 6$.* In some cases it was necessary to increase l/w to avoid an awkward design.

(5) TRAFFIC SIGNALS. Capacity according to formulae given in this chapter.

(a) Necessary widening extends for 250 ft from nearest kerb line of cross-road.

(b) Cycle time = 120 seconds. Lost time = 2 seconds per phase plus all red periods.

(c) Make g ratio and s ratio = $\sqrt{\text{(flow ratio)}}$.†

(d) Increase basic road widths (given above) at intersections to values gives by 5 (c).

(e) Average of 1 to 4 R.T. per cycle. On single carriageways no special R.T. lane required. Effect on their own stream allowed for by increasing width and hence s according to rule 1 R.T. = $1\frac{3}{4}$S.A. On dual carriageways assume no effect on s by allowing R.T. 6 ft of central reserve.
R.T. disperse at rate of 1000 veh/h during intergreen period, which is therefore increased to allow $3 \cdot 6$ seconds for each R.T. (no tidal flow, all roads at capacity).

(f) Average of 5 or more R.T. per cycle. Separate phase required. R.T. occupy exclusively one or two 10-ft lanes. Calculate width needed for R.T. by taking a fraction $\sqrt{\text{(R.T./S.A.)}}$ of the width for S.A. If this is: 0–15 ft, take 1 lane; over 15 ft take 2 lanes, for R.T.
Calculate exact g necessary for R.T.
Calculate width necessary for S.A. during remaining g. Assume with dual carriageways that 6 ft is available from central reserve. With double R.T. lanes allow 4-ft island between R.T. and S.A. Widen junction to give 14-ft lanes for right turners half-way through their turn and minimum radius of curvature of 35 ft.

(g) Exit width (for 250 ft) = entry width for S.A. (whether or not they have exclusive right to these lanes)—subject to minimum of original widths of feeder roads.

---

* These ratios obtained from sample of existing roundabouts.
† This rule minimizes total number of lanes and hence area assuming widening always goes back fixed distance on approaches. This usually leads to a reasonable design (see Ref. 12).

Chapter 7

Urban Traffic and Roads

SYNOPSIS

Traffic surveys: in London, Glasgow, Edinburgh, provincial towns; London traffic census; travel patterns in Greater London; survey of commercial traffic in London; peak-hour travel in London. Space requirements of traffic in towns: road space required for a journey; road space required in a town centre; numerical example; capacity and utilization of ring roads.

INTRODUCTION

In general, traffic congestion is greater in urban than in rural areas, and tends to be greatest in the centres of large towns. In urban areas there is usually a complex network of roads and what happens on or to one part of the network may sometimes affect traffic over a wide area. The effect of any improvement will depend partly on the character of the neighbouring area—if there are bottlenecks each side of the improvement then the usefulness of the improvement is limited by the capacity of the bottlenecks. The elimination of a bottleneck may remove long queues of slowly moving or stationary vehicles from a considerable length of street. For example, the widening of 150 yards of the Strand, London, in 1958-59 led to an increase in speeds in a section of 0·4 miles from Wellington Street to Trafalgar Square.[1]

Present conditions of congestion in urban areas often restrict the growth of traffic and, therefore, any improvement is likely to result in a large amount of new traffic as well as the diversion of traffic from other routes.

Various methods have been proposed to alleviate the problem of urban congestion, and some are considered in this chapter, but they are not discussed in detail. Proposals fall fairly clearly into one of three classes: (i) provision of new facilities, (ii) making the best use of the present facilities, and (iii) restraining traffic.

New facilities may be provided in a variety of forms—urban motorways, other new roads, major road widenings, new underground railways or mono-rails. There are of course many ways in which road networks can be designed; in particular there is often a choice between ring roads and radial roads. Urban motorways are favoured for their speed and safety, but they are opposed because it is said that they place artificial barriers in a town and that by increasing the ease with which vehicles can reach the centre the amount of congestion in the centre is increased.

To make the best use of the existing system is obviously desirable, irrespective of the policy regarding new roads. The use made of the existing streets may be improved by adopting traffic management measures such as one-way working, junction control and parking control (see Chapter 10). Such measures should have regard to effects on all traffic, pedestrian as well as vehicular, and to effects on amenity. Staggering of working hours could lead to an easing in traffic conditions in the peak hours. Changes in the form of transport may also enable better use to be made of the road; these may take the form of using smaller vehicles or may affect the choice between public and private transport.

Urban speeds could be increased by restricting the amount of traffic in towns. One method which had been proposed is to prohibit certain classes of vehicle from entering the central areas of towns during peak travel periods.

Another method assumes that the correct level of congestion will be found if road users have to pay the full costs that they impose upon the road system and on other road users in the form of delay. (This is discussed more fully in Chapter 15.) Charges could be collected by means of a system of special licences, by parking fees, or by some form of meter.

Planning regulations, which affect the amount of building that can take place, the uses to which it can be put and the amount of parking space that must be provided, will affect the amount of traffic.

One essential before any attempt is made to assess the effect of any measure to improve the traffic conditions in urban areas is to have data on flows, speeds, and delays, and on the details of journeys that are made and the reasons for making them.

The first part of this chapter discusses investigations that have been carried out to measure some of the factors mentioned above, the main emphasis being on those carried out by or for the Laboratory. The second part of this chapter discusses the theoretical space requirements of traffic in towns.

TRAFFIC SURVEYS

Traffic surveys in London

Between 1947 and 1960 the Laboratory made eight surveys of traffic conditions on main streets in central London.[2] In 1961 and 1962 similar surveys were made jointly by the London Traffic Management Unit of the Ministry of Transport and the Laboratory. The observations were made on weekdays, between 9.30 a.m. and 5 p.m., and each survey covered a period of three or four weeks in September and October. In addition, six surveys of traffic conditions during the evening peak hour (5-6 p.m.) were made between 1952 and 1962.

The network of streets covered by the surveys originally measured 36 miles, but new routes have been added from time to time and the total length covered in 1962 was 44 miles. These streets vary considerably in character; an example of a particularly busy shopping street is shown in Plate 7.1. In each survey a vehicle moving with the traffic stream made 15 journeys on every part of the network in each direction, and an observer in the vehicle recorded the times spent moving and stationary for each section of the route. These times were used to find:

(a) Percentage of time spent stationary at intersections controlled by traffic signals or police.
(b) Average journey speed.
(c) Average running speed (excluding time stopped at controlled intersections.)

In the surveys made between 1947 and 1960 the flows of traffic on the survey routes were measured by the moving-observer method (see Chapter 3). This method cannot be used for one-way streets and, because the number of one-way streets has been increasing, in the 1961 and 1962 surveys use was made of a different method, in which stationary observers recorded the flows at a large number of points distributed over the whole survey network.

The average flow between 9.30 a.m. and 5 p.m. on all the streets covered in the 1962 survey was 1705 vehicles per hour (both directions combined). Of these vehicles 42 per cent were cars, 4 per cent motorcycles, 34 per cent commercial vehicles, 7 per cent buses, and 13 per cent taxis and other vehicles. During the evening peak hour (5–6 p.m.) the average flow was 28 per cent higher than in the off-peak period (9.30 a.m.–5 p.m.). The flow of cars increased by 55 per cent, motorcycles by 390 per cent, and buses by 25 per cent. Commercial vehicles decreased in the evening peak period by 30 per cent and taxis decreased by 20 per cent.

The average journey speed in 1962 was 10·4 miles per hour in the off-peak period and 9·4 miles per hour in the peak period, and the corresponding running speeds were 15·3 and 14·6 mile/h. The proportion of time spent stopped at controlled intersections was 32 per cent in the off-peak period and 35 per cent in the peak period.

The results for the off-peak period in the ten surveys made between 1947 and 1962 are summarized in Table 7.1 and Figure 7.1. Because of additions that have been made to the survey network and the introduction of one-way streets, the overall average figures for the whole network are not always comparable from year to year. The figures given in Table 7.1 are based on those sections of the network which are comparable from one year to another, and the 1962 figures therefore differ slightly from those quoted above for the whole network.

It will be seen that flows have increased fairly steadily since the 1950 survey (the first after the end of petrol rationing). The average rate of increase for all vehicles (except pedal cycles) between 1950 and 1962 has been 2 per cent per annum.

Increases in flow have generally been accompanied by decreases in journey speed: this is to be expected unless deliberate administrative action is taken to increase the capacity of the streets. Increases in journey speed occurred between 1950 and 1952, when trams were withdrawn from parts of the survey routes, and between 1960 and 1961, when a number of one-way schemes, parking restrictions, and bans on right turns were introduced by the London Traffic Management Unit.

Thus the trends in London traffic exhibit three features which would probably be found in town centres throughout the country:

(a) Flows are increasing.
(b) Speeds are decreasing as a consequence.
(c) The downward trend in speeds can be temporarily checked or reversed where measures are taken to increase capacity.

Traffic surveys in Glasgow

Four surveys similar to those made in London were made on main streets in Glasgow (see Plate 7.2) between 1954 and 1961.[3] The observations were

TABLE 7.1

Flows and speeds on main streets in central London

	1947	1949	1950	1952	1954	1956	1958	1960	1961	1962
Flow (vehicles per hour)										
Private vehicles . . .	435	350	430	475	540	560	660	700	740	745
Commercial vehicles .	470	525	525	555	575	580	605	630	650	635
Buses, taxis, etc. . .	395	405	380	370	345	335	320	305	315	325
Total	1300	1280	1335	1400	1460	1475	1585	1635	1705	1705
Journey speed (mile/h) .	11·1	11·4	10·9	11·5	11·2	10·7	10·3	10·0	10·9	10·6
Running speed (mile/h) .	15·1	15·0	15·7	15·6	16·0	16·3	16·1	16·1	16·9	15·5
Time stopped (per cent) .	27	25	31	26	30	34	36	38	36	32

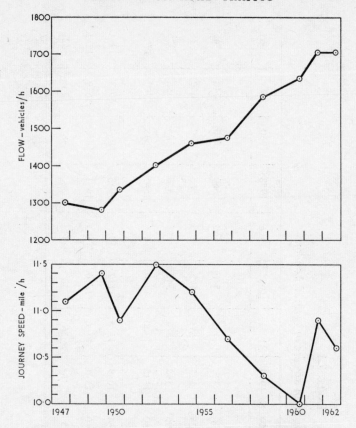

Fig. 7.1. Flows and journey speeds on main streets in central London (9.30 a.m.–5 p.m. on weekdays, September–October)

taken between 8.30 a.m. and 6.30 p.m. on ten weekdays in October, and the total length of the streets covered was six miles.

The results of the four surveys are summarized in Table 7.2. The flow of vehicles has increased at an average rate of 5 per cent per annum. The journey speed increased between 1954 and 1956 and also between 1958 and 1961. A large part of the latter increase can probably be attributed to the introduction of parking restrictions. Another factor contributing to the increase in speed has been the reduction in the number of trams on the survey routes.

Traffic surveys in Edinburgh

Traffic surveys were made on main streets in central Edinburgh (see Plate 7.3) in 1957 and 1959.[3] The observations were taken between 9 a.m. and 5.30 p.m. on six weekdays in October and November, and the total length of the streets covered was ten miles. The results are shown in Table 7.3. There was an increase in flow between 1957 and 1959, amounting to 8 per cent per annum, and this was accompanied by a decrease in speed.

TABLE 7.2
Flows and speeds on main streets in central Glasgow

	1954	1956	1958	1961
Flow (vehicles per hour)				
Cars	*	370	390	525
Commercial Vehicles	*	315	345	375
Buses, trams, and taxis	*	190	175	175
Total	775	875	910	1075
Journey speed (mile/h)	7·8	8·2	8·1	9·2
Running speed (mile/h)	11·7	12·8	13·0	14·8
Time stopped (per cent)	34	36	37	38

* Vehicles classified differently in 1954.

TABLE 7.3
Flows and speeds on main streets in central Edinburgh

	1957	1959
Flow (vehicles per hour)		
Cars	475	575
Commercial Vehicles	265	310
Buses and taxis	175	185
Total	915	1070
Journey speed (mile/h)	13·8	13·1
Running speed (mile/h)	16·3	16·0
Time stopped (per cent)	15	18

Conditions in provincial towns

Traffic conditions were studied in three provincial towns—Stafford, Stamford and Worcester—in 1956.[4] Speeds were measured along a main route through each town for a distance of 0·7 miles in Stamford and 1·2 miles in the other two towns. Mean journey speeds and flows between 8.0 a.m. and 6.0 p.m. on weekdays are shown in Table 7.4 where they are compared with the speeds and flows found in three large cities.

TABLE 7.4
Comparison of speeds and flows in three cities and three provincial towns in 1956

	Total flow (veh/h)	Journey speed (mile/h)
Large cities:		
Edinburgh*	915	13·8
Glasgow	875	8·2
London	1475	10·7
Provincial towns:		
Stafford	1070	14·2
Stamford	520	14·3
Worcester	730	12·0

* 1957.

London Traffic Census

Another source of information about flows of traffic in central London is the census carried out by the Metropolitan and City of London Police.[5] The first of these took place in 1904, and they are now held every two years. The 1960 census covered 122 points spread over the whole of the Metropolitan Police area. These points comprise the busiest intersections in the area and almost all the river crossings. At each point a count is made between 8 a.m. and 8 p.m. of the number of vehicles in each of 14 categories entering the intersection from each approach, and the results are recorded as hourly totals. The counting is normally spread over four Tuesdays in July.

Because the census points are deliberately placed at the busiest intersections, where the spare capacity is probably least, the figures may underestimate the rate of increase of the traffic from year to year. However, they illustrate the way in which the rate of increase varies from one part of the census area to another. Table 7.5 shows that between 1954 and 1960 flows (measured in passenger car units, see Chapter 6) increased more than twice as fast on the outskirts of London as in the centre.

TABLE 7.5

Annual rates of percentage increase of traffic flow in London, measured in passenger car units, 1954-60

Distance from Charing Cross (miles)	Daytime (8 a.m.–8 p.m.)	Peak hour (5 p.m.–6 p.m.)
Less than 2	2·5	1·8
2–4	3·6	3·5
4–6	4·5	4·9
More than 6	5·8	5·5

The increase was about the same in the peak hour as during the rest of the day except in the central area, where the traffic increased less in the peak hour than at other times.

The police census figures are also useful in indicating the composition of the traffic and the way it has changed from year to year. Table 7.6 gives the percentage of vehicles in each of seven categories from 1939 to 1962. There have been increases in the proportions of cars and motorcycles, and decreases in the proportions of commercial vehicles, public-service vehicles, and pedal cycles.

It is convenient to have a single figure which will serve as an index of traffic composition. An appropriate figure is the average passenger car unit factor, which may be obtained by dividing the flow measured in passenger car units by the corresponding flow in vehicles. This may be regarded as a measure of the "size" of the average vehicle, size being interpreted in terms of traffic flow. Average passenger car unit factors for London have been

TABLE 7.6

Percentage of vehicles of each type in London, 1939-1962

	1939	1949	1952	1954	1956	1958	1960	1962
Cars	34	29	34	38	41	43	47	49
Commercial vehicles	22	30	29	29	28	27	26	27
Public-service vehicles	13	13	12	10	9	8	6	6
Taxis	8	12	8	8	8	7	7	6
Motorcycles, etc.*	2	3	6	6	7	8	9	8
Pedal cycles	19	12	11	9	7	7	5	4
Others	2	1	0	0	0	0	0	0
Total	100	100	100	100	100	100	100	100

* Solo motorcycles, motorcycle combinations, scooters, and mopeds.

evaluated from the police census figures for 1954 and 1960, and they have been found to be decreasing in the central area and increasing slightly on the outskirts, as shown in Table 7.7.

TABLE 7.7

Annual rate of percentage change of average passenger car unit factor in London, 1954-1960

Distance from Charing Cross (miles)	Daytime (8 a.m.–8 p.m.)	Peak hour (5 p.m.–6 p.m.)
Less than 2	− 0·9	− 1·4
2–4	− 0·5	− 0·6
4–6	− 0·2	− 0·4
More than 6	+ 0·4	+ 0·6

Travel patterns in Greater London

Observation of vehicles on the roads can provide information about traffic flows and speeds, but information about the people in the vehicles, the journeys they make, and the reasons for their journeys can be obtained only by personal interviews.

The first survey of this nature was carried out on behalf of the London Transport Executive in 1949;[6] this was rather limited in scope, being concerned only with journeys by public transport and except for a small sub-sample only with regular journeys. In 1954 a larger survey was carried out by the Social Survey on behalf of the Laboratory and the London Transport Executive.[7, 8] To complete the picture of travel in London a survey of travel by commercial vehicles in London was carried out in 1960.[9]

A comprehensive survey on a much larger scale was carried out in 1961–63 on behalf of the Ministry of Transport and the London County Council;[10] this entailed interviewing the members of 50 000 households, collecting details of journeys made by 35 000 commercial vehicles, and 65 000 roadside interviews with drivers crossing a cordon located between 15 and 20 miles from central London.

The 1954 survey covered all journeys (other than those on foot) which had been made during the previous seven days and interviews were obtained with nearly 12 000 persons who were resident in Greater London (the survey area was slightly larger than the London Conurbation) and about 4400 in six nearby country towns. The methods used in carrying out the survey are described in greater detail in Chapter 4. The analysis carried out by the London Transport Executive[8] was mainly in terms of number of journeys and the main interest was in journeys by public transport. The analysis by the Laboratory[7] was in terms of passenger-miles and was restricted to journeys or parts of journeys which took place within a rectangle of 25×24 miles centred on Charing Cross, this being the area covered by the atlas which was the basis of the grid from which the mileages were calculated. The results have been adjusted as far as possible to represent 1958 conditions, using various sources of information.

The distribution of travel between different forms of transport is given in Table 7.8, which shows that in 1958 buses, trolley-buses, and coaches accounted for 50 per cent of the total passenger-mileage, and cars for 35 per cent. The proportion of travel by car was higher at week-ends, and higher on Sundays than on Saturdays.

Table 7.9 gives the distribution of weekday travel by hour of day and form of transport. The most striking feature is the very large proportion of travel which was concentrated in the morning and evening peak periods: four hours, 7–9 a.m. and 5–7 p.m., accounted for almost exactly 50 per cent of the total. The hourly distributions of car and bus travel were very similar, the only noticeable difference being that the morning peak for car travel started to build up an hour later than that for bus travel; cycle travel, however, differed from car and bus travel in three respects—the peaks were more pronounced, the morning peak was an hour earlier, and there was a third noticeable peak at lunch-time.

TABLE 7.8

Percentage distribution of total travel between different forms of transport, for weekdays, Saturdays and Sundays (all hours)

Form of Transport	Weekdays	Saturdays	Sundays	All days
Bus	41	34	25	38
Trolleybus	10	9	7	9
Coach	2	3	3	3
Taxi	1	*	*	1
Car	31	41	53	35
Motorcycle combination	1	2	3	1
Solo motorcycle	4	4	4	4
Powered cycle	1	1	*	1
Bicycle	9	6	5	8
ALL FORMS	100	100	100	100

* Less than 0·5 per cent.

The people interviewed were asked to state the purpose of each of the journeys they had made, and Table 7.10 shows the percentage distribution of the total passenger-mileage by bus, car, and taxi, on weekdays between 8 a.m. and 6 p.m., according to the purpose of the journey. Two-thirds of the mileage on buses and trolley-buses was covered by travel to or from work or school. Three-quarters of car travel was connected with work, 48 per cent for the journey to work and 28 per cent in working time.

TABLE 7.9

Percentage distribution of weekday travel according to time of day and form of transport

Time	Bus, trolley-bus and coach	Car and taxi	Motorcycle and bicycle	All forms of transport
Midnight– 5.0 a.m. .	0·2	0·3	0·1	0·6
5.0– 6.0 a.m. .	0·4	0·2	0·1	0·7
6.0– 7.0 a.m. .	1·6	0·1	0·4	2·1
7.0– 8.0 a.m. .	6·2	2·3	3·1	11·6
8.0– 9.0 a.m. .	7·2	4·6	1·9	13·7
9.0–10.0 a.m. .	2·9	2·0	0·3	5·2
10.0–11.0 a.m. .	1·4	1·0	0·1	2·5
11.0–noon . .	1·3	0·9	0·1	2·3
noon– 1.0 p.m. .	1·7	0·8	0·6	3·1
1.0– 2.0 p.m. .	2·4	1·3	0·9	4·6
2.0– 3.0 p.m. .	1·8	1·6	0·3	3·7
3.0– 4.0 p.m. .	1·9	1·3	0·2	3·4
4.0– 5.0 p.m. .	4·2	2·0	0·5	6·7
5.0– 6.0 p.m. .	7·4	4·1	2·9	14·4
6.0– 7.0 p.m. .	6·2	3·5	1·5	11·2
7.0– 8.0 p.m. .	2·5	2·3	0·5	5·3
8.0– 9.0 p.m. .	1·1	0·9	0·3	2·3
9.0–10.0 p.m. .	1·0	0·8	0·2	2·0
10.0–11.0 p.m. .	1·4	1·2	0·3	2·9
11.0 p.m.–midnight .	0·7	0·9	0·1	1·7
ALL DAY . .	53·5	32·1	14·4	100·0

TABLE 7.10

Percentage distribution of travel on different forms of transport according to purpose of journey (weekdays 8.0 a.m.–6.0 p.m.)

Purpose of journey	Bus and trolleybus	Car	Taxi	All motor vehicles with 3 or more wheels
Travel in working time .	4	28	22	13
To or from work . .	56	48	23	53
School . . .	12	3	2	8
Shopping . .	11	4	4	8
Cinema/theatre . .	1	*	1	1
Sport . . .	*	1	0	1
Other reasons . .	16	16	48	16
ALL REASONS .	100	100	100	100

* Less than 0·5 per cent.

Survey of commercial traffic in London

The survey of commercial traffic[9] only covered vehicles which were licensed and garaged in the survey area; this was the 25×24 mile rectangle used by the Laboratory in the passenger survey. (This restriction is more important in the case of commercial traffic than the restriction of the passenger survey to persons resident in Greater London.)

A one per cent sample of vehicles was drawn and a response rate of between 70 and 80 per cent was achieved. Details were collected of all journeys made during a week in April or May 1960. Of the 864 vehicles for which usable records were kept 110 vehicles were not used on any day in the week concerned, and the remaining 754 made 7840 journeys consisting of 41 500 stages, (only 22 000 of which were recorded in detail) in the course of which they travelled 102 500 miles and performed 82 300 ton-miles.

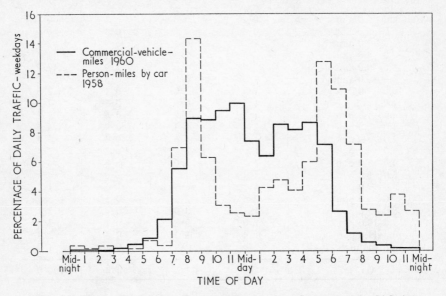

Fig. 7.2. **Hourly distributions of person-miles by car and commercial vehicle in central London**

The distribution of weekday travel by commercial vehicles by time of day measured in vehicle-miles is shown in Figure 7.2 where it is compared with the distribution of travel by car measured in person-miles. The main feature of the distribution of commercial travel is the absence of the peaks which are associated with personal travel. The period Monday to Friday covers 84 per cent of the vehicle-miles by commercial vehicles compared with 61 per cent of the person-miles by road transport. The distribution of ton-miles by time of day shows a steady decrease in average load throughout the day.

TYPE OF JOURNEY

For some aspects of planning, the type of journey (classified by length, number of stops and the relationship of the stops to each other) will be important. The percentage distribution of the number of journeys and of the vehicle-mileage according to the type of journey is given in Table 7.11 as well as the average length and number of stages in journeys of different types.

TABLE 7.11

Analysis by type of journey

Type of journey	% distribution		Average length of journey within the area (miles)	Average no. of stages per journey
	Journeys	Vehicle-mileage		
Between a point inside the survey area and a point more than 10 miles beyond it:				
Without stopping in the survey area . . .	7	6	11·5	1
With one or more stops in the area. . . .	1	2	22·4	3
Between a point inside the survey area and a point not more than 10 miles beyond it.*	18	16	11·6	3
Journeys entirely within the survey area:				
To a single destination . .	14	5	5·0	1
To a single destination and return	21	18	10·9	2
To several destinations within 3¼ miles of base .	18	15	10·5	11
To several destinations journey extending beyond 3¼ miles from base . .	21	38	23·9	9
ALL JOURNEYS . . .	100	100	13·0	5
TOTALS IN SAMPLE . .	7843	102 565		

* The boundary of the survey area was an artificial one and so journeys which went outside the area were divided into those going more than and less than 10 miles beyond it; many of the journeys which only went a short distance beyond it would be similar to a large number which took place entirely within the area.

Travel surveys have also been carried out in other cities. An early example is a survey made of the use of public transport in Bristol;[11] two of the largest and most comprehensive are the recent surveys connected with future road planning in Manchester[12] and Glasgow.[13]

Peak-hour travel in London

Nearly all traffic problems are affected by the problem of peak travel (seasonal or diurnal) and this is particularly true of urban travel. The numbers entering central London in the peak hour are counted annually by the London Transport Board. Each November a one-day count is made of those arriving by public transport between 7.00 a.m. and 10.00 a.m. and of those departing between 4.30 p.m. and 6.30 p.m.; and each July in conjunction with the London County Council a count is made of those arriving by private transport.[14] Table 7.12 shows the estimated numbers entering the central area in the morning peak by different forms of transport since 1948. (The total entering by rail is less than the sum of those entering by London Transport Railway and by British Railways due to double counting of those who arrive in the central area by British Railways and then proceed by "Underground".)

The table shows that there has been a steady increase in the number arriving by rail and a decline in the number of persons arriving by road but this reduced number of persons has been carried by an increased number of vehicles.

There is a considerable divergence between the comparative use of the different means of transport in different parts of the region. In particular over fifty per cent of cars entering the Central area between 7.00 a.m. and 10.00 a.m. come from the North-west sector.

There is a concentration within the peak period but this is much more pronounced on the railways than on the roads: in the busiest half hour on the railways the flow is $1 \cdot 7$ times the average over the peak period; the corresponding figure on the roads is $1 \cdot 3$.

TABLE 7.12

Number of persons entering the central area of London
between 7.00 a.m. and 10.00 a.m. according to class
of transport (thousands)

	Rail			Road				Total
	British Railways	London Transport Railways	Total*	Public-Service Vehicle	Car	Motorcycle and Pedal cycle	Total	
1948	350	450	720	290	30	30	350	1070
1952	380	455	750	285	45	25	355	1105
1956	415	470	790	260	65	25	350	1140
1960	450	505	860	215	85	30	330	1190
1962	475	545	900	215	95	30	340	1240

* See text.

To measure the proportion of all travel, on each system, which is accounted for by peak-hour travel to the central area on weekdays, the daily journeys to the central area in the morning peak (given in Table 7.12) plus the daily journeys away from the central area in the evening peak (4.30–7.0 p.m.) are multiplied by 260 and expressed as a percentage of all journeys. (The data are not available to make the calculation in terms of passenger-miles.) These figures are given in Table 7.13. Apart from travellers to the central area in peak hours there is also a concentration of much of the travel in other parts of London in these hours so the percentages in Table 7.13 by no means show the total proportion of travel which takes place in the peaks.

TABLE 7.13

Weekday peak-hour journeys into the central area as a percentage of all journeys made over each network during the whole week

Form of Transport	1952	1962
	%	%
British Railways – London lines . . .	42	46
London Transport Railways	35	41
London Transport Central Road Services .	4	5

One obvious way of relieving congestion, and one which would entail no capital expenditure, is to stagger working hours. It is not possible to make a direct estimate of the proportion of people who would have to change their hours of work in order to achieve any pre-determined amount of relief in congestion as the hours of work of all those employed in central London are not known. A comparison of the percentage distribution of hours of work and time of arrival or departure from the central area is given in Table 7.14. The figures for hours of work are taken from the Report of the Committee for Staggering of Working Hours in Central London[15] and relate to the hours of about half a million people employed in just under 2000 establishments. There are several points which may affect the comparison: not all persons travelling at these times will be going to or from work, not all workers adhere rigidly to the official hours of work (particularly to finishing times), and there must nearly always be some time-lag between arriving in the central area and arriving at the place of work (as the arrival and departure times used here are largely based on main-line termini and points near the edge of the central area the average delay could be appreciable).

The number who would need to change their hours of work depends primarily on the standard laid down for relief of congestion, but, given this, one needs to know more details of hours of work, particularly the relationship between times of starting and of finishing work. To achieve a levelling of travel within the peak at least a quarter of those working in Central London would have to change their hours of work.

TABLE 7.14

Comparison between times of travelling and of
starting/finishing work

	Morning			Evening	
Time	Percentage Starting Work	Percentage Arriving in previous ¼ hour	Time	Percentage Finishing Work	Percentage Departing in following ¼ hour
7.30	3	4	4.30	5	6
7.45	1	6	4.45	7	8
8.00	17	8	5.00	24	14
8.15	2	8	5.15	15	15
8.30	11	10	5.30	33	18
8.45	13	13	5.45	6	14
9.00	31	16	6.00	8	12
9.15	9	15	6.15	1	8
9.30	12	12	6.30	1	5
9.45	1	8			
	100	100		100	100

THE SPACE REQUIREMENTS OF TRAFFIC IN TOWNS

The road space required for a journey

An approach to the problem of congestion in towns has been made by considering the amount of space required for travel.[16, 17, 18, 19, 20, 21] Some figures have been found for the area of road required for a one-mile journey in the peak period, and these values may be multiplied by the estimated number of person-miles travelled in the peak period to give the total amount of road space required.

The concept of the area of road required for a journey is applicable whenever a road or a network of roads is occupied to capacity for a definite period of time. It is important to note that the concept is meaningful only if all the journeys take place within a fixed-time period. In these circumstances any additional journeys to be made within the same period will require additional road space, but if the period is not restricted it is clear that any section of road can provide an indefinite amount of travel. The idea of the space required for a journey finds its chief application in the study of traffic in the central areas of towns during the peak periods.

The concept may be illustrated by a numerical example. Consider a busy urban street, 44 feet wide. It has been found that in average central London conditions the flow of cars which can pass along such a street at an average running speed of 10 miles per hour is 2800 per hour (both directions conbined). If we consider a one-mile section of this road, the amount of travel which can take place on it during the peak period, which we shall assume to last for two hours, is $2 \times 2800 = 5600$ car-miles. The area of this section of road is $44 \times 5280 = 232,320$ square feet, so that the amount of road space per car-mile travelled is $232\,320/5600 = 41$ square feet. This is also the space required per person-mile if there is one person in each car. but if there are, say, four persons in each car, then the area of 41 square feet provides four person-miles, and the area per person-mile is 10 square feet.

In the general case, suppose that

Width of road $= w$ feet,
Capacity of road (both directions combined) $= c$ vehicles per hour,
Length of peak period $= T$ hours,
Average number of persons per vehicle $= n$.

Then a one-mile section of road has an area of 5280 w square feet, and provides cT vehicle-miles, or ncT person-miles, during the peak period. Thus

area of road required per person-mile = $5280w/ncT$ square feet.

Some values of the area of road required per person-mile for different conditions are given in Table 7.15, together with the capacities on which they are based. It has been assumed that the peak period lasts for two hours, that a car carries 1·5 persons and a bus carries 32 passengers (average figures for the peak period in central London), and that a bus is equivalent to three passenger car units. It will be seen from Table 7.15 that a one-mile journey by car requires an area of road space in the approximate range 20–70 square feet on multi-purpose roads, or 11 square feet on urban motorways. A similar journey by bus (on multi-purpose roads) requires only 4–10 square feet. It is interesting to compare these figures with the corresponding values for journeys on foot and by rail. It has been found that a one-mile journey on foot requires about three square feet of footway, while a one-mile journey by rail may need as little as 1–2 square feet.

TABLE 7.15

Road space required per person-mile

	Speed (mile/h)	Capacity (p.c.u./h)	Road space per person-mile (square feet)	
			Car	Bus
Urban street 24 feet wide				
In central London.	15	610	69	10
In central London.	10	990	42	6
With few pedestrians or inter sections	30	1400	30	
Urban street 44 feet wide				
In central London.	15	1970	39	6
In central London.	10	2790	28	4
With few pedestrians or inter- sections	30	4400	17	
Urban motorway	40	2000 per 12-ft lane	11	

The road space required in a town centre

The idea of the space required for a journey may be used to estimate the area which should be devoted to roads in a town, if the total amount of travel is known. A simple theoretical model will be considered. Attention will be confined to the central area of a town during the peak period, and only journeys to and from work will be considered. It will be assumed that the central area is circular, and that all the people who work in the central area live outside it. It will also be assumed that the point at which a worker enters the central area is not correlated with the position of his place of work, and that the number of workers entering the central area is the same at all parts of the circumference.

To find the distances travelled in the central area, some assumption must be made about the distribution of work-places. Two types of distribution will be considered: a uniform distribution, and a distribution in which the density of work-places is inversely proportional to the distance from the centre. The distribution of work-places in London has been found to approximate to the second type.

It is also necessary to make an assumption about the routes by which workers travel from the edge of the central area to their destinations. Three types of route will be considered: these are illustrated in Fig. 7.3. A *direct*

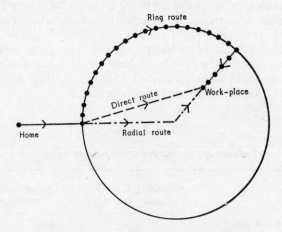

Fig. 7.3. The three types of route considered

route follows a straight line from the edge of the central area to the destination; a *radial* route follows a straight line to the centre of the town and then another straight line to the destination; and a *ring* route follows the circumference of the central area (clockwise or anti-clockwise—whichever is quicker) to the radius on which the destination lies, and then follows that radius inwards to the destination.

The average distance travelled from the point at which the central area is reached to the destination can now be calculated for each of the three types of route and for each of the two distributions of work-places. These average distances are given in Table 7.16.

It will be seen that radial routes are on average considerably longer than direct routes, and that ring routes are longer still. The ring route, however, has the advantage that the distance travelled within the central area (as distinct from round its perimeter) is very much less than on a direct route or a radial route. For a given means of transport, type of road, and length of peak period, these differences in distance travelled in the central area with different routeing systems will be reflected in proportional differences in the area of road required.

TABLE 7.16

Average distance travelled from points on the circumference of the central area to destinations inside it

Type of route	Average distance travelled	
	Uniform density of work-places	Density of work-places inversely proportional to distance from centre
Direct	$1 \cdot 13r$	$1 \cdot 09r$
Radial	$1 \cdot 67r$	$1 \cdot 50r$
Ring		
Total distance . . .	$1 \cdot 90r$	$2 \cdot 07r$
Distance within central area .	$0 \cdot 33r$	$0 \cdot 50r$

(r is the radius of the central area)

Let the number of people working in the central area be N. Then if we denote the average distance travelled in the central area (given in Table 7.16)[14] by Kr, r being the radius of the central area in feet, the total distance travelled in the central area on the journey to work is $NKr/5280$ person-miles. It follows that if the road space required per person-mile (given in Table 7.15) is A square feet, then the area of road required in the central area for the journey to work is $NKAr/5280$ square feet. If no part of the carriageway is used both for the journey to work and for the journey from work, then the road space required for the double journey will be twice this amount, i.e. $NKAr/2640$ square feet.*

It will be assumed that the ground-space required in the central area for all purposes other than travel is proportional to the number of workers, and that each worker requires P square feet for parking and G square feet for other purposes (working, recreation, etc.). Expressing the fact that the sum of the areas for different purposes equals the total area, we get

$$NKAr/2640 + N(G+P) = \pi r^2.$$

This is a quadratic equation in r and can be used to calculate r if N, K, A, G, P, are given. When r is known the area of road space and its ratio to the total area can be found.

A numerical example

As an example of the use of the above equation, it is interesting to find the area of road that would be necessary to enable all workers to travel to work by car. If we assume the streets to be 44 feet wide and of the type

---

* In practice part of the carriageway will always be used for both journeys and the space required will be less; see Reference (21).

found in central London, with traffic moving at 10 miles per hour, 1·5 persons per car, and a peak period of 2 hours, then $A = 28$ square feet per person-mile (see Table 7.15). G, the ground-space per worker, varies very considerably in actual towns: the average value for central London, which will be used here, is 245 square feet. P, the parking space per person, will be taken to be 25 square feet, which corresponds approximately to six-storey car parks with 1·5 persons per car. The density of work-places is assumed to be inversely proportional to the distance from the centres and the values of K given in Table 7.15 for the three routeing systems are used.

In the case of ring routeing, it is for some purposes more appropriate to find the road space required within the central area, excluding the ring road, than the total road space, and the value of K given on the bottom line of Table 7.15 has accordingly been used. The reason for excluding the area of the ring road is that the ring road does not conform to some of the assumptions that have been made: the same parts of the road would be used for the inward and outward journeys, and there would probably be fewer parked vehicles and pedestrians than on other roads.

Fig. 7.4 shows the amount of road space required per person calculated

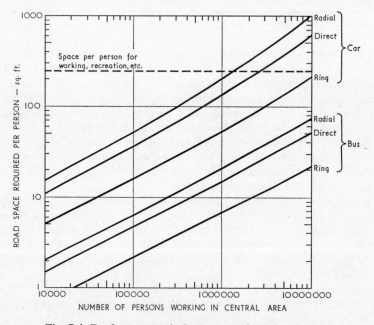

Fig. 7.4. Road space required per person for travel by car and bus with various routeing systems

from the equation given above and plotted against the number of persons working in the central area. In addition to the results for travel by car, lines representing travel by bus have been included, based on a value of A of four square feet per person-mile, with P equal to zero. The space per person for working, recreation, etc. ($G = 245$ square feet) is shown as a horizontal line.

Parking in Upper Brook Street, London

PLATE 8.1

Extensive transverse parking in St. James's Square, London

PLATE 8.2

(a)

(b)

In Coventry extensive parking areas have been provided on the roofs of buildings with bridge connexions

PLATE 8.3

Double right-turning lanes at an intersection in Slough, Bucks

PLATE 9.1

Carriageway markings for double left-turning lanes at a signal-controlled
junction in Düsseldorf, Germany. (Right-hand rule of the road)

PLATE 9.2

Examples of some types of roundabout: (a) round central island
PLATE 9.3 (a)

Examples of some types of roundabout: (b) square central island
PLATE 9.3 (b)

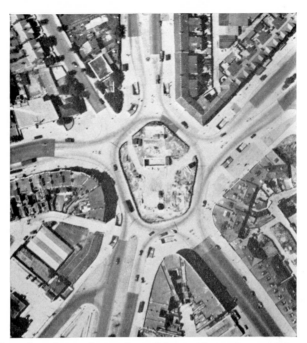

Examples of some types of roundabout: (c) complex roundabout
PLATE 9.3 (c)

Track marks on a roundabout showing that shape affects the use
made of the width of a weaving section
PLATE 9.4

A "locked" roundabout in Leeds

PLATE 9.5

Traffic signals at a roundabout on the outskirts of London

PLATE 9.6

Large loop vehicle detector installation for controlling traffic signals at a roundabout on the outskirts of London. The loop indicated by the black line is installed about 2 in. below the surface on a slot $\frac{3}{8}$ in. wide

PLATE 9.7

Experimental "Give Way" sign

PLATE 9.8

Use of broad (18-inch) broken line in conjunction with priority-rule at a roundabout

PLATE 9.9

Fig. 7.4 illustrates the general point that with the type of model assumed the road space required per person increases with the number of persons working in the central area, so that the road space should form a higher proportion of the total area in large towns than in small ones. When the proportion of road space is not very high, the road space per person increases approximately in proportion to the square root of the number of workers.

Fig. 7.4 should not be regarded as representing the situation in central London, although most of the data used do relate to London. In London there are no road systems of the types assumed, and the roads cannot all be used to their full theoretical capacity. Nevertheless, approximations to routes of the types assumed may be followed, and Fig. 7.4 probably indicates correctly the pattern of variation and the order of magnitude of the variables.

In central London the road space amounts to about 40–50 square feet per person working in the area. Within a two-mile radius of Cleopatra's Needle there were 1 246 000 people working in 1954, of whom 1 158 000 lived outside the area. The situation within this circular area therefore approximates roughly to that assumed for the theoretical model on which Fig. 7.4 is based. Most journeys to work probably approximate to direct routes, and Fig. 7.4 suggests that the road space available is insufficient to allow everyone to travel by car, but more than would be needed if everyone travelled by bus. If all drivers were to use ring routes, however, it appears that it would be much more feasible for everyone to travel by car. On the other hand, in smaller towns with about 100 000 workers in the central area, about 50 square feet of road space per person should permit everyone to travel by car and to use direct or radial routes.

It should be emphasized that a number of artificial assumptions have been made in obtaining these results. The numerical values in particular should be treated with caution, and should be regarded mainly as illustrating the possibilities of the method.

Capacity and utilization of ring roads

If all workers entering the central area follow ring routes then, with the assumptions made earlier, it is easy to find the flow of traffic along the ring road. The distance travelled along the ring road by a particular worker may be anything between zero and half the circumference, and its average value will be a quarter of the circumference. Any point on the ring road will therefore be passed by a quarter of the persons entering the central area. It follows that the capacity of the ring road in vehicles per hour must be a quarter of the rate at which vehicles enter the central area. For example, if 100 000 vehicles enter the central area in two hours, the capacity of the ring road must be 12 500 vehicles per hour. The assumptions made, however, overestimate to some extent the capacity required of a ring road, since there is in practice a tendency for people to live and work on the same side of a town.

It has been shown that if a ring road is used to the full extent it can lead to a very considerable reduction in the amount of travel taking place in the central area. However, a ring route is always longer than a direct route, so that drivers will not choose the ring route unless they are forced to do so or unless the higher speed on the ring road compensates for the greater distance. Some calculations have been made to find the parts of the central area to which a ring route is quicker than a direct route from a given point on the circumference, with various values of the ratio of the speed on the ring road to the speed in the central area. The results of these calculations are shown in Fig. 7.5.

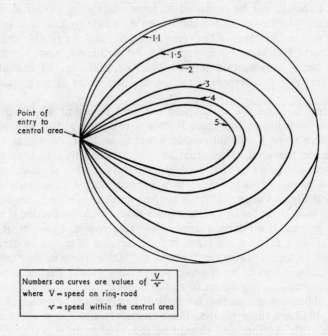

Point of entry to central area

Numbers on curves are values of $\dfrac{V}{v}$
where V = speed on ring-road
v = speed within the central area

To reach destinations between curve and circumference it is quicker to travel by ring route.

Fig. 7.5. Destinations which it is quicker to reach by a ring route than a direct route

REFERENCES TO CHAPTER 7

1. DAWSON, R. F. F.Traffic effects of Strand widening. *Traff. Engng & Control*, 1960, **2** (1) 26-8.

2. EATON, J. E. Flows and speeds in central London 1952-62. *Traff. Engng & Control*, 1963, **5** (8), 468-71.

3. TYLER, J. W., and J. MILLER. Traffic surveys in Edinburgh and Glasgow *Traff. Engng & Control*, 1962, 4 (7), 382-5, 390.

4. DEPARTMENT OF SCIENTIFIC AND INDUSTRIAL RESEARCH. Road research 1956. The report of the Road Research Board with the Report of the Director of Road Research. London, 1957 (H.M. Stationery Office).

5. METROPOLITAN AND CITY OF LONDON POLICE. Census of traffic 1960. London, 1961 (Metropolitan and City of London Police).

6. LONDON TRANSPORT EXECUTIVE. London travel survey 1949. London, 1950 (London Transport Executive).

7. DAWSON, R. F. F., and J. G. WARDROP. Passenger-mileage by road in Greater London. *Department of Scientific and Industrial Research, Road Research Technical Paper* No. 59. London, 1962 (H.M. Stationery Office).

8. LONDON TRANSPORT EXECUTIVE. London travel survey 1954. London, 1956 (London Transport Executive).

9. DAWSON, R. F. F. Survey of commercial traffic in London. *Traff. Engng & Control*, 1963, 5 (4), 246-50.

10. DRAKE, G. L. London's comprehensive traffic study—survey by home interview. *Traff. Engng & Control*, 1962, 4 (1), 26-30.

11. BRITISH TRANSPORT COMMISSION. Bristol on the move. A travel survey. London, 1953 (British Transport Commission).

12. SOUTH-EAST LANCASHIRE AND NORTH-EAST CHESHIRE HIGHWAY ENGINEERING COMMITTEE. A highway plan 1962. Manchester, 1962, (South-east Lancashire and North-east Cheshire Highway Engineering Committee.)

13. HODGEN, R. Prediction of Glasgow's future traffic pattern. *Traff. Engng & Control*, 1963, 4 (11), 606-11, 615.

14. LONDON TRANSPORT EXECUTIVE. London Transport in 1960. London, 1961 (London Transport Executive).

15. MINISTRY OF TRANSPORT AND CIVIL AVIATION. "Crush-hour" travel in Central London. Report of the first year's work of the Committee for staggering of working hours in Central London. London, 1958 (H.M. Stationery Office).

16. SMEED, R. J. The traffic problem in towns. Manchester, 1961 (Manchester Statistical Society).

17. SMEED, R. J. The space requirements for traffic in towns. *Symposium on Urban Survival and Traffic, University of Durham*, 1961. London, 1962, pp. 136-45.

18. SMEED, R. J. Road development in urban areas—the effect of some kinds of routeing systems on the amount of traffic in the central areas of towns (with particular reference to journeys into and out of the central areas). *J. Instn Highw. Engrs*, 1963, 10 (1), 5-26.

19. SMEED, R. J. The road space required for traffic in towns. *Town Plann. Rev.*, 1963, 33 (4), 279-92.

20. SMEED, R. J., and G. O. JEFFCOATE. Traffic flow during the journey to work in the central area of a town which has a rectangular grid for its road system. *Second International Symposium on the Theory of Road Traffic Flow, London, 1963.* (To be published).

21. SMEED, R. J., and E. M. HOLROYD. Some factors affecting congestion in towns. *Engineering for Traffic Conference*. London, 1963, (Printerhall Ltd.) pp. 83-91.

Chapter 8

Parking

SYNOPSIS

Growth of street parking in London. Origins of urban parked vehicles. The detailed study of parking intensity: indices of parking intensity; parking duration. Methods for parking surveys. Off-street parking.

INTRODUCTION

As the flow of traffic in towns increases so does the number of vehicles parked in the streets. These tend to reduce the speed of traffic, and methods of reducing their effect have to be found. The use of controlled parking (parking meters) was tried experimentally in a small area of the West End of London during 1958 and 1959, and the use of meters was fairly rapidly extended thereafter in central London. The virtual elimination of long-period parking from the meter zones aggravated the shortage of off-street parking space and gave rise to an accelerated programme of garage construction. Construction of large municipal and commercial off-street garages has also increased recently in British provincial cities.

In this chapter the development of parking congestion in pre-meter London is discussed briefly and simple survey methods for the study of street parking are described. The control of street parking by regulation, including the use of parking meters, is discussed in Chapter 10. Some problems of off-street garage construction in Britain, and standards for off-street parking facilities, are touched upon. No detailed treatment of garage design has been attempted as this subject already has an extensive literature.

GROWTH OF STREET PARKING IN LONDON

As in most industrialized countries, the problem of vehicle parking in urban areas increased rapidly in Britain after the 1939–45 war. The case of central London, though more serious than the average, illustrates some interesting features of increasing urban parking during the years before the appearance of parking meters (see Table 8.1 and Plate 8.1).

It will be seen that in less than a decade between 1951 and 1959, the total number of street-parked vehicles in the central area doubled, but whereas the increase between 1951 and 1955 was 68 per cent, that between 1955 and 1959 was only 19 per cent. The corresponding percentage increases in total registered vehicles in the London County Council Area were 38 per cent and 32 per cent respectively, showing that the increase in street parking during the second period was disproportionately smaller than the increase in total registrations. The probable explanation of the phenomenon appears in Fig. 8.1, which shows the increases in street parking during the two periods. By 1959 the density of standing vehicles per mile in the areas marked 2, 3, 4, 11, 12, 13, 14 and 15, representing the West End, was rapidly approaching or had actually passed the practical saturation limit

TABLE 8.1

The growth of parking in the Inner London area

Year	Number of street-parked vehicles in Inner London (private and commercial) (a)	Rounded figures of the number of vehicles Licensed in the L.C.C. licensing area			$\dfrac{(a)}{(b)} \times 100$	$\dfrac{(a)}{(c)} \times 100$
		Cars (b)	Other vehicles	Total (c)		
1951	25 400	142 750	183 790	326 540	17·8	7·8
1955	42 700	237 000	213 020	450 020	18·0	9·5
1959	50 700	315 000	280 550	595 550	16·1	8·5
Per-cent inc.						
51–55	68	66	16	38		
55–59	19	33	32	32		
51–59	100	33	53	82		

of approximately 400 vehicles per mile of street for longitudinally parked vehicles. The exceptionally high figure for Zone 14, St. James's, was accounted for by extensive transverse parking (see Plate 8.2). Thus the rate of increase in a large part of central London had, in fact, been cut down by sheer lack of further kerbside space.

TABLE 8.2

Time required for car parking operations in the West End (1954)

Movement	Times for types of parking (minutes)		
	Street	Garage	
		Attendant parked	Customer parked
Moving into and out of parking space . . .	0·68	1·16*	2·73†
Walking from parked car to chosen address and back[2] .	4·57	8·48	8·48
Total movements if car is parked first . .	5·25	9·64	11·21
Cruising streets if starting at chosen address . .	3·45	3·98	3·98
All movements if address is passed first . .	8·70	13·62	15·19

* Unparking time only.
† Assuming driver can park and unpark as quickly as attendant.

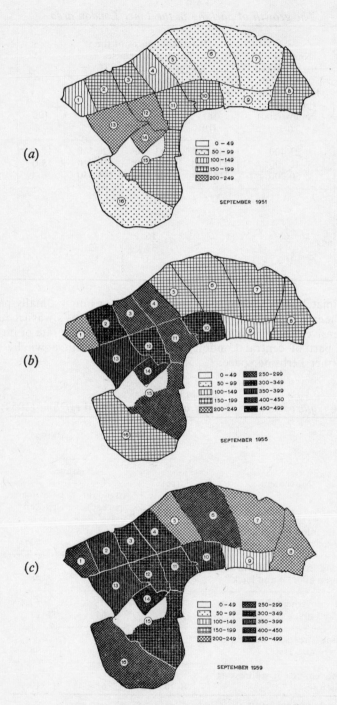

Fig. 8.1. Densities of standing vehicles per mile
of street in Inner London area

Another aspect of the shortage of parking space is shown by the figures in Table 8.2 which gives the time taken up by parking and walking during visits to certain addresses in the West End in about the same conditions as those of the 1955 census in Table 8.1, and corresponding to the distribution of density shown in Fig. 8.1(b). At a walking speed of three miles per hour, the average distance walked when using street parking corresponds to just less than one quarter of a mile. Although no comparable figures were available for 1959, the density in Fig. 8.1(c) shows that conditions had evidently deteriorated still further. Table 8.2 also shows that, in the mid-1950's no time was saved by using the off-street garages then available.

These conditions of acute parking congestion led to the introduction of the first experimental controlled parking, or parking meter, zone in Mayfair in 1958, and since that date the meters have spread rapidly within central London, giving rise to an entirely different situation in street parking.

ORIGINS OF URBAN PARKED VEHICLES

The origin of urban street-parked vehicles, particularly cars which are mainly responsible for parking congestion, has been studied extensively in the U.S.A. and to a much smaller extent in Britain. The matter may be studied in two aspects, first the origins and purposes of the drivers who park their cars in cities, and secondly the characteristics of various types of building when regarded as sources of generators of concentrations of parked vehicles.

In the summer and early autumn of 1955 the Social Survey of the Central Office of Information made, on behalf of the Road Research Laboratory, a pilot survey of the amount of parking generated by buildings of three kinds—offices, shops and factories—in or near central London. The proportions of people in various income groups travelling to the buildings, including staff and visitors, who owned cars are shown in Table 8.3.

TABLE 8.3

Car ownership and income of people using the buildings
(1955)

Income	Number of person using buildings	Percentage of car owners
Less than £500 p.a.	4499	16
£500–£1000 p.a.	3834	42
More than £1000 p.a.	995	76
All groups	9328	30

The distribution of the distance from Aldwych travelled by those who parked at these buildings is given in Table 8.4.

TABLE 8.4

Distribution of distance from Aldwych travelled by parkers (1955)

Distance (miles)	Percentage of parkers
0–2½	20
2½–5	13
5–7½	13
7½–10	6
10–15	26
Over 15	22

The average walking time from the place of parking to the final destination was three minutes, but in about 81 per cent of cases the walking time was less than this figure.

The results of a questionnaire suggested that parking difficulties and traffic congestion were the main deterrents to the use of a car; they were of about equal importance.

Counts of vehicles parked overnight were made at two post-war local-authority housing estates. All vehicles observed either on or off the carriage-way after midnight were counted and an estimate was made of the numbers of vehicles in garages. The number of housing units per parked vehicles was 3·7 on one estate and 3·0 on the other.

The numbers of parked vehicles associated with factories were studied by counting all vehicles observed on four factory estates and by counting vehicles at each of seventeen factories. In both cases the number of vehicles was related to the floor area of the factory or factories and to the number of people employed. These relations were found to vary considerably between different factory estates and even more markedly between factories. The number of square feet of floor space per car varied between about 500 and 14 000 with a mean of 400 and the number of employees per car ranged from three to 40 with a mean of 14.

The extent to which football matches attract parked vehicles was investigated by counts made in 1957 of parked vehicles at 15 Association Football grounds on Saturday afternoons and at three during evening and mid-week matches; all but one of the grounds were in the South-East of England. Within the range of attendances of 4000 to 36 000 it was found that the number of parked cars was given approximately by

Number of cars = $675 + 0.044 \times$ (number of spectators)

The amount of parking near cinemas was studied at 10 cinemas in South-East England in 1955 and 1956. The total numbers of cars and motor-cycles parked were found to vary considerably between cinemas and from week to week, although a definite seasonal variation could be distinguished. The numbers of cars parked were related to the seating capacity of the cinema and to the number of admissions. The average for seven of the cinemas, mostly in the London area, over a period of one year, was 340 cars parked per week per 1000 seats, with a range between individual cinemas of 240 to 450. At six of the cinemas there were, on the average, 62 cars parked per 1000 admissions, with a range between individual cinemas of 48 to 71. Some of this variation was probably associated with the type of neighbourhood in which the cinema was located. The number of vehicles parked on Saturdays was over 20 per cent of the total number parked during the week.

THE DETAILED STUDY OF PARKING INTENSITY

Indices of Parking Density

The density of parking may be measured in terms of vehicles per unit area or per unit length of street; however a more instructive index is given by the actual occupancy as a percentage of available space. Some years ago the Ministry of Transport[1] recommended the use of 20 ft of kerbside space per vehicle and this is the length used in most of the parking meter bays in central London. Adopting this standard, the number of cars actually standing along a given kerb, expressed as a percentage of the number of 20-ft lengths along the kerb has been defined at the Laboratory as the Parking Index.

Parking indices may be calculated for the separate kerbs of individual streets, for whole streets, or even for the aggregated usable lengths of street within an area. Table 8.5 shows the parking indices for whole areas for the central London zones used in parking censuses carried out by the Laboratory. It will be noticed that indices of 84 and 92 per cent were reached in Area 14, St. James's, these exceptionally high figures were due to the extra transverse parking already referred to. For the longitudinal kerbside parking to which the index normally refers, the index of 74 per cent for Area 13 represented street conditions bad enough to necessitate the drastic remedy of controlled (meter) parking which, since 1959, has reduced the indices in all the most congested West End zones.

Parking duration

OVERALL DISTRIBUTION OF PARKED PERIODS

A rather more important consideration than mere surface density, and one which greatly affects the chances of finding a parking place in a congested area, is the duration of parking. Table 8.6 taken from a Ministry of Transport[2] report shows a straight distribution of the parked times of cars standing in the streets of Inner London in May-June 1956.

An alternative graphical representation of the same sort of information, based on an investigation carried out by the Laboratory in Mayfair in 1951, is shown in Fig. 8.2; from such lines the percentage of the total daily turnover of vehicles, which were parked for less than any given period, can be read off directly. For example, in South Audley St. 92 per cent of all the vehicles parked in the course of the whole day remained for less than one hour, but in Green Street the figure was 41 per cent. It will be noticed that streets accommodating vehicle users of certain distinct types have characteristically shaped cumulative percentage lines.

10*

TABLE 8.5

Occupancy of available kerbside space in the Inner Area of London

Area Number (see Fig. 1)	Description	Length street in miles	Parking Index—percentage of total usable length of street		
			1959	1955	1951
1	Marylebone (South-West) .	7·0	50·4	39·0	24·0
2	Marylebone (Central) .	9·3	67·0	64·6	37·0
3	Marylebone (South-East) .	8·7	61·7	53·9	33·9
4	Holborn (Museum) . .	7·6	62·9	53·1	26·8
5	Holborn and St. Pancras .	10·5	46·0	33·8	16·9
6	Finsbury (West) . . .	19·5	47·3	32·6	18·2
7	Finsbury (South) and City (North)	18·9	38·6	30·3	18·1
8	City (East)	11·2	45·5	37·7	29·4
9	City (St. Paul's) . . .	8·1	25·8	20·5	12·3
10	City (Fleet St.) . . .	6·2	66·9	59·3	35·8
11	Holborn and Westminster (Covent Garden) . .	9·7	62·9	50·8	33·0
12	Westminster (Soho) .	7·9	58·7	61·8	39·0
13	Westminster (Mayfair) .	13·4	68·0	74·0	46·4
14	Westminster (St. James's) .	3·4	92·0	83·9	41·8
15	Westminster (Whitehall and Royal Parks) . . .	16·3	61·0	49·5	30·6
15	Westminster (Whitehall excluding Parks) . .	15·0	63·4	51·4	33·3
16	Westminster (Pimlico and Belgravia) . . .	22·7	48·9	33·3	16·8
Total	Inner London Area . .	180·4	53·6	44·8	26·6
	Inner London Area (excluding Royal Parks) .	179·1	53·6	44·9	26·8

TABLE 8.6

Total number of cars parked for different durations

Duration of parking	Up to ½ hr	½–1 hr	1–2 hr	2–4 hr	4–6 hr	6–10 hr	Over 10 hr	Total	Additional cars parked	
									5.30 p.m.–6 p.m.	6 p.m.–6.15 p.m.
Totals	50 768	25 872	26 416	19 616	10 048	12 576	1328	146 624	2992	4800
Percentages	34·6	17·7	18·0	13·4	6·8	8·6	0·9	100·0		

AVERAGE DISTIBUTION OF PARKED CARS AT ANY INSTANT

Data such as the foregoing are, however, of limited value in planning parking accommodation because, for the latter, it is important to know how much space should be provided for the vehicles in different duration categories which are observable in a given street or area at any instant

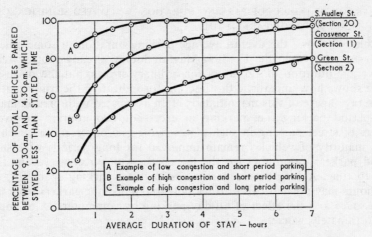

**Fig. 8.2. Cumulative percentage distributions of parked periods
for vehicles in three Mayfair streets in 1951**

throughout the day on an average—or more particularly at times of peak demand. This information is obtained by weighing distributions, such as those just described, by the average waiting time; the method of doing this will be described in detail later in this chapter. Fig. 8.3 illustrates the simple cumulative distribution lines and the corresponding weighted distributions obtained for Mayfair and central Leeds at about the same date. It is interesting to notice for example that 45 per cent of the total daily turnover of vehicles parked in Mayfair for less than half an hour constituted only 5 per cent of those seen to be parked, on an average, at any instant.

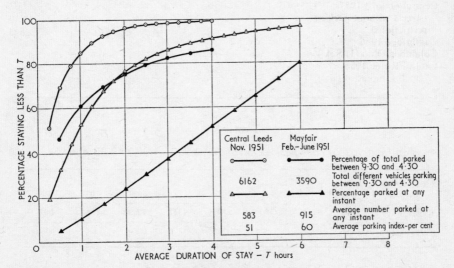

**Fig. 8.3. Proportions of vehicles parking for various times in selected streets in Leeds
and Mayfair**

COMPARISON OF INDICES OF PARKING DURATION   LIMITED SIGNIFICANCE OF
THE OVERALL AVERAGE PARKED TIME

Table 8.7 shows the overall average parking duration in some cities in
which surveys were made. The 1951 Mayfair Survey, already quoted, yielded
an average duration of 1·6 hours for ordinary streets, but the discussion
above shows how unrealistic this figure is for indicating the true situation;
an average figure of this magnitude is often associated with predominantly
long-period parking (i.e. parking in excess of two hours), the overall
picture of street parking in such places being one of streets in which the
large majority of vehicles remain unmoved for long periods with short-
period parkers scrambling for the few spaces which become vacant from
time to time. A long-period parker occupying a parking space for, say,
two hours may prevent two or three potential half-hour parkers from finding a space and the effect of all-day parking by commuters is, of course,
proportionately worse.

TABLE 8.7

Some results from parking duration surveys

Place and time	Average duration of parking (hours)	Percentage remaining for more than 2 hours	
		Of all vehicles	Of vehicles observed at any instant
Mayfair 1951 . . .	1·6 (streets— excluding squares)	20	60
Central Leeds 1951 . .	—	4	—
Central London 1955 (Ministry of Transport survey) . . .	2	30	—
Central Oxford 1957 (streets without parking restrictions) . . .	1·5	18	47
Cambridge 1956 . .	over 2	—	—
Columbus Ohio (U.S.A.) .	3	—	—
Central Rome 1958 (small samples of cars) .	2·8	—	—

TABLE 8.8

Total number of cars parked during peak hour 1.30 *to* 2.30 *p.m.*

Duration of parking	Up to ½ h	½–1 h	1–2 h	2–4 h	4–6 h	6–10 h	Over 10 h	Total
Totals	5840	3536	5904	6848	7952	12 560	1344	43 984
Percentages	13 ·4	8 ·0	13 ·5	15 ·5	18 ·0	28 ·6	3 ·0	100 ·0

Confirmation of the preponderance of long-period parking in central
London before metres were introduced is shown in Table 8.8. which gives

the percentage distribution of cars parked during the hour of peak demand, 1.30–2.30 p.m.; here only 13·4 per cent of the vehicles were parked for up to half an hour.

In central Leeds, although about 70 per cent of all the vehicles that were parked between 9.30 a.m. and 4.30 p.m. stayed for less than half an hour, at any instant during this period only about 33 per cent were in this duration category. The average parking index in these streets was 51 per cent; hence a motorist seeking a parking space would find about $0·67 \times 0·51$, that is about one third of the available kerbside space occupied by vehicles parking for more than this time.

In Mayfair the average parking index was about 60 per cent, and $0·95 \times 0·60$, or 57 per cent, of the available kerbside parking space was occupied at any time by vehicles staying longer than half an hour; 12 per cent was occupied by vehicles staying longer than six hours.

METHODS FOR PARKING SURVEYS

The scope of surveys

The scope and sophistication of parking surveys depend largely on the resources available for the work. With sufficient resources exhaustive parking surveys combined with origin-and-destination studies, involving extensive interrogation of vehicle users, can be employed using procedures developed by traffic consultants in the U.S.A. Such studies are capable of yielding detailed information on sources and characteristics of urban parking as well as the optimum theoretical location of parking facilities to suit a given population of street parked vehicles.[3,4,5]

Parking surveys yield conclusions relating to existing conditions and in planning parking accommodation from them allowance should be made for future trends in traffic and for the effects of changes in land use, population migration and similar factors.

Simple parking survey

SURVEY OF GENERAL DISTRIBUTION

The simplest type of useful parking survey includes a general census of parked vehicles and a more or less complete duration survey.

In an area about which nothing is known in advance the work should start with a pilot survey of the general distribution of street-parked vehicles and the extent and use of off-street parking facilities. This information should be entered on a map of the area to be surveyed. A knowledge of the periods of the day during which peak demand for parking space occurs is also necessary for planning subsequent work—the peak periods can be identified by maintaining a detailed half-hourly count all day in a few specially congested streets and possibly a few off-street parking places.

The general census of parked vehicles should be completed as far as possible during the peak period, and may be carried out by teams of two observers, each travelling in a car, or by a larger number of pedestrian enumerators. Where manpower is limited the former method is preferable, and for this a foolscap size outline map of the streets should be mounted on an observation board beside a convenient table on which the vehicle counts can be recorded. On the map should be drawn a continuous vehicle route designed to cover all the streets with the minimum of travelling. The vehicle route should then be divided up into numbered sections corresponding to convenient street lengths within which private and commercial standing vehicles can be counted. During the journey in the car the standing vehicles on the near and offsides of the street are conveniently counted by one or two back-seat observers using small four-bank mechanical counters scoring the vehicles in the order Private, Commercial (Nearside), Commercial (Offside), Private (Offside), the numbers being called out for tabulation by the scribe and vehicle navigator sitting beside the car driver. After the dictation of the count at the end of each numbered section of the street route, the counters are quickly re-set. During the general census the vehicle navigator should note on the street map the limits of no-waiting street sections and official parking places so that provision for these features may be made in later work.

PARKING DURATION SURVEY

PREPARATORY WORK. The general census shows the overall distribution of standing vehicles but reveals nothing about the duration of waiting; the purpose of the duration survey is to determine the duration characteristics of the parked-vehicle population with special reference to the peak parking demand. Ideally the duration study should include all the vehicles in the surveyed area, but in practice sampling generally suffices. As the duration survey depends on the regular periodic recording of all vehicles in the selected streets, it is important that the interval between successive recordings, the so-called Trip Interval, shall be short enough to detect an adequate proportion of the short-period parked vehicles. The effects of the choice of the trip interval on the results obtained have been examined in a particular case. Observations taken at $\frac{1}{4}$-hour intervals were analysed to give results corresponding to $\frac{1}{2}$-hourly observations, and Table 8.9 shows the average number of vehicles parked during the period of observation compared for $\frac{1}{4}$- and $\frac{1}{2}$-hourly intervals.

TABLE 8.9

Comparison of the results for $\frac{1}{4}$- and $\frac{1}{2}$-hourly intervals

Interval between observations	Average number at any instant	Total number of vehicles seen
$\frac{1}{4}$h	28·9	293
$\frac{1}{2}$h	29·2	213

It has been calculated that in this particular case, observations at $\frac{1}{2}$-hourly intervals would give adequate information about total vehicle-hours of parking and the proportions staying for various times, but would considerably underestimate the total turnover of parked vehicles and would not, of course, provide detailed information about vehicles staying for less than half an hour. Experience in the West End of London has shown that, where the proportion of vehicles remaining for less than half an hour does not exceed about 15 per cent, as determined by continuous close observations of small samples of the parked vehicle population, a duration survey based on a half-hour trip interval yields adequate information, but where the percentage of vehicles which parked for less than half an hour substantially exceeds this figure, a trip interval of 15 minutes may be required. Unfortunately a short trip interval enormously increases the labour of analysis.

After deciding the correct trip interval, a sample of streets representative of all varieties of parking within the survey area must be selected. These streets are then grouped into closed circuits each of which can be covered within the trip interval under the most congested traffic conditions likely to be experienced. In actual practice the foregoing generally resolves itself into the selection of several closed circuits each of which can be traversed within half an hour. Using a car, low densities of parked vehicles, up to 200 per mile, can be recorded over a route up to two miles long by two observers, one writing down the indentification marks of vehicles on the nearside, and the other, those on the offside of the street, but for higher densities of parking, such as are found in the centres of large towns, it is necessary to use four observers, one dicating and a second writing down the numbers of vehicles for each side of the street. Where vehicles are dense only intermittently, a three-observer team can cope with the work, the third observer helping with dictation on whichever side of the street the vehicle density may require it. The street route must be traversed in the same direction on each circuit and, since the work goes on all day, reliefs for the observers and the vehicle driver must be arranged.

When manpower is limited but the available observers are reasonably skilled, modern portable sound recorders may be used with advantage. Since failure of the apparatus during any of the recording spoils the whole day's work, only thoroughly reliable and constantly checked recorders with adequate supplies of recording tape are suitable. The recording procedure should be carefully rehearsed, and time must be allowed for sample checking of the recording after each trip. With these precautions sound recording is capable of faster, more accurate and more comprehensive recording than the other methods, and it is also less exhausting for the observers. With careful intermittent operation of the recorder, for the maximum economy of tape, a surprisingly large amount of information can be placed on office recorder size tapes and the consumption is not excessive. Using a sound recorder an observer, with driver, riding in a car can cope with high-density parking along one side of the street over a two-mile route with a trip interval of half an hour, thus saving the use of one extra observer for each side of the street as compared with the manual method described above. The sound recordings must of course be transcribed on to forms for subsequent analysis, but this has incidental advantages over direct manual recording in the production of clearer and more legible tabulation. It has been found with sound recording that recording errors due to overworking of the observers at places of high congestion are less frequent than with the manual method, and useful extra comments on special features, which could not be written down, can be dictated on to sound records.

Much parking survey work is also done by comparatively unskilled observers working on foot. Here the closed street circuits have to be much shorter than when a car is used, and it is most important that the instructions for the work should be clearly understood and the observers should not be burdened to the point where observations are spoilt by inaccuracy or incompleteness. Two formulae given by the Ministry of Transport for calculating the capacity per observer on quarter-hour trip intervals routes are as follows:

$$nd = 80\,000 \quad \cdots \cdots \cdots \cdots \quad (1)$$

$$d + 5n = 1250 \text{ (Maximum)} \quad \cdots \cdots \cdots \quad (2)$$

where n = number of vehicles and d the route length in yards. An alternative for (1) is $n = 720T/V$ where T is the trip interval in hours and V the travelling speed in miles per hour. Formula (1) is unrealistic for low densities of parked vehicles, while (2) allows a fixed time per vehicle ($3\frac{1}{2}$ sec) plus a fixed speed of travel (about three miles per hour). Both these formulae agree over the medium range of parking density.

COLLECTION AND ANALYSIS OF FIELD DATA. Work may now be started on the duration survey proper. The trip routes must be memorized before the travelling begins. Special recording forms are used for recording the identification marks of parked vehicles between say 8.30 a.m. and 6 p.m. On the field recording sheet shown in Fig. 8.4 only the last three figures

Please complete all the headings carefully   Use pen or sharp pencil

Investigation: Central Oxford   Date: 31.8.57   Street: Keble Rd. Nearside – P

1	2	3	4	5	6	7	8	9	10	11	12	13	14	15	16	17	18	19	20	21
8.30	9.0	9.30	10.0	10.30	11.0	11.30	12.0	12.30	1.0	1.30	2.0	2.30	3.0	3.30	4.0	4.30	5.0	5.30	6.0	6.30
634	325	325	374	374	374	374	444	254	444	444	801	376	376	376	99	99	99			
434	903		325	885	885	325	906	444	985	365	733	733	733	271	376	271	271	271		
575	863		844	325	647	985	325	153	51	366	365	365	365	093	271	344	344	344		
837	207	207	207	184	325	833	985	325	153	67	67	67	67	486	349	325	093	093		
	644	644	644	91	985	644	833	985	575	575	575	575	612	923	093	486	486	67		
	922	922	922	226	833	171	644	737	40	40	40	62	575	166	486	923	923	432		
	434			207	91	922	171	575	922	183	183	183	62	67	923	166	166	814		
	575	575	575	644	226	183	922	644	183	572	572	252	183	612	166	67	67	200		
	837	837	837	922	644	572	183	171	572	960	960	960	252	429	67	612	432	44		
				575	171	960	572	922	960					62	612	429	814	760		
				837	922		960	183						588	429	588	588			
					575			572						183	814	200	200			
					837			960						20	62	62	760			
														252	588	176	176			
														176	200					
															176					

Fig. 8.4. Field observation sheet for parking duration work

of the vehicles registration number are recorded, one observer using a sheet for nearside vehicles and another observer a second sheet for offside ones. If, for the subsequent calculation of parking indices, all the street lengths are measured in advance, the number of vehicles which can be recorded per sheet and hence the most convenient sheet changing points may be estimated allowing about 20 ft of kerb length per vehicle in crowded streets plus about 20 per cent spare space on each sheet. For convenience in the later work, it is an advantage to use a single sheet, such as the one here illustrated, for the whole day rather than spreading the field observations across two sheets. With sound recorders no sheets or boards are normally required on the road, though the field sheets may be used for the subsequent transcription of the dictated records. If possible the duration survey over each selected route should be repeated on at least two weekdays,

Site Keble Road Parking place nearside Date Sat. 31 8 57

Period 8.30 a.m.–6.0 p.m.

Vehicle number	Number of times seen																				Total number of times seen
	Time and trip number																				
	8·30	9·0	9·30	10·0	10·30	11·0	11·30	12·0	12·30	1·0	1·30	2·0	2·30	3·0	3·30	4·0	4·30	5·0	5·30	6·0	
	1	2	3	4	5	6	7	8	9	10	11	12	13	14	15	16	17	18	19	20	
634	1																				1
434	2	2																			2
575	6	6	6	6	6	6															6
837	6	6	6	6	6	6															6
325		8	8	8	8	8	8	8	8												8
903		1																			1
863		1																			1
207		4	4	4	4																4
644		8	8	8	8	8	8	8	8												8
922		9	9	9	9	9	9	9	9	9											9
374				4	4	4	4														4
944				1																	1
885					2	2															2
647					1																1
184					1																1
91					2	2															2
226					2	2															2
833						3	3	3													3
171						4	4	4	4												4
985						4	4	4	4												4
183							9	9	9	9	9	9	9	9	9						9
572							6	6	6	6	6	6									6
960							7	7	7	7	7	7	7								7
444								4	4	4	4										4
906								1													1
575									6	6	6	6	6	6							6
254									1												1
153									2	2											2
737									1												1
385										1											1
51										1											1
40										3	3	3									3
365											4	4	4	4							4
366											1										1
67											9	9	9	9	9	9	9	9	9		9
801												1									1
733												3	3	3							3
376													1								1
62													5	5	5	5	5				5
252													3	3	3						3

Table incomplete

Fig. 8.5. First stage analysis for parking duration observation

one of which should be the busiest or market day but, if available manpower is limited, it is best to concentrate on the weekday of worst parking congestion, since any parking accommodation planned as a result of the survey must provide for the worst conditions.

Fig. 8.5 shows a convenient form for the first stage of the analysis. The vehicle identification numbers are entered in the first column and the number of times the vehicles are seen is recorded in the manner shown, for convenience in the next stage of the work.

The table shown in Fig. 8.6 summarizes the data in the table shown in Fig. 8.5 in a form convenient for cross-checking and further calculations. The total vehicle-trips (a) divided by the total number of trips throughout the day—nineteen in this case—gives the average number of vehicles seen per trip. The total vehicle-trips divided by the number of trip intervals in the corresponding parking duration yields the total number of different

---

Site Keble Rd. Oxford.   Length 18 x 20 ft. (effective)   Average width..........
Nearside parking
(street parking place)

Date Sat. 31.8.57   Time 8.30 a.m – 6.00 p.m

Trip interval and unit of parking duration.....½ hour.....

Parking Duration in trip intervals	Trip number (A.M. 1–8 / P.M. 9–20)																				Total vehicle-trips (a)	Average number per trip (b)	Total No. of different vehicles parked (c)
	1	2	3	4	5	6	7	8	9	10	11	12	13	14	15	16	17	18	19	20			
1	1	2		1	2				1	2	2	1	1	1					1	1	16	0.8	16
2	1	1		3	3				1	1			1	1	1	1	3	3			20	1.1	10
3			1	1	1		1		1	1	2	2	2	3	3	3	1				21	1.1	7
4	1	1	2	2	3	3	3	3	1	2	1	1	2	4	5	5	4	1			44	2.3	11
5									1	2	5	5	5	4	3						25	1.3	5
6	2	2	2	2	2	2	1	1	2	2	2	2	1	1							24	1.3	4
7				1	1	1	1	1	1	1	1										7	0.4	1
8	2	2	2	2	2	2	2	2													16	0.8	2
9	1	1	1	1	1	1	2	2	2	2	2	2	2	2	1	1	1	1			27	1.4	3
10																							
11																							
12																							
13																							
14																							
15																							
16																							
17																							
18																							
19																							
20																							
Total (Vehicles per trip)	4	9	6	5	12	12	10	11	13	10	9	9	9	10	15	15	15	14	5		200		59
Parking index per cent																							

Fig. 8.6. Second-stage analysis form for parking duration data

vehicles observed throughout the day which stayed for that duration; for example, sixteen different vehicles stayed for one half-hour, $20 \div 2$ stayed for two half-hours, etc. The sum of the figures (c) in the last column shows that 59 different vehicles parked in the street during the day. The relevant length, in feet, of street kerb divided by 20 gives the acceptable maximum number of vehicles which could park in the street at any one time, and the

Site Central Oxford. Length 681 x 20 ft. spaces. Average width...............
Sample of streets with (Maximum kerbside space)
unrestricted parking

Date Sat. 24th August 1957 Time 8:30am to 6:00 p.m.

Trip interval and unit of parking duration ½ hour...............

Parking Duration in trip intervals	Trip number																				Total vehicle-trips (a)	Average number per trip (b)	Total No. of different vehicles parked (c)
	A. M.								P. M.														
	1	2	3	4	5	6	7	8	9	10	11	12	13	14	15	16	17	18	19	20			
	0800-0830	0830-0900	0900-0930	0930-1000	1000-1030	1030-1100	1100-1130	1130-1200	1200-1230	1230-0100	0100-0130	0130-0200	0200-0230	0230-0300	0300-0330	0330-0400	0400-0430	0430-0500	0500-0530				
1	6	15	13	19	14	24	22	24	13	9	5	9	12	15	18	13	13	7	15		266		266
2		3	10	22	22	25	28	16	11	9	7	6	10	14	17	20	16	17	9		262		131
Subtotal to '2'	6	18	23	41	36	49	50	40	24	18	12	15	22	29	35	33	29	24	24		528		
3	1	3	5	9	14	25	25	23	12	10	8	10	8	11	17	26	28	16	8		261		87
4		1	4	7	7	12	11	11	14	9	10	8	9	18	22	26	22	12	5		208		52
Subtotal to '4'	7	22	32	57	57	86	86	74	50	37	30	33	38	58	74	85	79	54	37		997		
5	2	2	4	5	7	7	11	10	12	10	8	4	4	5	13	13	13	12	8		150		30
6			5	7	9	10	11	11	6	4	3	4	8	8	8	8	7	5			114		19
7	1	3	4	6	6	6	7	6	5	4	2	4	4	3	3	2	2	2			70		10
8		1	1	2	2	3	3	5	5	4	6	7	7	6	6	4	4	4	2		72		9
Subtotal to '8'	10	28	41	75	79	111	117	106	83	61	50	51	58	80	104	112	106	79	52		1403		
9	1	1	1	1	1	1	3	3	8	3	3	2	2	2	2	2					27		3
10			1	1	1	1	1	1	1	1	1	1									10		1
11	1	1	1	1	1	1	2	2	2	4	4	4	3	3	3	3	3	2	2	2	44		4
12		1	2	2	2	2	2	2	2	2	2	2	2	2	1						24		2
Subtotal to '12'	12	30	43	79	84	119	125	114	93	70	59	59	66	87	108	116	108	81	54		1503		
13	1	1	1	1	1	1	1	3	3	3	3	3	3	2	2	2	2	2	2		39		3
14			1	1	1	1	1	1	1	1	1	1	1	1	1	1					14		1
15																							0
16		2	3	3	3	3	3	3	3	3	3	3	3	3	3	3	1				48		3
17																							0
18	1	2	2	2	2	2	2	2	2	2	2	2	2	2	2	2	1				36		2
19	1	1	1	1	1	1	1	1	1	1	1	1	1	1	1	1	1	1			19		1
20																							
Total	15	34	49	86	91	127	135	124	103	80	69	65	76	96	118	125	117	90	60		1664		624

Fig. 8.7a. Summary sheet for the calculation of parking indices

observed vehicles per trip, at the foot of the table, expressed as a percentage of this figure is the so-called parking index.

Data of the kind shown in Fig. 8.6 may be aggregated for numbers of streets to give tables like those in Fig. 8.7(a) and 8.7(b). By the insertion of subtotals such as those shown in the first of these tables for 2, 4, 8 and 12 trip intervals, the intermediate parking indices for durations of 1, 2, 4, and 6 hours respectively can be calculated as shown at the foot of Fig. 8.7(a), and exhibited graphically as in Fig. 8.8. The latter shows clearly that the peak-parking densities occur at approximately 11.30 a.m. and 4.00 p.m. and the curves show how much the parking index would be reduced by the imposition of various time limits on parking. For example, the restriction of parking to two hours would reduce the 11.30 a.m. peak index from 19.8 to 12.6 by the removal of $135-86 = 49$ parked vehicles and the 4 p.m.

Site Central Oxford. Length All non-restricted. Average width..................
streets on duration survey

Dates Wednesday, Friday and Saturday, Aug. 1957 Time 8:30 a.m. - 6:00 p.m.

Trip interval and unit of parking duration ½ hour.................

Parking duration in trip intervals	Trip number																				Total vehicle-trips (a)	Average number per trip (b)	Total No. of different vehicles parked (c)
	1	2	3	4	5	6	7	8	9	10	11	12	13	14	15	16	17	18	19	20			
1																					(17.4) 2743	144.4	(47.5) 2743
2																					(14.8) 2328	122.5	(20.2) 1164
3																					(12.2) 1911	100.6	(11.0) 637
4																					(8.5) 1336	70.3	(5.8) 334
5																					(7.4) 1160	61.1	(4.0) 232
6																					(6.5) 1026	54.0	(3.0) 171
7																					(6.0) 945	49.7	(2.3) 135
8																					(4.6) 728	38.3	(1.6) 91
9																					(3.8) 594	31.3	(1.1) 66
10																					(1.8) 290	15.3	(0.5) 29
11																					(2.0) 308	16.2	(0.5) 28
12																					(1.5) 228	12.0	(0.3) 19
13																					(1.4) 221	11.6	(0.3) 17
14																					(1.3) 210	11.1	(0.3) 15
15																					(1.0) 150	7.9	(0.2) 10
16																					(1.6) 256	13.5	(0.3) 16
17																					(1.5) 238	12.5	(0.2) 14
18																					(3.4) 540	28.4	(0.5) 30
19	Average vehicle per trip for morning peak = 990				Average vehicles per trip for afternoon peak 2.30-4.30 p.m. = 982														(3.3) 513	27.0	(0.5) 27
20																							
Total	Vehicles per trip																			15725		5778
Parking index per cent	Average vehicles counted per trip during census hrs. 10 a.m. - 10 a.m. = 335																			15725 vehicle ½ hrs = 7862·5 veh./hrs. ÷5778 = 1·36 h (=1 hr. 22 minutes) = Average duration of parking [All subject to (*) on page (i)]		

Fig. 8.7b. **Summary sheet for cumulative distributions and parking peaks**

peak index from 18.4 to 12.5 by the removal of $125-85 = 40$ vehicles. Thus, appropriately situated off-street car parks for say 50 vehicles would house the long-period parkers. Of course fresh short-period parkers might well move into the kerbside places vacated by the long-period parkers so that a permanent reduction in the parking index might not ensue.

Fig. 8.7(b) shows some further analysis of the same kind of material as that in 8.7(a). In this table only the summary figures in the marginal columns have been reproduced. The percentage distribution of the total vehicles trips (figures in brackets in the "(a)" column) may be plotted as cumulative distributions showing the percentage of vehicles which, at any instant, were waiting in the streets for less than a given period. A similar distribution, based on the figures in the last column of the table, shows the total number of different vehicles which parked throughout the day for one, two, three, etc., trip intervals. Cumulative distributions of these two kinds for Mayfair and central Leeds have already been discussed elsewhere in this chapter.

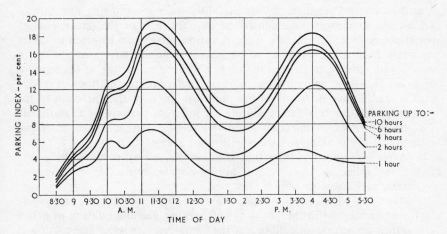

Fig. 8.8. Variation of the parking index due to vehicles parked for various periods in a sample of unrestricted streets in a provincial town (data from Fig. 8.7a)

In Fig. 8.7(b) the grand total of vehicle-trips is 15 725 and this number divided by the grand total of different vehicles parked throughout the day, 5778, yields the average duration of parking in terms of trip intervals—the figure in this case is 1·36 hours or 1 hour 22 minutes.

The array of total vehicles per trip, shown along the bottom of the table, (i.e. 320, 599, 718 etc.) shows the variation of parking during the day. These figures may be expressed as percentages of the total different vehicles parked (5778) and drawn as a histogram alternative to Fig. 8.7 to show the periods of peak parking demand. The morning peak is shown on Fig. 8.7(b) as occurring between 11 and 12 noon and the afternoon peak between 3.30 and 4.30 p.m. To assess accurately the peak demand, the general census of parked vehicles should ideally be completed during the higher of the two levels of parking. This was impracticable, as would normally be the case with limited manpower, and the census actually continued between 10 a.m. and 1 p.m. To raise the count so obtained to the peak levels they were multiplied by $(900/935) = 1·059$ for the morning peak, and by $(992/935) = 1·061$ for the afternoon peak, the derivation of these factors being explained in the table. If the distribution of durations for the peak period alone is required, it may be obtained for the morning peak, for example, by using only the figures in the columns for the corresponding trip numbers, namely columns 6 and 7 for 11.00 a.m. and 11.30 a.m. respectively.

To estimate the distribution of parking durations among the total vehicles parked in a town, the cumulative percentage distributions obtained from the duration survey, and exemplified by Fig. 8.3, can be applied to the peak number of parked vehicles obtained from the general parking census in the manner described above.

Presentation of the results of a simple parking survey

The results of a simple parking survey may be presented in tabular and graphical forms of the kinds already illustrated. The results of the general census of parked vehicles may be presented as maps showing numbers of vehicles in each street, the density per square mile or the parking index per street or area. The results of the duration survey can be given as tables showing the average duration of parking in separate streets or groups of streets with either unrestricted parking or waiting restriction of one kind or another. However, probably the most instructive representations of results are the cumulative distribution lines and the lines for the variation of the parking index due to vehicles waiting for different periods, and familiarity with these forms of illustration should enable the engineer to make a rapid estimate of the parking situation within an area.

It is perhaps worth noting that the parking survey methods here described as applied to street parking are, of course, applicable to surveys of off street parking with only slight modifications.

Tests of the park-and-visit type, referred to in Table 8.2, are instructive for those concerned in the provision of parking accommodation in urban areas, they constitute an acid test of the actual usefulness of any particular regime of urban parking control.

OFF-STREET PARKING

General economics

Within the last few years the rapid spread of parking meters particularly in central London, has accentuated the shortage of off-street parking space. However, the excess revenue from meters has to be devoted to the provision of off-street parking space and councils are thus encouraged to provide such space. Private developers are also encouraged to provide space in metered areas at an economic cost. There is, however, understandable caution over the construction of large off-street parking garages, specially where these are not combined with vehicle servicing facilities to improve profits; indeed the economic viability of many recently built large purely parking garages is still uncertain though economic returns generally tend to improve slowly. A novel solution to the problem has been adopted in Coventry where extensive parking areas are provided on the roofs of buildings with bridge connexions (see Plate 8.3).

General problems of intake and discharge as affecting traffic congestion

The structural aspects of garage construction are more the province of the civil than the traffic engineer, but the latter may concern himself with certain general features of design as they affect traffic. During peak intake periods the access arrangements for non-mechanical (customer parking) garages, or the reservoir space for mechanical ones should be sufficient to avoid any street congestion outside the garage. Some guidance on reservoir space has been given by Ricker.[6]

The peak discharge of large off-street garages also calls for special planning. The peak discharge rate of a large off-street garage may be as much as 1000 vehicles within an hour, and it is most important that these vehicles shall be enabled to leave without obstructing each other within the garage or causing traffic congestion in the streets outside—the discharge just quoted would be enough almost to fill one traffic lane of a main road.

Stall sizes and general features of design

A convenient average size for a car parking stall is 16 ft × 8 ft in Britain (somewhat larger in the U.S.A.) and the floor areas of off-street garages or ground level parking lots may be laid out on this basis. A few simple configurations given by Manzoni[7] are shown below (Table 8.10). More exhaustive tables of dimensions have been given by Baker and Funaro[8] and these can be adapted to local requirements.

Garage attendants can park cars in smaller spaces than drivers can, and hence smaller standard stalls can sometimes be used where all vehicle storage is done by them. However, the high price of labour may more than offset the saving in floor space allowance.

To a great extent the floor layout schemes used for multi-storey non-mechanical garages may be used for ground level car parking areas and the following general requirements, quoted from a Ministry of Transport Memorandum[1] for parking places, may be taken as applicable to both:

(i) One-way circulation of vehicles on the floor or ground area.
(ii) Avoidance of reversing movements as far as possible.
(iii) Arrangement of vehicles should be such that any one vehicle can be taken without disturbing any other.
(iv) Layout must provide for quick intake and despatch of vehicles.
(v) Vehicles should be parked in such a manner that the front is pointing in the outgoing direction.

Individual parking stalls should be clearly marked either by painted lines, bumper posts or kerbs, this is specially important in customer-parking parks. As a guide to centering the parked car in the stall, a strip wide enough for the opening of doors should be marked distinctively between the parking spaces. Segregated pedestrian paths may be necessary for safety in large parks. In ground level open parks some illumination is usually recommended on the grounds that it discourages theft and reduces the chance of accidents. Groups of lock-up garages such as are constructed by local authorities and others for private use should be made to a minimum size of 16 ft × 8 ft.

Table 8.10

BASIC DIMENSIONS FOR SOME SIMPLE PARKING STALL LAYOUTS

e = Floor space per stall

	Type of parking		Dimensions (based on 16 ft × 8 ft parking stalls)
1	90° Straight parking	a	16 ft
		b	20 ft*
		c	52 ft
		d	8 ft
		e	208 sq. ft
2	45° Intermeshed	a	16 ft 9 in (a' = 11 ft 3 in)
		b	12 ft†
		c	52 ft
		d	11 ft 3 in (d' = 16 ft 9 in)
		e	225 sq. ft
3	60°	a	17 ft 9 in
		b	14 ft‡
		c	49 ft 6 in
		d	9 ft 3 in
		e	228 sq. ft
4	45°	a	16 ft 9 in
		b	12 ft†
		c	45 ft 6 in
		d	11 ft 3 in
		e	256 sq. ft

* Two-way movement in aisles.
† Aisle operation unspecified.
‡ One-way movement in aisles.
Notes: All floor areas quoted are on the basis of stall area plus half aisle width and include no allowance for intermeshing of adjacent rows except in 2 (45° intermesh). The ceiling heights of garages are less frequently given, the minimum found in American literature was 7 ft 6 in for car garages.

Although not aesthetically ideal, something may be said for the idea of increasing the capacity of open ground level parks, when necessary, by the installation of customer-operated mechanical chain-and-platform installations. One of these devices, occupying a ground area of only 24 ft × 20 ft, with a height of 75 ft, houses 20 cars and is reputed to deliver a car on demand in 30 seconds on an average. Units of this kind could be installed as required with only limited capital commitment.

Comprehensive information on the design requiremens of parking garages is given by Ricker[6] and by Vahlefeld and Jacques.[9]

Provision of parking space in conjunction with the new buildings

Many local authorities specify or encourage the provision of parking space in conjunction with new buildings. At the time of writing there were no national standards for this sort of accommodation; a useful recent summary of existing standards is given in a report by the Institution of Municipal Engineers.[10]

REFERENCES TO CHAPTER 8

1. MINISTRY OF TRANSPORT. Memorandum on parking places. *Memorandum* No. 597 London, 1946 (H.M. Stationery Office).

2. MINISTRY OF TRANSPORT AND CIVIL AVIATION. Parking survey of Inner London. Interim report. London, 1956 (H.M. Stationery Office).

3. U.S. DEPARTMENT OF COMMERCE, BUREAU OF PUBLIC ROADS. Parking study manual. Instructions for a comprehensive study. Washington, D.C., 1949 (U.S. Department of Commerce).

4. SMITH, W., and Associates. Parking study. Central Business District, New New Orleans, Louisiana. Volume I. Parking and needs. Volumn II. Parking program. New Haven, Conn., 1960 (Wilber Smith and Associates).

5. WILSON, B. A do-it-yourself parking survey. *Struct. Engr*, 1960, **5** (12), 26–8, 32, 49.

6. RICKER, E. R. Traffic design of parking garages. Saugatuck, Conn., 1957 (Eno Foundation for Highway Traffic Control).

7. MANZONI, H. J. Public parking garages. *J. roy. Inst. Brit. Archit.*, 1958, **65** (5), 147–56; Discussion, 157–9.

8. BAKER, G., and B. FUNARO. Parking. New York, N.Y., 1958 (Reinhold Publishing Corporation).

9. VAHLEFELD, R., and F. JACQUES. Garages and service stations. London, 1960 (Leonard Hill Books Ltd.).

10. INSTUTION OF MUNICIPAL ENGINEERS. Provision of car parks in shopping and commercial centres. London, 1961 (Institution of Municipal Engineers).

Chapter 9

Traffic Control at Intersections

SYNOPSIS

Priority-type intersections. Traffic signals: signal aspects; intergreen period; types of signal available; special facilities for vehicle-actuated signals; co-ordinated control systems; pedestrian signals; warrants for signals; phasing; clearance periods; filter signals, detectors. Geometric design of signal-controlled intersections. Delay at traffic signals. Roundabouts: geometric design; traffic operation.

INTRODUCTION

Factors which determine the choice of a particular type of intersection include cost, the required capacity, delay, safety and aesthetic considerations. Capacity is rarely a problem in rural areas but is usually of considerable importance in urban areas. Cost, safety and delay are important in all areas. It is desirable to allow traffic to move without any stops if possible, but in urban areas drivers generally expect to have some stops and are more willing to tolerate delays.

This chapter deals only with single-level intersections, the main types of which fall into the following categories:

(1) Uncontrolled intersections, where the intersecting roads are of equal importance and there is no priority. These are not considered here.

(2) Priority intersections, where one road takes precedence over the other and virtually no delay is caused to the main road traffic. They effectively allow vehicles on the minor road to enter or cross the main road during any "spare time" on the major road. To this category belong intersections where the minor road is controlled by "HALT", "SLOW" or "YIELD" signs, or by road markings, or where the layout indicates which is the main road.

(3) "Time sharing" intersections, which give right of way first to one set of streams, then to another, and if necessary to others in sequence. Intersections with traffic signals or police control belong to this type.

(4) "Space sharing" intersections, which allow continuous "weaving" to take place. Roundabouts and gyratory systems in general belong to this group.

Though capacity, delay, driver behaviour, safety, cost and amenity are really interdependent this chapter deals with intersections particularly from the points of view of delay and driver behaviour. Capacity is dealt with in Chapter 6, and safety in Chapters 11 and 13.

PRIORITY-TYPE INTERSECTIONS

Observations of driver behaviour have been made to determine vehicle speeds at intersections and the time intervals between vehicles in a stream which are accepted by other drivers who wish to enter or cross that stream. Delays at priority-type intersections have been investigated and comparisons made with delays at signal-controlled intersections.

Speed of approach

In an unpublished study, reported by Charlesworth and Tanner,[1] Duff recorded minor road approach speeds of between 8 and 12 mile/h at about 20 ft from the major road at a few intersections mainly in built-up areas. Observations by the Laboratory to determine the effect of "HALT" and "SLOW" signs showed that the average speed between points 150 ft and 50 ft from the major road was 14·6 mile/h; it was independent of the type of junction, the type of control, or the traffic flow on the major road. It was also found that the time taken to travel the last 50 ft to the junction was independent of these factors if there was no vehicle on the major road and the minor road vehicle did not halt at the intersection. In these circumstances the average speed was 7·4 mile/h. However when vehicles were passing on the major road then the time taken to travel the last 50 ft did vary with the type of control and the flow on the major road, as shown in Fig. 9.1.

Speeds have been measured at a rural T-junction in Buckinghamshire before and after converting it from a square junction to a "Bennett" type junction. Vehicles on the major road and those turning right into, and left

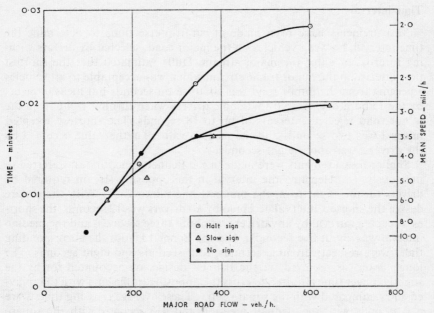

Fig. 9.1. Time and mean speed of vehicles for
last 50 ft before junction

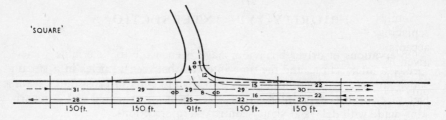

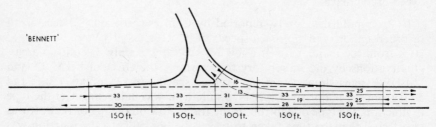

Fig. 9.2. Average speeds at a rural junction before and after conversion from a square to a "Bennett" type junction

from the minor road were timed past a number of fixed points. The resulting space-mean speeds are shown in Fig. 9.2 for the various sections. The principal points to notice in this figure are the higher entrance and exit speeds to and from the minor road and the smaller reduction of speed of the vehicles on the major-road as they pass the intersection with the Bennett layout (see also Chapter 13).

Time intervals

Measurements have been made at rural intersections to determine the time interval, between vehicles on the major road, selected by drivers wishing to cross or enter the major stream. Duff[1] estimated that the shortest time interval in the major traffic stream which was acceptable to all vehicles emerging from the minor road was six to seven seconds but measurements by the Laboratory showed that some drivers when turning right from the minor road rejected intervals of up to 18 seconds. The shortest accepted interval was two seconds and the median value, i.e. the value accepted by the drivers, was about eight seconds.

Similar measurements were made in the Bennett junction test, referred to previously, to determine the interval in the opposing stream required by drivers turning right from the major to the minor road. With the square design the shortest interval accepted by all drivers was 12 seconds, the shortest accepted interval by any driver was about three seconds, and the median interval was about five seconds; with the Bennett layout the corresponding times were respectively nine seconds, four seconds and eight seconds. The longer intervals required for the Bennett design are accounted for by the slightly longer time required to cross the opposing traffic lane with the splayed entry compared with the square entry. These average crossing times were 6·0 seconds with the Bennett junction and 4·3 seconds with the square junction.

Similar measurements were also made when investigating the effect of replacing "HALT" and "SLOW" signs by "YIELD" signs. The median acceptance values of the available time intervals in the major traffic stream are given in Table 9.1, for left-hand, right-hand and straight-over movements at "SLOW" and "HALT" controlled intersections. These results relate only to intervals in the major road traffic approaching from the right of the minor road traffic.

TABLE 9.1

Time interval, in seconds, in major traffic stream accepted by 50 per cent of drivers when emerging from minor road

Movement from minor road	SLOW sign	HALT sign
Left turn	4·6	6·5
Right turn	6·4	8·3
Straight over	5·5	6·7

As would be expected drivers require more time to execute a right-hand turn and longer intervals are needed at Halt-controlled intersections. After substituting "YIELD" signs at some of these junctions the gaps accepted by minor road vehicles were not significantly different from the above figures, suggesting that the behaviour of drivers is determined by the type of junction rather than the control sign, the sites at which "SLOW" signs were placed being naturally easier to emerge from than the ones where "HALT" signs have been placed.

Delays to minor road traffic

Tanner[2] has considered theoretically the average delay to vehicles on the minor road at a junction where the traffic on the major road has absolute priority. He assumed that vehicles on the major road arrived at random, and passed through at intervals of not less than a time β_M, that vehicles on the minor road arrived at random and passed through at intervals of not less than β_m and further, that they could not enter the junction within a time α after the previous vehicle on the major road. Thus one minor-road vehicle could pass through a gap of duration between α and $\alpha + \beta_m$ in the major road traffic, two could pass in a gap of between $\alpha + \beta_m$ and $\alpha + 2\beta_m$, and so on. He derived a formula for the average delay to vehicles on the minor road when the system was in statistical equilibrium. He used this formula to provide tables of delay to minor road traffic for several values of the parameters: q_M, q_m (flows on the major and minor road respectively) β_M, β_m, and α. These tables show, as expected, that, as the traffic builds up on the major road and fewer gaps become available, delays increase, theoretically to infinity. A few examples of delay/flow curves are shown in Fig. 9.3.

Comparison of priority-type intersections and traffic signals

When traffic volumes are very heavy "HALT" signs and "SLOW" signs are inadequate and more positive forms of control are necessary. Calculations made by the Laboratory[3] show that traffic signals generally offer greater

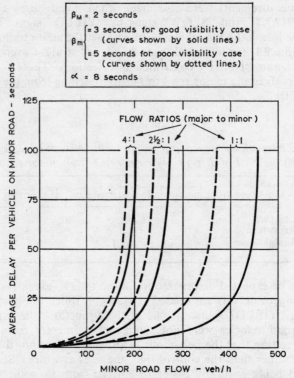

Fig. 9.3. Theoretical delay/flow curves for various
traffic conditions at a priority-type intersection

capacity than priority-type control and Fig. 9.4 illustrates this in some
hypothetical cases. This does not mean that all priority-type intersections
should be replaced by traffic signals. On the contrary, at light flows the
priority-type intersection offers less delay than with traffic signals. Figure
9.5 compares the delay/flow curves for the same hypothetical cases. It can

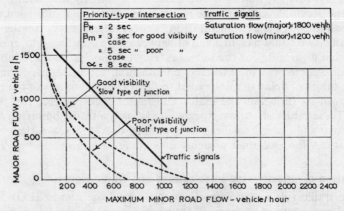

Fig. 9.4. Capacity of a hypothetical intersection with traffic
signals or priority-type control

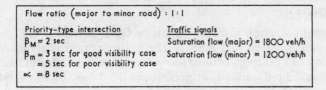

Flow ratio (major to minor road) : 1 : 1

Priority-type intersection
β_M = 2 sec
β_m = 3 sec for good visibility case
= 5 sec for poor visibility case
$\propto$ = 8 sec

Traffic signals
Saturation flow (major) = 1800 veh/h
Saturation flow (minor) = 1200 veh/h

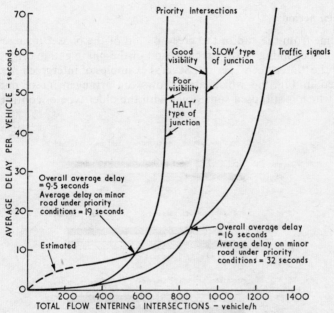

Fig. 9.5. Theoretical delay/flow curves for particular cases of
traffic signal and priority intersections

be seen that at a certain level of flow the average delays become equal. This might, in some circumstances, be regarded as the point at which traffic signals should be installed, though strictly other factors such as cost and maintenance of signals, and accidents should be taken into consideration. In urban areas priority-type intersections which have become overloaded are usually signalized in order to increase their capacity, but in rural areas channelization is often employed to enable the minor-road traffic to negotiate the two halves of the main road separately. This step is sometimes taken as an intermediate one prior to a roundabout or flyover being built.

TRAFFIC SIGNALS

Results of research and general practice have been used to provide guidance on the geometric design of signal-controlled intersections. Investigations have also been made of delays at traffic signals and of signal timings which minimize delays. A description of present-day traffic signals together with some considerations of practical interest in the use of traffic signals is given at the beginning of this section.

Signal aspects

The signal sequence of traffic signals in Great Britain is red, red/amber shown together, green and amber. The amber period is standardized by the Ministry of Transport at three seconds and the red/amber at two seconds The two-second red/amber is at present provided only by the latest type of signal controller, the older types giving a three-second red/amber.

Intergreen period

The time from the end of the green period of the phase* losing right-of-way to the beginning of the green period of the phase gaining right-of-way is called the "intergreen" period. Several examples of intergreen periods are illustrated in Fig. 9.6 which also shows the arrangement of concurrent ambers which is still used sometimes with the older type of controller.

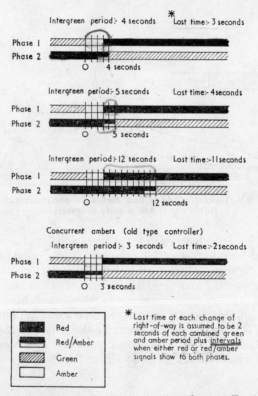

Fig. 9.6. Possible signal aspects at a two-phase traffic signal

Types of signals available

There are essentially two types of signal in general use—fixed-time and vehicle-actuated. Although most fixed-time signals have been replaced by

---

* A phase is the sequence of conditions applied to one or more streams of traffic which, during the cycle, receive identical signal light indications.

vehicle-actuated signals in Great Britain, in some countries fixed-time signals are far more numerous than the vehicle-actuated type. Detailed des-
criptions of traffic signals are given by Tyack,[4] Harrison and Priest,[5] Inglis,[6]
Thorpe and Green,[7] and Thorpe.[8]

With fixed-time signals the green periods and hence the cycle times are
pre-determined and are of fixed duration, but with vehicle-actuated signals
the green periods are related to the traffic demands. With the latest British
vehicle-actuated equipment the controller consists of several low voltage
electronic timers to give the following facilities:

MINIMUM GREEN PERIOD

This is the shortest period of right-of-way which is given to any phase and
is long enough for vehicles waiting between the detector and the stop line
to get into motion and clear the stop line. On the latest controllers the min-
inum green period varies according to the number of vehicles waiting. Under
light flow conditions this facility automatically reduces the minimum green
period and permits a quicker change of right-of-way thus reducing overall
delay to vehicles, particularly when three or four phases are in use.

VEHICLE-EXTENSION PERIODS

After the minimum green period has been timed off, each vehicle, as it
crosses the detector, extends the green period by an amount called the
vehicle-extension period. In many of the older controllers this extension
was of a fixed duration but in the latest controllers the extension relates to
the speed of the vehicle, as measured at the detectors. It is automatically
varied to enable each vehicle to reach 10 or 20 ft beyond the stop line.
Extensions are individual and not additive and the associated timer is only
re-set to a new value if the next extension is for a period longer than the
unexpired time of the previous extension. When the interval between vehicles
crossing the detector becomes greater than the vehicle-extension period,
right-of-way is transferred to the other phase if so required (this is called a
"gap" change of right-of-way).

MAXIMUM GREEN PERIOD

To prevent vehicles on one phase from waiting indefinitely in the event
of a continuous stream of traffic on the running phase a maximum period
is timed off, after which the signals change right-of-way irrespective of the
state of the vehicle-extension period. The maximum period starts at the
beginning of the green period if vehicles are waiting on the halted phase or
at the time the first vehicle passes over the detector on the halted phase
whichever is later. When a change of right-of-way occurs due to the expiry
of the maximum period arrangements are made for the right-of-way to
return to this road as soon as traffic conditions on the other roads permit
(this is called maximum reversion).

If the traffic is fairly dense on all phases the green periods may successively run to maximum, giving, in effect, fixed-time operation. Many signals
in large cities are operating in this manner during the peak periods and some
signals do so for practically the whole day.

II

VARIABLE INTERGREEN PERIOD

Sometimes the intergreen period is of fixed value and is set to provide adequate clearance time to cover normal traffic conditions. Occasionally, however, a longer clearance period may be required for safety and this can be catered for on the latest controllers by the provision of a variable intergreen period. This allows the intergreen period to be increased if the detectors on the phase losing right-of-way indicate a possibly dangerous situation.

Special facilities of vehicle-actuated signals

Amongst the many special facilities which may be provided are:

(1) EARLY CUT-OFF

To facilitate a heavy right-hand turning movement from one approach the green time of the opposing arm can be cut-off a few seconds early.

(2) LATE START

An alternative way of dealing with the same problem is to make the opposing traffic start a few seconds late.

Co-ordinated control systems

The object of co-ordination is to establish a definite relationship between the appearance of the green periods at two or more intersections so that interference to the through traffic streams is reduced to a minimum.

When two intersections are very close to each other some form of linking is often used to prevent the queue of vehicles at either intersection from extending back and interfering with the other. With vehicle-actuated signals it is often achieved by repeating the detector pulses from one intersection to the other, thereby requesting or retaining right-of-way at the other intersection. The controllers can be arranged to be interlocked so that the maximum green periods run concurrently.

Several forms of linking the intersections on a main traffic route are available:

(1) SIMULTANEOUS SYSTEM (SYNCHRONIZED SYSTEM)

All the signals along the controlled section display the same aspect to the same traffic stream at the same time. This type of system encourages speeding by drivers who may try to get through as many intersections as possible before the signals change.

(2) ALTERNATE SYSTEM (LIMITED PROGRESSIVE SYSTEM)

With this system adjacent signals show opposite indications alternately along a given road. The aim is that vehicles travel one block in half the cycle time. Drivers find that if they exceed the design speed of the system they are stopped at each signal. This system is not very suitable for streets where the distance between intersections varies appreciably. Variations on this basic scheme and on the simultaneous scheme can be made with both fixed-time and vehicle-actuated signals under the control of a master controller. The alternate system can be extended to allow adjacent groups of synchronized signals to show opposite indications along the main route.

(3) FLEXIBLE PROGRESSIVE SYSTEM

The cycle time for each intersection in the system is fixed, but the "go" periods are displaced with respect to each other according to the desired road speed. This is intended to give a "progression" of green periods along the road in both directions. A compromise is usually effected between the requirements of the main road and the side-road traffic. With unevenly spaced junctions a compromise has also to be made between the two directions and the resulting system often is basically a mixture of "alternate" and "synchronized" working. This system could be used to give a "preferential" movement, e.g. in the morning peak to favour the inbound flow at the expense of the fewer vehicles travelling in the opposite direction and vice versa in the evening peak.

This system requires a master controller to keep the "local" controllers at each intersection in step. Either fixed-time or vehicle-actuated signals can be used. If vehicle-actuated signals are used the local controllers at each intersection in the system operate according to the over-riding progressive plan whilst there are continuous demands from all detectors, but if the flow falls, the individual intersections are allowed to operate as isolated vehicle-actuated signals provided that there is no interference with traffic progressing in accordance with the progressive plan. This proviso means that in light traffic the progressive system may be less flexible than an unlinked system of vehicle-actuated signals. A time switch could be arranged to link and unlink all the signals in a system and could also change the "plan" in a predetermined manner. Alternatively, traffic integrators (devices for counting traffic) could be used to change the traffic plan according to the measured flows at one or more locations.

(4) TAILOR-MADE SYSTEMS

At the present time many schemes of linked signals in Great Britain are "tailor-made" for the particular location. These systems do not generally have a master controller because this sometimes leads to less efficient control at particular key intersections in the system. These "key" intersections are usually allowed to operate in a fully vehicle-actuated manner and to impose conditions on the times at which the right-of-way is changed at the neighbouring intersections. As traffic progresses through the system the link is passed from one intersection to the next to request right-of-way.

LINKING A NETWORK OF STREETS

All the above systems can be applied to a network of streets. If the network consists entirely of one-way streets with alternate directions a useful basic system is the one in which the green periods at adjacent intersections are displaced by $\frac{1}{4}$ cycle. This system often gives a more acceptable cycle length than the alternate system.

Pedestrian signals

Pedestrians at intersections controlled by signals are catered for in two ways in Great Britain. One method is to provide a crossing marked out in studs in front of the stop line (see Fig. 9.7) whereby pedestrians crossing the road fit in with the signal timings, i.e. no special phases are given for them. The second method is to provide a special phase for the pedestrians and in this case the pedestrians' movements are signalled. The pedestrian signals have two aspects: one displaying the word "WAIT" (red on black background) and the other displaying the word "CROSS" (green or white on black background). The pedestrian phase may be included in the cycle, whether or not pedestrians require it or may be brought in by push buttons to avoid unnecessary delay to vehicles. The "CROSS" signal is usually preceded and followed by all-red periods.

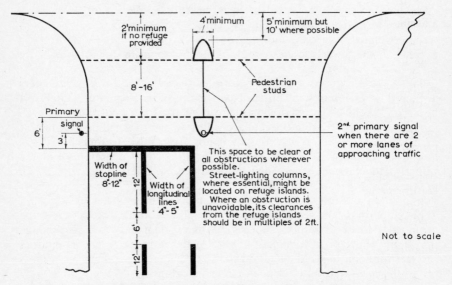

Fig. 9.7. Typical layout suggested by the Ministry of Transport for stop lines and pedestrian crossings at signal-controlled intersections

Pedestrian crossings between junctions can be signalled in the same way. With one type of pedestrian-operated signal no vehicular detector is installed and right-of-way normally rests with the traffic. In the absence of demands from pedestrians it would remain so indefinitely but when the pedestrian push-button is depressed the pedestrian receives right-of-way immediately or as soon as a predetermined period for the traffic expires. If detectors are installed for the vehicular traffic the signals act as normal 2-phase vehicle-actuated signals.

Warrants for signals

In Great Britain, the Ministry of Transport does not lay down set conditions which must be attained before signals can be considered and each case is judged on its merits. Broadly speaking, the three primary aims of signal control are:

(a) To reduce traffic conflicts and delay. A total of about 300 veh/h with at least 100 veh/h on the side road, averaged over 16 hours of the day, would be regarded as the minimum justification for signal control.

This would be equivalent to a peak hour value (taken as 10 per cent of the 16 hour total) of 480 veh/h. Many intersections with flows substantially in excess of this figure work quite satisfactorily with no control at all and some examples of hypothetical intersections showed that about twice this volume was required to make the average delay the same with and without traffic signals.

(b) To reduce accidents.[9]

(c) To economize with police time.

In the U.S.A. the traffic warrants given in "Manual on Uniform Traffic Control Devices for Streets and Highways"[10] are more rigid.

Phasing

The phasing depends mainly on the number of roads entering the junction and the amount of right-turning traffic. It is desirable to reduce the number of phases required to the least number which will work satisfactorily. Normally 2-phase control is satisfactory for straight cross-roads when there is not too much right-turning traffic. With appreciable numbers of right-turners, an early cut-off or late start feature (as mentioned earlier) is often incorporated in the cycle. A third phase may be necessary in the case of a cross-road with an exceptionally heavy right-turning movement.

A 3- or 4-phase controller may be necessary at more complicated junctions with five or more roads, at certain T-junctions where the early cut-off feature is not adequate and at ordinary cross-roads where a pedestrian phase is required.

With vehicle-actuated signals it is usually arranged that if no demand for a particular phase is received then that phase is omitted from the cycle and delay to vehicles is consequently reduced.

Clearance periods

The intergreen period is arranged on the latest controllers to have a minimum of four seconds (on the older type controllers concurrent ambers gave a minimum intergreen of three seconds). It is suggested that the intergreen period should be extended if necessary from the minimum of four seconds to some suitable value on the following occasions:

(1) To allow vehicles to clear the intersection when the distance across the junction is greater than normal or when the road carries a large number of slow moving vehicles.

(2) To improve safety when the roads carry fast traffic.

(3) To improve safety for pedestrians and to assist them in crossing the road at intersections where there is a high pedestrian flow, though pedestrians are better catered for by having their own phase.

Filter signals

Filter signals mounted alongside the main signals are sometimes used to permit movement of vehicles in the direction shown by the green arrow even though the main signal is showing red. Drivers who make use of a filter should therefore proceed with extreme caution as other traffic movements may be taking place in the intersection at the same time. Filter signals can be dangerous to pedestrians who may cross a line of waiting vehicles and walk right into the path of vehicles moving in accordance with a filter signal. Special precautions may have to be taken depending on the site conditions, e.g. by using guardrails to prevent pedestrians crossing the approach with the filter movement or if that cannot be done by setting the stop line about 20 ft from the pedestrian crossing to give drivers and pedestrians a better view of each other.

An alternative which is sometimes preferable to a left filter is a left turn slip-road which allows traffic to turn left continuously without coming under the control of the signals.

Detectors

Detectors used in Great Britain are normally of the pneumatic type and are unidirectional, i.e. they are only operated by vehicles approaching the intersection. With single channel detectors, vehicles leaving an intersection, especially on a narrow road, are liable to cross the centre line (e.g. in passing a parked vehicle) and operate the detector for that approach causing the signals to prolong the green period unnecessarily and thereby increasing the delay to waiting traffic.

The normal recommended distance of the detector from the stop line is 130 ft but on roads in urban areas which are narrow, winding or having appreciable gradients or where speeds are not likely to exceed 30 mile/h, the detectors are located between 100 and 120 ft from the stop line. At T-junctions with awkward turns the detectors on the side road are usually only 60 ft away.

For high-speed roads a new type of controller has been developed which has detectors at some considerable distance away from the stop line (of the order of 500 ft) in addition to detectors in the normal position. Until trials of the prototype equipment have been completed and a production model is available, a system known as double detection is being used with two detectors at approximately 130 ft and 240 ft. Equipment for high-speed roads is described later.

GEOMETRIC DESIGN OF SIGNAL-CONTROLLED INTERSECTIONS

The approach

Figure 9.7 shows the layout of an approach to a signal-controlled intersection as approved by the Ministry of Transport. In addition to the two primary signals a secondary signal is normally placed diagonally opposite the nearside primary signal (i.e. on the back of the signal post carrying the primary signal heads for the opposing traffic). The radius of curvature of the corners should not be so small that vehicles have difficulty in negotiating them nor so great that clearance times for vehicles and pedestrians are increased unnecessarily. The Ministry of Transport have suggested that a radius of 35 ft is generally satisfactory.[11]

Because the signals permit traffic movement from any approach for only proportion of the time, it is sometimes necessary to have the intersection approaches, where queueing takes place, wider than the roads which feed these approaches (see simplified layout in Fig. 9.8) in order to pass the required flow. If the intersection already exists the timing of the signals can be adjusted for a given flow pattern to make the best use of the layout. If the intersection is in its design stage, or if some change can be made to the layout of an existing intersection, then a choice of approach widths is available. Having selected particular approach widths the green times can be adjusted to give the correct capacities for those approaches.

Possible ways of designing an intersection which appear obvious at first sight are (a) to have equal approach widths and then set the green times on each approach in proportion to the flows; (b) to have approach widths in proportion to the flows and to equalize the green times; (c) to give main road approaches not only greater widths but also longer green times than minor road approaches.

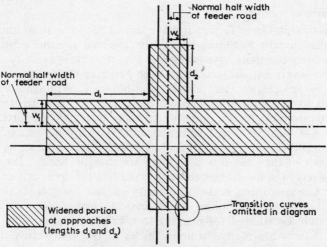

Fig. 9.8. Simplified diagram of widened approaches at signal-controlled intersection

The selection of approach widths was considered by Webster and Newby[12]. It was concluded that whatever ratio of w_1/w_2 was adopted it made very little difference to the area of intersection and approaches assuming that the maximum possible rate of flow past the stop line is proportional to the width of the approach (w_1, w_2), and also that the widened section of the approach is just long enough (d_1, d_2) to accommodate the queue which can pass through the intersection during a fully saturated green period. It was also thought that it may be desirable to avoid extreme ratios of widths and green times which methods (a) and (b) sometimes give, since such ratios make the intersection less adaptable to changes in flow pattern in the surrounding area. Method (c), on the other hand, avoids extreme ratios; furthermore, if

$$\frac{w_1}{w_2} = \sqrt{\frac{q_1}{q_2}}$$

the total width of approaches at the intersection is reduced to a minimum for a given capacity.[12] With this rule the green times (and hence the length

widened should also be in the same proportion. There are several advantages in reducing the total width of approaches to the minimum necessary for a given capacity, e.g.

(1) The narrower the roads entering the intersection the more convenient (and perhaps the safer) for pedestrians crossing the road;

(2) Clearance distance (and hence all-red time) is reduced;

(3) Encroachment on to footways and frontage development is reduced.

In some cases the presence of existing buildings near to the intersection may prevent uniform widening of the approach from being carried out and it may only be possible to flare the approach.

Where the approach is a dual carriageway extra space can be gained by reducing the width of the central reserve (if more than four feet) to four feet.

Lane widths

It is normal in Great Britain to have lanes 10 ft wide at an intersection, though occasionally 9-ft lanes have to be accepted at some existing intersections. Some countries have found that in certain cases capacity is increased by having very narrow lanes[13] (down to 7 ft) even though drivers of some of the wider vehicles are unable to keep within them. With lanes wider than 10 ft it is likely that capacity would be wasted, though this depends on traffic composition; for example, where there is a high proportion of bicycles or wide vehicles it may be beneficial to have a wider nearside lane.

Many traffic engineers recommend having the same number of lanes on the exit side of the intersection as there are straight-through lanes (partly or exclusively used by straight-through traffic) on the approach side.[14,15] If, however, site conditions make it necessary to have fewer lanes on the exit side of the intersection, observations indicate that a distance of about 300 ft should be allowed for merging to take place, though this could be reduced if there are many turning vehicles at the intersection, i.e. fewer vehicles going straight ahead. It is most desirable that vehicles travelling in through lanes should not be obstructed either by parked vehicles or by waiting right-turners, and the latter should wherever possible have their own lane or lanes.

Layout for right-turning vehicles

Opposing right-turners can turn either on the offside of each other or on the nearside. In the former case they have good visibility and can see an approaching gap in the opposing stream in which to complete their turn. On the other hand, if there are too many turners from the two directions for the storage space within the intersection, the two streams may interlock causing congestion in the intersection. With the nearside method locking cannot occur but visibility is often restricted and drivers usually have to wait until the end of the green period before turning in order to be sure that there is no opposing straight-through traffic. If the nearside method of turning right is used there may be advantages in off-setting the central reserve so that more space is available to traffic approaching the intersection than to traffic leaving it (see Fig. 9.9). This method places opposing right-turners practically opposite each other, hence it is applicable only to cases where the nearside method of turning is used. The layout suggested in Fig. 9.10

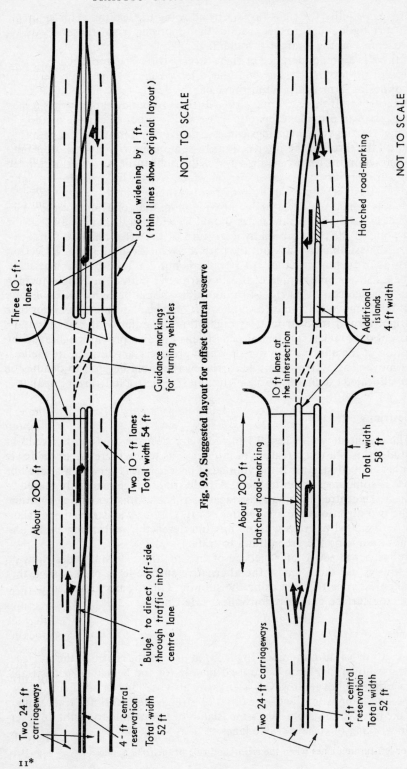

NOT TO SCALE

Three 10-ft. lanes

Local widening by 1 ft. (thin lines show original layout)

Guidance markings for turning vehicles

Two 10-ft lanes
Total width 54 ft

'Bulge' to direct off-side through traffic into centre lane

About 200 ft

Two 24-ft carriageways

4-ft central reservation
Total width 52 ft

Fig. 9.9. Suggested layout for offset central reserve

NOT TO SCALE

Hatched road-marking

Additional islands
4-ft width

10 ft lanes at the intersection

Total width 58 ft

About 200 ft

Hatched road-marking

Two 24-ft carriageways

4-ft central reservation
Total width 52 ft

Fig. 9.10. Offset central reserve with improved visibility for right-turning vehicles

11*

improves visibility for right-turners by allowing the leading vehicles in the right-turning queues to see round the opposing right-turners without encroaching on the straight-through lanes.

If there is a preponderance of right-turners from one approach the green period of this approach may continue after the end of the green period of the opposing arm sharing the same phase ("early cut-off" feature, mentioned earlier). If there are many right-turners from both approaches it may be necessary to provide a separate phase and to use the nearside method of turning. Carriageway markings can assist drivers in following the path they should take through the intersection. In some countries dotted stop lines are marked in the right-turning lanes* if the right-turners are not prohibited from turning during the green period which is used by opposing straight-through traffic. Where the flow of right-turning vehicles is exceptionally high, it is sometimes necessary to provide more than one lane for them (see Plate 9.1). In such cases the lanes should be widened to at least 14 ft at the mid-point of the turn, especially if the turn is sharp (less than 50-ft radius). It is also desirable to mark out the path the vehicles should take with paint or studs in such a way that cross traffic is not confused by the markings. Plate 9.2 shows an example of this in Germany. With double right-turning lanes it is necessary that right-turning traffic should be signalled separately and should move only on its own phase. It may be desirable also to separate the right-turning traffic from the straight-through traffic by means of islands. This not only makes it safer for pedestrians but also provides a site for the location of the appropriate signals which are necessary to indicate the various movements. Arrows on the carriageway should be used to denote the lanes allocated exclusively to right-turning vehicles (or left-turning vehicles).

Pedestrians

The layout shown in Fig. 9.7 includes a pedestrian crossing marked out in studs; this is a usual feature of intersections where there are appreciable numbers of pedestrians. If the volume of pedestrians is very high a separate phase is sometimes given to them. A pedestrian refuge is usually placed at or near the centre of a single carriageway if the widths remaining to traffic in the two directions are greater than 14 ft. On one-way streets pedestrians can be signalled to cross without any interference from turning traffic and without reducing the green times to traffic.

Subways provide a safer method of crossing the road but pedestrians do not always use them unless the alternative surface-level path is such that it takes less time to cross using the subway. Guard rails are often used to make the surface path less convenient (see Chapter 12).[16]

Islands

Islands of 4-ft minimum width placed at or near the centre of the carriageway, as shown in Fig. 9.7, are used mainly for the benefit of pedestrians, as mentioned above, However, islands are also used for channelizing traffic: sometimes, opposite islands are offset to give greater width for traffic entering the intersection; sometimes the islands are moveable to facilitate reversible working of certain traffic lanes.

* or left-turning lanes when the right-hand rule of the road applies.

DELAY AT TRAFFIC SIGNALS

It is estimated that in Great Britain delays at traffic signals amount to about 100 million vehicle-hours each year. If a saving of only a few per cent could be effected by using new methods to set signals the financial saving would be considerable.

Although delays at signals have been studied on the road most of the work has been done by simulating traffic behaviour at signals, firstly by using a special purpose computer[17] and later using a general purpose digital electronic computer (the pilot ACE which was at the time housed at the National Physical Laboratory).[18] Until this work was done no reliable method was available for calculating the delay at signals as all the methods assumed that traffic arrived at an intersection at a uniform rate.[19] The arrival rate has been shown to be much more nearly random[20] and in the simulation technique, which was used artificially, generated traffic of a random nature was used to feed the computer. It was also assumed that once the signals turn green, traffic discharges during the green period at a constant rate whilst the queue remains (called the saturation flow).

Fixed-time signals

Computations of delay were carried out for a variety of flows, saturation flows and signal settings and from the results a formula was deduced for the average delay on any single approach to an intersection controlled by fixed-time signals (or, of course, vehicle-actuated signals operating on a fixed cycle because of heavy traffic demands, i.e. during peak periods). The details of the simulation method are given in Reference 18 and only the results are given here. It was found that

$$d = \frac{c[1-(g/c)]^2}{2[1-(q/s)]} + \frac{x^2}{2q(1-x)} - 0.65\left(\frac{c}{q^2}\right)^{\frac{1}{3}}x^{(2+5g/c)} \qquad . \qquad . \qquad . \ (1)$$

where

d = average delay per vehicle on the particular arm,
c = cycle time,
g = green time,
q = flow,
s = saturation flow,
x = the degree of saturation. This is the ratio of the flow to the maximum possible flow under the given settings of the signals and equals cq/gs.

The last term of the equation has a value in the range 5 to 15 per cent of d in most cases. A rough approximation to the delay may therefore be given by

$$d = \frac{9}{10}\left\{\frac{c[1-(g/c)]^2}{2[1-(q/s)]} + \frac{x^2}{2q(1-x)}\right\} \qquad . \qquad . \qquad . \qquad . \qquad . \ (2)$$

To enable the delay to be estimated more easily, equation (2) has been rewritten as

$$d = cA + \frac{B}{q} - C \qquad . \qquad . \qquad . \qquad . \qquad . \qquad . \qquad . \qquad . \qquad (3)$$

where $A = \dfrac{(1-(g/c))^2}{2(1-(q/s))}$ $B = \dfrac{x^2}{2(1-x)}$ and C is the third term.

A and B have been tabulated (see Tables 9.2 and 9.3) and C has been calculated as a percentage of the first two terms of equation (3) and is given in Table 9.4 in terms of x, g/c, and M where $M(=qc)$ is the average number of vehicles arriving per cycle.

The delay formula has been tested under actual road conditions at several fixed-time and vehicle-actuated intersections and the variation between observed and calculated values was no greater than would be expected due to random fluctuations (see Fig. 9.11).

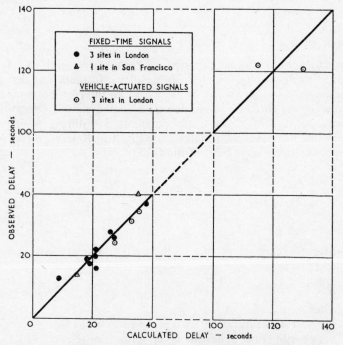

Fig. 9.11. Observed and calculated average delays at traffic signals

The way the delay varies with traffic flow is illustrated in Fig. 9.12 in a typical case ($g = 30$ seconds, $c = 60$ seconds, $s = 1800$ veh/h).

It will be seen that when the flow reaches about 90 per cent of the capacity (as shown by the vertical asymptote to the curve) the delay rises sharply. Computations of delay were made for values of x up to 97·5 per cent of saturation. Theoretically the delay increases to infinity as the flow tends to capacity but in practice the level of flow rarely remains at a high value for

TABLE 9.2

$$\text{Tabulation of } A = \frac{(1-g/c)^2}{2(1-q/s)}$$

x \ g/c	0·1	0·2	0·30	0·35	0·40	0·45	0·50	0·55	0·60	0·65	0·70	0·80	0·90
0·1	0·409	0·327	0·253	0·219	0·188	0·158	0·132	0·107	0·085	0·066	0·048	0·022	0·005
0·2	0·413	0·333	0·261	0·227	0·196	0·166	0·139	0·114	0·091	0·070	0·052	0·024	0·006
0·3	0·418	0·340	0·269	0·236	0·205	0·275	0·147	0·121	0·098	0·076	0·057	0·026	0·007
0·4	0·422	0·348	0·278	0·246	0·214	0·184	0·156	0·130	0·105	0·083	0·063	0·029	0·008
0·5	0·426	0·356	0·288	0·256	0·225	0·195	0·167	0·140	0·114	0·091	0·069	0·033	0·009
0·55	0·429	0·360	0·293	0·262	0·231	0·201	0·172	0·145	0·119	0·095	0·073	0·036	0·010
0·60	0·431	0·364	0·299	0·267	0·237	0·207	0·179	0·151	0·125	0·100	0·078	0·038	0·011
0·65	0·433	0·368	0·304	0·273	0·243	0·214	0·185	0·158	0·131	0·106	0·083	0·042	0·012
0·70	0·435	0·372	0·310	0·280	0·250	0·221	0·192	0·165	0·138	0·112	0·088	0·045	0·014
0·75	0·438	0·376	0·316	0·286	0·257	0·228	0·200	0·172	0·145	0·120	0·095	0·050	0·015
0·80	0·440	0·381	0·322	0·293	0·265	0·236	0·208	0·181	0·154	0·128	0·102	0·056	0·018
0·85	0·443	0·386	0·329	0·301	0·273	0·245	0·217	0·190	0·163	0·137	0·111	0·063	0·021
0·90	0·445	0·390	0·336	0·308	0·281	0·254	0·227	0·200	0·174	0·148	0·122	0·071	0·026
0·92	0·446	0·392	0·338	0·312	0·285	0·258	0·231	0·205	0·179	0·152	0·126	0·076	0·029
0·94	0·447	0·394	0·341	0·315	0·288	0·262	0·236	0·210	0·183	0·157	0·132	0·081	0·032
0·96	0·448	0·396	0·344	0·318	0·292	0·266	0·240	0·215	0·189	0·163	0·137	0·086	0·037
0·98	0·449	0·398	0·347	0·322	0·296	0·271	0·245	0·220	0·194	0·169	0·143	0·093	0·042

TABLE 9.3

Tabulation of $B = \dfrac{x^2}{2(1-x)}$

x	0·00	0·01	0·02	0·03	0·04	0·05	0·06	0·07	0·08	0·09
0·1	0·006	0·007	0·008	0·010	0·011	0·013	0·015	0·017	0·020	0·022
0·2	0·025	0·028	0·031	0·034	0·038	0·042	0·046	0·050	0·054	0·059
0·3	0·064	0·070	0·075	0·081	0·088	0·094	0·101	0·109	0·116	0·125
0·4	0·133	0·142	0·152	0·162	0·173	0·184	0·196	0·208	0·222	0·235
0·5	0·250	0·265	0·282	0·299	0·317	0·336	0·356	0·378	0·400	0·425
0·6	0·450	0·477	0·506	0·536	0·569	0·604	0·641	0·680	0·723	0·768
0·7	0·817	0·869	0·926	0·987	1·05	1·13	1·20	1·29	1·38	1·49
0·8	1·60	1·73	1·87	2·03	2·21	2·41	2·64	2·91	3·23	3·60
0·9	4·05	4·60	5·28	6·18	7·36	9·03	11·5	15·7	24·0	49·0

TABLE 9.4

*Correction term of equation (3) as a percentage
of the first two terms*

x	g/c \ M*	2·5	5	10	20	40
0·3	0·2	2	2	1	1	0
	0·4	2	1	1	0	0
	0·6	0	0	0	0	0
	0·8	0	0	0	0	0
0·4	0·2	6	4	3	2	1
	0·4	3	2	2	1	1
	0·6	2	2	1	1	0
	0·8	2	1	1	1	1
0·5	0·2	10	7	5	3	2
	0·4	6	5	4	2	1
	0·6	6	4	3	2	2
	0·8	3	4	3	3	2
0·6	0·2	14	11	8	5	3
	0·4	11	9	7	4	3
	0·6	9	8	6	5	3
	0·8	7	8	8	7	5
0·7	0·2	18	14	11	7	5
	0·4	15	13	10	7	5
	0·6	13	12	10	8	6
	0·8	11	12	13	12	10
0·8	0·2	18	17	13	10	7
	0·4	16	15	13	10	8
	0·6	15	15	14	12	9
	0·8	14	15	17	17	15
0·9	0·2	13	14	13	11	8
	0·4	12	13	13	11	9
	0·6	12	13	14	14	12
	0·8	13	13	16	17	17
0·95	0·2	8	9	9	9	8
	0·4	7	9	9	10	9
	0·6	7	9	10	11	10
	0·8	7	9	10	12	13
0·975	0·2	8	9	10	9	8
	0·4	8	9	10	10	9
	0·6	8	9	11	12	11
	0·8	8	10	12	13	14

* M is the average flow per cycle $= qc$

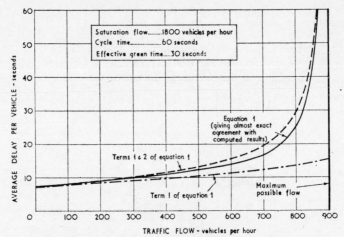

Fig. 9.12. Typical delay/flow curve obtained from computations
on fixed-time traffic signals

a long period, for example, the flow falls off at the end of the peak period, and the queues generally have not time to build back to such lengths to
give such long delays. In addition, vehicles seeing the end of the queue at
some distance from the intersection would usually turn off and find some
alternative route under these conditions and this has in fact been observed
at a particular junction in central London which was running to capacity
for a large proportion of the day.[21] The average delay at this junction was
several minutes.

The average delay is usually quoted and used in calculations but it is often
useful to know the variability of delays. These fluctuations in delay are
primarily due to random fluctuations in the numbers of vehicles arriving
at an intersection. Results obtained from observations of delays at several
sites in London have shown the standard deviation to be about $\frac{3}{4}$ of the
mean delay, but computations carried out on the computer using purely
random traffic indicate that the standard deviation is greater than this.

A factor that considerably affects the delay to vehicles at an intersection
is the presence of a parked vehicle on the approach to an intersection.[3]
The parked vehicle reduces the saturation flow (sometimes by up to $\frac{1}{3}$) often
raising the degree of saturation to greater than unity, e.g. if on an approach
to an intersection 12 vehicles can be discharged on the average per green
period and 11 arrive the degree of saturation is 11/12 or 92 per cent. If a
vehicle parks and reduces the saturation flow by $\frac{1}{3}$ only eight vehicles can be
discharged each green period and a queue builds up at the rate of three
vehicles per cycle. If the cycle time is one minute and the vehicle stops for
20 minutes there will be a queue of 60 vehicles by the time the parked vehicle
leaves (over and above the queue which would have formed). When the
vehicle leaves, this queue will be reduced by one vehicle every cycle and it
will be an hour before the queue is back to normal. Vehicles arriving during
this time will be unaware of the cause of the long delays.

The computations of delay already referred to were carried out assuming
steady conditions, i.e. traffic varying randomly about a constant mean, but
as soon as a vehicle is parked on the approach the degree of saturation is

suddenly raised and it takes a finite time for the queue (and therefore the mean delay) to reach equilibrium again. Similarly when the parked vehicle leaves a finite time is required before equilibrium is restored. These transition periods were studied by simulation using the computer and the results in a typical case are shown in Fig. 9.13. It can be seen that when the degree of saturation is raised to over unity the queue continues to increase, as in the example given above, and the delay also. More details are given in reference 22.

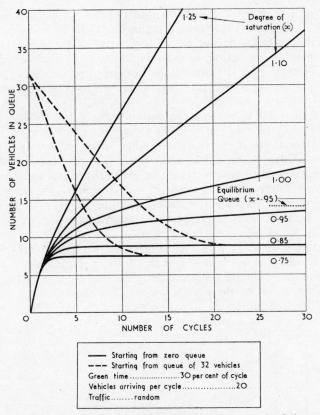

Fig. 9.13. Variation of average queue with time at fixed-time traffic signals

Calculations have shown that a parked vehicle may cause a total delay to other road users equal to many times (in some cases many hundreds of times) the duration of parking and the effects of the parked vehicle may last for hours after the vehicle has left.

Optimum settings: Fixed-time signals

CYCLE TIME

In deducing an expression for the cycle time which gives the least delay to all traffic, it has been found to be sufficiently accurate to select one arm only from each phase to represent that phase. Providing (as is usually the case) the lost times are more or less the same for different arms of the same phase, the arm is selected with the highest ratio of flow to saturation flow and this value is denoted by the symbol y.

By differentiating the equation for the overall delay at an intersection with respect to the cycle time it was found that the cycle time for which the delay is a minimum could be represented by

$$c_o = \frac{1 \cdot 5L + 5}{1 - y_1 - y_2 - \ldots y_n} \text{ seconds} \qquad \qquad \ldots \qquad \ldots \qquad (4)$$

where $y_1, y_2 \ldots y_n$ are the maximum ratios of flow to saturation flow for phase $1, 2 \ldots n$, and L is the total lost time per cycle (in seconds), i.e. it is the sum of the lost times for each phase (due to starting delays and the reduced flow during the amber period, usually amounting to about two seconds per phase on average) plus the sum of the intergreen periods less the sum of the amber periods. This cycle time will be referred to as the "optimum cycle time".

Under light traffic conditions the optimum cycle time as deduced from this formula may be very short. From a practical point of view, including safety considerations, it may be undesirable to have cycles less than, say, about 25 seconds. This could be regarded as a lower limit. In addition it may be undesirable to have a cycle time greater than one and a half or two minutes, particularly since the gain in capacity with very long cycles is often insignificant. Two minutes could therefore be regarded as an upper limit to be exceeded only in exceptional circumstances (e.g. at multi-phase junctions).

The variation of delay with cycle time is shown in Fig. 9.14 for a few hypothetical cases. It has been found that for cycle times within the range $\frac{3}{4}$ to $1\frac{1}{2}$ times the optimum value the delay is never more than 10 to 20 per cent over that given by the optimum cycle. For most practical cases this result may be used in deducing a compromise cycle time when the level of

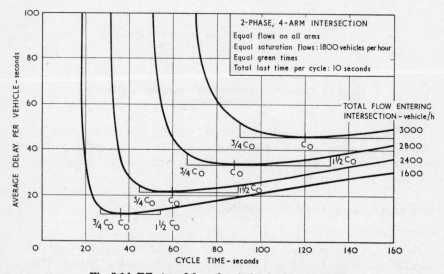

Fig. 9.14. Effect on delay of variation in the cycle length

flow varies considerably throughout the day. It would be of course better either to change the cycle time to take account of this or, as is more common, to use vehicle-actuated signals.

It should be noted that constant saturation flow has been assumed in the derivation of the cycle time formula. If the saturation flow falls off with green time (e.g. owing to heavy right-turning movements) this formula does not hold and a more complicated procedure is necessary to arrive at a reasonable cycle time.

The use of the formula is not straightforward when there is an early cut-off or late start feature or when the lost times and saturation flows are both different for different approaches of the same phase. Trial and error method should be used considering each arm of the phase in turn as the "predominant" one. The longest cycle time deduced is the optimum one.

More complications arise when there are special left-turning and right-turning lanes.

GREEN TIMES

A simple rule for setting the green times to give the least overall delay to all traffic using the intersection was derived from the delay equation. It was found that the ratio of the effective green times should equal the ratio of the y values, i.e.

$$\frac{g_1}{g_2} = \frac{y_1}{y_2} \qquad . \qquad . \qquad . \qquad . \qquad . \qquad . \qquad . \qquad . \qquad . \qquad (5)$$

where g_1 and g_2 are the effective green times of phase 1 and 2 respectively. This rule can be extended to three or more phase operation. Where the two arms of a single phase have different values of the ratio q/s, approximately minimum overall delay is still obtained by dividing the cycle according to the y values.

Just as it was necessary to have limits on the cycle time for practical purposes so it is necessary to avoid having green times too short and this is catered for automatically with existing controllers which have a minimum green period of seven seconds.

PRACTICAL ASPECTS OF THE RESULTS

Minimum overall delay has been used as the criterion in deducing optimum signal settings. Consistent with safety requirements this appears to be reasonable provided that the delay to any particular stream does not become intolerably high in relation to that of other streams. The delay formula or tables may be used to check that delays are reasonable.

If other junctions are close by it is desirable to know how far the queue is likely to extend, and a formula has been derived for predicting the average queue at the beginning of the green period (N). This is generally the maximum queue in the cycle and is given approximately by

$$N = q\left(\frac{r}{2} + d\right), \text{ or } N = qr, \text{ whichever is larger} \qquad . \qquad . \qquad . \qquad (6)$$

where r is the red time, q is the flow and d is the average delay per vehicle. A more exact expression is given in Reference 18.

Perhaps of more importance than the average queue is the extent of the queue in certain infrequent cases, and tables, showing the queue which will be exceeded only once in 20 cycles and the queue which will be exceeded only once in 100 cycles, have been computed and are given in Reference 18. The queues exceeded once in a 100 cycles are given also in Table 9.5.

TABLE 9.5

Queues which are exceeded only once in 100 *cycles*

Degree of saturation	M* / g/c	2·5	5·0	10·0	20·0	40·0
0·3	0·4	6	9	14	23	38
	0·6	5	6	11	17	28
	0·8	3	5	7	12	17
0·5	0·2	7	9	17	29	53
	0·4	6	9	14	23	38
	0·6	5	7	11	17	28
	0·8	4	5	7	12	18
0·7	0·2	9	12	17	28	50
	0·4	9	9	15	23	38
	0·6	8	9	12	18	28
	0·8	7	7	8	12	18
0·8	0·2	13	15	19	28	50
	0·4	12	13	17	24	39
	0·6	12	13	14	20	28
	0·8	11	12	12	15	18
0·9	0·2	29	25	29	38	55
	0·4	28	24	27	33	46
	0·6	27	24	26	28	42
	0·8	27	23	24	25	29
0·95	0·2	40	36	38	47	65
	0·4	40	34	37	44	55
	0·6	40	32	30	42	48
	0·8	39	32	34	36	40
0·975	0·2	82	70	79	69	93
	0·4	83	66	75	65	82
	0·6	82	70	69	59	79
	0·8	79	65	66	57	79

* M is the average number of vehicles arriving per cycle, i.e. g/c.

An expression for the proportion of vehicles which stop at least once and an expression for the average number of stops and starts per vehicle have also been deduced and are given in Reference 18. These factors may be important when considering wear and tear of vehicles, fuel consumption and annoyance to drivers.

Vehicle-actuated signals

All the above results refer to fixed-time signals or to vehicle-actuated signals which are operating on a fixed cycle because of heavy traffic demands.

SIGNAL SETTINGS

The electronic computer referred to earlier was used to simulate traffic conditions at an intersection controlled by vehicle-actuated signals, assuming that traffic was random and that saturation flow was constant. The variation of calculated delay with vehicle-extension period and maximum period is shown for a particular case in Fig. 9.15. It would appear that for

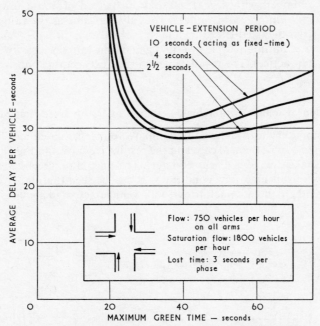

Fig. 9.15. Calculated effect of the vehicle-extension period and the maximum period on delay at vehicle-actuated signals

minimum delay a fixed vehicle-extension period should be as short as is practicable so that the signals just allow the queue to disperse before changing to the other phase if there is waiting traffic. This is difficult to attain in practice because, unlike the theoretical model assumed so far, the discharge rate varies within a cycle and between cycles and a vehicle-extension period which is just greater than the average discharge interval would, under actual conditions, frequently cut off part of the queue. This would have an adverse effect on delay. However, safety requirements demand that a fixed vehicle-extension period should not be too short (say, at least four seconds) so that this state of affairs is not likely to arise.

It will be seen from Fig. 9.15 that the best value of the maximum period does not vary much with different vehicle-extension periods and the results of the fixed-time work may reasonably be used to deduce the best value of the maximum period. In any case, in heavy traffic the majority of vehicle-actuated signals act virtually as fixed-time signals.

Delay at vehicle-actuated signals

When the green periods are running to maximum because of heavy traffic demands (i.e. during peak periods) the formulae derived for fixed-time signals may be used to estimate the average delay per vehicle, the number of vehicles in the queue, etc. This has been tested in practice at several vehicle-actuated intersections in the London area and good agreement was obtained between observed and theoretical values.

When the signals are not running to maximum it is much more difficult to derive a simple method for predicting the delay to vehicles. However, a few computations of delay using the electronic computer have shown that the delay obtained with a vehicle-extension period of about four seconds (i.e. the minimum practical value) is roughly the same as the value of delay obtained from the fixed-time formula, by substituting in this formula calculated values of optimum cycle time and green time (not necessarily the values observed in practice). The results given in the next section confirm this finding.

Comparison of delays with vehicle-actuated and with fixed-time signals

The computer has been used to compare vehicle-actuated and fixed-time operation in a hypothetical case and the results are shown in Fig. 9.16 (curve B is a special case and is discussed later). The maximum greens were chosen arbitrarily to suit high flow conditions. It can be seen that under light flow conditions the delay is much lower with vehicle-actuated signals, although

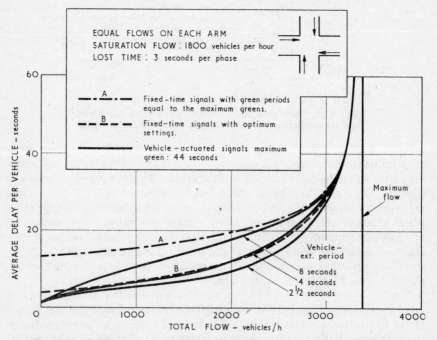

Fig. 9.16. Comparison of vehicle-actuated with fixed-time signals (four-way intersection)

the absolute value of delay even with fixed-time signals is quite low. At higher flows the vehicle-actuated signal is running to maximum more often and the two types of curve converge. The point at which this occurs depends largely on the value of the vehicle-extension period. In this example the saturation flow is assumed to be constant at 1800 veh/h, corresponding to a discharge interval of two seconds, so that when the vehicle-extension period is $2\frac{1}{2}$ seconds the signals change soon after the queue has dispersed. With a longer vehicle-extension period the signals run to maximum at much lower flows.

In the fixed-time case (curve A) the green periods were equal to the maximum greens of the vehicle-actuated signal. When the green periods are optimum values (according to rules given in this chapter) at each value of flow the delay is represented in Fig. 9.16 by curve B, which is practically identical with the vehicle-actuated curve corresponding to a vehicle-extension period of four seconds. It should be noted however that only one setting of the vehicle-actuated signal is necessary to cater for the whole range of flows shown in Fig. 9.16.

A comparison of vehicle-actuated and fixed-time working has also been made for cases where the total flow entering the junction is assumed to be constant, but the ratio of the flows on the two phases varies from 1:1 to $2\frac{1}{2}$:1. This is illustrated in Table 9.6, where it can be seen that the vehicle-actuated signal for low vehicle-extension periods, without any change in setting, gives no increase in delay as the traffic pattern alters and only a slight increase when the vehicle-extension period is eight seconds, whereas

TABLE 9.6

Effect on delay of a change in traffic pattern

2500 vehicles per hour entering the junction.
Saturation flow on each arm: 1800 veh/h
Lost time: 3 seconds per phase.
Maximum green times with vehicle-actuated signals: 44 seconds.

Details of controller		Average delay per vehicle (seconds)		
		Ratio of flows (A/B)		
		1·0	1·5	2·5
Vehicle-actuated signal with vehicle extension periods of (seconds):	$2\frac{1}{2}$	15	15	14
	4	18	18	17
	8	22	24	33
Fixed-time signal	44 sec green per phase	23	29	Over-loaded
	Optimum settings	18	17	16

the fixed-time signal becomes overloaded with the 2½:1 flow ratio. If the fixed-time controller could provide optimum settings for each flow ratio chosen then the delays would be comparable with those of the vehicle-actuated signal working with a short vehicle-extension period.

Thus, the real value of a vehicle-actuated signal is not that it caters for the random variation of traffic, i.e. variations in flow from cycle to cycle, but that it can deal satisfactorily with long-term variations both in the mean values of the total flow and in the flow ratio of the phases, provided the vehicle-extension period is sufficiently short.

Under steady flow conditions (i.e. when variations from hour to hour are small*), the fixed-time signal has been shown to give delays comparable with a vehicle-actuated signal operating on a short vehicle-extension period†). However, the fixed-time signal is less able to cope with variable traffic conditions (particularly when the flow ratio of the phases changes) than the vehicle-actuated signal.

High-speed roads

Existing traffic signals are not entirely suitable for high-speed roads, as drivers may be driving at such a speed that, when the signals change to amber, they can neither stop in time nor, by continuing at the same speed, reach a safe point by the time the red period commences. Investigations have been made under controlled conditions to find the position on the road for various speeds from which, when the lights turn to amber, most drivers can stop comfortably and at what position drivers decide to carry on and cross on the red. The main results are shown in Table 9.7.

TABLE 9.7

Distance from stop line from which 50 and 90 per cent of drivers stop when amber commences

Speed (mile/h)	Distance (ft) from stop line from which 50 per cent of drivers stop	Distance (ft) from stop line from which 90 per cent of drivers stop
30	105	135
40	160	205
50	235	300
60	345	440
70	525*	650*

* Estimated.

There is a section (called the critical section) where a driver travelling at a particular speed may be in a dilemma if the signals change to amber (see Fig. 9.17). For example, a driver travelling at 60 mile/h would cover 264 ft during a three-second amber period: if the "collision" point were 64 ft

* This is typical of many large cities during the daytime.
† Many vehicle-actuated signals have vehicle-extension periods greater than four seconds.

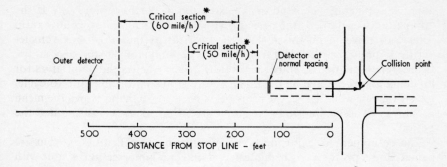

Note:* A critical section is that section of road in which a vehicle travelling at a given speed may not be able to stop in time if the signals ahead change to amber, nor continue and clear the collision point before the red signal appears.

Fig. 9.17. Critical sections for vehicles approaching traffic signals on high-speed roads

beyond the stop line any driver further than 200 ft from the stop line at the commencement of the amber signal would be unable to clear the collision point before the appearance of the red signal; Table 9.7 shows that 90 per cent of drivers travelling at 60 mile/h will stop comfortably if they are 440 ft from the stop line when the signals change to amber. Therefore between 440 ft and 200 ft from the stop line a driver travelling at this speed may be uncertain whether to stop or to continue; in fact he may be unable to take either action with safety. It has been found that only 10 per cent of drivers moving at 60 mile/h stop satisfactorily if they are 275 ft from the intersection when the signals change to amber.

With the present signal system a vehicle registers its presence when it crosses the detector (usually located 90-130 ft from the stop line) and its green time extension is started at this time. Thus, drivers travelling at medium and high speeds will have passed through their critical sections and will already have decided their course of action long before they reach the detector. It has been mentioned earlier that a system known as "double detection" is currently in operation, it goes part of the way towards meeting the needs of high-speed roads, though there are some disadvantages associated with it. Two detectors at 130 ft and 240 ft (approximately) are installed and vehicles receive an extension of right-of-way on passing over each detector, the length of the extension being just sufficient to take the vehicle at its measured speed from one detector to the next and from the second detector to the intersection. The disadvantages with this method are (1) 240 ft is not far enough away from the intersection for vehicles travelling at over 45 mile/h to stop in time, and (2) slow vehicles are given two fairly long extensions of right-of-way which decrease the chances of a "gap" change of right-of-way, though in some systems the outer detectors are installed only in the fast lane(s).

Because of the difficulties with present control equipment at traffic signals on high-speed roads, additional equipment to the normal vehicle-actuated controller has been devised by the Laboratory. This additional equipment measures a vehicle's speed when it is 500 ft from the intersection and delays placing a demand for an extension of the green time until a certain period has elapsed; the period is equal to the time that it would take a vehicle to travel from this distant detector, at its measured speed, to its "critical" point, i.e. the point from which it could no longer stop in comfort. If the signals change to amber before the driver reaches the point at which his demand is registered he should be able to stop comfortably. If the signals are still green when he reaches this point then his demand is placed in the usual way. These extensions are, of course, limited by a maximum green period.

The equipment is being developed jointly by two British signal companies, and a prototype is being tested at an actual intersection.

ROUNDABOUTS

Some details affecting the design of roundabouts, including recommended dimensions for the weaving sections, the central island, and the entry and exit layouts, have been given by the Ministry of Transport.[11,23] It should be noted that the Ministry of Transport Memorandum 575[23] is now under revision. Detailed discussions of roundabout design have also been given by Manton,[24] and Clayton.[25,26]

This section does not make recommendations for the dimensions of roundabouts but discusses the general principles involved. The results of theoretical calculations and also investigations at actual roundabouts have led to the derivation of a method of estimating the expected delay at a roundabout.

Geometric design

SHAPE OF CENTRAL ISLAND

When the central island of a roundabout is exceptionally large or contains buildings the system of weaving sections is often referred to a as "gyratory" system. With large gyratory systems the shape of the central area or island is often of secondary importance, being the result of converting in the cheapest way an area containing buildings and streets into a system of weaving sections of the required dimensions (see Fig. 9.18.)

With conventional roundabouts at normal cross-roads the central island is usually round or square (with rounded corners) but oval shapes are sometimes used at "scissors"-type intersections. At intersections where more than four roads converge or at sites which are hemmed in by buildings in places which prohibit a free hand in construction, irregularly shaped roundabouts often result. Figure 9.19 shows some examples of variously shaped roundabouts (see Plate 9.3). An almost square central island would be expected to create a certain amount of difficulty to drivers going from one weaving section to another as well as placing them at a disadvantage with respect to traffic entering the roundabout. This would tend to give the wrong type of priority, as will be seen later. For this reason it is preferable to round off considerably the corners of a square roundabout. Thus, if the radius of curvature of the corners is made at least 60 ft, "square" roundabouts must have sides considerably longer than 120 ft to retain something approaching a square shape.

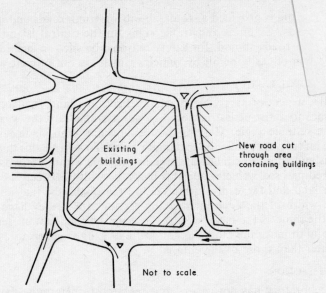

Existing buildings

New road cut through area containing buildings

Not to scale

Fig. 9.18. Example of gyratory system formed mainly from existing streets

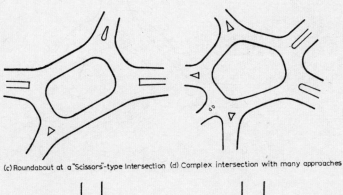

(c) Roundabout at a "Scissors"-type Intersection   (d) Complex intersection with many approaches

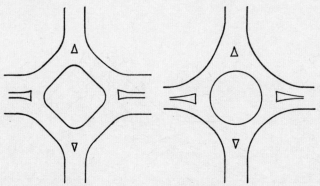

(a) Square central island at normal 90° cross-road

(b) Circular central island at normal 90° cross-road

Fig. 9.19. Layout at some actual roundabouts. Not to scale

Street lighting is provided at roundabouts on trunk roads and important classified roads. Columns and traffic signs on the central island opposite the approach roads should, for safety reasons, be sited in such a position that they cannot easily be hit by vehicles which are out of control.

ENTRY AND EXIT LAYOUT

Usually, a pedestrian refuge or channelization island is placed on the approaches to assist pedestrians and to guide traffic into the weaving sections at a suitable angle. Merging manoeuvres are often made easier when vehicles, on entry, are confined to definite paths. To achieve this the channelization island should be made as large as possible without encroaching on the desired paths of vehicles. On this basis the width between the channelization island and the central island could reasonably be the same or less than the width of the adjacent weaving sections (or if they have different widths, the same as the mean width). To keep the roundabout free-flowing it is helpful to make the radius of curvature of exits as generous as possible and greater than those of the entries.

WEAVING SECTIONS

The Laboratory has not carried out research to determine the effect of different shapes of weaving section (other than rectangular shapes), but

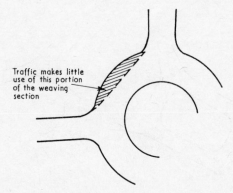

Traffic makes little use of this portion of the weaving section

(a) With this layout the weaving section is partly wasted

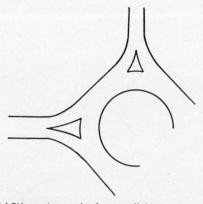

(b) This weaving section is more efficient

Fig. 9.20. Shapes of weaving sections

certain facts appear to be fairly obvious; for example, the concave sections of a circular roundabout (shown shaded in Fig. 9.20 (a)) are unlikely to contribute much to capacity (see track marks shown in Plate 9.4), and therefore the type shown in Fig 9.20 (b) appears to be more practical.

The main factors which affect the capacity, delay and driving conditions are weaving length (l), weaving width (w), entry width (e) and the proportion of weaving traffic (p). With a rectangular weaving section and a suitably shaped channelization island for entering traffic the meanings of these terms are fairly obvious (see Fig. 6.10). This diagram also shows how the proportion of weaving traffic is determined. With weaving sections of irregular shape, effective dimensions may have to be assumed for purposes of calculation and these should be based on the likely paths of vehicles through the weaving section. This also applies when there is a normal pedestrian refuge island instead of a channelization island, and Fig. 6.13 indicates how the effective entry widths and weaving length should be determined.

In practice, weaving widths tend to have standard values, such as 24 ft, 30 ft, 40 ft, 50 ft, or 60 ft. In rural areas on busy trunk roads the usual practice is to have a weaving width of 30 ft with a weaving length of about 150 ft, although other widths and lengths have been observed. In urban and suburban areas the dimensions of the weaving sections of roundabouts appear to be less standardized, perhaps because capacity is more of a problem in these areas and the design has to be governed much more by economic considerations.

In rural areas speeds tend to be high and weaving would be expected to take place at higher speeds than in urban areas. Longer weaving sections are therefore favoured, but a high length/width ratio is not as economic in land usage as a lower one. However, this objection is generally of minor importance in rural areas where land values are much lower than in urban areas. In towns, however, capacity is important and speeds are much lower, so that a lower ratio of length/width is both satisfactory and economic. To assist in the selection of the length/width ratio the dimensions of a number of weaving sections of roundabouts in Great Britain have been studied. The mean values, according to location and type, are shown in Table 9.8.

TABLE 9.8

*Mean ratios of length/width ratio (l/w) of
weaving sections observed at a selection of
roundabouts of various types*

Description of site	Class of road	
	Trunk	Non-trunk
Rural . . .	4·8 (54)*	4·4 (34)
Suburban . .	3·8 (119)	3·9 (147)
Town . . .	3·4 (81)	

*The figures in brackets denote the number of weaving sections in the sample; the sample of roundabouts was approximately one-quarter of this

Assuming the shapes of weaving sections of roundabouts have, on the whole, been satisfactory in relation to location and traffic requirements, then this past experience can be used in designing new roundabouts when the required capacities of the weaving sections are known. If the length/ width ratio l/w is denoted by r and is given the value appropriate to the particular category, as listed in Table 9.8 and if e/w, for simplicity, is assumed to be unity then the formula for capacity (Q_p p.c.u./h) (see Chapter 6) may be rearranged to provide a means of estimating w as follows:

$$w = \frac{[1+(1/r)]Q_p}{172(1-\frac{1}{3}p)}$$

where p is the proportion of weaving traffic. The nearest "standard" width to the value deduced, provided it is greater than the width of the approach road, might then be regarded as a suitable width for the weaving section. From the ratio assumed the length of the weaving section can then be calculated.

PEDESTRIANS

Pedestrian crossings of the zebra type are frequently placed at the entrances and exits to roundabouts, and although subways would in many cases be safer and cause less vehicular delay the presence of pedestrian crossings on the approach carriageway would not be expected to have an adverse effect on the operation of the roundabout. However, this is not always true for zebra crossings on the exit carriageways, where pedestrians might hold up vehicles and cause a queue to extend back into the roundabout. This can increase the chance of the roundabout locking. Sometimes the crossing is placed further back on the approach roads but this causes difficulty to pedestrians.

Traffic operation

FLOW CHARACTERISTICS THROUGH ROUNDABOUTS

Since a roundabout is made up from a number of weaving sections, each one will react on its neighbours, e.g. if traffic has difficulty manoeuvring through one weaving section, then this may prevent further vehicles entering from the previous weaving section. This interaction can cause congestion within the roundabout and sometimes complete "locking" of the roundabout (see Plate 9.5) when all vehicles are brought to a standstill; vehicles neither being able to get in nor out of the roundabout. Fig. 6.14 shows a delay/flow curve at a particular roundabout when a blockage was just beginning: the flow entering the roundabout became less as the delay increased. If the weaving section occupies a large area it can usually provide sufficient storage space for vehicles which temporarily cannot enter the following weaving section. Often, the temporary blockage disperses before there are any harmful effects on the operation of the previous weaving section. Thus locking is more likely to occur in smaller roundabouts (in the absence of any priority rule). Usually, the police take over control of a roundabout once it has become congested and it has been found that rarely can they relax control until the queues on the approaches have dispersed (usually at the end of the peak period.)

WAYS OF REDUCING THE CHANCES OF LOCKING

(a) USE OF TRAFFIC SIGNALS (see Plate 9.6). Traffic signals have been installed on the approaches to a number of roundabouts in an attempt to improve capacity and reduce the chances of locking.[27,28] In all cases the roundabouts were such that prior to signal control being tried they required police assistance during most peak periods. In each case the signals were installed between 100 and 200 ft from the roundabout so that drivers, even though they had had a green signal, would approach with caution and would not expect a "guaranteed" free passage. Also it was intended that by setting the signals back drivers would observe the zebra crossings, which had to be retained as the signals were operating only during peak periods. Signal control was found to increase the capacity over police control by about 10 per cent at two of the roundabouts where there were four approaches, but gave no increase at two others where there were five or more approaches. Locking was not entirely eliminated, however, and usually occurred when the traffic signals temporarily allowed more traffic to enter the roundabout than could leave. It was found that increasing the "all-red" periods as traffic increased reduced quite substantially the number of occasions when locking took place, without causing a decrease in capacity.

In periods of moderate flow, when there was no danger of locking, a shorter all-red period reduced delay. The all-red periods at these experimental sites were compromise values: they were set to give reasonable flexibility in times of moderate flow yet having a small chance of locking in times of peak flow, but were such that they could be extended manually beyond the set time during any cycle when the policeman on duty felt conditions required it. Experiments have been carried out at the roundabout, using a loop detector surrounding the central island, to assess the amount of traffic in the roundabout and automatically to adjust the all-red in each cycle accordingly (see Plate 9.7). Locking was virtually eliminated using this presence detector (now commercially available). Vehicle presence detectors are described in Chapter 10.

(b) USE OF "OFF-SIDE" PRIORITY RULE Signs asking drivers to give way to traffic on their right (see Plates 9.8 and 9.9) have been installed at a number of roundabouts[29] which regularly became congested during peak periods. In all cases the signs virtually eliminated locking and the roundabouts no longer required the assistance of police. The flow could be maintained at the "capacity" value even in overload conditions, i.e. with long queues on all approaches. Delays were reduced owing to the increase in capacity, which ranged from 6 to 14 per cent, over police control. At two roundabouts which had previously been signalized, the priority rule gave about the same increase in capacity over both signal control and police control, but it should be mentioned that at these two sites signal control showed no improvement over police control. Accidents with the priority rule in operation were reduced by about 40 per cent.

DELAY AT ROUNDABOUTS

The delay at roundabouts can be regarded as consisting of two components: (1) delay caused by slowing down, travelling the extra distance round the roundabout and accelerating to the normal speed of the road; (2) delay caused by queueing to get into the roundabout and by obstruction by other vehicles while in the roundabout.

Table 9.9 shows the results of some calculations for the delay described under (1). In these calculations it was assumed that vehicles slowed down with a deceleration of 0·2g, negotiated the roundabout at such a speed as to cause a radial acceleration of 0·2g, and on leaving the roundabout accelerated to the normal speed of the road with an acceleration (shown in the table) appropriate to the difference between the initial and final speeds, these accelerations having been derived from published figures in motoring journals. It can be seen that, roughly, the delay is about nine seconds for roads with an average speed of 30 mile/h, 12½ seconds for roads with a speed of 40 mile/h and 17 seconds for roads with a speed of 50 mile/h. The radius of curvature of the roundabout island appears to make little difference since the larger the island the greater the extra time spent negotiating it but the smaller the time losses due to deceleration and acceleration.

A few observations have indicated that actual delays are about 2 seconds

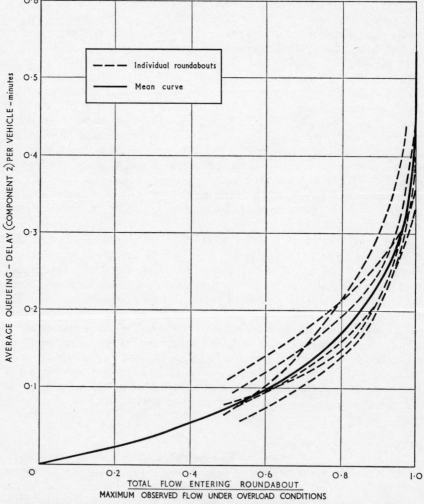

Fig. 9.21. Queueing-delay/flow curves for six roundabouts (ignoring the effect of "locking")

TABLE 9.9
Calculated delay (component 1) at roundabouts

Time losses (sec) at roundabouts

Radius of curvature of path of vehicle (ft)	Speed round roundabout (mile/h)	30 mile/h				40 mile/h				50 mile/h			
		Decelerating (0·20g)	Round about	Accelerating (0·20g)	Total	Decelerating (0·20g)	Round about	Accelerating (0·15g)	Total	Decelerating (0·20g)	Round about	Accelerating (0·10g)	Total
50	12	1·2	6·5	1·2	8·9	2·2	7·1	3·0	12·3	3·3	7·4	6·4	17·1
75	14	0·9	7·4	0·9	9·2	1·8	8·3	2·5	12·6	2·9	8·7	5·5	17·1
100	16	0·6	7·9	0·6	9·1	1·5	9·0	2·0	12·5	2·5	9·7	4·8	17·0
125	18	0·4	8·2	0·4	9·0	1·2	9·7	1·7	12·6	2·2	10·5	4·2	16·9
150	20	0·3	8·4	0·3	9·0	1·0	10·1	1·4	12·5	1·9	11·1	3·7	16·7
200	24	0·1	8·4	0·1	8·6	0·7	10·7	1·0	12·4	1·5	12·0	2·9	16·4

12

less than the calculated values given above because in practice drivers tend to follow a straight path.

Values for delay described under (2) above have been found from a study of six roundabouts and are shown in Fig. 9.21. The solid curve gives the mean value and could be used to give a first approximation to this delay. These curves refer to conditions when locking did not occur, as the delay during conditions of locking is not amenable to calculations. The sum of the component delays (1) and (2) gives the correct delay for comparison with the delay associated with traffic signals.

REFERENCES TO CHAPTER 9

1. CHARLESWORTH, G., and J. C. TANNER. Road junctions in rural areas. *Department of Scientific and Industrial Research, Road Research Technical Paper* No. 47. London, 1960 (H.M. Stationery Office).

2. TANNER, J. C. A theoretical analysis of delays at an uncontrolled intersection. *Biometrika*, 1962, **49** (1/2), 163–70.

3. WEBSTER, F. V., and J. G. WARDROP. Capacity of urban intersections. *Sixth International Study Week in Traffic Engineering, 10–14 September 1962, Salzburg, Austria.* London, undated (World Touring and Automobile Organisation.)

4. TYACK, F. G. Street traffic signals, with particular reference to vehicle-actuation. *J. Instn elect. Engrs*, 1938, **82**, 125–53.

5. HARRISON, H. H., and T. P. PREIST. Automatic street traffic signalling. London, 1934 (Sir Isaac Pitman & Sons, Ltd).

6. INGLIS, B. G. Traffic signal systems. *J. Instn munic. Engrs*, 1954, **80** (8), 369–92.

7. THORPE, E., and R. G. GREEN. Modern vehicle-actuated road signals. *Contractors Rec.*, 1954, **65**, 25–9.

8. THORPE, E. Recent developments in vehicle-actuated traffic signal control. *Surveyor, Lond.*, 1960, **119** (3537), 285–6.

9. GARWOOD, F., and J. C. TANNER. Accident studies before and after road changes. *Publ. Wks. munic. Services Congr.*, 1956, *Final report*, 329–54; Discussion, 374–80.

10. AMERICAN ASSOCIATION OF STATE HIGHWAY OFFICIALS, INSTITUTE OF TRAFFIC ENGINEERS and NATIONAL CONFERENCE ON STREET AND HIGHWAY SAFETY. Manual on uniform traffic control devices for streets and highways. Washington, D.C., 1948 (U.S. Public Roads Administration).

11. MINISTRY OF WAR TRANSPORT. Design and layout of roads in built-up areas. London, 1946 (H.M. Stationery Office).

12. WEBSTER, F. V., and R. F. NEWBY. Research into the relative merits of roundabouts and traffic-signal-controlled intersections. *Proc. Instn civ. Engrs*, 1964, **27**, 47–76.

13. HERZOG, A. Design of intersections in urban areas from the capacity point of view. *International Study Week in Traffic Engineering, 10–14th September, 1962, Salzburg, Austria*, London, undated (World Touring and Automobile Organisation).

14. CHRISTOFFERS, C. Practical experience in the design of high capacity urban intersections. *International Study Week in Traffic Engineering, 10–14th September, 1962, Salzburg, Austria.* London, undated (World Touring and Automobile Organisation).

15. GULSTAD, E. Design of intersections in urban areas from the capacity point of view. *International Study Week in Traffic Engineering, 10–14th September, 1962, Salzburg, Austria*. London, undated (World Touring and Automobile Organisation).

16. MOORE, R. L. Psychological factors of importance in traffic engineering. *International Study Week in Traffic Engineering, 1–6th October, 1956, Stresa, Italy*. London, 1956 (World Touring and Automobile Organisation).

17. HILLIER, J. A., P. D. WHITING and J. G. WARDROP. The Automatic delay computer. *Department of Scientific and Industrial Research, Road Research Laboratory Research Note* No. RN/2291/JAH. PDW. JGW. Harmondsworth, 1954 (Unpublished).

18. WEBSTER, F. V. Traffic signal settings. *Department of Scientific and Industrial Research, Road Research Technical Paper* No. 39. London, 1958 (H.M. Stationery Office).

19. WARDROP, J. G. Some theoretical aspects of road traffic research. *Proc. Instn civ. Engrs. Part II*, 1952, **1**, (2) 325–62; Discussion, 362–78.

20. ADAMS, W. F. Road traffic considered as a random series. *J. Instn civ. Engrs*, 1936, **4**, 121–30.

21. SMEED, R. J. Traffic flow. *Operat. Res. Quart.*, 1957, **8** (3), 115–23; Discussion, 142–8.

22. SMEED, R. J. The traffic problem in towns. 1961 (Manchester Statistical Society).

23. MINISTRY OF TRANSPORT. Memorandum on the layout and construction of roads. *Memorandum* No. 575. London, 1943 (H.M. Stationery Office).

24. MANTON, B. G. Traffic flow at roundabouts. A review of theory and practice. *Highw. & Br.*, 1958, **26** (1238) 8, 10; (1239) 4, 6; (1240) 4, 6; (1244) 4, 6.

25. CLAYTON, A. J. H. Traffic capacity of roundabouts at road intersections. *J. Instn civ. Engrs*, 1945, **23**, 149.

26. CLAYTON, A. J. H. Working capacity of roads. *Proc. Instn. civ. Engrs*, 1955, **4** (3), 625–73; Discussion, 673–96.

27. WEBSTER, F. V. Greenford roundabout experiment. *Traff. Engng & Control*, 1962, **2** (5), 266–71.

28. DEPARTMENT OF SCEINTIFIC AND INDUSTRIAL RESEARCH. Road research 1960. The report of the Road Research Board with the report of the Director of Road Research. London, 1961 (H.M. Stationery Office), pp. 34–5.

29. BLACKMORE, F. C. Priority at roundabouts. *Traff. Engng. & Control*, 1963, **5** (2), 104–6.

Chapter 10

Regulation and Automatic Control

SYNOPSIS

Control of speed. Waiting restrictions: growth of parking; control of kerbside parking; all-night parking in London streets. One-way systems. Channelization. Automatic control: linked traffic signal systems; traffic funnels and pre-signals; automatic diversion of traffic; vehicle guidance and control.

INTRODUCTION

Traffic regulation can be regarded as including all those measures designed to control traffic so as to improve road conditions and prevent the movement of road users from conflicting. This control can be imposed by physical means, which are usually effective but sometimes expensive, or by legal regulations, which are usually cheap but which depend appreciably on the degree of enforcement provided to support them.

Administrative orders to regulate traffic can be broadly sub-divided into two groups, namely, those which apply everywhere and those which apply only in specified circumstances. Those which are so general as to apply everywhere and which are not indicated by signs, e.g. keep left on the highway, are accepted by almost everyone as justified and consequently require very little enforcement.

The second group includes regulations such as speed limits, waiting restrictions and the prohibition of turning which relate to particular places or classes of vehicle, and are indicated by signs or symbols. Regulations of this type require more positive enforcement and in framing them it is important to take this into account. From a practical standpoint a regulation which is not acceptable to most road users is usually unsatisfactory since it is very difficult to enforce.

This chapter first discusses some of the more common forms of regulation, and then deals with the use of automatic central control to co-ordinate traffic movement throughout an area. Intersection control, pedestrian control and safety fences are considered in Chapters 9, 12 and 14 respectively. The use of carriageway markings as a means of controlling and regulating traffic is discussed in Chapter 11.

CONTROL OF SPEED

Effect of speed limits

A speed limit of 30 mile/h in built-up areas was first introduced in Great Britain in 1935. Little information is available, however, on the effect of the speed limit on traffic speeds at that time. Although other changes were made at the same time, including the introduction of driving tests and pedestrian

324

crossings, the sudden change from a rising trend in accidents to a fall is ascribed to the introduction of the speed limit in built-up areas (see Chapter 6 of the Companion Volume).[1]

More recent observations of the effect of a 30 mile/h speed limit have been made at sites where the limit has been either removed or imposed. The effect of changes made at about 40 sites during 1948 and 1951 were studied and Table 10.1 compares the numbers of accidents that occurred with the numbers that might have been expected had no change been made.

TABLE 10.1

Effect of 30 mile/h speed limit on accidents

	Limit imposed	Limit removed
Observed accidents after · · · ·	190	51
Expected accidents after · · · ·	221	36
Apparent change · · · · · ·	−14%	+42%

In neither case was the effect statistically significant; the average length of the before and after periods was two years.

Later investigations have shown that a high proportion of vehicles exceed the speed limit in fringe areas and that the effect on the mean speeds is small. However, there is a slight reduction in the mean speed of cars and a substantial reduction in the proportion of vehicles travelling at the higher speeds.

A speed limit of 30 mile/h was imposed on the roads of built-up areas of Northern Ireland in October 1956. Prior to this date only certain commercial vehicles and coaches were subject to a speed limit. The Royal Ulster Constabulary embarked upon a campaign, which received widespread press publicity, to detect by means of a radar speedmeter those drivers who exceeded the limit. Observations at a number of sites before and about one year after the introduction of the limit[2] showed a reduction of 7 mile/h, from 36 mile/h to 29 mile/h, in the speed of cars on roads in the outer surburbs of Belfast. There were correspondingly smaller reductions in the mean speeds of slower vehicles. The proportion of vehicles exceeding 30 mile/h was reduced by 75 per cent and almost all speeds greater than 40 mile/h were eliminated. These speed changes were much greater than those observed in connexion with speed limit changes over limited lengths of road in Great Britain, and it is thought that this was largely attributable to the campaign of police enforcement and the publicity given to the use of the radar speedmeter. Personal-injury accidents in a six-month period unaffected by the petrol shortage of 1956/57 showed a reduction of 24 per cent in built-up areas, there being a slight increase in non-built-up areas; this reduction was equivalent to a saving of about 700 accidents in one year.

In 1958 and 1959 a speed limit of 40 mile/h was imposed at a number of selected sites on main roads in the London traffic area. They covered about 100 miles of main traffic routes where some restriction of speed was necessary but where the normal limit of 30 mile/h was considered unrealistic. About two-thirds of the mileage was unrestricted before the change. In studying the effect of this regulation[3] it was convenient to divide the roads into two groups, one group consisting of sections of road which were previously derestricted and the other of sections which were previously limited to 30 mile/h. Speeds were measured at a number of these sites and also at control sites where the regulation would not have been expected to have affected speeds. After allowance had been made for the upward trend of about 1·5 mile/h at the control sites it was found that the 40 mile/h limit did not appear to have affected vehicle speeds on roads that had previously been limited to 30 mile/h; where there had previously been no limit the average speed of cars was about 3 mile/h less (and that of light commercial vehicles about 2 mile/h less) than they would have been if the limit had not been imposed. On dual-carriageways the proportion of cars exceeding the limit was 28 per cent and on single carriageways 13 per cent, and these were about one-half of what would have been expected if there had been no limit.

A study of accidents[4] covering nearly two years before and two years after the introduction of the 40 mile/h limit showed that relative to accident trends on all roads in the surrounding districts, those on roads formerly restricted to 30 mile/h were slightly in excess of the expected number (7 per cent more in the case of fatal and serious accidents) but for these roads the changes were not statistically significant. Injury accidents on roads formerly derestricted were about 19 per cent fewer than expected and fatal and serious accidents were about 28 per cent fewer than expected, after the 40 mile/h limit was imposed. These changes were statistically significant.

A 50 mile/h speed limit was imposed on certain trunk roads during summer week-ends in 1960 and 1961, when about 750 miles were affected. The operational period of the speed limit was from 6.00 a.m. on Friday until mid-night on Monday when a Bank Holiday was included, but during normal week-ends the limit was imposed from noon on Friday until mid-night on Sunday. Speed measurements at one site showed a reduction of nearly 4 mile/h in the mean speed of cars and of just over 2 mile/h in the speed of light commercial vehicles. The percentage of vehicles exceeding 50 mile/h was approximately halved; the percentage of cars exceeding the limit fell from about 40 to 20 and that of light commercial vehicles from 18 to 9. The percentage of cars exceeding 60 mile/h fell from 13 to 3 per cent.

A comparison of injury accidents on trunk roads during summer week-ends during 1959 (before the week-end speed limit was started) and 1961, is shown in Table 10.2. The "control" roads were 1000 miles of other roads not subject to speed limits but carrying a similar type and volume of traffic to that carried on the roads used as test sites. A very similar table was obtained when considering only fatal and serious casualties. It can be seen that the injury accidents were reduced by about one-quarter where the speed limit was imposed. It is interesting to note that at the "control" sites there was also a reduction of about one-fifth in the number of accidents. Further speed measurements[5] at two sites, one controlled and the other not controlled, at week-ends during the early summer of 1962 have indicated that there was probably also a significant reduction in the average speed of vehicles at sites other than those directly subject to the week-end speed limit.

TABLE 10.2

Injury accidents on trunk roads during summer week-ends

Type of road	Number of injury accidents			
	1959	1961	change	percentage change
50 mile/h speed limit in 1961 ·	1137	842	−295	−26
"Control", subject to no limit in either year · · · ·	756	595	−161	−21

The effect of a radar speedmeter

A number of police forces have adopted the radar speedmeter as a means of enforcing speed limits. To determine its effect on driver behaviour, observations were made of vehicle speeds before and after a police check point in Slough, where the police were using a radar speedmeter to stop and warn violators of the 30 mile/h speed limit. Speeds of traffic in both directions were measured about $\frac{1}{2}$ mile before and after the police check point. It was found that there was a reduction of about $1\frac{1}{2}$ mile/h in the average speed of vehicles after they had passed the check point and also a reduction in the number of vehicles exceeding the speed limit. The display of warning boards alone on the day following the police check had much the same effect on the speeds of vehicles as the police check itself.

Control of speeds by linked traffic signals

A study of accident records for 1952 and 1953 showed that about 15 per cent of the casualties in Slough occurred on a section of A.4 between the town centre and the western borough boundary. It was believed at the Laboratory that if some method of effectively controlling vehicles speeds could be found, it might result in a reduction in the numbers and severity of accidents on this section of road. The effect would apply particularly at night when the risk of a serious or fatal casualty per mile travelled was more than twice that during the day. Proposals were being made for traffic signals to be installed at certain important junctions on this section of A.4, and it was suggested that if a system of linked fixed-time signals were used instead of isolated vehicle-actuated signals it might be possible to regulate traffic speed. In December 1956 signals were installed at 11 points along the 2·2-mile section, with fixed cycle times to limit the progression speeds to about 26 mile/h in peak periods and to about 28 mile/h in off-peak periods.

During the first four years of operation serious and fatal casualties were estimated to have been reduced by about 55 per cent. Detailed study[6] of the accidents occurring in the first 18 months of operation of the signals showed that the reduction in the serious accident rate was greater by night than by day and apparently occurred over the whole length of the system. There was a greater reduction in the number of casualties among pedestrians and occupants of vehicles than among cyclists and motorcyclists.

The effect of the fixed-time installation was to increase average journey times through the system by about one minute. Informal comment showed that motorists tended initially to regard the signals as a nuisance because their free choice of speed was checked. However, when told of the saving in casualties their reaction was one of acceptance of the extra delay in view of the benefits derived from the signals. Another common comment from motorists was that the signals were obviously not needed during the night period when there was so little traffic about, whereas the accident statistics indicated that the risk per mile travelled at night was twice as great as that during the day before the signals were installed. After the installation the day and night accident rates were lower and similar.

General effect of speed limits

These and other investigations give weight to the hypothesis that a reduction in speed leads to a reduction in accidents. In summarizing speed data from many sources in Europe and America, Smeed[7] concluded that speed limits are disobeyed on a very large scale but they nearly always affect the speed of traffic. The number of vehicles travelling at high speed is usually considerably reduced. He also concluded that speed limits seem to have a marked effect in reducing fatal accidents in urban areas although they have much less effect on slight or damage-only accidents. There is some evidence that motorcyclist and pedal cyclist fatalities are especially affected by speed limits. The imposition of speed limits on a number of main roads, including motorways, also seems to have been beneficial in reducing road accidents. The effect of speed limits on traffic speeds and accidents is considered in greater detail in Chapter 6 of the Companion Volume.[1]

WAITING RESTRICTIONS

The growth of parking

The rapid increase in urban parking in recent years can be illustrated by the following figures for an area of inner London, before the advent of controlled parking. Between 1951 and 1955 the number of street-parked vehicles in this area increased by 68 per cent, from 25 400 to 42 700 vehicles. Since street-parked vehicles are normally predominantly cars it is interesting to note that the number of cars licensed in the London County Council licensing area rose by 66 per cent in the same period, from 142 750 to 237 000, (see Table 8.1).

In the most congested areas of the West End of London the annual rate of increase of kerbside parking between 1951 and 1955 was 20 per cent compound, but after 1955 the rate decreased considerably as a result of the exhaustion of available kerbside space and the spread of "No Waiting" regulations. In the area of inner London mentioned above the number of street-parked vehicles increased by only 19 per cent between 1955 and 1959 compared with the 68 per cent increase in the previous 4-year period. Since 1959 the number of street-parked vehicles has been drastically reduced in the areas in which meters have been used to control parking.

In an urban area the degree of parking congestion can be expressed as a percentage of the available kerb space which is already occupied by standing vehicles in a length of street. The Ministry of Transport has recommended 20 ft as the desirable kerbside space allowance for a longitudinally parked vehicle and Table 10.3 shows the increase of the parking index (see p. 265) in inner London in recent years.

TABLE 10.3

The growth of parking congestion in inner London

Year	Standing vehicles per mile of street		Parking index (per cent)	
	Average	Range	Average	Range
1951	141	65 to 245	27	12 to 46
1955	237	108 to 443	45	21 to 75
1959	283	136 to 486	54	26 to 92

The amount of kerbside space which is available for vehicle parking is difficult to estimate owing to the requirements of bus stops, yard entrances and driveways, but the parking index of 75 per cent which appeared in parts of the City of Westminster in 1955 represented approximately saturation conditions. Increases above this level are associated with double-banking of parked vehicles and the infrigement of no-waiting regulations.

Control of kerbside parking

In Great Britain the Ministry of Transport has issued a Memorandum of Advice to Councils[8] regarding the control of traffic by traffic regulation orders. This memorandum gives general advice as to the sites and times of waiting restrictions, both along roads and at intersections. Restrictions on waiting may be imposed on traffic, safety or amenity grounds, but cannot be imposed if their effect is to deny reasonable access. In urban areas they can rarely be justified on Sundays or after 6.00 p.m. or 7.00 p.m., although in places where holiday traffic is a problem restrictions may be imposed only at week-ends and at Bank Holidays. Where there is much waiting for the purposes of loading and unloading, a time limit of, say, 20 minutes on waiting by commercial vehicles may be introduced; this further restriction is normally only applied for up to six hours in any period of 24 hours.

NO WAITING

No-waiting orders prohibit waiting but exceptions can be made for certain purposes, including loading and unloading. On trunk roads they usually operate from 8.30 a.m. or 9.00 a.m. to 6.00 p.m on weekdays, and until 12.30 or 1.00 p.m. on Saturdays. The actual hours can be chosen to suit local conditions and there are many complicated variations. Where conditions justify it they can apply for 24 hours per day. No-waiting orders are indicated by a circular sign with black letters on a yellow background, often giving the period and the days for which the regulation holds.

On the 27th May, 1947 the first no-waiting restrictions were applied to a number of main streets in the central London area. Observations made by means of a test vehicle driven at the speed of the traffic, and by means of aerial photographs, showed that there was a reduction of approximately 60 per cent in the number of parked vehicles; journey time improvements averaged 10 per cent.

Further no-waiting regulations were introduced at a number of sites in the Metropolitan area in September 1949. Observations from a test vehicle showed that decreases in parking ranged from zero to 65 per cent, producing small changes in the journey speed of the test vehicle, generally below 10 per cent. The average decrease in parking was about 30 per cent and the average increase in speed about 3 per cent, but this latter change was not statistically significant. These results are summarized in Table 10.4.

TABLE 10.4

Effect of "no-waiting" regulations in the London Suburbs, 1949

Site	Item	Before	After	Percentage change
London suburbs 1949	Waiting vehicles per mile	42	29	−31
	Journey speed mile/h	14·7	15·2	+3

The main conclusions of this work were that in an average surburban High Street a reduction of up to 30 per cent in vehicle parking, from an existing parking level of about 40 vehicles per mile, was unlikely to produce traffic speed increases exceeding a few per cent when the total traffic flow was below about 1000 vehicles per hour. At levels exceeding this figure there is some indication that the speed gained might exceed 10 per cent but such conditions are not common outside the central London area.

No-waiting regulations were introduced in central Glasgow in 1952. The results of a "before-and-after" study are given in Table 10.5. There was a marked decrease in the number of parked vehicles and a 14 per cent increase in mean journey speed.

TABLE 10.5

Effect of "no-waiting" regulations in Glasgow, 1952

	Before regulations in force	After regulations in force	Difference (per cent)
Parked vehicles per mile	171	53	−69
Mean total flow (veh/h)	690	730	+6
Mean journey speed (mile/h)	6·9	7·9	+14
Mean running speed (mile/h)	9·3	10·8	+16
Stopped time as percentage of journey time	26	25	

In October 1958 new regulations were introduced which considerably extended the no-waiting restrictions in the central area of Glasgow. The traffic flows, speeds, delays and the concentrations of parked vehicles were measured in selected streets and the results are given in Table 10.6. They relate to 5·9 miles of streets that were not previously restricted in 1952.

TABLE 10.6

Effect of "no-waiting" regulations in Central Glasgow, 1958

	Before regulations (Sept/1958)	After regulations (March/59)	Difference per cent.
Average number of parked vehicles per mile	100	32	−68
Mean total flow (veh/h) . .	945	995	+5
Mean journey speed (mile/h) .	10·0	11·2	+12
Mean running speed (mile/h) .	14·0	14·2	+5
Stopped time as percentage of journey time	27	24	−11

The density of parked vehicles fell by two-thirds and despite an increase of 5 per cent in traffic flow the average journey speed rose by 12 per cent. The effect of the regulations on journey time was greatest at the intersections, delays there being reduced by 23 per cent.

The effect of standing vehicles on accidents is not fully understood but the 1947–48 report of the London and Home Counties Traffic Advisory Committee[9] stated that during the period when the number of personal injuries sustained in the whole of Metropolitan Police District increased by 8 per cent, the accident rate in about 10 miles of no-waiting streets decreased by about 30 per cent during no-waiting hours.

During the year following the introduction of the no-waiting regulations in Glasgow accidents also decreased by an estimated 30 per cent.

UNILATERAL WAITING

Unilateral waiting regulations are a variation of the normal no-waiting regulations, allowing parking on one side of the road at a time. They usually apply during similar hours and for trunk roads usually consist of a waiting prohibition on even days on one side of the road and on odd days on the other side. Waiting is often limited on the side where it is not prohibited. Unilateral waiting regulations are also indicated by the circular yellow sign with a black legend.

Observations of traffic speed under conditions of (a) unilateral waiting and (b) waiting and no-waiting mixed in short sections, were made between 9.00 a.m. and 5.30 p.m. in High Street, Slough, which is part of A.4 and also a main shopping street. On the average fewer vehicles were parked under the mixed waiting and no-waiting condition; average speeds were about the same in each case. It was concluded that if the amount of parking and interference from other factors such as pedestrians, had been the same in each case, speeds would have been about 3 per cent slower under the mixed waiting conditions than with unilateral waiting.

There is, of course, still a need for enforcement of unilateral waiting regulations. When studying some newly established unilateral waiting streets in the West End it was found that 19 per cent of the total vehicles parked in the regulated streets were standing on the wrong or no-waiting side of the street.

RESTRICTIONS ON LOADING AND UNLOADING

Restrictions on loading and unloading usually operate only at peak hours e.g. 8.30 to 9.30 a.m., 11.30 a.m. to 1.30 p.m., and 4.00 p.m. to 6.00 p.m. They are usually coupled with no-waiting, limited waiting or unilateral waiting regulations and are applied at places such as bottlenecks or intersections where the presence of a single vehicle can be very obstructive. These regulations are indicated by a circular sign with a yellow background and a black legend.

Experimental loading and unloading restrictions were tried in central London in 1955. Observations were made of saturation flow (the maximum rate of discharge of vehicles from a queue during the green period at a traffic signal) and of the number of waiting vehicles in the affected zones before and after the restrictions were imposed on the approaches to 10 intersections. The ban was imposed for five hours daily.

During the hours that the restrictions were enforced the average number of waiting vehicles in the affected zones was only one-third of that before the ban and the average capacity of these streets was increased by about 150 veh/h; this increase was almost independent of the level of saturation flow. During the five hours of the ban there was a decrease of about 55 per cent in the average number of hours in which one or more waiting vehicles were observed. Both before and after the ban, only two-thirds as many vehicles were waiting within 150 ft of the intersections on the nearsides of the approaches as on the offsides (or exits from the intersections).

PARKING METERS

The use of parking meters in Britain began in July 1958 with the experimental installation of nearly 650 in a small area in the West End of London. By the end of 1963 there were about 14 000 in use in central London. A parking meter scheme increases the turnover of parking places by discouraging long-term parking. Fewer parking spaces are available in the area after introduction of the scheme and this often means that surrounding areas experience an increase in parking congestion. Traffic flow through the area covered by the scheme is improved because double-parking is eliminated (see Plate 10.1.)

No legal powers were available to make a charge for parking on the highway until the Road Traffic Act of 1956. This Act laid down the conditions under which parking meters could be used for this purpose making the important provision that any surplus revenue obtained was to be devoted to the provision of parking facilities off the street.

A parking meter scheme is set up in an area known as a "controlled parking zone". Special signs are used to indicate to drivers that they are entering or leaving the controlled zone; the signs have a yellow background

(a)

(b)

North side of Grosvenor Square, London: (a) before, and (b) after installation of parking meters

PLATE 10.1

with a black legend and usually indicate the times for which the parking meter scheme is in operation. Within the zone all existing waiting and loading restrictions signs are normally removed and certain conditions which are summarized below apply during the specified times. Parking is prohibited in the area except at the meter spaces, where parking is allowed for a limited period and upon payment of the appropriate charge. Loading and unloading of goods is allowed except at places where special restrictions apply (shown by means of a continuous yellow line in the carriageway near the kerb). Solo motorcycles and scooters may park without charge or time limit in specified places known as "cycle parking areas".

The parking meter is basically a timing mechanism which is started by the insertion of a coin. It can be either a "manual" meter or an "automatic" meter. With the former the driver turns a handle when inserting the coin and this winds the mainspring of the instrument and sets the timing mechanism in motion. Automatic meters are wound once a week by an attendant and the insertion of a coin starts the mechanism timing for the appropriate period. The meters can be designed to give a single fixed period of time for the insertion of a single coin or to allow the option of one or more periods according to the number or value of coins inserted. For example, in most meters in London the insertion of sixpence buys one hour and the insertion of two sixpences or one shilling buys two hours. Both the period and the amount can be varied and the 1960 Act allows the standard period to be split into two equal parts and with proportional payment.

At the expiry of the time paid for, which is indicated in London by the appearance of a yellow flag, the driver becomes liable for an excess charge which must be paid within a certain number of days to the local authority either in person or by post. No offence is committed. The excess charge in London is ten shillings. Only at the end of a further period covered by payment of the excess charge is an offence committed and the driver becomes liable to prosecution and to have his car towed away. In London this excess period is timed by the meter and at the end of the period a second red flag appears to denote that an offence has been committed.

It is an offence to return and insert a further coin in the meter (meter feeding). It is also an offence* to use the unexpired portion of time left by a previous driver without inserting a coin, although the meters in London are designed to add on this time to the time paid for up to a maximum of two hours. However, among other proposals[10] for the revision of parking meter regulations, the Ministry of Transport have suggested that the free use of unexpired time should be allowed.

Studies of the effect on traffic of some of the first metered zones showed that within the zones the number of parked vehicles was halved and traffic speeds increased by 16 per cent, from about 8·2 mile/h to about 9·6 mile/h. There were small increases in the amount of parking in the areas surrounding these zones. A study of changes in the first metered parking zone showed that the daily turnover of parked vehicles during the hours of control decreased by 27 per cent. The number of vehicles staying for up to two hours decreased by 14 per cent over the whole day but remained virtually unchanged during the peak period 1.30 p.m. to 2.30 p.m. Of the parked vehicles found at this time of day 40 per cent remained for over two

* This was true at the time of writing.

hours, 14 per cent for between six and ten hours and nearly 1 per cent for over ten hours. Not all the overstaying vehicles were using parking meters; some were commercial vehicles not obliged to use meter bays but subject to the limited waiting for loading and unloading.

The total time necessary for a visit, including street parking and walking to and from the chosen address, was averaged for several visits and it was found that the mean visiting time decreased in the metered zones. Observations after the meters had been in use for about two years showed that the overall availability of street parking space continued to be better than before controlled parking, but that visits in the surrounding uncontrolled area were taking about 20 per cent longer than they took before the appearance of the meters.

THE EFFECT ON ACCIDENTS OF PARKING METER SCHEMES. To find the effect on accidents of the first controlled parking scheme in London personal-injury accident figures have been examined for a four-year period, starting one year before the meters were installed. To eliminate the effects of other factors the accidents in the controlled parking zones and the neighbouring areas were compared with those in all the Metropolitan boroughs. After controlled parking was introduced accidents decreased by 21 per cent in the meter zones and increased by 22 per cent in the neighbouring areas. The latter change may have been partly due to a transfer of parked vehicles, with associated traffic congestion, from the controlled areas. A study of the effect of parking meters in one zone on accidents in the area as a whole, i.e. comparing the total accident experience in meter zone plus its surrounding areas with what would have been expected had the meters not been installed, showed no statistically significant change. Personal-injury accidents in the combined area were 8 per cent greater than would have been expected and fatal and serious accidents combined were 34 per cent greater than would have been expected.

PARKING CONTROL BY DISC IN BLUE ZONES, PARIS

In the most congested part of central Paris an area known as the "Blue Zone" has been designated inside which parking is limited to one hour. The scheme now applies to 200 streets totalling $43\frac{1}{2}$ miles; within the zone parking between 9.00 a.m. and 7.00 p.m. Mondays to Saturdays is limited to periods varying from one to one-and-a-half hours, but between 11.30 a.m. and 3.30 p.m. four hours parking is permitted to allow for the long Parisian lunch time. In many lengths of street no waiting or only unilateral waiting is allowed and considerable use is made of one-way working. Commercial vehicles are not allowed to enter or operate in a zone between the hours 1 p.m. to 7 p.m.

During the restricted hours every vehicle parked in the area must display a special cardboard disc. This consists of a folded square of cardboard with two small apertures on each side and inside which rotates a disc with arrival and departure times. On arrival the driver sets the disc so that the hour of arrival appears in one apperture and the second aperture then automatically displays the time by which the driver is required to leave. Overnight parking is allowed for residents without the use of a disc but the vehicle must be removed by 9.00 a.m. If a disc is displayed showing arrival "before 9.00 a.m." the vehicle is allowed to stay until 10.00 a.m.

The discs are distributed free of charge by various industrial and commercial undertakings who are allowed to have advertising matter on part of the disc which must otherwise be of the approved pattern. Several million discs have been issued to cover an area containing some 5200 parking places.

The disc system has been adopted by other towns in France, Austria, Italy, Switzerland and Greece. A principal disadvantage of the system is that the amount of enforcement required tends to be expensive in staff.

CLEARWAYS

Clearways were first introduced on roads in South-East England in August 1959. On these roads stopping as well as waiting, loading and unloading are prohibited, and putting down and picking up passengers are also prohibited except by public-service vehicles. Lay-bys are provided since the restrictions apply for 24 hours per day. Clearways are indicated by a sign with a black background and a white legend bearing the distinctive split-arrow symbol.

A comparison of accidents during the first year of clearway operation with those in the preceding year showed that, relative to trends on similar roads in the same police districts, there was no statistically significant change. Total accidents in the twelve-month period were 5 per cent fewer, and fatal or serious accidents combined were 14 per cent fewer than expected.

Peak-hour clearways are at present applied by regulation in the London Traffic Area although they may be introduced elsewhere. Ordinary clearway limitations of stopping and waiting are applied during specified peak hours. The sign indicating these restrictions has a black background and a white legend including two split-arrow symbols pointing horizontally in each direction.

All-night parking in London streets

In the Metropolitan Police District and the City of London lighting regulations for parked vehicles during hours of darkness were amended in September 1955. Under the amended regulations cars and some classes of commercial vehicle may be parked at night without lights on roads which are subject to a 30 mile/h speed limit and which are not bus routes providing:

(a) The nearside of the vehicle is close to and parallel with the kerb or verge and facing the "right" way. In one-way streets it may be parked on either side of the road as long as it is facing in the same direction as the traffic.

(b) No part of the vehicle is within 15 yards of a road junction whether or not the junction is on the same side of the road.

(c) No part of the vehicle is more than 25 yards from a lit street lamp, unless the lamp goes out accidentally. If such a vehicle is over 25 yards but less than 100 yards from the lamp, whether the lamp is lit or not, an approved parking light must be displayed on the offside of the vehicle. A vehicle not subject to the lighting exemption is now allowed to be parked with only a parking light.

An investigation into the accidents occurring at night before and after this concession showed that fatal and serious injury accidents, involving parked vehicles subject to this exemption and on roads with the speed limit in the London area, increased by over 50 per cent. Parked vehicles hit in the front or side accounted for nearly all this increase. A survey carried out in a central London borough and in an outer London borough of parking behaviour at night gave the following main findings:

Of the vehicles subject to the lighting exemption and not on bus routes, about 55 per cent were breaking the regulations. Of these about half were facing the wrong way.

In each borough on roads which were not bus routes, more than 90 per cent of the vehicles that were required to show their own light were parked without lights or with parking lights only.

Of the small number of vehicles seen on bus routes, more than 40 per cent in each borough were parked incorrectly.

ONE-WAY SYSTEMS

One-way systems reduce conflict points at intersections, eliminate head-on collisions and dazzle, make conditions easier for pedestrians and allow efficient progression in linked traffic signals. The capacity of any given street is usually increased and this effect is greater when there is an odd number of traffic lanes. If the extra capacity is not required one lane can often be given up to parking. However, journey times and distances may be increased and for the benefit of public-transport passengers the two directions of any route must not be too widely separated. Signs must be erected to direct strangers. Opposition to the scheme may be encountered from local business men.

Results of "before and after" studies on one-way systems are given in Table 10.8.

In all cases the one-way systems involved longer distances but the vehicles were able to travel faster. At the first site the mean journey time increased, at the second there was little change, while at the other two it decreased. Journey times through each one-way system were less variable than those on the alternative two-way system and this is of benefit because with less variable journey times, less time has to be allowed for any journey with a known arrival time.

A number of one-way systems have been introduced in central London by the London Traffic Management Unit with the co-operation of the police and the various London boroughs. In all a total of 31 miles have been included in recent schemes. Observations of traffic behaviour reported by the Unit in six major schemes showed that reductions in average journey time ranged from 3 to 35 per cent with an overall average reduction of about 20 per cent, although journey distances were usually increased. A study covering six months before and six months after the introduction of the schemes showed a reduction of 14 per cent in slight injury accidents but a rise of 8 per cent in fatal plus serious accidents. Accidents involving pedestrians fell by about 40 per cent.

A study of the effect of a number of other one-way systems on accidents

TABLE 10.8

One-way systems

Site		Mean Journey			Standard deviation of journey time (min)	Total flow (veh/h)
		Length (miles)	Speed (mile/h)	Time (min)		
1	Before	0·43	13·8	1·88	0·55	940
	After	0·52	15·2	2·06	0·47	
	Percentage change	+21	+10	+10	−16	
2	Before	0·44	13·1	2·01	0·67	1090
	After	0·48	14·3	2·03	0·44	
	Percentage change	+9	+9	+1	−34	
3	Before	0·42	13·2	1·93	0·52	2400
	After	0·46	15·9	1·73	0·35	
	Percentage change	+10	+20	−10	−33	
4	Before	0·43	10·8	2·38	0·50	760
	After	0·46	12·5	2·21	0·49	
	Percentage change	+7	+16	−7	−2	

has led to the tentative conclusions that on the average one-way systems result in fewer accidents.

Some calculations have been made of the extra distances which are travelled due to the introduction of one-way operation in an area of London, ½ mile by ¼ mile, which includes about 4½ miles of streets, about 75 per cent of the street mileage being one-way.

Distances were measured by the shortest route (i) assuming no one-way streets, and (ii) with the present one-way streets, between all the possible combinations of pairs from 19 representative points chosen on the network, seven of the points were on the periphery of the network and 12 inside the area, chosen at random. The results are shown in Table 10.9. The one-way system increased the average distance travelled by 28 per cent; average speeds would need to increase by the same amount if the journey times were to remain the same. Vehicle mileage and hence average flows also increased by 28 per cent. It follows that the average capacity of the streets affected by the one-way system had to be increased by considerably more than 28 per cent to attain the same average journey time.

The area on which these calculations were based was selected because it

TABLE 10.9

*Journey distance changes caused by a one-way system in
Central London*

	Average distance (miles)		
	No restrictions	One-way streets	Difference
Through　.　.　.	0·375	0·48	0·105 (+28 per cent)
Stopping　.　.　.	0·34	0·44	0·10 (+29 per cent)
Internal　.　.　.	0·30	0·41	0·11 (+37 per cent)
Average journey assuming 80 per cent through traffic, 20 per cent stopping and a negligible amount of internal traffic	0·37	0·47	0·10 (+28 per cent)

was relatively self-contained and it included a high proportion of one-way streets. It may not be representative of central London as a whole but this example serves to indicate that substantial increases in capacity must be achieved if a one-way system is to reduce journey times. The results of other one-way systems quoted earlier show, of course, that such increases in capacity can sometimes be achieved.

Similar work by Bunton and Blunden[11] in New South Wales, Australia showed that one-way flow on a rectangular grid of city streets will inevitably result in many drivers having to travel longer distances than with two-way flow. In the case of 100 randomly selected trips over a 6 × 6 grid, the increase in journey distance with complete one-way working was found to be about 45 per cent. This result did not take into account the volume of traffic which might be expected on each movement; in a practical application the one-way arrangement would probably be arranged to suit any major movements and consequently the average increase in journey time might be substantially less than 45 per cent.

In another investigation[12] average travel distances and average numbers of turns per trip on a hypothetical square grid were compared for two alternative modes of operation, all two-way streets and all one-way streets. It was found that the introduction of one-way operation in alternate directions increased the average travel distance between pairs of points by two block lengths, as compared with normal two-way operation. The average number of turns per trip with normal two-way operation was $1\frac{1}{2}$, half being right turns. If one-way operation was introduced the average number of turns per trip was increased to $2\frac{1}{2}$, but there were no longer any turns which involved crossing an opposing flow of traffic.

CHANNELIZATION

When passing through an intersection the driver has to make many decisions in a short time. Apart from deciding his own route he has to relate his movements to those of several other streams of traffic and pedestrians. A single false decision may produce an accident. Channelization physically separates the traffic streams and requires the driver to make fewer decisions at any one time. When traffic signals are used, straight-through and turning streams can be treated separately if necessary. Channelizing islands are extra hazards to vehicles in bad visibility conditions and should be marked having regard to the speeds prevailing on the road. Good signposting is also necessary since the motorist usually has no second chance once in the wrong lane.

Pedestrian refuges are a simple form of channelization and segregation, intended to allow pedestrians to cross one traffic stream at a time. They can also be used at some intersections to assist vehicular flow.

Plate 10.2(a) shows the site of an experiment carried out in 1952 at a junction in Streatham, London, controlled by 3-phase signals. The phases were so arranged that traffic going northwards from the intersection was passed through on two phases but traffic going southwards was restricted to one phase. It was suggested that an island should be placed in the 37-ft wide carriageway to assist pedestrians because traffic was always passing this point on one phase or other of the signal control. An experiment was carried out to determine where the pedestrian refuge should be placed. A portable refuge was made by putting sand into a metal container (see Plate 10.2(b)) which was placed in various positions. The sides of the container were covered with white elastoplast so that it was possible to count the number of times the container was scraped by passing vehicles. The maximum flow past the island was observed under various conditions and the results are given in Table 10.10.

TABLE 10.10

Effect on maximum flow of varying the position of a refuge

Refuge	Traffic entering intersection		Traffic leaving intersection	
	Available road width (ft)	Max flow from queue (veh/h)	Available road width (ft)	Max flow (veh/h)
No		2000		1500
Yes	16	1950	17	1500
Yes	18	2000	15	1450
Yes	20	2250	13	1400

The effect of the central refuge was to reduce by 3 per cent the saturation flow, i.e. the flow when vehicles entered the intersection at minimum spacings from the queue. Off-setting the refuge by 2 ft to favour the traffic entering the intersection restored this saturation flow to its original value, while a 4-ft off-set increased it by a further 12 per cent. Traffic in the opposite direction was relatively unaffected by the refuge except when it was off-set by 4 ft. In this case the maximum rate at which vehicles could leave the intersection was reduced by 6 per cent which could be tolerated owing to the elongated shape of this particular intersection.

Even at signal-controlled intersections where the proportion of turning traffic is small, it has been found that a given traffic flow sometimes required less road width when leaving an intersection than it required when approaching it.

AUTOMATIC CONTROL

It has been evident for some time that the demand for road transport in many areas has been increasing at a greater rate than can be accommodated by the present rate of construction of new roads in those areas. This is particularly the case in urban areas, where the result has been growing congestion. In these circumstances proposals have been put forward by a number of people that the best use should be made of the existing road network by adopting co-ordinated systems of controlling traffic over large areas, usually referred to as area traffic control. This section describes some of the more important existing forms of co-ordinated traffic control and the research on the subject that has been carried out at the Laboratory.

Linked traffic signal systems

Police control of conflicting traffic streams at an intersection was first superseded by a mechanical device in 1928 in the United States of America, where fixed-time traffic signals were used. After a few years vehicle-actuated traffic signals were introduced and they were subsequently adopted in Britain. The development of traffic signal control in Britain differed from that in the United States mainly in the use of vehicle-actuated equipment rather than fixed-time equipment. It was soon recognized that the movement of vehicles through a series of fixed-time traffic signals could be improved if they were linked, so that the green period available to a traffic stream at successive intersections coincided with the arrival of the traffic at these points. Similar advantages were obtained from the linking of vehicle-actuated signals, although to a lesser degree.

In Great Britain vehicle-actuated signals close to one another are often co-ordinated so that the movement of through traffic is facilitated. Several schemes of linking have been tried but the one most commonly used for the larger systems is the vehicle-actuated flexible progresssive system, in which a master controller, common to all the signals in the area, supervises a local controller at each signallized intersection.

The master controller determines a common cycle and exerts overriding control of the local vehicle-actuated controller at certain points in this cycle. For each phase there is a period of the master cycle during which that phase can obtain right of way immediately on demand, holding it for the remainder of the period irrespective of other traffic demands on either phase; normal vehicle-actuated signal changes can occur after the control period has elapsed. If right of way is obtained during a control period and there is a continuous demand on the phase no change from that phase can occur until the beginning of the control period for the other phase. The normal maximum green control (see Chapter 9) is not operative when the linked system is functioning correctly. If there is a continuous demand on all the phases at all the signals there will be no vehicle actuated changes; the signals will operate as a fixed-time system in which individual signals change at the points in the master cycle corresponding to the start of the overriding control periods. The position of the control periods is chosen so that under these conditions of continuous demand the signals operate as a normal fixed-time progressive system, (see Chapter 9).

The length of the overriding control period can be varied and is set long enough to ensure that the main platoon of traffic from the previous signal arrives before the period ends; if the period is not long enough traffic on the other phase could hold up the platoon. Additional overriding controls prevent signal changes that would cause the need for a minimum green on one phase to conflict with a demand for an immediate change of right of way by the other phase.

The master cycle time can be fixed or it can be varied to suit traffic conditions, either by a time switch or by counts of vehicles at a representative point. In the latter case, the cycle time is changed at the end of each counting period to the predetermined value appropriate to the number of vehicles counted; each count usually lasts for five minutes. The cycle time is divided into 50 equal steps that are used to define the limits of the control periods at the local controllers; the same steps are used for this purpose whatever the cycle time.

If the master controller breaks down the local controllers continue to operate as isolated vehicle-actuated installations. Where there are more than five intersections linked together it is normal to provide duplicate master controllers so that if the one in operation breaks down it can automatically be replaced by the other.

Some typical examples of vehicle-actuated flexible progressive schemes can be found in Oxford Street, Marylebone Road and Edgware Road in London, and Slough High Street. The system co-ordinating signals on Marylebone Road and Baker Street was installed during the 1930's and included a total of 54 signals.

The fixed-time system of 11 signals along a $2\frac{1}{4}$ mile length of trunk road at Slough, was described earlier in the section on speed control (see p. 327).

In some installations, particularly in Europe and the United States, more extensive systems of control have been used. The signals controlling all intersections in a large area are co-ordinated from a central station. Examples of such installations can be found in Newhaven, Washington, Baltimore, and Toronto.

NEW HAVEN, CONNECTICUT

The central area of New Haven still retains the gridiron layout of early Colonial days. The city now has about 210 signal-controlled intersections, almost all of which are supervised by radio from a central control room.

At each of the signal-controlled intersections there is a controller which offers choices between three cycle times and between three types of progression with each cycle time, in addition to amber flashing facilities for use during the small hours. (This is known as a "3-dial triple off-set* fixed-time controller"). The individual intersections are supervised from the central control room by a Motorola radio control system. This control system gives facilities for six alternative programmes of traffic control, each covering a period of seven days, and also the option of manual control

---

* An off-set is the time interval between a fixed instant in the master cycle and the start of the "main road green" at a given junction.

of individual signals. The alternative programmes are for use under different weather conditions, exceptional traffic flows and the like. At any time the one most appropriate for the prevailing conditions is selected manually from the six available by the operator at the central control. The traffic signal settings employed in the various programmes are based on previous traffic studies at the appropriate times of day. The actual operation of the signals therefore depends on the time of day and the judgement of the operator, who selects what he considers to be the most appropriate programe for the prevailing conditions.

In the past year or two approximately £180 000 have been spent on radio control of 200 signals, about 90 replacement local controllers and the provision of modern mast-arm and pedestal signal mountings. No before-and-after studies have been made of the benefits of these changes, partly because of changes in road layout in the city.

An interesting feature of the New Haven installation is the provision of "fire lanes" in the wrong direction down one-way streets. Some of the wider roads which are normally used as one-way streets have special signs suspended above them, which in the event of a fire alarm indicate to traffic using the road in the normal way that they should move to the right side of the road to allow fire engines to travel in the wrong direction down the one-way street.

Owing to the high radio frequency used, 952·5 megacycles per second, it was necessary to use "point to point" radio transmission paths. To achieve this the transmitter aerial was placed on a high point overlooking the town and signals are sent from the central control via leased telephone line to this aerial.

MOTOROLA RADIO TRAFFIC CONTROL SYSTEM. In view of the increasing use of this system for controlling traffic signals by radio, further details of its method of operation are given below. The system is capable of controlling up to 1000 intersections, or groups of signals with identical timing, and can carry out 36 functions at each intersection. For this purpose a function is the switching on or the switching off of a single circuit or the selection of one out of three mutually exclusive conditions, e.g. the selection of one out of three cycle lengths.

As was mentioned above, the setting of the traffic signals for any condition is dependent upon studies, which have been made beforehand, and 8-hole perforated paper tape is used to carry the instructions which are derived from the traffic studies. Each tape carries instructions covering a complete week and there is almost no limit to the number of instructions which can be given during that period. Six alternative programmes can be included on one tape.

Instructions are transmitted between the central control and the individual signals by pulses of audio frequency tones which may be used individually or in combination. Each local controller has two addresses, an individual address and a group address. By using a group address a number of signals in the same group can be controlled by a single instruction. Both individual and group addresses are reached by transmitting two pulses each consisting of two audio tones. At each local controller there are four "vibrasponder" reed relays for the individual address and four for the group address. If the correct combination of tones is received for either of these two addresses then the equipment is alerted to react to the signal change control function which is transmitted next.

The signal control function is also initiated by the transmission of a pulse of two audio tones. At the local controller 12 "vibrasponder" frequency sensitive reed relays are used to form a 6 by 6 matrix giving a total of 36 possible control functions.

Each local controller thus has a total of 20 vibrasponder frequency sensitive reeds. Nine audio frequencies are required for reaching 1000 addresses and 12 audio frequencies are needed to operate the 6 by 6 function matrix.

The cycle length is determined by the time taken for one revolution of a dial driven by a synchronous motor. If the cycle length is changed then a different dial is used. Each local controller normally has three possible dials. In order to maintain all the synchronous motor driven dials in synchronism over the whole city the central control sends out a continuous series of tones which ensure that any local controller which has temporarily fallen out of step is arrested and restarted at the correct time in the next cycle.

WASHINGTON, D.C.

As in New Haven, the traffic control policy in Washington, D.C.[13] is based on the assumption that traffic flows are repetitive over a weekly cycle and, that the appropriate pre-determined signal settings can be selected according to the time of day. The city has a large number of fixed-time signals co-ordinated on a common cycle by a combination of radio and wire interconnection.

In 1947 about 400 signals in the central business district were connected by wire to a single master controller in the municipal centre and the signals were co-ordinated to give progression into, and out of, the city centre. Other movements were not particularly catered for. In 1948 a number of the traffic signals on main arterial roads entering the central business district were connected by the Motorola radio system to the central control and were used to extend the progressions on the main arterials in co-ordination with the down-town wire controlled signals. As a result of a continued policy of replacing old local controllers in the outer areas by new 3-dial triple off-set units under radio control, the total number of signals co-ordinated by the master controller reached about 1000 in 1963. The next stage will be to modify the local controllers now on the down-town wire system to respond to the Motorola pulsed-tone instructions and thereby introduce greater flexibility to the signal programming. The system will ultimately be extended to include signals on sections of radial arterials now under the jurisdiction of surrounding communities.

The signals are normally operated on an 80-second cycle. Between 6 a.m. and 7 a.m. green-time ratios and off-sets appropriate to off-peak conditions are used. These are changed between 7 and 9 a.m. to accommodate the peak in-bound flow. Off-peak operation is resumed until 4 p.m. when out-bound peak flow settings are used. At 6.30 p.m. the system reverts again to off-peak settings, which remain in operation until 1 a.m. on weekdays or 3 a.m. at weekends. For the rest of the night until 6 a.m. the signals revert to flashing amber on the main road and flashing red on the side road. Special arrangements are made to cope with emergency services or events such as parades and football games.

The green-time ratios and progressive systems are under continual review by the Traffic Bureau staff. No "before-and-after" study has been carried out to assess the benefits attributable to the central control of the signals. Local studies have indicated that to minimize delay progression speeds should be set about two or three miles per hour slower than the speed limit.

The traffic authorities in Washington recognize that the arrangement described above may not provide the best settings to minimize delay over the whole system. As a first step towards achieving optimum setting of the signals a computer programme has been written to simulate a section of the central business district in the city. By using this programme the Traffic Bureau hope to determine the most effective settings of the signals for all traffic movements in this area instead of providing mainly for the arterial flows; the technique can be extended to include the whole of the system.

BALTIMORE, MARYLAND

At the beginning of 1963 there were 1008 signallized intersections in Baltimore. 821 were on a master co-ordinated system under the control of equipment at the Traffic Department Headquarters. The co-ordinated area is divided into seven sections each having a master-controller. About 30 per cent of the signals are semi-vehicle-actuated and all are centrally controlled by the PR system manufactured by Automatic Signal Division of Eastern Industries Inc. Norwalk, Connecticut (see below). A small number of fully vehicle-actuated signals are used as buffers between the seven sections.

The signals are linked to the central control by cable installed, maintained, and owned by the City. Each intersection is connected by 15 conductors to central control although only 12 are essential for signal operation, the others are used for spares and for telephone communications. Radio inter-connection was considered to be more expensive and less reliable.

The system is traffic responsive and uses magnetic, radar and sonar (ultrasonic) detectors to measure prevailing traffic conditions. The detectors most frequently used are radar detectors which cover the traffic in one lane only. On an installation on a four-lane one-way street the detector is installed over the second lane out from the kerb. The master control equipment associated with each area can have up to eight traffic sampling points connected to it. If the area covered has predominantly tidal flows four detectors can be used to count inbound traffic and four outbound traffic. If the area contains a grid in which the flows are predominantly at right angles one set of detectors can be used to sample flows on streets in one direction; the remaining set can be used on streets in the other direction. Information from these detectors is used to select cycle lengths and progression arrangements. When under automatic control the signals are essentially fixed time on pre-determined progression arrangements; the traffic data collected by the detectors being used to select the appropriate setting. The signal timings used at different flow levels were selected by trial and error.

The City has a very large number of service and maintenance lorries associated with the Traffic Department and in direct radio communication with it. Using these facilities an extremely high standard of maintenance is possible and a constant check can be kept on the behaviour of critical points.

Experiments are now being carried out with equipment based on sonar vehicle presence detectors to measure concentration instead of volume, because the former is a more suitable parameter in congested conditions. In one area both concentration and flow are measured and comparisons of the two methods are being made.

In the central area it was found that traffic demands in all directions were very balanced and therefore the computer always gave average settings with a long cycle. To accommodate known fluctuations in demand, use is now made of information from detectors on other roads leading to the centre to determine when peaks are arriving and special programmes are used to benefit certain streets. It has been found that traffic changes its route to take advantage of a favourable progression.

At one important bridge traffic flows on the approaches are measured and are used to control reversible lane working on the bridge with a signal progression favouring the major flow.

No "before-and-after" studies have been carried out to determine the precise benefit of the traffic signal system, largely because when it was introduced by Henry Barnes in 1953 a number of other traffic engineering measures were undertaken at the same time as the installation of the first master control. Although an undoubted improvement resulted it was not possible to separate out the effect of the various contributory factors. It is estimated that since 1953 the Traffic Department has spent about £2½ million on signal co-ordinating equipment.

PR SYSTEM. This equipment is produced by the Automatic Signals Division of Eastern Industries for controlling a number of fixed-time linked signals. Pre-determined cycles, green-time ratios and arrangements for progression are selected automaticaly by the equipment, depending on the prevailing traffic conditions at several representative points on the road network. An installation consists of a number of units, the most important of which are the cycle computer, the system selector, the cycle generator, the translator, and the switching panel. Additional equipment which is available for certain applications includes an amplifier, for boosting signals over long distances, and a chart recorder for maintaining a permanent record of traffic demands and of the manner in which the controller responded to them.

(a) Cycle computer. This unit totals the traffic information from up to four detectors, each collecting data about the same stream or movement, i.e. all north-bound movements or south-bound movements or one of the major movements in a network. The information from each group of detectors is fed to a single input in order to minimize the effect of random variations in flow at any one sampling point. The flow is averaged exponentially (see Chapter 2) with a time constant which can be varied between one and nine minutes. Time constants between four and nine minutes are normally used in operation; shorter time constants are used for testing. The average traffic flow is displayed on a meter with variable sensitivity which is usually adjusted so that the expected mean peak volume per lane registers approximately 100 per cent on the meter, which is calibrated from 0 to 150 per cent.

The equipment permits the allocation of a different cycle length to each of six flow groupings between 0 and 150 per cent of the expected mean peak volume per lane. In order to prevent instability the point of transition between cycle X and cycle Y when flows are increasing is always made higher than the point of transition between cycle Y and cycle X when the flows are falling.

(b) System selector. This unit takes the output from two cycle computers, one operating on the traffic demand in one direction and the other on the traffic demand in the opposite direction. It selects the longer of the two cycles calculated by the computers. It also determines what type of progression shall be used by comparing the two cycles. If they are the same or differ by only one step, then the "Average" progression is normally selected, since neither traffic stream is appreciably heavier than the other. If the cycles differ by more than one step then a progression arrangement which favours the heavier direction of traffic is selected. The two alternatives are usually referred to as "Inbound" and "Outbound".

An additional feature is the option of simultaneous operation under conditions of heavy loading. It can be applied to selected signals, and is operated according to the length of cycle, usually only with the longest or next longest cycles. The remaining signals continue to function on the normal cycle and progression system described above.

(c) Cycle generator. This unit enables the six cycles to be specified in units of five seconds between 40 and 80 seconds and by 10 second units between 80 and 120 seconds.

(d) Translator. The translator produces two 3-phase A.C. electrical outputs on the lines between the master controller and the local controllers. One 3-phase signal is a 400-cycle reference and the other a slightly lower frequency. The difference in frequency is very small, there being one complete phase change in a traffic signal cycle.

(e) Switching panel. The main function of the switching panel is to enable an operator to override the automatic selection of cycle lengths and progression systems and to select the appropriate settings manually.

(f) Recorder. The recorder unit incorporates an Esterline Angus chart recorder on which three pens record the progressive system in use, two pens record the flows and five pens show which of five main cycle settings is in use. The sixth cycle setting is shown by the absence of any signal on these five pens.

(g) Local controllers. The local controllers used in conjunction with the PR master controllers can be either fixed-time or semi-vehicle-actuated. Models with two or three traffic signal phases are available. The side-road phase normally consists of two parts, one a fixed proportion of the cycle time and the other of fixed duration. Three settings for the side road phase are provided, any one of which can be connected with each of the four progression systems, inbound, outbound, average and simultaneous.

TORONTO, ONTARIO

One of the first applications of a digital computer to the direct control of traffic signals was in Toronto, Canada. During a pilot experiment in

1959 a computer was used to control 16 signal installations, nine on a main road and the others on cross streets. A form of control rather similar to normal British linked vehicle-actuated operation was compared with the fixed-time system used previously, in which adjacent signals were linked together in small groups, the various groups having different cycles.

The computer control gave the following improvements:

(i) Average delays during the evening peak period were reduced by about 10 per cent;

(ii) Average delays during the morning peak period were reduced by about 25 per cent.

Following this experiment, the installation of a large system which will ultimately include 1000 signals was started in Toronto.[14] The first stage of the project involved about 100 signals and was intended to establish the best arrangement for traffic detectors for the various circumstances which might arise and to provide experience with data transmission and monitoring systems.

Various types of detector have been considered during the project including radar, sonar, infra-red, fluxgate, and magnetic loops. Loop detectors appeared to be the most promising. Detectors were placed at mid-block points in the main streets to give vehicle counts, while on minor streets they were placed near the intersections as for normal signal actuation.

The signal installations are connected to the central control by leased telephone lines. Three pairs of lines are necessary for a typical local controller. One pair carries traffic data and signal monitoring data using eight tones between 350 and 2900 cycles per second. Five of the tones are normally used to monitor the signal indications, and the others are used for transmitting information received from the vehicle detectors. The other two pairs of lines form three D.C. circuits with a common return by which three relays in the local controller can be operated by the central control. One relay is used to transfer an intersection from local to central control and to disconnect the local "manual" facilities, one steps the signal phase sequence under the computer's control and the third is available for the operation of any special facilities, for example, special green-time ratios or extra phases which might be required.

The main control computer is a Remington-Rand UNIVAC 1107. This computer has a thin-film memory with a cycle time of two-thirds of a micro-second. There are six magnetic tape units which may be used to carry programme information or can be used to record incoming traffic data and signal operation instructions for subsequent analysis if required.

A Remington-Rand 418 computer is used as a buffer between the 1107 and the data-links. Its function is to convert incoming information to binary form, store it, and feed the 1107, and also to take the binary output from the 1107 and convert it into a form suitable for transmission to the local controllers. The 418 can itself control the signals on a simple linked fixed-time basis, which means it can be used to take over the control of the signals if the main computer breaks down or is undergoing service.

The traffic detectors are scanned 64 times a second which enables a profile of detector pulses to be built up by the computer so that speed, concentration, and flow information can be obtained. (Speed and concentration are obtained by assuming an average effective vehicle length).

LOS ANGELES, CALIFORNIA

The Department of Traffic in Los Angeles has a Thompson Ramo Wooldridge computer controlling 26 signal-controlled intersections on about 3½ miles of Sunset Boulevard, a four lane two-way surface street. Traffic information from positive contact detectors at five points on the main road is transmitted by leased telephone line to the central control at Los Angeles City Hall. One data transmission system is used to send signal-control pulses and another to collect traffic data. Both systems code information on to the telephone lines by frequency-shift type modulation with 12 circuits on each pair. In 1963 the computer was controlling the signals in a manner very similar to the PR system used in Baltimore. Sunset Boulevard was divided into two sections with independent PR Systems which would, however, co-ordinate if they chose a common cycle. There were additional special features to handle the very large surges of traffic generated by a baseball stadium situated in the centre of the system. No "before-and-after" studies of the benefits of computer control had been made.

SIMULATION OF SIGNAL NETWORKS

The simulation on a digital computer of traffic behaviour at a signal controlled intersection has led to some important conclusions as to the most efficient way of setting an isolated signal. This work has been described in Chapter 9. In order to study linked signals, a computer programme was prepared for the Laboratory by the National Research Development Corporation to simulate traffic on a road network with fixed-time traffic signals. It has been used to test the effectiveness of two simple linking schemes under typical traffic conditions.

The programme was used to evaluate delays at a series of simple intersections along a straight road 0·7 miles long carrying two-way traffic, shown diagramatically in Fig. 10.1. The intersections had differing proportions of turning traffic and varying degrees of saturation ranging from

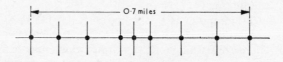

Fig. 10.1. Diagram of simulated layout

65 to 90 per cent. The data used were based on observations of actual traffic in London, although it was not intended that the simulation should represent any particular location. The average speed and range of speeds used in the simulation were determined from observations of those vehicles which were not delayed by signals or a queue at the signals; delays caused by pedestrians, by stopping buses or by other traffic causes were included.

In the first linking scheme the offsets were fixed so that, for one direction of traffic, a platoon of vehicles travelling at a given average speed would arrive at each junction as the signals changed to green. However, vehicles which turn on to the main road from side streets along the linked system are clearly a potential obstruction to the smooth passage of a platoon, and a second, modified, linking scheme was studied in which allowance was made for the presence of such vehicles. This scheme was also designed to give a progression for vehicles in one direction only.

The effect of various progression speeds on the average delay to traffic travelling in the favoured direction is shown in Fig. 10.2(*a*). With the first

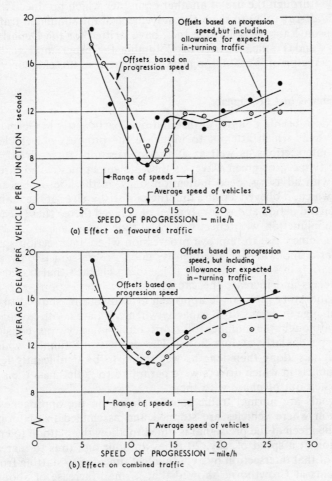

Fig. 10.2 Effect of speed of progression on delay at
signals linked to favour one direction of traffic

scheme there was a pronounced reduction in average delay when the speed of progression was about one mile/h faster than the mean running speed of the traffic. The same effect was produced by the second scheme with a progression speed the same as the mean running speed. With both schemes the delays increased more rapidly when the progression speed was too slow than when it was too fast.

Both schemes were intended to benefit traffic travelling in one direction. It can be seen from Fig. 10.2(*b*) that in this particular case the average delay to traffic in both directions changes with progression speed in a similar manner to the average delay to traffic in the favoured direction, although the effect is less marked.

The U.S. National Bureau of Standards has been responsible for a simulation programme[15] to study 10 intersections, seven of them signal-controlled, on a 0·6 miles section of a heavily used street in Washington, D.C. In addition to the usual printed output of this programme a film was made (through the use of another computer which produced a display on a cathode-ray tube) to show the movement of the simulated traffic.

Thompson Ramo Wooldridge Inc., have written for the Department of Highways and Traffic, District of Columbia the programme to simulate traffic in a region of Washington mentioned earlier in this chapter.

Traffic funnels and pre-signals

There have been a number of installations, particularly in Germany,[16] of signal systems which attempt to influence the progress of vehicles when between intersections as well as at the intersections themselves.

Traffic funnels, or green waves as they are sometimes called, are linked systems with advisory speed indication signs on the approaches to intersections which, if obeyed, ensure that the motorist arrives at the main signal on a green indication and is not stopped or delayed there. These systems are used in conjunction with effectively fixed-time linked signals and are intended in some cases to improve progression where intersection spacing is not uniform and where, consequently, good progression is only possible with variation in speed. Although it has been claimed that traffic funnels reduce delays and increase the capacity of the intersections, experiments by the Laboratory on a single approach at Crowthorne showed that there was no change in delays or in capacity when compared with normal traffic signals, although the number of stops on a journey was considerably reduced, particularly at low flows. The capacity of funnels which had "stop" signals along their lengths was found to be significantly less than that of funnels in which drivers were permitted to "idle" past the advisory signals when out of phase with them.

Pre-signals are normal traffic signals placed on the approaches to an intersection where vehicles are stopped and assembled in platoons. The start of the green at the pre-signal is timed to allow the platoon to enter the intersection at a speed of, say, 20 miles an hour and thus to increase the capacity of that intersection by avoiding lost time due to starting from rest. Experiments at Crowthorne showed that a small increase of about 5 per cent in the capacity of one signal approach could be achieved; this gain would probably be offset by the need to have longer inter-green periods for safety since the danger of collisions would be greater.

The General Motors Corporation has developed Pacer,[17] a version of the traffic funnel, in Detroit, Michigan. On a 4-mile section of road there are nine signal-controlled intersections originally on isolated fixed-time operation. The Pacer installation consisted of interlinking between the main intersections, the introduction of speed advisory signs at approximately 1500 ft, and of pre-signals at about 500 ft before each intersection. At the pre-signal site there is also a speed indication to show motorists passing through on the green signal the advised speed in order to make most effective use of the green at the main intersection. In all there were 43 speed signals and 11 pre-signals. Studies showed that there was no difference in journey time between the Pacer and normal linked operation but that the number of stops was considerably reduced by the Pacer system. The traffic at this site was not sufficient to give evidence on increase in capacity.

Automatic Diversion of Traffic

It has been suggested that roads in urban and rural areas have a reserve capacity and that, in the near vicinity of congested areas, there are often uncongested roads which drivers would use if they had anticipated congestion, if they knew of the alternative routes and the routes had been sign-posted.

It has been pointed out that congestion does not always occur in the same places and consequently conventional methods of indicating diversions are often quite an unreliable guide to actual traffic conditions.

To make best use of the road networks, various proposals [18,19,20,21] have been made that traffic conditions should be measured continuously at strategic points throughout the area under control and that a central "computer" should decide whether control devices should direct traffic away from areas of congestion. The traffic control devices would include variable direction signs, variable speed signs, prohibitions of entry to certain streets and, possibly, restrictions on entry to a whole area.

EQUIPMENT

An automatic diversion project requires equipment to assess the traffic situation, to determine what action should be taken and to display the signs necessary to implement the decision. The following paragraphs give brief details of equipment that has been developed for these purposes.

VEHICLE PRESENCE DETECTORS. Most existing vehicle detectors are sensitive to the movement of vehicles and do not respond to the presence of a stationary vehicle. When problems of congestion are being considered a detector which will respond to the presence of a vehicle, whether it is moving or stationary is very desirable. Such a device is called a "vehicle presence detector".

A number of detectors that depend on detecting the mass of metal in a vehicle have been developed. These usually use a loop of electrical cable buried in the road surface; the change in impedance of the loop due to the presence of a vehicle operates the detector. The size of the loop can be varied to suit particular applications but experiments by the Laboratory have shown that a loop 12 ft long and 6 ft wide (see Plate 10.3) is a convenient size for detecting individual vehicles in a single lane and for distinguishing between free flow and congestion.

Vehicle presence detectors with loops usually need balancing electrically after installation but at least one model is self balancing when the loop is unoccupied; the self balancing feature is disconnected when the loop is occupied to prevent the detector returning to the "unoccupied" position with a vehicle still stationary over it.

A number of presence detectors that use sensing elements mounted over the carriageway have been developed; both infra-red and ultrasonic techniques have been used.

CONGESTION DETECTORS. The pattern of the output signal from a vehicle presence detector can be used to detect whether there is a queue of stationary or slow moving traffic over the detector. Equipment has been built with an integrating circuit that produces an exponentially weighted average* of the occupancy of a presence detector; observations have shown that if a loop detector 12 ft long is used then the average occupancy exceeds 0·75 when there is a queue over the loop and that if the occupancy is less than 0·25 it is very unlikely that there is a queue. Averaging time constants of the order of 30 seconds appear to be satisfactory although the actual value is not very critical.

If a number of congestion detectors are placed along a road it is possible to assess approximately the length of any queue present and hence the number of vehicles waiting in it. By dividing this number by the rate at which vehicles are leaving the queue it is possible to estimate the delay to vehicles joining the queue.

AUTOMATIC MEASUREMENT OF CONCENTRATION. A new type of presence detector which is particularly suitable for use with detector loops of large circumference has been designed at the Laboratory. It has been used with a detector loop 400 ft long and 8 ft wide (see Plate 10.4) to give an output signal proportional to the amount of metal over the loop; the output can be calibrated to give an indication of the number of vehicles over the loop at any instant and hence the concentration in vehicles per mile on the strip of road in which the loop is installed.

AUTOMATIC MEASUREMENT OF JOURNEY TIME. The average time for a vehicle to travel the length of the 400 ft loop described above can be obtained by dividing the average number of vehicles over the loop by the average flow of vehicles leaving it. Since the flow is the reciprocal of the average interval between vehicles a simple practical method of obtaining the journey time is to multiply the output of the long loop detector by the successive intervals between vehicles leaving the loop. The intervals may be obtained from a small loop presence detector. Tests by the Laboratory with equipment of this kind have achieved reasonable correlation between the journey times obtained at the same time by this and other methods.

QUICKEST ROUTE COMPUTERS. In simple networks it may be easy to determine the best route for each movement to take in a particular traffic situation. As the size of network increases it becomes more important to have a device that will compute the quickest route for each movement with current traffic conditions.

A small demonstration electro-mechanical computer for deriving quickest routes has been constructed at the Laboratory (see Plate 10.5). Each link of the road network is represented by a stepping switch in which the time taken to travel along the link is represented by the number of

---

* If $\delta(t)$ is a function of the time t that has the value unity if the presence detector is occupied at time t and zero otherwise, the exponentially weighted average occupancy at time T is:

$$\frac{1}{a}\int_{-\infty}^{T} \delta(t)e^{-\left(\frac{T-t}{a}\right)}dt$$

where a is a constant, usually referred to as the time constant.

(a)

(b)

Experiment on the effect of moving a pedestrian refuge laterally: (a) site, (b) portable refuge

PLATE 10.2

Detector loop: 12 ft long and 6 ft wide

PLATE 10.3

Detector loop 400 ft long and 8 ft wide

PLATE 10.4

Small demonstration electro-mechanical quickest route computer

PLATE 10.5

Automatic diversion sign installed at Malton, Yorks. Illuminated arrow indicates the less congested route

PLATE 10.6

A vehicle, equipped for experiments in automatically controlled steering, following a buried guidance cable

PLATE 10.7

steps before a marked contact is reached. To carry out the calculation of the quickest routes to all destinations from a particular origin, the switches representing each link connected to the origin are set stepping simultaneously. All switches step at the same rate and when a particular switch has reached its marked contact it is stopped; the destination at the end of the link has then been reached. All other switches connected to this destination are then started unless they are already stepping in which case they are stopped. The stepping process continues until all destinations are reached. The stepping switches that have reached their marked contacts represent the links that form the minimum paths. Journey times on the individual links can be adjusted to current values by changing the position of the marked contacts.

A quickest route computer has been built by Decca Radar Ltd.[22] in which the links forming a network are represented by strings of small neon lamps, each with a constant striking voltage. The number of lamps forming a link is proportional to the journey time along it. The quickest route between any two points can be found by applying a high voltage source (with a high internal impedance) to the points; the neons making up the quickest route will strike. The journey times can be changed by inserting or removing lamps.

VARIABLE DIRECTION SIGNS. The design of signs with a variable legend is not as simple as it might appear since the correct indication must always be clearly visible even in bright sunlight while the other indications must always be invisible to drivers. These requirements rule out the use of the internally illuminated stencil type signs which are often used in less bright surroundings.

The "theatre sign" indicators in which the appropriate lamps in a large matrix are illuminated to display the required legend work fairly well in sunlight, but relatively high power lamps are required and each symbol must be formed from a fairly large number of lamps (say 5×7) if it is to be clearly legible; the capital cost and the running cost are therefore high unless the legend is very short. Neon tube signs are effective providing that the tubes are enclosed in slots to prevent the light spreading.

Signs with mechanically moving parts are not affected by the level of ambient lighting but they require a high standard of construction if they are to be reliable. Signs with legends on rotating discs or drums have been tried; another design uses a matrix of discs which can be rotated individually to show either a black or a white face.

DATA TRANSMISSION. An automatic diversion project requires an extensive communication network between the equipment collecting traffic data, the central control and the variable signs. Direct wire connections are probably the most reliable method of interconnection but radio communication has the advantage that the position of the roadside equipment can be changed more easily.

Equipment has been designed at the Laboratory which can have up to 20 remote stations connected by two-way radio links to a central control station. Some of the remote stations collect information about the traffic, using congestion detectors, and send it back to the central station when interrogated. The central station would use this information to determine the routes to be recommended and, by appropriate radio signals, would operate automatic direction signs at the other remote stations.

EXPERIMENTS

A number of experiments on automatic diversion and surveillance have been carried out in this country and in America. As described above, suitable equipment for the purpose has been successfully developed but some difficulty has been experienced in finding sites where suitable alternative routes are available. A number of places in and near London have been investigated, but in nearly all it was found that alternative routes congested more or less at the same time as the main routes. This experience may have been partly because, for simplicity, only small-scale schemes were considered and partly because, in most problems involving commuter or similar regular journeys, some drivers are already seeking alternative routes.

MALTON, YORKSHIRE. An experiment was carried out in Malton at Whitsun 1961, where a queue from a level crossing frequently became long enough, particularly at holiday times, to block the main intersection in the town, thus preventing any traffic movement (see Fig.10.3). Using

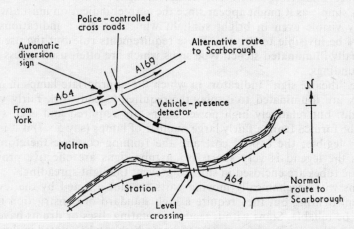

Fig. 10.3. Layout of main roads in Malton, Yorkshire (not to scale)

automatic detection equipment it was possible to sense when the queue was approaching a critical length. When this happened an automatic sign (see Plate 10.6) was operated to divert traffic travelling between York and Scarborough on to an acceptable alternative route. Observations showed that with the normal indication two-thirds of the traffic from the direction of York turned right towards the level crossing. When the sign changed its indication, only one-third of the traffic turned right. With this system in operation the queues did not extend over the detector for more than five minutes at a time and the intersection remained clear. It is likely that similar routes carrying holiday traffic would offer most scope for diversionary techniques.

BLACKWALL TUNNEL. Another experiment was undertaken in Greenwich, London, where traffic crossing the Thames by the Blackwall Tunnel frequently encounters serious delays. Preliminary measurements showed that at an alternative crossing, the Rotherhithe Tunnel, traffic was very rarely congested and it was found that the journey from south to north of the Blackwall Tunnel crossing could be made via the Rotherhithe Tunnel in about 30 minutes. The alternative route was about $6\frac{1}{4}$ miles long compared with the direct crossing of about two miles.

Equipment was installed on the southern approach to the Blackwall Tunnel to detect when the estimated journey time on the direct crossing would be expected to exceed 30 minutes. The equipment worked very successfully but, unfortunately, because of natural increases in traffic and other causes, the congestion on the alternative route through the Rotherhithe Tunnel increased considerably soon after the start of the experiment. Consequently diversion to the alternative route was very rarely beneficial and the experiment was discontinued.

M.4 CHISWICK. The new section of the M.4 motorway from Langley to Chiswick is the first example of a motorway penetrating into London. For most of its length it has three lanes plus a shoulder in each direction but at Chiswick, where the motorway is on an elevated structure, there are only two lanes in each direction, without shoulders. The possibility of serious congestion on the section, arising from accidents, breakdowns or abnormal traffic conditions, has led to the installation by the Ministry of Transport of a surveillance and control system based on loop-type vehicle presence detectors and television. The control centre is about three miles away at Hounslow police station, where the officer on duty will be alerted by automatic congestion detectors in the event of trouble. Signs to divert traffic from the congested section can be operated either automatically or by the officer, who decides on the appropriate emergency action, e.g. calling ambulances and police patrols, on the basis of the television monitors.

THE JOHN LODGE FREEWAY SURVEILLANCE PROJECT, DETROIT, MICHIGAN.
In 1960 an experimental surveillance project was set up on a part of the John Lodge Freeway in Detroit.[23] This is a sunken motorway carrying heavy volumes of traffic into and out of the town centre—more than 160 000 veh/day in 1962. Fourteen television cameras were installed to provide almost continuous viewing of a section $3 \cdot 2$ miles long, part of which was dual four lanes and part of which was dual three lanes. Each camera is connected by land-line, laid down the central divider of the expressway, to its own monitor screen in the control centre. Remote control of the camera allows the operator to focus, pan, tilt, and change from normal to telephoto lens. In addition a remotely-controlled iris on each camera enables the amount of light received by the tube to be altered either manually or automatically according to prevailing light conditions.

After some experience with the use of the television surveillance system a traffic control system of lane signals and advisory speed signs was installed in the spring of 1962. Signals to control the opening of certain on-ramps were added in 1963. The lane signals show either a red "X" or a green arrow to indicate whether a lane is closed or open to traffic. The red "X" over a lane implies that there is an obstruction ahead and the driver should leave that lane as soon as it is safe to do so. The lane control signals are installed at 11 locations on the study section, six on the northbound carriageway and five on the southbound. Variable advisory speed signs, intended to indicate the recommended speed under the prevailing traffic conditions, are also mounted at 21 points in the study section. The signs can show speeds ranging from 20 to 60 in units of five. Sonar detectors are used to collect traffic information, which is automatically processed at the control centre to select the appropriate speeds to be shown by the advisory signs. In the first design of this equipment the speed control signs were grouped in two's and three's having the same speed indications. Experience has shown that it would be desirable to have the speed control signs operated individually.

In addition to the lane signals and advisory speed signs, ramp signals have been installed on each of the on-ramps in the expressway study section. These signals enable the central control to close a ramp if congestion has occurred on the freeway; when the ramp is closed the ramp signal shows the legend, "Don't enter ramp".

The effect of traffic control using the lane signals and speed signs was studied in 1962. The use of the lane signals to indicate an obstruction was found to increase the speed of the vehicles passing the blockage by between 40 and 60 per cent and to reduce the number of vehicles stationary behind the blockage to about 10 per cent of the previous number. In general lane changes occurred much earlier. The capacity of the lanes passing obstructions has been increased by about 30 per cent using the lane signals.

It was found that the television surveillance could be used without difficulty to give journey-time measurements comparable with those obtained by orthodox methods. Comparison of travel times on the freeway before and after the introduction of the lane and speed control system showed reductions ranging between five and 25 per cent. It is anticipated that the use of ramp closures in conjunction with lane signals and speed signs will provide further benefits.

THE CONGRESS STREET EXPRESSWAY SURVEILLANCE PROJECT—CHICAGO, ILLINOIS. The Congress Street Expressway is a sunken motorway running west out of Chicago. A surveillance project[24] was set up in 1961 to develop a pilot scheme for traffic data collection and control, with the ultimate aim of reducing travel time and increasing flow on the road network. After preliminary studies a 5-mile length of the outbound (westbound) carriageway of the expressway was selected for field trials.

The section selected was in part four lanes in each direction and in part three lanes in each direction. Congestion was experienced where the four lanes merged into three lanes and also where a heavily loaded on-ramp, carrying between 1200 and 1500 vehicles per hour for a short period, merged with the 3-lane section at the top of a short hill. The combined flows in the two directions on the study section exceeded 100 000 vehicles per day.

Traffic studies have shown that the conditions on the expressway are closely reflected by the concentration of traffic on it. Concentration is measured in vehicles per mile and is closely related to occupancy. At concentrations up to 35 vehicles per mile per lane it was found that speeds were relatively unaffected by the presence of other traffic; at concentrations between 35 and 60 vehicles per mile per lane speeds were affected, but the volume of traffic passing remained approximately constant; between 60 and 100 vehicles per mile both the speed and the volume of traffic passing fell progressively, while at concentrations over 100 vehicles per mile speeds were lower than 10 mile/h, i.e. there was serious congestion.

In 1962 sonar (ultrasonic) vehicle presence detectors were installed on each of the entrance and exit ramps serving the 5-mile test section. Another 23 were distributed, one per lane, at seven points on the carriageway itself. These detectors were connected by landline to the control centre where 21 analogue computers were mounted under a diagrammatic display of the section of expressway under surveillance. Each analogue computer produces an exponentially weighted average flow and occupancy (see footnote on page 352). The outputs from the analogue computers are connected to level monitors which determine the level of occupancy beneath each detector. The output from the level monitors is used to illuminate coloured lights on the display, a green light, an amber light, a red light and flashing red being used to show the four stages of increasing occupancy.

The equipment also includes four sonar speed and flow detectors which are sampling four lanes on the expressway. The data from each of these detectors is presented on meters as average flow, average speed, and the speed of the last vehicles measured. There is an automatic indication of dry road, wet road, or ice.

In addition to the visual displays already described the traffic data can be recorded on an automatic plotter or on printed tape or punched on standard 5-hole tape for subsequent detailed analysis.

Experimental control of traffic entering via the congested ramp mentioned earlier was attempted in 1963. It was preceded by very detailed studies of traffic movements both on the freeway and on the surface streets. As a result of the studies it was decided that the ramp could be closed to some traffic on the onset of congestion but that the remaining traffic which really had no suitable alternative route, should be allowed to continue to use the ramp. This traffic was metered on to the expressway at rates according to the state of congestion on the expressway; in the preliminary experiments the metering was done manually by a police officer. Estimates of journey times both on the expressway and on the main surface streets indicated that this form of control saved about 90 vehicle-hours per hour and consideration is now being given to more ambitious control schemes.

Vehicle guidance and control

Mention should be made of the work being carried out by the Road Research Laboratory on the uses of electronics for the guidance and control of road vehicles.[25] From a technical point of view the completely automatic operation of road transport is feasible, although the cost would be very high, and the standard of reliability would leave something to be desired. However, progress in electronics is so rapid that the position may be completely changed in the future. Meanwhile, the indications are that some of the features of a fully automatic system might make worthwhile contributions to the safety and efficiency of traffic even now—particularly in foggy conditions—and it is this aspect of the problem with which the work at the Laboratory is at present mainly concerned.

Hitherto, most of the work on electronic guidance and control for road vehicles has been carried out in the U.S.A., where work on a completely automatic system was begun in 1953 by the Radio Corporation of America.[26] Since then, two complete schemes have been developed for experimental trial, one by the Radio Corporation of America, and the other by the General Motors Corporation.[27] It is understood that the United States Bureau of Public Roads is studying in general terms the ways in which electronics might be used in present and future traffic conditions and work is in progress at Ohio State University.[28]

In Britain, the Road Research Laboratory, besides starting exploratory investigations on some of these possibilities, has established contact with the American workers in this field. Meanwhile, certain British firms are marketing successful automatically controlled trucking systems for use in factories and railway goods yards where the maximum speed required is about 5 mile/h and the vehicles are operated over fixed routes.

BASIC SYSTEM REQUIREMENTS

For the fully automatic operation of vehicles the basic elements are (i) a method of guiding the vehicle along its desired path, and (ii) means for preventing collisions and controlling the vehicle's speed. Since all vehicles using a road may not be equipped for automatic control it may be desirable to detect the presence of vehicles by apparatus located in the road itself and means are then needed for communicating to vehicles information about the presence and speed of other vehicles in their vicinity. An ideal road installation is therefore required to provide facilities for vehicle guidance, for the detection of the presence of vehicles and for communication of information from road to vehicle.

GUIDANCE

For guiding vehicles along a traffic lane the general scheme is to lay a trail which can be followed by a device mounted on the vehicle. Various methods have been suggested, for example a buried cable carrying an electric current, a painted line which can be tracked by using an optical device, a line of radioactive particles, the detection of a metallic strip or the use of a radar-type unit.

Of the above possibilities, the most attractive at present seems to be the buried cable, which is unaffected by weather, requires only relatively simple equipment in the vehicle, and can be buried far enough below the road surface to be unaffected by resurfacing. Such a cable has been installed in the Laboratory's research track at Crowthorne and investigations carried out there using experimental equipment have shown that in this method a generator is required to energise the cable at intervals of 2–3 miles along a road. The experimental system uses a current of 0·15 amps. r.m.s. at a frequency of 5 kc/s.

With this kind of installation the electronic apparatus in the car may be used either to operate an indicator to enable the driver to keep to his traffic lane in conditions of bad visibility, or to operate the vehicle steering directly through an electro-hydraulic servo system. The principle of a simple vehicle installation which has been used experimentally to provide drivers with guidance information is shown in Fig. 10.4. A car which has been equipped with an experimental automatic steering system for use on the track is shown in Plate 10.7.

DETECTION OF VEHICLES

The prevention of collisions is the most difficult and the most costly part of any automatic system. The ideal system involves the detection of a vehicle's presence, together with some measure of its speed and distance from other vehicles, so that the control equipment in the other cars can compute a safe following distance for the particular speed and road conditions. The various methods of vehicle detection which are available include devices using radio waves or ultrasonics, infra-red detectors,

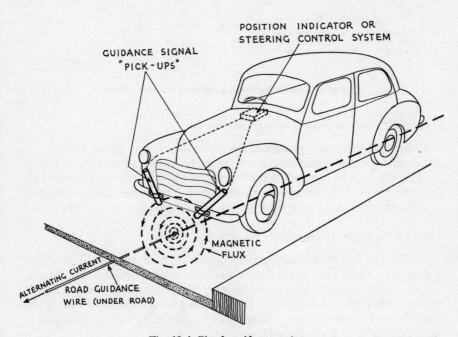

Fig. 10.4. Simple guidance system

buried loops of wire (with associated electronic circuits which react upon the presence of a vehicle's metallic construction), and sensitive magnetometers which detect (by the Hall effect) changes in the earth's magnetic field caused by the presence of the vehicle.

At present, the type of detector using a buried wire loop seems to be the most attractive since its area of operation can be more easily defined by the layout of the loop. This method of detection involves the laying of wires in the road. Fig. 10.5 shows a schematic layout of such a vehicle detector installation. In the Laboratory's research track this type of detector has been installed for experimental purposes. The wire loops are 13 ft × 5 ft and are spaced two feet apart so that individual vehicles can be detected.

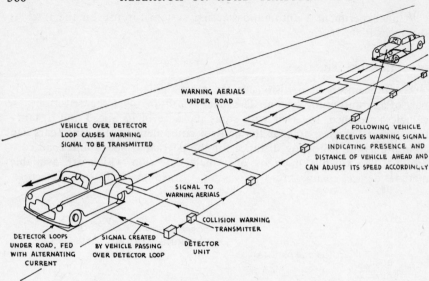

WARNING AERIALS
UNDER ROAD

VEHICLE OVER DETECTOR
LOOP CAUSES WARNING
SIGNAL TO BE TRANSMITTED

FOLLOWING VEHICLE
RECEIVES WARNING SIGNAL
INDICATING PRESENCE AND
DISTANCE OF VEHICLE AHEAD AND
CAN ADJUST ITS SPEED ACCORDINGLY

SIGNAL TO
WARNING AERIALS

COLLISION WARNING
TRANSMITTER

DETECTOR LOOPS
UNDER ROAD, FED
WITH ALTERNATING
CURRENT

SIGNAL CREATED
BY VEHICLE PASSING
OVER DETECTOR LOOP

DETECTOR
UNIT

Fig. 10.5. Basic detection and collision warning system

COMMUNICATION BETWEEN ROAD AND DRIVER

Under full automatic guidance, the anti-collision and speed information obtained from the vehicle detectors must be conveyed to the vehicle to operate the vehicle controls. Experiments at Crowthorne have shown that this can be done by means of an induction-type communication system which confines the relevant information to the traffic lane in question.

PRESENT DAY APPLICATIONS

Whilst the completely automatic control of road vehicles is probably a long way ahead, and is then only likely to be practicable on restricted-access roads, some of the basic ideas may be used with advantage even in present day traffic conditions. It is this aspect of the question with which current work at the Laboratory is chiefly concerned. Typical examples of such applications are as follows:

(i) Guidance in fog: the simple guidance system described above might be used to assist a driver to follow the road under conditions of bad visibility or when snow covers the lane markings and verges. This might be applied to motorways and, perhaps, selected bus routes where it is important to keep services running in fog. It might also be applied to roundabouts and intersections where drivers at present find difficulty in fog. The outstanding requirement for these applications is a suitable indicator to be installed in vehicles which would provide the driver with steering directions without, at the same time, distracting him from keeping a lookout for obstacles ahead. From a safety point of view, it would probably be advisable to have, in addition, a simple obstacle detector mounted on the guided vehicle but, at present, a suitable, cheap system does not appear to be technically feasible.

(ii) Speech communication with drivers: the communication part of a complete electronic guidance system can be adapted to provide a "talking road sign" which would supplement the ordinary road sign. Using a wire induction system for the roadside transmitting station would confine the messages to that part of the road for which they were intended and the signals would be received by a small amplifier unit in the vehicle, the information being presented verbally to drivers by means of a loudspeaker. "Talking road signs" might be used in advance of intersections on main roads and motorways where they would augment the conventional road signs. This could be particularly valuable in fog and mist, or even in darkness in situations where glare from vehicle headlights may cause difficulty in reading signs. Another use might to be give reminders of a change in speed limit.

Other possible uses might be to give emergency warning about road conditions and accidents, or to give details and advance warnings of any diversions. It would also be possible to link each installation to a central control station by means of telephone lines and to operate any group of installations by remote control, changing the messages or re-recording them at will, thus providing a flexible system, capable of meeting any situation.

(iii) Presence detection: vehicle detectors could be used to operate roadside warning lights or signs at sharp bends, or other places with restricted field of view, to warn oncoming traffic of the presence of other vehicles.

(iv) Excessive speed: vehicle detectors can be installed in pairs to measure vehicle speeds and to operate excess-speed warning signs if the vehicle exceeds a pre-set speed. Such devices, which have already been tried in the United States, might be useful at the approaches to roundabouts, at the ends of lengths of motorway or at places where speed limits change.

Vehicle guidance does not lie directly in the field of area traffic control, but the transmission of information to drivers is clearly an essential part of diversionary systems.

REFERENCES TO CHAPTER 10

1. DEPARTMENT OF SCIENTIFIC AND INDUSTRIAL RESEARCH, ROAD RESEARCH LABORATORY. Research on road safety. London, 1963 (H.M. Stationery Office).

2. COBURN, T. M., and N. C. DUNCAN. The effect on speeds and accidents of a 30 mile/h speed limit in built-up areas in Northern Ireland. *Internat. Rd Saf. Traff. Rev.*, 1959, **7** (3), 21–2, 24.

3. BLACKMORE, D. H. Effect on vehicle speeds of imposing a 40 mile/h speed limit in the London Traffic Area. *Surveyor, Lond.*, 1959, **118** (3505), 634–5.

4. NEWBY, R. F. 40 m.p.h. Effect on accident frequency in London Area. *Traff. Engng & Control*, 1962, **3** (11), 678–9.

5. BLACKMORE, D. H., and J. D. G. F. HOWE. Effect of 50 mile/h speed limit on vehicle speed. *Traff. Engng & Control*, 1963, **5** (8), 466–7, 471.

6. HILLIER, J. A., and M. J. ARNOLD. Linked fixed-time traffic signals. *Surveyor, Lond.*, 1958, **117** (3472), 1085–6.

7. SMEED, R. J. The influence of speed and speed regulations on traffic flow and accidents. *Rds & Rd Constr.*, 1960, **38** (456), 393–7; 1961, **39** (457), 15–24; *Internat. Rd Saf. Traff. Rev.*, 1961, **9** (1), 51–64; Discussion, 64–6.

8. MINISTRY OF TRANSPORT. Road Traffic Act, 1956—Section 33. *Memorandum* No. 747. London, 1957 (Ministry of Transport).

9. LONDON AND HOME COUNTIES TRAFFIC ADVISORY COMMITTEE. London traffic 1947–48. Ministry of Transport, 1949 (H.M. Stationery Office).

10. MINISTRY OF TRANSPORT. Parking—the next stage. London, 1963 (H.M. Stationery Office).

11. BUNTON, R. B., and W. R. BLUNDEN. An analysis of route factor for one-way and two-way street systems. *Proc. First Conference, Australian Road Research Board*, Canberra, 1962.

12. FAIRTHORNE, D. Average travel distances and numbers of turns per trip on a square grid. *Department of Scientific and Industrial Research, Road Research Laboratory Research Note* No. LN/377/DF. Harmonsworth, 1963 (Unpublished).

13. TWISS, F. E. Centralized control of a metropolitan signal system. *Traff. Engng*, 1962, **32** (10), 20–3.

14. HEWTON, J. T. Toronto installs all-purpose electronic computer for traffic signal control. *Traff. Engng & Control*, 1964, **5** (10), 589–94.

15. EDWARDS, J. A. Simulating traffic flow patterns on a computer. *Data Processing*, 1962, **4** (3), 192–6.

16. STEIN, W. VON. Traffic flow with distant signals and the signal funnel. *Proceedings of the Symposium of Theory of Traffic Flow*. Detroit, Mich., 1959 (General Motors Ltd.).

17. MORRISON, H. M., A. F. UNDERWOOD and R. L. BIERLEY. Traffic pacer. *Bull. Highw. Res. Bd, Wash.*, 1962, (338).

18. GERLOUGH, D. L. Control of automotive traffic on an area basis. *Institute of Transportation and Traffic Engineering*. Los Angeles, 1959 (unpublished).

19. WALTON, J. H. D. (Private communication).

20. REXWORTHY, D. R., and D. W. W. KING, Freeing city traffic by computer. *New Scientist*, 1960, **7** (167), 167, 197.

21. DECCA RADAR LTD., (Private communication).

22. PARKER, E. Trafficometry. *Traff. Engng & Control*, 1962, **4** (6), 318–23.

23. GERVAIS, E. F. The John Lodge Freeway surveillance system. *Traff. Engng*, 1962, **32** (10), 15–9.

24. MAY, A. D. The Congress Expressway surveillance project. *Proc. 2nd Int Symposium on Theory of Road Traffic Flow*. London, 1963 (To be published).

25. GILES, C. G. Guiding and controlling cars by electronics. *New Scientist.* 1962, **15** (306), 664–6.

26. FLORY, L. E. Electronic control of highway vehicles. *J. Instn Elect. Engrs*, 1961, **77** (7), 271.

27. MORRISON, H. M., A. F. WELSH and E. A. HANYSZ. *Trans. Soc. Automot. Engrs*, 1961, **69**, 31.

28. OHIO STATE UNIVERSITY. Study of electronic devices as traffic aids. *Transportation Engineering Center Report* No. 176–1. Columbus, Ohio, 1961 (Ohio State University).

Chapter 11

Traffic Signs and Carriageway Markings

SYNOPSIS

Direction signs: size of letters and symbols; design and spacing of lettering; layout; colour. Signs other than direction signs. Making signs effective at night: brightness requirements; illuminated signs; reflectorized signs. Siting and mounting of signs. Carriageway markings: longitudinal lines; use of lane lines at controlled intersections; double white lines; transverse lines at controlled junctions, at uncontrolled junctions; written messages; visibility of carriageway markings at night.

INTRODUCTION

When a driver has made a particular journey a number of times he will usually be able to adjust his speed and to position himself for each hazard or change in direction of the route without difficulty or hesitation; he will also know the sections of road where speed limits and other regulations are in force. Ideally, by means of signs a newcomer should be given all the information which the regular user has acquired by experience. Each item of information should come at the right time, not too early nor too late. Travelling at the operating speed of traffic a driver should be able to perceive, read and understand the signs sufficiently early to take any necessary action with safety: he should not have to divert his attention unduly from the task of driving. Moreover the signs should be effective by night as well as by day. To meet these provisions, signs must fulfil the following requirements:

(1) Be sufficiently striking to attract the driver's attention;
(2) Be legible at long range;
(3) Be understandable at a glance;
(4) Be sited so as to leave the driver sufficient time to take the necessary action safely;
(5) Be provided with an effective system of illumination or reflectorization.

DIRECTION SIGNS

Size of letters and symbols

The most important requirement of a sign is legibility and the most important factor governing the legibility of signs carrying written messages is the size of the lettering (provided certain fairly obvious rules are followed with regard to other factors).

Since small signs cannot be read when vehicles are moving at high speed but are easily read when drivers are travelling slowly, different sizes of lettering are required for fast and for slow roads. The British signs regulations have not always made provisions to suit the signs to the road. For example, in the 1950 regulations,[1] the standard size of lettering for place names on directional signs was 2 in. with up to 4 in. in a few cases (route numbers could, however, be larger). The 1957 regulations[2] brought an improvement with a standard letter size for place names of 3 in. and a maximum of 6 in. in a few special cases. The erection of signs with small lower case letters 12 in. tall (and even taller capitals) on the Preston By-pass motorway at the end of 1958 heralded the introduction of a new signing policy.[3]

In the U.S.A., on the other hand, the need to vary the letter size to suit the conditions had long been recognized: the 1948 edition of the Manual of Uniform Traffic Control Devices[4] quoted *minimum* letter sizes of 6 in. for main rural roads and 4 in. for other roads. In addition, Mitchell and Forbes[5] had developed rules for treating specific cases which can be expressed in the following formula for letter height:

$$\frac{N.V}{50} + \frac{S}{10} \text{ inches} \qquad \qquad . \qquad . \qquad . \qquad . \qquad . \qquad . \qquad . \qquad . \tag{1}$$

where N is the number of names on the sign,
                 V is the velocity of the vehicle in mile/h,
                 S is the distance of the sign from the vehicle's path in ft.

Further work carried out at the Road Research Laboratory on the reading of place names on signs has led to the development of a slightly different formula.[6] The letter sizes recommended in the report of the Advisory Committee set up to consider signs on all purpose roads[7] are in accordance with the new formula which was developed on the same basis as that used by Mitchell and Forbes, but new values have been derived for some of the parameters.

Obviously it is dangerous for a driver to direct his gaze sideways to read a sign whilst travelling fast. The driver should finish reading the sign before he is close to it otherwise he will have to divert his gaze through a large angle from the road ahead. It is thought that if this angle is small enough the driver will still be aware of what is happening ahead of him whilst he is scanning the sign. Thus, if θ in Fig. 11.1 is the maximum permissible divergence angle and S ft the sideways displacement of the sign from the driver's path then the driver should finish reading by the time he has reached a point B such that

$$BC = S \cot \theta \text{ ft} \qquad . \qquad . \qquad . \qquad . \qquad . \qquad . \qquad . \qquad . \tag{2}$$

To find the total range AC at which the driver must be able to begin reading the sign it is necessary to add the distance AB which he travels whilst reading it. Thus, if his speed is V mile/h and he takes T seconds to read the sign then the minimum value of AC is given by

$$AC = S \cot \theta + 1.47 \ VT \text{ ft} \qquad . \qquad . \qquad . \qquad . \qquad . \qquad . \tag{3}$$

If L is the measure of the legibility of the lettering to be used expressed

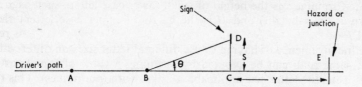

Fig. 11.1. Calculation of the size of lettering necessary. θ is the maximum permissible divergence angle (i.e. the maximum angle through which the driver would have to divert his gaze from the road ahead). The driver should therefore finish reading the sign by the time he reaches B. The letter size must be chosen so that the driver will be able to begin reading at a point A. The point A must be chosen so that the driver will have sufficient time to read the sign whilst travelling from A to B. The siting distance Y is dealt with on page 380.

as feet of reading distance per inch of letter height then the minimum acceptable letter height is given by

$$\text{Letter Height} = \frac{AC}{L}$$

$$= \frac{S \cot \theta + 1.47 VT}{L} \text{ inches} \qquad . \qquad . \qquad . \qquad . \quad (4)$$

The following values were selected as the most appropriate for insertion in the formula.

$$\theta = 10°$$

$$T = T(\max) = 0.31N + 1.94 \text{ seconds}$$

$$L = \begin{cases} L_x & = 50 \text{ ft/in. (for lower case lettering)} \\ L_H & = \tfrac{3}{4} \times 50 \text{ ft/in. (for upper case lettering)} \end{cases} \qquad . \quad (5)$$

The value for θ is that recommended by Mitchell and Forbes[5] and seems the most reasonable one to take in the light of the evidence available. The value of T is an estimate of that for reading the whole of the sign; on many occasions a driver will succeed in obtaining the required information without reading the whole of the sign. The values of L quoted do not, however, make full allowance for drivers whose eyesight only just allows them to scrape through the acuity test on the driving licence application form: for them L_H would have to be 21 ft/in. It seems reasonable to assume, however, that drivers with such poor eyesight will normally tend to drive more slowly than drivers with normal eyesight. When these values are substituted in (4) and some rounding off carried out the following formulae are obtained:

$$x = \frac{S}{10} + \frac{V}{100}(N+6) \text{ inches}$$

$$H = \frac{4}{3}\left[\frac{S}{10} + \frac{V}{100}(N+6)\right] \text{inches} \qquad . \qquad . \qquad . \qquad . \quad (6)$$

In these formulae x is the height of small lower case letters such as x and z (known as the x-height) and H is the height of upper case letters such as H and I.

The inconvenience of having to use different letter sizes on different signs on the same road can be avoided by assuming a value of four for N (i.e. always using the letter size applicable to signs with four names). This seems quite reasonable since the addition or subtraction of two names would in any case only alter the letter size by ± 25 per cent. Assuming therefore that $N = 4$, the formulae (6) then reduce to

$$x = \frac{S+V}{10}$$

$$H = \frac{4}{3}\left(\frac{S+V}{10}\right) \qquad \qquad \qquad \qquad (7)$$

Table 11.1 lists the x-heights for lower case letters derived in this way. The corresponding heights for upper case letters would be greater by a factor of 4/3 but the signs would be similar in area.

TABLE 11.1

The x-height of lower case letters for advance direction signs with four names

Vehicle speed V (mile/h)	Sideways displacement of sign from driver's path S (ft)				
	10	20	30	40	50
30	4	5	6	7	8
40	5	6	7	8	9
50	6	7	8	9	10
60	7	8	9	10	11
70	8	9	10	11	12

How should the value of V be chosen for a particular road? For roads with a speed limit this limit may be used for V and on modern roads with a specific design speed the design speed may be used for V. On older roads which often vary considerably along their length the mean speed of cars is probably a satisfactory value to take.

Design and spacing of lettering

Different alphabets are legible from different distances even when the letter height is the same. Many factors are known to affect legibility in addition to the type of lettering (upper and lower case, with and without serifs etc.), e.g. letter width, stroke width, spacing between letters, proximity of borders and other lettering, the contrast in colour and brightness between the lettering and its background, and even the level of brightness. Moreover it has been shown that these different factors[8,9] interact and this may account for the conflicting results which have been obtained when these factors have been studied individually.

Generally, narrow (condensed) letters are less legible than wide letters. In Germany a series of three alphabets with different letter widths and the same stroke width are used and a different legibility distance is quoted for each.[10]

For the optimum stroke width Berger[11] obtained one-eight of the letter height for black letters on a white ground and one-thirteenth for white letters on a black ground, (the stroke width for white letters is less than that for black letters as the visual image of a bright area appears to spread into an adjacent dark area, a phenomenon called irradiation). However, these values may be peculiar to the rather unusual letters with which he worked. Other workers have recommended greater stroke widths, e.g. Lauer[12] recommended one-fifth or one-quarter. The stroke width of the Gill-type Ministry of Transport alphabet[2] is one-sixth, the same as that of the commonly used American series E alphabet. A range of alphabets is in use in the U.S.A., the stroke width varying in conjunction with the letter width.[13]

The legibility of signs can be increased by increasing the spacing between letters. Solomon[14] found that in certain American reflectorized signs maximum legibility was obtained when the length of a place name was 40 per cent greater than normal but that a greater improvement could be obtained by using the extra area to accommodate larger letters at normal spacing. Similarly the legibility of lettering of a given size can be improved by increasing the space between the letters and the edge of the sign, but for maximum legibility with a given size of sign it pays to use the maximum possible letter size and, according to the results of one experiment, the border need be no wider than the stroke width for black letters on white ground.[15] The results of a laboratory experiment with Ministry of Transport white upper case letters on a black ground suggest that maximum legibility distance for a given area of sign would be obtained with a spacing of about 2-stroke widths between names and between the legend and the border[16] (see Fig. 11.2).

It is often claimed that lower case lettering (small letters usually with an initial capital) is more legible than upper case lettering (all capitals), because the ascenders and descenders of such letters as "b" and "y" give a characteristic shape to a name which facilitates recognition. In an experiment carried out in the U.S.A.[17] the legibility distance of familiar and expected names was about 10 per cent greater in lower case lettering than in upper case lettering when signs of equal area were used. However, the tests can be criticized on the grounds that only single name signs were tested, the marginal spaces were too large for maximum legibility to be obtained and more space was left empty on the upper case signs than on the lower case signs. An experiment carried out at the Laboratory has shown that with signs designed for maximum legibility distance the differences between good examples of upper and lower case scripts are negligible,[16] (see Fig. 11.3). Signs of equal area were used, the x-height of the lower case letters being approximately three-quarters the height of the upper case letters.

The legibility of lettering is affected by details of design. One suggestion which is sometimes made is that letters with serifs (i.e. a thickening of the ends of the strokes of the letters) would be more legible than the sans-serif letters normally used for road traffic signs. A serified upper case script (see Fig. 11.3) was included in the comparison of upper and lower case lettering

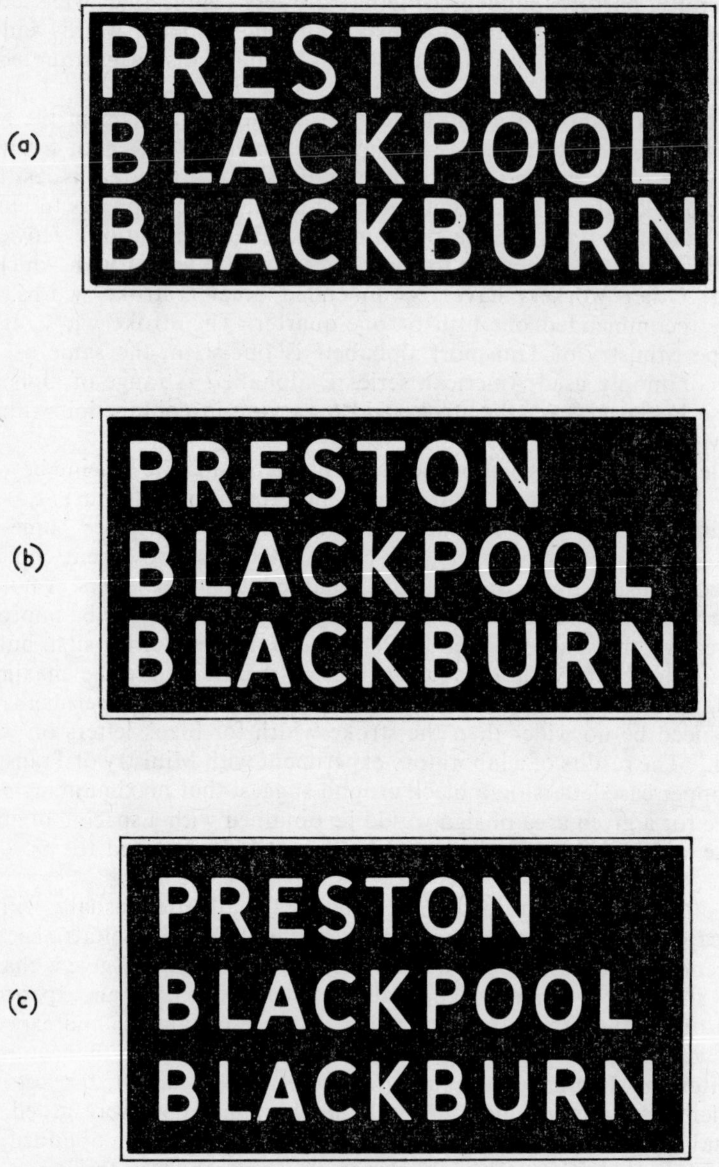

(a)

PRESTON
BLACKPOOL
BLACKBURN

(b)

PRESTON
BLACKPOOL
BLACKBURN

(c)

PRESTON
BLACKPOOL
BLACKBURN

Fig. 11.2. Effect on legibility of the width of space between lines and between legend and border. Spacing: (a) 1-stroke width, (b) 2-stroke widths, (c) 3-stroke widths. The areas of the signs are equal. (b) gave a slightly greater legibility distance than either (a) or (c)

mentioned above; from the results it appears that if there is any advantage in using serifs, it is small. It should be possible to obtain a greater improvement by emphasizing the distinguishing features of the letters[18] (e.g. by exaggerating the horizontal bar on the G to distinguish it from C); it is doubtful whether this could be done in a way which is aesthetically acceptable.

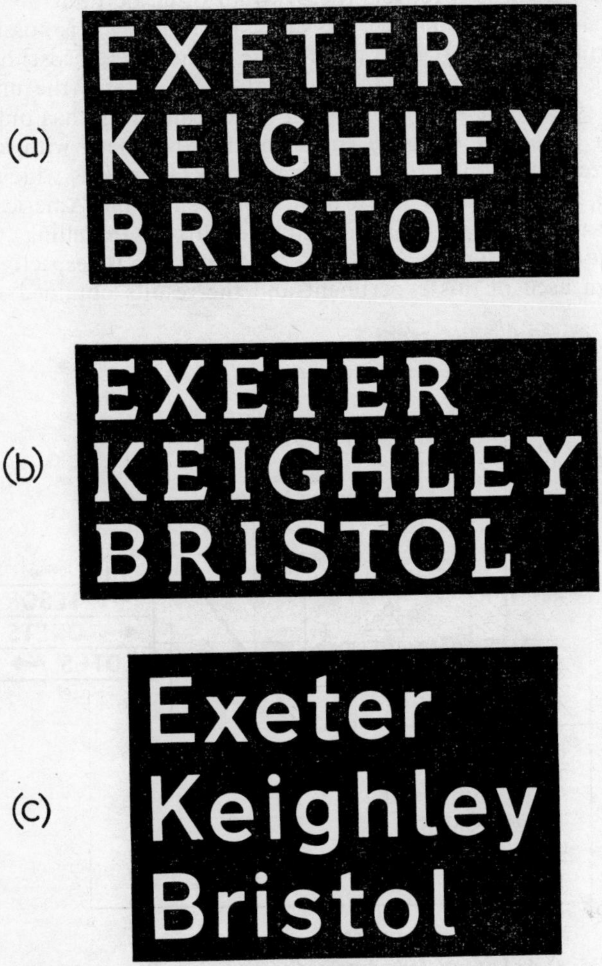

Fig. 11.3. Examples of the signs used in a comparison of upper and lower case lettering. The three signs have the same area. The relative legibility distances were

    (a)   100
    (b)   103
    (c)   100

Layout of advance direction signs

According to the current (1957) regulations[2] advance direction signs should normally be of the map type with the place names and route numbers inside framed panels. This gives a neat design and the fact that it is rather uneconomical in space is not so important when the size of lettering to be used is 3 in. (the standard size in the 1957 regulations). However, as has been shown earlier, much larger lettering is required on fast roads, and if the same pattern of sign were merely enlarged to enable the larger lettering to be used, they would be unnecessarily large and expensive as their cost goes up roughly in proportion to their area, i.e. in proportion to the square of the letter heights. Moreover, there would often be difficulty in finding sufficient space to accommodate the signs. Fortunately it is possible to use larger lettering without so great an increase in the size (or cost) of the signs by adopting other layouts. A Continental design retains the map feature but dispenses with the little panels. An American design has only a list of names with an arrow opposite each. In an experiment with a panel of standard size, it was found that the maximum letter sizes which could be used were 4, 5 and 6 in. for the British, Continental and American layouts respectively and the average distances at which drivers travelling at 50 mile/h finished reading the signs were 165 ft, 250 ft and 315 ft respectively.[19] The types of sign used in this experiment and the results obtained are shown in Fig. 11.4.

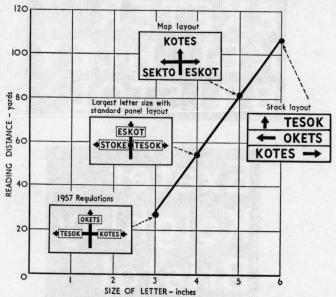

Fig. 11.4. Layouts for advance direction sign. Distance away at which direction of chosen place was indicated. All signs have exactly same total area

Whilst the American type appears quite satisfactory for simple junctions, difficulties of interpretation arise at complex junctions. This point is illustrated by results obtained in a further experiment which included signs for both 4-way junctions (simple cross-roads) and 5-way junctions. Examples of those for 5-way junctions are shown in Plate 11.1. In this experiment, the observers read signs of equal area at 30 mile/h and had to indicate the direction in which a particular destination lay. The recognition distances and errors made are given in Table 11.2.

Although in both cases the American list layout could always be read further away because it permitted the greatest letter size, there were considerably more errors with the American type at a 5-way junction. Thus it appears desirable to use a map layout at complex junctions such as 5-way junctions and probably also at 4-way junctions if the layout has unusual features. Similar conclusions[20] were reached by the Medical Research

TABLE 11.2

Comparison of three types of advance direction signs

Junction	British "map and panel" type (4-in. letters)	Continental "map" type (5-in. letters)	American "list" type (6-in. letters)
Recognition distance (ft)			
4-way . .	280	375	463
5-way . .	277	350	420
Mistakes in interpretation (per 100 trials)			
4-way . .	1·5	1·5	5
5-way . .	1·5	2	16

Council's Industrial Psychology Unit who also showed that drivers are capable of dealing with a mixed set of signs which included both map and list layouts.

Map-type advance direction signs have been installed on the motorways and on some by-passes built to motorway standards. The general applications of such signs to all-purpose roads has been reconsidered by the 1963 Traffic Signs Committee.[7] Plate 11.2 shows experimental signs erected by the Laboratory to assist the Committee.

Colour

It is generally agreed that there should be a difference in brightness as well as a difference in colour between the legend and the background of a sign: one should be light and the other dark.[21] In practice the light colours are limited to white and yellow and the dark ones to black and dark greys, blues, greens and reds, though not all combinations of these are entirely satisfactory. According to Lauer[12] legibility falls off if the reflection factors of the legend and background differ by less than 0·45 but this does not appear to be an infallible guide.

Investigations into the relative legibility of black letters on a white ground and white letters on a black ground have frequently been made, with somewhat discordant results[6,8,9,12,22,23] probably because several other factors (such as stroke width and spacing) affect the result. On the whole the evidence for the more usual types of alphabet seems to favour light letters on a dark ground, and the results of day and night tests carried out by the Laboratory with the Ministry of Transport upper case alphabet tend to confirm this.[24]

However, other considerations help to determine which way the colour contrast should go. If the sign is a small one, e.g. 20 sq. ft, background colour affects the ease with which the sign is picked out against its background. Tests[25] have shown that the following areas of sign give roughly equivalent target value at a range of 250 yd: 14 sq. ft yellow, 16 sq. ft white, 18 sq. ft red, 20 sq. ft blue, 22 sq. ft green, 36 sq. ft black. For small signs there are, therefore, disadvantages in using blue, green or black grounds but large signs, especially those on motorways, are conspicuous because of their size alone.

In the case of large reflectorized signs, there is an economic advantage in adopting a dark background as it is more effective to reflectorize the white part of the sign than the dark and the letters occupy the smaller part of the sign. Therefore on large signs such as direction signs for motorways it is usual to have white letters on a dark ground,[24] for example, dark green on the Interstate Highways in the U.S.A.[26] and dark blue on British motorways such as the M1.[3]

SIGNS OTHER THAN DIRECTION SIGNS

Important as they undoubtedly are, direction signs constitute only a small proportion, possibly about one-sixth, of the total number of traffic signs on our roads; the majority are concerned with how a driver should proceed. Since the system of signs used in Britain for this purpose is peculiar to this country it has often been suggested that, in the interests of international uniformity, a change should be made either to the system set out in a United Nations Protocol of 1949,[21] and used in most European countries, or to the system used in the U.S.A.[27] and some other countries such as Canada.[28] A third possibility is to change to the so-called "World System", set out in a United Nations Draft Convention of 1953, which is essentially a compromise between the European and American systems. This system is based on considerable research[29] carried out by experts in the U.S.A., France, South Africa, Chile, India and Turkey, in a wide variety of climatic and environmental conditions. It is logical and from the user point of view, possibly the most satisfactory system. However, since earlier systems were well entrenched in Europe and the U.S.A., only a few countries (including Eire, Egypt, Turkey) have changed over to it. Nevertheless, some features of the symbolism in it merit careful examination for they appear to be superior to the system set out in the Protocol.

Main characteristics of the British, European and American systems of signs

Both the European and American systems make use of combinations of shapes and colours to distinguish the main classes of sign (warning, regulatory and informatory), and the European even subdivides regulatory signs into mandatory (positive instructions) and prohibitory (negative instructions). The way in which this coding is done is indicated in Table 11.3. The borders referred to are wide enough to serve as an important element of the signs. British signs incorporate many of the distinguishing features of European signs though usually in a weaker form. For example, the triangular and circular signs of the European system become rectangular signs surmounted respectively by triangles and circles (or discs) in the British system.

In the European and American systems certain particularly vital signs are designed to be as easily distinguishable from all other signs as possible. Thus the American "STOP", "Priority Road Ahead" and "Ungated Level Crossing" signs are a red octagon, a yellow triangle point-down and a

TABLE 11.3

Main characteristics of European and American signs (other than directional signs)

Class of sign	Element of sign	System European	American
Warning[1]	Shape	Triangle	Diamond
	Colour of background	White (or yellow)	Yellow
	Colour of legend	Black	Black
	Colour of border[2]	Red	None
Mandatory[1]	Shape	Circle	Rectangle
	Colour of background	Blue	White
	Colour of legend	White	Black
	Colour of border[2]	None	None
Prohibitory[1]	Shape	Circle	
	Colour of background	White (or Yellow)	As Mandatory above
	Colour of legend	Black	
	Colour of Border	Red	
Informatory[1]	Shape	Rectangle	Rectangle
	Colour of background	Blue	White
	Colour of legend	White	Black
	Colour of border[2]	None	None

NOTES: [1] There are exceptions in nearly every case: some of the reasons are discussed in the text
[2] Narrow contrast borders intended only to outline signs are ignored for this purpose

yellow circle respectively, whilst the European "Priority Road Ahead" and "Ungated Railway Crossing" signs are a triangle point-down (other triangles are point-up) and two boards in the form of the cross of St. Andrew (sometimes) respectively. This dual aim, to make important signs specially easy to recognize and yet make different classes of sign clearly distinguishable, is one reason why there are a considerable number of exceptions to the simple systems indicated by Table 11.3.

One great difference between the European and American systems is that, whereas the European system makes considerable use of symbolism, both pictorial and abstract, the American system explains all but the simplest conceptions in words. The British system tends to use both. This difference affects both the ease with which signs can be distinguished at long range and the ease with which their meanings can be learned and remembered. Before discussing the question of learning, an account is given of experiments undertaken to determine the system that can be most easily recognized by a population of drivers thoroughly familiar with the meanings of the signs.

Long range recognition

A group of 16 signs was chosen for which counterparts existed (or could be invented) in each of the three systems tested, the British, the European and the American. At least two examples were included of each class with a definite shape and colour coding, together with important signs which have been singled out for individual treatment. Reduced scale models of the signs were constructed, all of equal area (in the case of a British sign the area included that of the surmounting symbol). The signs were mounted one at a time on top of a car and driven at a speed corresponding to 20 mile/h full-scale towards seated observers who each had two buttons to press, one when the class of sign was recognized and the other when the particular sign was identified. In this way the distances for type recognition and for detailed identification were obtained separately from each observer. The best basis of comparison would have been to compare signs of equal cost but since cost is roughly proportional to area it was considered satisfactory to work with equal area. The mean relative distances recorded are given in Table 11.4.

TABLE 11.4

Long range recognition of British, European and American signs (other than directional signs)

Mean relative[1] distances for:	British	European	American
(a) recognition of sign class	2·69	3·03	3·31
(b) identification of particular sign	1·00	1·15	0·93

NOTE: [1] The distances are given relative to the mean distance for the complete identification of the British signs taken as 1·00

In this experiment the European system emerged as superior to the British both with regard to the recognition of the class of sign and the identification of the particular sign, whereas the sole advantage of the American system appeared to be in relation to the first (and less important) of these two criteria. It was concluded that from the point of view of long range recognition there would be an overall advantage in changing to the European system of signs. The next stage was to examine the results for the most important individual signs to see whether any improvements seemed desirable.

It was noted that in the European system the identification distance for the "STOP" sign was only slightly greater than the mean for the whole system, whereas on the American system it was twice the mean. No improvement was, however, achieved when the European system was modified by the substitution of the American "STOP" sign for the Protocol version because it was confused at long range with the "No Entry" sign. An increase of

| (a)
British | (b)
Protocol | (c)
U.S.A. | (d)
1953 draft
convention | (e)
R.R.L.
suggestion,
quasi-protocol |

a. Several versions of the 'Halt' signs. Tests show that (e) identified 10 per cent further away than (b)

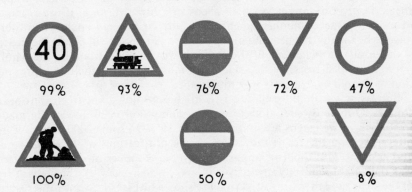

b. Proportion of drivers understanding Protocol signs.
Top row; Swedish drivers, their own signs
Bottom row; British drivers who had travelled on continent

| No Right Turn | No Entry | No Horns | No Cycles | No Parking | Turn Right |

c. Top row; consistency in signs of 1953 Draft Convention
Bottom row; lack of it in Protocol

Fig. 11.5. Warning, mandatory and prohibitory signs

about 10 per cent in the identification distance was obtained in a third experiment merely by modifying the present design as in Fig. 11.5a and it is hoped that this redesign will be considered for international adoption.

Although the identification distance for the "Priority Road Ahead" sign was good on the European system (50 per cent greater than the mean for the system) it was even better on the American system. Therefore in the second experiment the effect was tested of making the European sign yellow (like the American) whilst retaining white for the colour of all warning triangles. The identification distance was increased to twice the mean value for the system. The 1949 Protocol which says that white and yellow should be used consistently could with advantage be modified to permit the use of this colour distinction.

Learning the meaning of European-type signs

The ease with which the European signs can be recognized at long range stems from the symbolism used, whereby a worded message is conveyed by a single symbol.

Where these are simply pictures e.g., skidding cars or roadworkers they speak a universal language which needs very little learning. If use is made of more abstract symbolism such as a white bar in a red circle, road users have to be taught the meaning of the symbol. An important point, therefore, is to consider to what extent the symbols will be understood by the whole population of drivers, cyclists, etc. who must inevitably include a proportion of people of relatively low intelligence.

Surprisingly little information is available on this point from European sources. Only in Sweden does a serious attempt appear to have been made to study how well signs are understood. In 1953–54 some 2000 drivers were interviewed on the road; they were shown illustrations of 11 traffic signs and asked to give their meanings. The average number of signs recognized was only eight and only one driver in every seven knew all the signs. Five of the signs used in the investigation are shown in Fig. 11.5b with the results obtained for them. As might be expected written messages and direct pictorial representations were understood by nearly all drivers, whereas signs relying on purely abstract symbolism were not.

The experience of the Republic of Ireland tends to corroborate these findings. A system of signs based on the world system has been introduced there, most of the difficult signs being supplemented by explanatory plaques. The European "Priority Road Ahead" sign was used at first without explanation; later the Government felt obliged to add words within the sign.

One way of obtaining an estimate of how British drivers would cope with Continental type signs is to test drivers who have themselves driven on the Continent. A group of 63 such drivers was interviewed on behalf of the Road Research Laboratory by the Social Survey of the Central Office of Information as part of a much wider survey of drivers' understanding of traffic signs.[30] Some of the results are given in Fig. 11.5b. If the signs were introduced in Britain, the proportion of drivers that understands them would most probably be greater than that found in the survey; nevertheless the same overall picture emerges as from the Swedish experiment: no difficulty with pictorial representations but considerable difficulty with purely abstract symbolism.

Words and symbols

The use of words in conjunction with important abstract signs such as the "Priority Road Ahead", the "Closed To All Vehicles", and possibly, the "No Entry" signs would probably prove helpful to some drivers. According to the Protocol any worded explanations should go on separate plaques below the main signs. However, the signs in question have plenty of room for words on them and the effect of adding the words was tested in the second experiment referred to above. The results showed that words can be added without reducing the distance at which the signs can be recognized by those drivers who do fully understand their symbolism.

The signs of the 1949 Protocol[21] suffer from several defects which the 1953 convention avoided. One of them is the inconsistent use of the red cancellation bar across a sign. For example, to indicate a "No Right Turn" a white circle with a red edge bears a bent arrow cut through by a red bar. The reason for the bar here is obvious; if there were no bar, the sign would appear to be an invitation to turn right, the very opposite of what is intended. Now if the bar means "Don't do this" it should be used consistently, for example, the cycle in the "No Cycling" sign should also have a bar, similarly the overtaking car on the "No Overtaking" sign, but this is not done and these illogicalities and inconsistencies may make it more difficult for people to learn the meaning of the signs. The reason given for the omission of this bar is said to be that it tended to hide the symbol underneath, but tests carried out by the Laboratory showed that this is not a serious difficulty. Children can guess the meaning of signs with bars. A class of 11 year old children was divided into two groups, A and B, of equal intelligence. Group A was shown a set of Protocol signs, warning, mandatory and prohibitory; Group B was shown the same set of signs with bars added to four of the prohibitory signs which do not have them on the Protocol system (but do in the system proposed in the 1953 Draft Convention). Both groups were told only that triangles give warnings and circles commands (either do's or don'ts) and were asked to guess their meanings. It was found that 71 per cent of the answers given by Group B for the meanings of the four modified signs were correct, although they had never seen them before, whereas only 16 per cent of the answers given by Group A for the strictly Protocol versions of the same signs were correct. Moreover, 25 per cent of the answers to the Protocol signs were the exact opposites of the messages the symbols were intended to convey. There were no such errors with the modified signs.

It may be noted that one European country, Denmark, already uses the cancellation bars on these signs.[45]

Sizes of signs other than direction signs

For direction signs a rule has been given for estimating the size of lettering necessary for drivers to be able to read signs easily without diverting too much of their attention from the road ahead; the size of the sign then follows from the size of the lettering. If the same rule were to be applied to other types of sign, which contain only a single word or symbol, they would not be large enough to attract the driver's attention. In an experiment on a wide rural road, it was found that a white sign had to have an area of about 16 sq. ft for it to be judged as adequately conspicuous. Estimates of the sizes required on other types of road can be obtained by assuming that the areas of these classes of sign should be proportional to the areas of the direction signs (i.e. by making the linear dimensions of these signs proportional to the letter size used on the direction signs). From the foregoing the sizes shown in Table 11.5 are suggested for mandatory and prohibitory signs. "HALT" signs whch are of special importance should be made larger (say 50 per cent greater in area), whilst warning and informatory signs which are of less importance could be made a little smaller.

TABLE 11.5

Suggested sizes for circular mandatory and prohibitory signs

Height of lettering on advance direction signs (x-height in inches)	3–4	6–8	10–12
Diameter of mandatory and prohibitory signs (in.)* .	24	48	72

* For repeater signs in urban areas a specially reduced size could be used, say 20-in diameter

MAKING SIGNS EFFECTIVE AT NIGHT

The visibility and legibility of signs are much reduced at night unless the signs are illuminated by fixed lighting or reflectorized so that they appear bright in drivers' headlights. The 1963 Traffic Signs Committee[7] has recommended greater use of both lighting and reflective materials.

Brightness requirements

Research has been carried out both in the U.K.[31] and in the U.S.A.[23] on the ideal brightness (i.e. luminance) of signs at night. In unlit areas the ideal brightness of the light parts of the sign (sometimes this is the legend, sometimes the background) is about 10 ft L. A brightness of about 20 ft L seems to give the best results in well lit areas according to the pre-war British investigation: the American results agree so far as signs with a light legend on a dark surround is concerned but indicate a brightness of about 100 ft L for signs with a dark legend on a light surround. However, signs used in well lit areas have often to compete for the driver's attention with advertising signs with a brightness of 100–200 ft L and, therefore, brightnesses much greater than 20 ft L are certainly desirable in those circumstances, especially for small important signs.

Illuminated signs

B.S. 873:1959[32] contains a specification for the brightness of the white parts of externally illuminated signs according to which the average brightness should be 12–30 ft L and the variation over the signs should not exceed 10:1, 30:1, and 40:1 respectively for signs 2, 4 or 6 ft square. However, a study[33] of about 100 illuminated signs in the Home Counties showed that these requirements are rarely satisfied in practice. On few signs did the maximum brightness reach the lowest acceptable value specified for average brightness, the main reasons apparently being poor design and maintenance of the lighting units.

Even so the specification itself falls short of good modern practice. The permitted upper limit to the average brightness is much less than is now used with small internally illuminated mandatory and prohibitory signs (about 100 ft L). Moreover, the permitted variation of brightness over the sign is unnecessarily large: even on motorway signs 30 ft square a variation of only 5:1 has been achieved[34] (see Plate 11.3). The Association of Public Lighting Engineers has accordingly issued the following recommendations[35] in which M and m are the maximum and minimum brightnesses of the light coloured parts of the sign.

Average brightness $\frac{1}{2}(M+m)$: not less than 10 ft L
Variation of brightness M/m : not greater than 10:1
Maximum brightness M : not greater than 150 ft L.

It is, however, envisaged that the higher brightnesses will only be used in brightly lit areas and it is specifically advised that large light coloured signs on unlit roads should not have a maximum brightness exceeding 50 ft L.

Reflectorized signs

The light which falls on a reflectorized surface is returned in a narrow beam towards the source of light.[36] To anyone in the beam, the driver for instance, the sign appears much brighter than an ordinary white paint surface. To anyone outside the beam the sign may appear darker than an ordinary painted surface. The width of the returning beam (and therefore the brightness of the sign) can be varied by the manufacturers and reflection in a variety of colours is also possible. It should be noted that no useful effect can be expected from such a material if used in streets which are so well lit that headlights are not used.

Signs may be reflectorized in three main ways. Either beaded material (containing small glass spheres) may be used on the background or legend, or alternatively button reflectors may be set in the legend. Experiments have shown that the legibility distance for Ministry of Transport letters covered with beaded material is (1) approximately equal to that of letters fitted with button reflectors returning the same total amount of light, and (2) slightly better than for the black letters of the same form with a background of the same beaded material. The button reflectors used in the past were often of poor quality and very variable in performance. Consequently, in recent years, the tendency has been to use beaded materials instead of button reflectors.

It should be noted that unless the beads are immersed in a suitable medium so as to give a smooth outer surface the reflective power may be seriously reduced when the sign is wet; the reflective power may also be reduced by dirt retained in the interstices between the beads.

It is difficult with reflective materials to achieve the ideal brightness of about 10 ft L for large signs placed well away from the path of the vehicle. However, it has been shown that a legibility distance of over 90 per cent of the maximum possible value can be obtained with a brightness of about 2 ft L. A specification for the reflective power of reflectorizing materials, based on an average brightness of 2 ft L in full headlights, is given in BS.873:1959.[32] This specification should be raised when reflectorizing materials improve. For the measurement of reflective power a photometer developed by the Laborotary is especially convenient.[36]

It is important that signs which have to be read in the light of headlights should be so angled that the driver will not see mirror reflections of his head-lights from the glossy surface of the signs which can obliterate the contrast between the legend and its background. This is dealt with on page 382.

THE SITING AND MOUNTING OF SIGNS

Siting of signs in relation to junctions, etc.

All signs which give warning or information about hazards or junctions, etc., ahead should be sited sufficiently far in advance for a driver to be able to make the appropriate manoeuvre without endangering himself or others. Clearly, signs should be sited further from the points at which action is required on roads carrying fast traffic than on slow roads.

If the letter height on advance direction signs has been chosen according to Table 11.1 the driver should finish reading the sign at a distance of S cot $10°$ (see Fig. 11.1) or more from the sign. If the sign itself is Y ft from the junction, then the distance $Y + 5 \cdot 7S$ ft must be equal to or greater than the minimum safe stopping distance

$$\text{i.e. } Y + 5 \cdot 7S \geqslant 1 \cdot 5 RV + 1 \cdot 1 \cdot \frac{V^2}{A}$$

where A is the maximum safe deceleration of the vehicle in ft/sec,[2] V its initial speed in mile/h and R the driver's reaction time in seconds. It will be appreciated that the application of such a formula can only be used as a guide since the layout of the road and the presence of other roads will have to be taken into account in practice. It is suggested that for V the average speed of cars at the site in question should be taken and that for A a value of deceleration should be chosen between that achieved by simply removing the foot from the throttle and that following a general application of the brakes, i.e. a value between $0 \cdot 05g$ and $0 \cdot 2g$. A value of $0 \cdot 15g$ appears reasonable and can be obtained on the majority of wet roads. When the roads are icy, drivers will be travelling more slowly. Experiments have shown that R is about 1 second. Since the formula can only be considered as an approximation it is suggested that a single set of values of Y computed for $S = 20$ ft and rounded off will give a satisfactory guide in practice (see Table 11.6).[45]

There is little value in erecting a sign based on the principles enumerated if in that position trees, lamp columns, other signs or street furniture obscure it. These must be moved so that a driver in the nearside lane can have a clear view of the sign from a distance equal to 50 ft for each inch of x-height of the lettering. This may mean that on major roads in urban areas where street lamps are at the edge of the carriageway one or more columns will have to be shifted.

TABLE 11.6

*Approximate distances at which advance signs should be
sited from the points at which action is required*

Average speed of cars (mile/h)	Distance of sign from junction, hazard etc. (ft.)
30	150
40	300
50	500
60	750
70	1000

Positions of signs relative to the carriageway

Signs on roads where there are no obstructions are most easily read if they are low and close to the edge of the carriageway; this is especially true at night in the case of signs which have to be read in the light from dipped headlamps. However, there are two disadvantages in siting signs in this position. The first disadvantage is that they suffer severely from the effect of mud splash; Fig. 11.6 shows how the reflective power of reflex reflectors

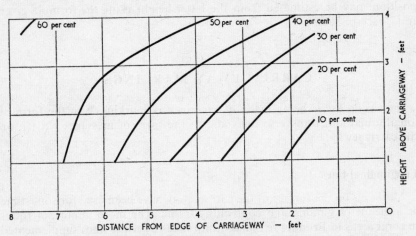

Fig. 11.6. The effect of mud splash on reflective power of reflex reflectors on posts. Reflective power after exposure for 26 days in March, expressed as a percentage of the original reflective power

in different positions relative to a busy trunk road was reduced after 26 days' exposure during the month of March (six days were wet and the total rainfall was 0·5 in.).[43] The second disadvantage is that signs close to the carriageway may obstruct the view of drivers and may constitute hazards, at least on fast roads. Clearly, compromise is necessary and recommended, practice may be summarized as follows:

(1) Signs should be sited with their lower edges at a height of not less than 3 ft 6 in. except in the case of signs on footways under which pedestrians must pass and for which a minimum height of 6 ft 9 in. is required.[7]

For motorways, on which the signs are larger and can be read from a greater range, a minimum height of 5 ft is recommended for the lower edge of the sign.

(2) On trunk roads and classified rural roads built to modern design standards signs should be about 4 ft back from the edge of the carriageway. On other all-purpose roads a clearance of at least 18 in. is required to prevent signs being struck by overhanging loads.

Angling of signs to prevent specular reflection

If a sign is turned in towards the road so that the approaching driver sees it square on, at night the contrast between the legend and the background may be obliterated by mirror-like reflections of headlamps. To avoid such reflections,[37] signs should be turned about a vertical axis away from the road through an angle of 5° in the case of all-purpose roads and 3° in the case of motorways. Although this means that the driver has a slightly oblique view of the sign the effect is small at the range at which signs are designed to be read. On straight roads and right-hand bends the angle may be measured from the tangent to the edge of the road opposite to the sign. On left-hand bends the angle should be measured from a line joining the point on the road edge opposite the sign to the point on the road edge opposite the position at which drivers can begin to read the sign (this position may be estimated from the letter height using the formula given in (7) (see p. 366).

CARRIAGEWAY MARKINGS

Increasing use is being made of carriageway markings[38] in the form of longitudinal and transverse lines and in the form of messages written on the carriageway.

Longitudinal lines

Markings on the surface of the carriageway have been used for some time as a means of guiding and controlling traffic. The more important roads in rural areas in Britain are marked into lanes by white lines supplemented for guidance at night by reflecting road studs or glass beads in the white line. Lane lines are much less common in towns but are becoming more popular.

Several varieties of longitudinal line may be used to divide the carriageway. The simplest form—the lane line—is a series of widely-spaced dashes. The warning line is also a broken line but has a greater mark/space ratio than the lane line: it tells the driver that he is approaching a hazard.

Solid white lines are sometimes used to outline continuously the edge of carriageways without raised kerbs where they butt on to flush shoulders or verges. According to a European agreement[39] lines used to mark the boundaries of the road should be of a different colour from those used for lane lines and, since there are only two possible easily distinguishable colours of lines, edge markings would have to be yellow in this country according to the agreement. However, the tendency in this country is to reserve yellow for lines denoting limitations on stopping and waiting.

Various varieties of yellow line along the edge of the carriageway have been tried out experimentally to indicate restrictions on stopping and waiting, and recommendations in favour of the adoption of such a system of yellow lines were made by the Traffic Signs Committee of 1963.[7]

The use of lane lines at controlled intersections

Lane markings are frequently used at controlled intersections and normally extend 90–100 ft back from the stop-line. By indicating to drivers when it is possible to form two or more lanes of traffic they encourage more efficient use of the green time at the signal. Lane widths of 10 or 11 ft are desirable but even sub-standard widths can be marked with advantage, since in most cities traffic is so mixed that it is worth-while encouraging small vehicles to form two lanes even when large vehicles cannot do so.

A study was made of the effect of the position of lane markings on one approach to a signal-controlled junction in Lambeth, London, where the road was 33 ft wide. Observations were made of the maximum flow of vehicles entering and leaving by this arm of the intersection when various temporary lane markings of self-adhesive tape were placed on the road. The results are given in Table 11.7.

TABLE 11.7

Effect on traffic flow of various lane markings on one arm of an intersection

Road markings	Flow per hour when departing from a queue	
	Traffic entering intersection	Traffic leaving intersection
None	1450	1800
One central white line .	1500	1800
Approach marked as two 9 ft 6 in. lanes . .	1700	1800

Off-set markings allowing 19 ft in two 9 ft 6 in. lanes to traffic approaching the signals increased the rate of discharge of that traffic by 17 per cent without affecting the opposing traffic flow. The tidal nature of the traffic and the irregular shape of the intersection contributed to the success of off-set markings in this instance.

Double white lines

A system of marking hazardous sections of the road was introduced by the Ministry of Transport in 1959. The chief innovation consisted of two parallel white lines, one for each direction of travel, laid longitudinally along the centre of the carriageway. The lines may both be continuous or one may be continuous and the other broken. A driver must not cross the lines if the one near his vehicle is continuous. If the line nearer the vehicle is broken, crossing for overtaking purposes is permitted if the driver judges that it is safe to do so. The location of each kind of line is decided according to a set of rules depending upon the distance ahead that a driver can see and the speed of traffic at the site.

Observations of driver behaviour were made at seven sites on trunk roads in Berkshire, Hampshire, and Wiltshire.[40] Visibility was restricted by horizontal curvature at six of the sites and by a hill crest at the seventh. Non-observance of the regulation was common and for purposes of comparison the percentages of all vehicles crossing the line per hundred yards was used as an index of behaviour. At the sites studied it was found that:

(1) Drivers respected the pairs of continuous lines more than they did the mixed pair—the violations being about 1 per cent as compared with 2·2 per cent respectively, this difference being statistically significant. (2) The violations of the regulations implied by the lines were due to overtakings or attempted overtakings: 80 per cent of overtaking vehicles were cars and 50 per cent of the overtaking vehicles were lorries or heavy commercial vehicles. (3) These overtakings were on average shorter in time and distance than permitted overtakings. (4) Drivers paid less attention to the lines on right-hand bends than on left-hand ones—the violations over a mixed pair of lines being 2·6 per cent on right-hand bends compared with 1·9 per cent on left-hand bends. Crossings where there was a broken line on the nearside (not a violation) were 3·6 per cent on right-hand and 3 per cent on left-hand bends.

Except at the exits from bends the rules for the layout of the double white lines make no allowance for the fact that, when attempting to overtake a vehicle on a left-hand bend, vision is obstructed to a greater extent than on a right-hand bend. Consideration might usefully be given to altering the sighting rules so that overtaking would sometimes be forbidden on left-hand bends whereas it would be allowed on equivalent right-hand bends.

A comparison[41] has been made of the number of injury accidents occurring on about 150 miles of main road in Southern England before and after the roads concerned were marked with double white lines and associated markings where appropriate. The changes in accident frequency on these roads were compared with the changes in the number of road casualties in the whole of the surrounding police districts during the corresponding periods. There were no statistically significant increases or decreases in accidents associated with the experiment as a whole. It is possible that drivers were not complying with, or even fully aware of, the requirements of the new markings during the introductory period.

Transverse lines at controlled junctions

The most important form of transverse line is the continuous stop line used at traffic signals and at "HALT" junctions and reserved for these positions.

Because of the oblique angle at which a driver views the road ahead of him a stop line appears extremely narrow even at a distance of 75 ft, the safe stopping distance from 30 mile/h. Fortunately advance warning is given by either a vertical "HALT" sign or by traffic signals. In addition the

Ministry of Transport now recommend that "HALT" should be written on the carriageway in advance of the stop line (see section on "Written messages" below).

Transverse lines at uncontrolled intersections

In the absence of vertical signs or traffic signals at a road junction there may be some doubt as to which of two vehicles approaching on different roads should give way. Many authorities have laid a white line across the carriageway of the minor road where it joins the main road; it is sometimes laid across the whole of the minor road and sometimes only over half but it is usually a broken line.

Injury accidents have been studied at several groups of junction before and after the provision of these transverse lines. Eight groups of junction (a total of 213 sites) were studied, covering a variety of districts, types of junction and several kinds of marking). In two areas there were 60 and 40 per cent fewer accidents after markings had been provided; the differences were statistically significant. After marking, the 213 junctions which were studied had 18 per cent fewer accidents then expected. The evidence also suggested that a longitudinal central line on the minor road adds to the value of the transverse line.

The 1963 Traffic Signs Committee[7] have, therefore, recommended the adoption of a distinctive transverse marking for this purpose and experimental installations of double broken lines are in use. A longitudinal hazard line is used in each case.

Written messages

For messages written on the surface of the carriageway it is common to increase to four or more times normal the longitudinal dimensions of the letters relative to their transverse dimensions. Even so the distance from which they can be read is limited to about 100 ft. Therefore, messages on the carriageway are possibly most useful where traffic speeds are restricted or where the messages are used to supplement vertical signs. In urban areas messages on the carriageway, often accompanied by arrows, are widely and successfully used to get traffic into the correct lines before junctions. Since 1960 it has been permissible to mark "Halt" on the carriageway to reinforce the message of the vertical sign.

The Laboratory has carried out several investigations at junctions controlled by "HALT" signs to discover if additionally painting the word "HALT" on the carriageway produced any improvement in the behaviour of drivers at these sites. Observations were made at five sites in 1954 of the effect of letters 2 ft high and 1 ft 6 in. wide. These showed no change in the percentage of drivers stopping. In 1955 letters 4 ft high and 1 ft 6 in. wide were put down and further observations showed an increase of 17 per cent in the drivers stopping before leaving the minor road.

To determine whether the increase was permanent or due in part to the novelty of the marking, further observations were made to find out if there was any consistent difference in behaviour between sites which had had "HALT" on the carriageway for a considerable period and those which had had only a stop-line. This investigation was possible because for a number of years some authorities had made a practice of using the additional markings. About 80 sites were studied, half with "HALT" and "STOP" road markings and half without.

The observations indicated that at these sites the effect of the markings was that an extra 7 per cent of drivers made some effort to conform to the requirement of the "HALT" sign. After making allowances for traffic conditions between sites there were about 40 per cent fewer personal-injury accidents to vehicles emerging from the minor road at sites with the additional carriageway markings than at the normal "HALT" sign. This change was statistically significant.[42] The Ministry of Transport now recommend that "HALT" should be marked on the carriageway.

The visibility of carriageway markings at night

In lighted streets at night the contrast between a surface marking and the carriageway is reduced (especially in the wet) because of their peculiar reflection properties at oblique angles. The effect is to reduce the range at which surface markings in the form of written messages can be read and therefore the time the driver has to read them.

On unlit roads, surface markings are visible in headlights only at short distances unless they are fitted with catseyes (self-cleaning reflecting studs) or are coated with ballotini (small glass spheres). The effect of catseyes on the visibility of lane lines is very marked; they are in fact the best indicator of the layout of a road, and are visible up to 300 ft in the dipped beam and 600 ft in the driving beam. Their visibility is not affected by rain. Lines incorporating ballotini are less common in Great Britain; their visibility distance is less than that of catseyes and is appreciably reduced when it rains heavily.

Attempts have been made to improve the visibility of raised kerbs by inserting reflectors or by shaping them so as to return more light to the driver but, because of the bad effects of road splash, results have been disappointing.[43] A more satisfactory alternative is the use of posts carrying reflectors alongside the road. However, even these suffer from mud splash and in bad weather frequent cleaning may be necessary.

A more difficult problem is the demarcation of the edge of the carriageway on motorways and similar roads designed for fast traffic. Such roads have no raised kerbs to separate them from the verge or shoulder which is at substantially the same level as the carriageway. There is little difficulty in daylight but on wet nights ordinary smooth white lines tend to appear dark in headlights. Lines containing ballotini are better but are still rather poor in the worst conditions of rain (they are affected too by the detritus which tends to collect on the edge of the road). Attempts have been made to improve the visibility of these markings; the alternative is to design them so that they cause unusual vibrations in a vehicle passing over them (the two methods can of course be combined).

With the co-operation of the County Surveyors, short lengths of a number of different types of edge-marking were laid in 1960 on the Oxton bypass, Nottinghamshire (A.6097), and on the Gatwick diversion, Surrey (A.23). Measurements were made of the visibility of markings in a variety of weather conditions and subjective estimates were also made of the effectiveness of some of them as generators of vibration.[44]

The tests showed that to ensure that the edge is visible in bad weather at night it is essential to use either an efficient retro-reflective device (such as a reflecting roadstud), or a surface that presents a large number of light-coloured surfaces, vertical or nearly vertical, to a headlamp beam. The following five types of edge marking gave promise of good performance visually and some of them gave, in addition, a useful noise signal:

(1) Concrete blocks with $\frac{1}{2}$–$1\frac{1}{2}$ in. calcined flint aggregate heavily exposed (Plate 11.4 (a)).

(2) Surface dressing of $\frac{1}{4}$ to $\frac{3}{8}$ in. calcined flint aggregate (similar in appearance to Plate 11.4 (a)).

(3) A white line marking with the addition of reflecting roadstuds (either single or in pairs) (Plate 11.4 (b)).

(4) A precast concrete kerb with the addition of reflecting roadstuds (Plate 11.4 (c)).

(5) A second type of precast concrete kerb without roadstuds (Plate 11.4 (d)).

These markings have been selected for the following reasons:

(i) The size of aggregate used in (1) and (2) is large enough to ensure that the marking has an open texture. In wet weather, therefore, the light-coloured stones project above any surface water and are clearly visible.

(ii) The white line marking in (3) is quite adequate by day, and moderately effective in dry weather at night. In wet weather at night, however, the addition of reflecting roadstuds is necessary.

(iii) The precast concrete kerb (4) was found to be an effective generator of vibration. It was not, however, easily visible at night in wet conditions and required the addition of reflecting roadstuds.

(iv) The second type of concrete kerb (5) was less effective in causing vibration than the first. It was, however, clearly visible in wet conditions at night.

REFERENCES TO CHAPTER 11

1. MINISTRY OF TRANSPORT. The traffic signs (size, colour and type) regulations, 1950. *Statutory Instruments*, 1950, No. 953. London, 1950 (H.M. Stationery Office).

2. SECRETARY OF STATE FOR SCOTLAND and MINISTER OF TRANSPORT AND CIVIL AVIATION. The traffic signs regulations and general directions, 1957. *Statutory Instruments*, 1957, No. 13. London, 1957 (H.M. Stationery Office).

3. MINISTRY OF TRANSPORT ADVISORY COMMITTEE ON TRAFFIC SIGNS FOR MOTORWAYS. Motorway signs. London, 1962 (H.M. Stationery Office).

4. U.S. PUBLIC ROADS ADMINISTRATION. Manual on uniform traffic control devices for streets and highways. Washington, D.C., 1948 (U.S. Public Roads Administration).

5. MITCHELL, A., and T. W. FORBES. Design of sign letter sizes. *Proc. Amer. Soc. civ. Engrs.*, 1942, **68**, (1), 95–104; Discussion, (5), 839–40; (6), 1073–4; (9), 1675.

6. MOORE, R. L. Traffic sign design. *Traff. Engng & Control*, 1962, **3**, (11), 685–8.

7. MINISTRY OF TRANSPORT. Traffic signs 1963. Report of the Committee on Traffic Signs for All-purpose Roads. London, 1963 (H.M. Stationery Office).

8. SOAR, R. S. Stroke width, illumination level and figure-ground contrast in numeral visibility. *J. appl. Psychol.*, 1955, **39** (6), 429–32.

9. CASE, H. W., and others. Analysis of certain variables related to sign legibility. *Bull. Highw. Res. Bd, Wash.*, 1952, (60), 44–54.

10. HELLER, F. Recommendations for the design and siting of traffic signs. *Strasse u. Autobahn*, 1957, **8** (12), 455–64.

11. BERGER, C. Stroke-width, form, and horizontal spacing of numerals as determinants of the threshold of recognition. *J. appl. Psychol.*, 1944, **28**, 208–31; 336–46.

12. LAUER, A. R. Certain structural components of letters for improving the efficiency of the stop sign. *Proc. Highw. Res. Bd, Wash.*, 1947, **27**, 360–71.

13. U.S. DEPARTMENT OF COMMERCE, BUREAU OF PUBLIC ROADS. Standard alphabets for highway signs. Washington, D.C., 1952 (U.S. Department of Commerce, Bureau of Public Roads).

14. SOLOMON, D. The effect of letter width and spacing on night legibility of highway signs. *Traff. Engng*, 1956, **27** (3), 113–20.

15. BRIDGEMAN, C. S., and E. A. WADE. Optimum letter size for a given display area. *J. appl. Psychol.*, 1956, **40** (6), 378–80.

16. CHRISTIE, A. W., and K. S. RUTLEY. Relative effectiveness of some letter types designed for use on road traffic signs. *Rds & Rd Constr.*, 1961, **39** (464), 239–44. (Appendix. A preliminary experiment to determine what marginal and interlinear spaces give maximum legibility distance.)

17. FORBES, T. W., and others. A comparison of lower case and capital letters for highway signs. *Proc. Highw. Res. Bd, Wash.*, 1950, **30**, 355–73; Discussion, 371–3.

18. BARTLETT, F., and N. H. MACKWORTH. Planned seeing. *Air Ministry Air Publication* 3139B. London, 1950 (H.M. Stationery Office).

19. MOORE, R. L. The design of traffic signs. *Fourth International Study Week in Traffic Engineering, 16–21 September, 1958, Copenhagen, Denmark*. London, 1958 (World Touring and Automobile Organisation).

20. WALKER, J. Perception of topographical information (with reference to road signs). *Nature, Lond.*, 1962, **195** (4840), 522.

21. UNITED NATIONS ECONOMIC AND SOCIAL COUNCIL. United Nations Conference on Road and Motor Transport, held at Geneva, September 1949. Final act and related documents. New York, N.Y., 1950 (U.N. Economic and Social Council).

22. NEAL, H. E. The legibility of highway signs. *Convention Group Meetings: papers and discussions: Cincinnati, Ohio, November 28–30, 1944*. Washington, D.C., 1945 (American Association of State Highway Officials), pp. 151–64.

23. ALLEN, T. M., and A. L. STRAUB. Sign brightness and legibility. *Bull. Highw. Res. Bd, Wash.*, 1956, (127), 1–14.

24. MOORE, R. L., and A. W. CHRISTIE. Direction signs for motorways. *Engineer, Lond.*, 1960, **209** (5442), 813–7.

25. ODESCALCHI, P. Conspicuity of signs in rural surroundings. *Traff. Engng & Control*, 1960, **2** (7), 390–3, 397.

26. AMERICAN ASSOCIATION OF STATE HIGHWAY OFFICIALS. Manual for signing and pavement marking of the National System of Interstate and Defense Highways. Washington, D.C., 1961 (American Association of State Highway Officials).

27. NATIONAL JOINT COMMITTEE ON UNIFORM TRAFFIC CONTROL DEVICES. Manual on uniform traffic control devices for streets and highways. Washington, D.C., 1961 (U.S. Department of Commerce, Bureau of Public Roads).

28. CANADIAN GOOD ROADS ASSOCIATION, JOINT COMMITTEE ON UNIFORM TRAFFIC CONTROL DEVICES FOR CANADA. Uniform traffic control devices for Canada. Ottawa, 1960 (Canadian Good Roads Association).

29. UNITED NATIONS ECONOMIC AND SOCIAL COUNCIL. Report of group of experts on road signs and signals. *Second Session, 13th August–8th September*, 1951. Geneva, 1951 (U.N. Economic and Social Council, Transport and Communications Commission).

30. GRAY, P. G., and R. RUSSELL. Drivers' understanding of traffic signs. *Central Office of Information, Social Survey* 347. London, 1962 (H.M. Stationery Office).

31. SMYTH, J. S. The brightness and legibility at night of road traffic signs. *Trans. Illum. Engng Soc., Lond.*, 1947, **12** (4), 71–86; Discussion, 86–94.

32. BRITISH STANDARDS INSTITUTION. British Standard 873:1959. The construction of road traffic signs and internally illuminated bollards. London, 1959 (British Standards Institution).

33. REID, J. A. Some measurements of the brightness of road signs at night. *Surveyor, Lond.*, 1962, **121** (3637), 189–92.

34. JEHU, V. J. A method of illuminating direction signs on motorways. *Lt & Ltg*, 1959, **52** (11), 338–40.

35. ASSOCIATION OF PUBLIC LIGHTING ENGINEERS. The lighting of traffic signs. *Technical Report* No. 1. London, 1963 (Association of Public Lighting Engineers).

36. CHANDLER, K. N., and J. A. REID. Reflex reflectors. *Department of Scientific and Industrial Research, Road Research Technical Paper* No. 42. London, 1958 (H.M. Stationery Office).

37. GREGSTEN, M. J. Advance direction signs and specular reflections. *Traff. Engng & Control*, 1961, **3** (6), 347–9.

38. SECRETARY OF STATE FOR SCOTLAND and MINISTER OF TRANSPORT AND CIVIL AVIATION. The traffic signs (amendment) regulations, 1959. *Statutory Instruments*, 1959, No. 761. London, 1959 (H.M. Stationery Office).

39. HOUSE OF COMMONS. European agreement on road markings. *Command Paper* 480. London, 1958 (H.M. Stationery Office).

40. OLDER, S. J. Driver behaviour at double white lines. *Traff. Engng & Control*, 1962, **4** (5), 260–2, 266.

41. DEPARTMENT OF SCIENTIFIC AND INDUSTRIAL RESEARCH. Road research 1961. The report of the Road Research Board with the report of the Director of Road Research. London, 1962 (H.M. Stationery Office), p. 59.

42. OLDER, S. J. Accident comparisons at halt or stop junctions. *Traff. Engng & Control*, 1961, **2** (11), 655–7.

43. CHRISTIE, A. W. Reflectors on roads with raised kerbs. *Traff. Engng & Control*, 1961, **3** (3), 169–71, 175.

44. CHRISTIE, A. W., J. A. REID, K. S. RUTLEY and A. E. WALKER. Edge markings for roads with flush shoulders. *Traff. Engng & Control*, 1963, **4** (9), 500–4, 509.

45. MOORE, R. L., and A. W. CHRISTIE. Research on traffic signs. *Engineering for Traffic Conference*. London, 1963 (Printerhall Ltd.), pp. 113–22.

Chapter 12

Pedestrians

SYNOPSIS

Methods of observation: speed measurements; density measurements; delay measurements. Pedestrians as traffic. Pedestrian crossing places.

INTRODUCTION

This chapter is concerned with the methods of studying pedestrian movement and behaviour and the results such studies have produced. Methods of measuring pedestrian speeds, delays and density of grouping are discussed and consideration is given to the effect of various factors on these measures. An analysis is made of the factors likely to affect pedestrians in judging when it is safe to cross the road and three types of crossing facility are mentioned and compared: uncontrolled crossings, controlled crossings, and bridges or subways. Finally the question of the establishment of criteria for the provision of a crossing facility is discussed.

METHODS OF OBSERVATION

It is difficult to adapt fully automatic methods to the recording of pedestrian movements so most methods require the presence of a human observer either directly or indirectly, as in the case of examination of a photographic record.

Speed measurements

The simplest method of measuring pedestrian speed is to have an observer record the journey time over a measured distance. Since it is not always possible to record all pedestrians, care is necessary in selection so that a representative sample is obtained of the types of people using the particular footway under study. Particular reference should be made to the proportions of old and young people, males and females, unaccompanied adolescents and people with young children, as these groups are known to have different walking speeds (see Table 12.1).

In some cases photographic methods are useful, particularly where it is necessary to relate speeds with other happenings such as, for example, changes in density. A film provides a permanent record and allows rechecking of results where necessary.

Density measurements

The estimation of the number of pedestrians in a given area can prove difficult if there are many and they are not standing still. Two methods of assessment have been used.

The first is by what is called the "moving observer" technique.[1] To obtain an estimate of the number of people on a given length of footway, for example, an observer traverses its length in one direction, counting every person he passes in whatever direction they happen to be moving and deducting those people who overtake him going in the same direction. He then traverses the section in the opposite direction doing the same thing. The average of the two totals he obtains will be the estimate of the average number of people on the footway.

This method is useful for reasonable lengths of footway, e.g. of the order of 100 yards, but it is not very accurate for short lengths where the "bunching" of pedestrians can cause great variation in density from one instant to another. The latter situation is more suited to the second method; the use of photographic recording on cine film. With this method an instantaneous count can be made of all the people on one frame of the film, and as many other counts made as necessary to obtain a reasonable estimate of the average density and its variation. The success of using a cine camera and film depends to a large extent on finding a suitable vantage point where the camera can be placed. The most suitable position is directly above the section to be photographed or as close to this as possible; from this angle pedestrians will not be hidden from view by others. It has been found in practice that lengths of about 50 ft can be covered easily, greater distances need care in analysis due to possible parallax errors and difficulties due to lack of resolution on the film, although the latter obviously depends on the types of film and camera used. Colour film has been found to add considerably to the ease of analysis of these studies where the densities were high.

In many applications of a cine camera to such work a speed of about four frames per second has been found useful. At this speed a pedestrian can be located to an accuracy of about one foot, this being the average distance moved between any two frames on the film.

Delay measurements

The most direct way of measuring delay is by recording the length of time that each pedestrian is stationary or, if change in delay is of interest, to record the difference in journey times over a given distance. Using normal stop-watch methods it is often impossible to time all pedestrians and some sampling system needs to be devised, with the same precautions already referred to in discussing speed measurements.

It is possible to obtain an estimate of the average delay to pedestrians in a slightly easier way, although information on individual differences is lost. The following method has given satisfactory results.[2]

The total pedestrian delay over a given period of time is equal to the average number of waiting pedestrians multiplied by the duration of the period. The average delay is obtained by dividing by the total number of pedestrians involved.

Since it is not usually practicable to record the number of waiting pedestrians continuously, this may be done at fixed intervals of time. Provided the interval is short enough to follow the pedestrian trend reasonably closely and long enough to enable the observer to count and record this number accurately then, on the average over a fairly long period of time, any difference between the true pedestrian flow curve and that obtained when observations are made at intervals will have no effect on the resulting delay.

In addition to recording the number of waiting pedestrians a count of the number of pedestrians who cross the road is also required.

If n represents the number of waiting pedestrians at the end of each short interval of duration t, and m equals the number of pedestrians crossing the road in time T, then the average delay per pedestrian is

$$\bar{d} = \frac{t\Sigma n}{m}$$

A reasonable interval for recording the number of waiting pedestrians is one-tenth of a minute since it is short enough to follow the pedestrian trends, convenient for the observer using a stop watch graduated in tenths and hundredths of a minute to see when to count the pedestrian queue, and long enough for the observer to record the count on paper.

An observer equipped with a watch graduated in one-tenth minutes and a recording board notes down the number of waiting pedestrians at one-tenth minute intervals. Also recorded is the number of pedestrians crossing the road. This number is counted on a hand tally and the cumulative pedestrian count is usually copied from the hand tally every five minutes. Then a calculation, which simply consists in multiplying the summation of the waiting pedestrians by $0\cdot1$ and dividing by the number of pedestrians, gives the average delay per pedestrian in minutes.

All pedestrians who are waiting at the instant the watch hand passes each tenth of a minute division must be recorded (whether waiting at either side of the road or in the central reserve, if any). If, however, a pedestrian is walking (even though he may have only just started to cross the road) he is not being delayed at that instant and consequently should not be recorded as a waiting pedestrian.

PEDESTRIANS AS TRAFFIC

The average speed of adult pedestrians has been found to be about $3\cdot4$ mile/h ($5\cdot0$ ft/s)[3] when walking on level ground. Average speed of individuals will vary about this depending on the conditions affecting the pedestrian at the time of observation. Age and sex are important factors as Table 12.1 shows.[4]

TABLE 12.1

Walking speeds

Age and Sex	Level walking speed	
	mile/h	ft/s
Men under 55 years of age	3·7	5·4
Men over 55 years of age	3·4	5·0
Women under 50 years of age	3·1	4·5
Women over 50 years of age	2·9	4·3
Women with small children	1·6	2·3
Children between 6 and 10 years of age . .	2·5	3·7
Adolescents	4·0	5·9

The speed of pedestrians crossing the road is only likely to have the above values in the absence of approaching vehicles. These vehicles cause the pedestrian to speed up,[3] as is shown in Table 12.2.

TABLE 12.2

Speeds of pedestrians crossing the road
at various times before the arrival of a vehicle

	Crossing speed
Vehicle 8 seconds or more away .	4·0 ft/s
Vehicle 6 seconds or more away .	4·1 ft/s
Vehicle 4 seconds or more away .	4·7 ft/s
Vehicle 2 seconds or more away .	6·5 ft/s

When pedestrian movement is not on level ground, in particular on the approaches to bridges or subways where there are ramps or stairs, speed on ramps is related, as might be expected, to the amount of gradient as Fig. 12.1 and Table 12.3 show.[5]

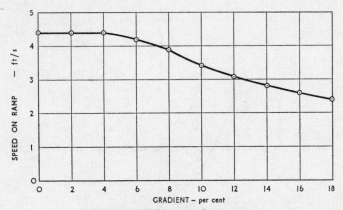

Fig. 12.1. Walking speeds on ramps

TABLE 12.3

Walking speeds on ramps
(A gradient of 4 per cent implies a rise of 4
vertical units in every 100 horizontal units)

Gradient	Speed (on ramp)
0%	4·4 ft/s
2%	4·4 ft/s
4%	4·4 ft/s
6%	4·2 ft/s
8%	3·9 ft/s
10%	3·4 ft/s
12%	3·1 ft/s
14%	2·8 ft/s
16%	2·6 ft/s
18%	2·4 ft/s

It will be seen that until a gradient of about 5 per cent is reached no appreciable decrease in walking speed occurs. The maximum gradient in common use is 10 per cent.

Stairs are an alternative to ramps although they have obvious disadvantages for old and infirm people. An average speed of ascent of stairways has been found to be about 0·5 ft/s in a vertical direction.[3] Other results for normal adults show a speed of about two steps per second ascending stairs although this varies with the design of the stairway.[5] Speeds decending stairways are only slightly faster than those ascending.

A further factor that affects walking speed is the concentration or density of the pedestrians. The greater the concentration of people on a footway the slower will be their walking speed. Emprical relations have been found by various workers[6,7,8] and these are shown in Fig. 12.2.

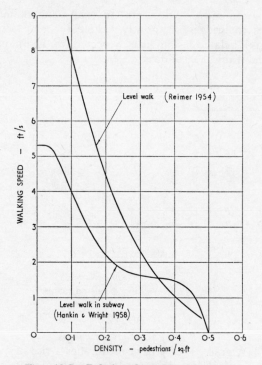

Fig. 12.2. Relation between pedestrian density and velocity (movement in one direction only)

These speed/density relations imply a speed/flow relation for any given width of footway, as illustrated in Fig. 12.3.[7] After a given density has been reached any increase in density is compensated by a decrease in speed so that the flow remains approximately constant. This critical density can be used to predict when a given footway will become congested. For level passages in subways this concentration is about 0·13 persons/sq. ft.[7] On footways it is likely that the critical level would be slightly greater than this. These relations are of course only applicable to unidirectional flows;

opposing flows would cause interaction and the resulting relationships do not yet appear to have been studied.

Above a minimum of about four feet the maximum flow in subways and on stairs is directly proportional to width. Below four feet multiples of shoulder widths become important.

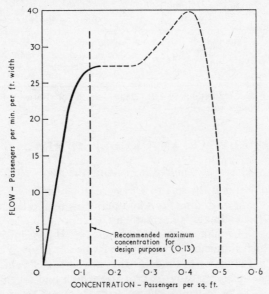

Fig. 12.3. Concentration and flow relation for pedestrians in level passageways (Hankin and Wright, 1958)

The slower speeds on stairs and ramps and the increased expenditure of energy required lead to discriminating use of bridges and subways in crossing the road. The relative time involved is a useful criterion in predicting the use of alternative routes at such facilities (see pp. 400-1).

The minimum footway widths in Great Britain, as suggested by the Ministry of Local Government and Planning in 1951,[9] are as follows:

Type of district	Type of street	Footway width
Industrial areas	Main street 30-ft carriageway . .	10 ft
	Minor street 22-ft carriageway . .	6 ft
Principal business areas	Main street 44-ft carriageway . .	15 ft
	Shopping street 44-ft carriageway .	15 ft
	Minor street 30-ft carriageway . .	12 ft
	Minor street 20-ft carriageway .	6 ft
Residential areas	Shopping street 22-ft carriageway . (minor traffic)	12 ft
	Shopping street 22-ft carriageway . (main traffic)	12 ft
	Main street 22-ft carriageway . . (no shops)	9 ft

It was pointed out by a Departmental Committee of the Ministry of War Transport in 1946[10] that in shopping districts there is a "dead" width of footway of up to 3 ft which is not available for pedestrian movement. The following guide for the adequacy of footway widths was also derived.

Persons per minute per 24-in. width*	Adequacy of footway
Under 20 .	Adequate
Between 20 and 30 .	Free passage inconvenient
Over 30 .	Unduly congested

* After deducting 3 ft "dead" width for footways in shopping districts.

PEDESTRIAN CROSSING PLACES

The problem—judgement required in crossing the road

A person standing at the side of a busy road which he wishes to cross has to look at traffic in both directions and make his own estimate of when it is safe to cross. His estimate is normally a correct one, but in about one case in a million or so he makes a disastrous mistake. It is of interest to examine the factors which influence his decision of when it is safe to cross.

Accordingly a study[3] was made of the movement of vehicles and pedestrians at a pedestrian crossing. A crossing which had a central refuge was chosen because the pedestrian's choice, to cross or not to cross, is simplified at such a place. The arrival of a pedestrian at the kerb and his subsequent pause and eventual movement across the road were recorded as were the movements of vehicles approaching the crossing.

Certain relationships were deduced from these observations. The probability that a waiting pedestrian will cross in front of a moving vehicle a given distance away was calculated for vehicles approaching at different speeds. It was found that the pedestrian makes an allowance for the speed of the approaching vehicle; for example 75 per cent of people will cross in front of a vehicle 60 ft away moving at 5–10 mile/h, but if the vehicle is travelling at 20–25 mile/h only 25 per cent of pedestrians will risk crossing. This suggests that pedestrians are concerned primarily with a time gap and not a distance gap in the traffic. It would be interesting to know how the pedestrian estimates the time gap in traffic. He may do this by estimating the speed of the vehicle and its distance away or more likely he has intuitive appreciation of the time of arrival of the vehicle.

To discover what happens to the people who take the greater risks, the time taken by the pedestrian to move across half the carriageway from the kerb to island was plotted against the expected time of arrival of the next approaching vehicle. It was seen that when the vehicle was less than seven seconds away the pedestrian, realizing his danger, increased his speed across the road.

The pedestrian's choice of a suitable time interval in which to cross the road rather than a distance gap is an economy of his time. At the crossing studied, for example, it has been estimated that if all pedestrians waited for a gap in the traffic of at least 100 ft before crossing the road the average loss of time by waiting at the kerb or refuge would be nine seconds per pedestrian; the actual pedestrian delay is only three seconds. Moreover this threefold increase in delay would not necessarily make for greater safety because it is known that there are numbers of vehicles on the roads today, with poor brakes, travelling at speeds such that they cannot stop in 100 ft. There is therefore some indication that economy of time or effort plays an important part in determining pedestrian behaviour.

Further work[3] on this subject of pedestrian judgement has been carried out under controlled conditions on a test track. Here it was possible to give a group of selected pedestrians the task of choosing the shortest safe time interval in which to cross the road before the arrival of a vehicle travelling at a known speed. This work confirmed the previous results but also showed that if the approaching vehicle was travelling at a high speed the time interval allowed by the pedestrian was overestimated (or the speed was underestimated). Special consideration must therefore be given to the difficulties of pedestrians crossing a road which carries high-speed traffic. It has also been shown that pedestrians underestimate the speed of vehicles on the far side of the road and the speed of small vehicles such as motor-cycles. These investigations are considered in greater detail in the Companion Volume.[11]

Types of crossing place

Protection can be provided for pedestrians crossing the road in three ways:

(*a*) Uncontrolled crossings (zebra crossings) where co-operation is necessary between drivers and pedestrians at certain recognized crossing places.

(*b*) Controlled crossings (police or traffic signals).

(*c*) Bridges and subways providing complete segregation, preventing the access of pedestrians to the carriageway.

More details of accidents to pedestrians at crossing places and elsewhere are given in the Companion Volume.[11]

CO-OPERATION AT ZEBRA CROSSINGS

Pedestrian crossings were introduced to help pedestrians cross busy roads. The original form of uncontrolled crossing, marked by two lines of metal studs on the carriageway and Belisha beacons on the kerb (see Plate 12.1), was found to be slightly safer than crossing elsewhere on the roads. However signal-controlled or police-controlled crossings were found to be safer especially where there were refuges.

A study, made in 1961, of seven roads in West London gives the following results:

Place		Relative risk
At, or within 20 yd of a junction	On signal-controlled crossing	0·20
	On zebra crossing	0·65
	Elsewhere (more than 50 yd from crossing) .	1·25
More than 20 yd from a junction	On zebra crossing	0·22
	Elsewhere (more than 50 yd from crossing) .	1·00*

*Arbitrarily taken as unity.

It can be seen from the above table that the risk of an accident to a pedestrian crossing the road is higher in the vicinity of road junctions than away from them. A pedestrian using a crossing is still much safer than one crossing the road well away from crossings, and safer on a signal-controlled crossing than on a zebra crossing. The risk to a pedestrian crossing the road near (within 50 yd of) crossings, although not given in the above table, appeared from the survey to be higher than anywhere else, probably because crossings tend to be placed on the more dangerous parts of the road. This finding is in need of further investigation, however.

Studies have been made of both pedestrians and drivers at these crossings, in particular to discover the effect on behaviour of the introduction of the zebra marking of the crossings generally introduced in October 1951. Pedestrian behaviour has been measured by the "Behaviour Index" i.e.:

$$100 \times \frac{\text{The number of pedestrians using the crossing}}{\text{The number of pedestrians crossing the road on and within 20 yards of the crossing}}$$

Driver behaviour has been measured by the "Stopping Index" which is the percentage of vehicles giving way to pedestrians. The effect of the striped marking is illustrated by the results from six crossings in London:

	Behaviour index	
	Before striping	After striping
Men	45·0	53·1
Women	63·4	68·6
	Stopping index	
Vehicles	2·6	4·0

The Stopping Index is dependent on pedestrian flow and increases with it; as a measure of driver behaviour it is only comparable for similar levels of pedestrian flow.

A long-term study of one crossing (see Plate 12.2) in North London has shown definite changes in the behaviour of pedestrians and drivers over the years. The level of pedestrian behaviour has improved from some 45 per cent of pedestrians using the crossing in 1948 to over 70 per cent using it in 1959 (see Fig. 12.4), largely owing to the greater difficulty in crossing elsewhere because of the greater traffic but also because of successive improvements in marking the crossing and in control of its use by regulations.

A recent study[12] at the sites of 21 zebra crossings in the London area has shown, by comparing the pedestrian flow with pedestrian accidents, that the risk of an accident on the crossing is only half that of an accident within 50 yards of a crossing.

Some pedestrians who would otherwise cross the road up to 100 yards away from the site of a new crossing will change their crossing place and use the crossing when it is constructed. The percentage moving to the crossing increases nearer the crossing and exceeds 50 per cent for distance of 60 yards or less, (see Fig. 12.5).

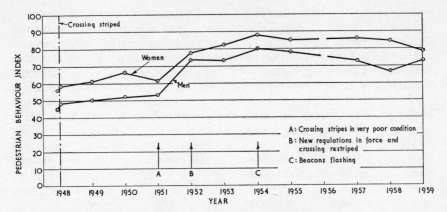

Fig. 12.4. Pedestrian behaviour indices at Crouch End, Broadway, 1948–59
(For constant level of vehicle flow)

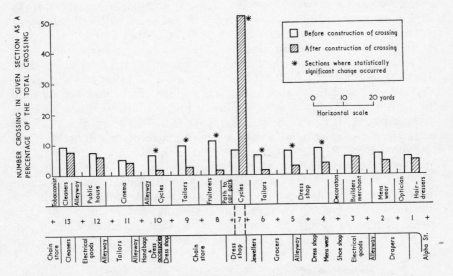

Fig. 12.5. Diagram of part of Slough High Street showing shops, sections of road compared and the percentage of total pedestrian cross-flow on each section

TRAFFIC CONTROL (SIGNAL-CONTROLLED CROSSINGS)

There are conditions in which positive control of traffic at crossings has advantages over the zebra crossing conditions. For example, where there are heavy vehicle and pedestrian flows it is possible for either group to establish a right of way over the crossing which the opposing group finds difficult to change, thus causing considerable delay and congestion. Over the range of vehicle and pedestrian flows normally found, the delay to vehicles increases linearly with increasing pedestrian flow at the rate of 0.5 seconds per vehicle for each 100 pedestrians per hour on the crossing.[13]

This uncontrolled delay can be avoided by signal-controlled crossings. In a comparison of signal-controlled and zebra crossings under similar conditions in Croydon, Ealing and Glasgow it has been found that with pedestrian flows greater than about 800–1000 p.p.h. less delay is caused to vehicles at the signal-controlled crossings. Delay to pedestrians is increased but in the "Cross Now" periods they can cross in greater safety.

The effect of the installation of the signal-controlled pedestrian crossings in the High Street shopping area of Slough (see Plate 12.3) in February 1956 has been investigated. The proportion of pedestrians crossing this section of road on pedestrian crossings has risen from 32 per cent on the four zebra crossings, to 51 per cent on the six signal-controlled crossings. Taking into account those pedestrians crossing at or near the traffic signals at either end of the High Street as well, this means that 86 per cent of all pedestrians crossing this section of road did so at positions where there was positive signal control of vehicular traffic.

BRIDGES AND SUBWAYS (SEE PLATES 12.4, 12.5, 12.6)

The one safe way to cross the road is by a pedestrian subway or a bridge. But these are expensive items: a cheap bridge, for example, may cost £3000 and a subway as much as £30,000. It is important, therefore to find under what conditions pedestrians will make use of these facilities.

Observations have been carried out at different sites where the situation is usually as follows: Pedestrians cross the road between two points A and B; they will be delayed by the traffic by an amount which can be measured. If a subway or bridge is built at C what proportion of pedestrians will use it? Assume that pedestrians choose the path requiring least time. Let the ratio of the time required to use the subway or bridge to the total time to cross the road be R. It is reasonable to suppose that if R is very large—if, for example, the subway is half a mile away—no pedestrians will use it; if, on the other hand R is less than unity, that is the subway or bridge is the quicker route, then nearly all pedestrians will use it. What is required, however, is the percentage of pedestrians who use the safe path for conditions intermediate between these two extremes. A tentative result was obtained by comparing values found at subways and bridges of different construction and at very different sites. It was seen that roughly 80 per cent of people will use the safe path if it takes the same time as the path across

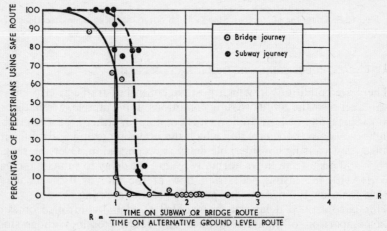

Fig. 12.6. The use of subways and bridges

the road. It would appear that to ensure that most pedestrians will use a subway or bridge when provided, some device to increase the inconvenience of the path of pedestrians at road level will have to be arranged. If by the use of pedestrian guard rails, for instance, the path across the road takes one third as long again as the safe alternative then all pedestrians may be expected to use the safe path. The results are illustrated in Fig. 12.6, see also Chapter 3 of the Companion Volume.[11]

Criteria for the establishment of pedestrian crossing places

Methods used in justifying the protection afforded by special crossing places are based on the frequency of the occurrence of adequate gaps in traffic for the use of pedestrians. They also assume in most cases, except Reference 14, that vehicles and pedestrians arrive at random intervals in time. No theoretical allowance is made for any saving in accidents in the methods referred to, although in practice some such allowance has to be made.

The most extensive analysis of the problem appears to have been made by Underwood.[15] He assumes that the maximum permissible delay to pedestrians should be that level at which the rate of increase in delay (with increasing vehicle flow) begins to accelerate. He derives minimum vehicle flow figures from this assumption. To define the minimum pedestrian flow necessary he makes the assumption that, on the average, no more than one pedestrian should be waiting to cross at any one time.

Using these facts he derives expressions from which the curves in Fig. 12.7 have been drawn. These indicate for various levels of vehicle and pedestrian flow, whether an uncontrolled crossing is needed or not.

In addition Underwood derives conditions for the establishment of traffic signal control, as shown on Fig. 12.7, by assuming that this was necessary if the proportion of time available to vehicles was less than 60 per cent of the total time. Further reference to traffic signal control, this time in the U.S.A., is given in Reference 16 where minimum flows of 250 pedestrians per hour and over 600 vehicles per hour are quoted as necessary for such an installation.

Other studies concentrate mainly on assessments of pedestrian delay; References 17 and 18 assume that the maximum delay between safe traffic gaps should not be more than a minute, while Reference 14 assumes that the proportion of time for which traffic gaps are less than the safe value should not be more than a certain criterion value.

The disadvantage of these analyses of the crossing problem is that they all depend on some necessarily arbitrary assumption concerning the level of pedestrian delay that can be permitted. This is a reflection of the fact that little information is available on the value of pedestrian time or the extent to which pedestrians are prepared to suffer delays.

Using the expression for pedestrian delay quoted by Tanner[19] and a relation of vehicle delay to pedestrian flow on uncontrolled crossings quoted by Smeed,[13] it is possible to consider the saving in man hours due to the introduction of an uncontrolled crossing (of a type similar to the present "zebra" crossing) for various levels of the relative importance of pedestrian and vehicle time. Assuming, as is shown by empirical data, that pedestrians are prepared to cross in a gap between vehicles which is 1·5 seconds shorter

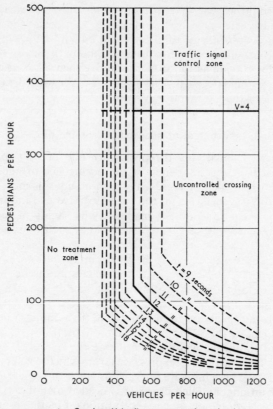

t = Gap in vehicle flow necessary for pedestrians
to cross road safely — seconds
v = Walking speed of pedestrians — ft./sec.

**Fig. 12.7. Criteria for the establishment of
pedestrian crossings**

at a crossing than elsewhere then the algebraic expression indicating the
loss or gain in man hours from installing a crossing is:

$$\frac{0 \cdot 75P}{3600} \left\{ \frac{e^{nI}(1 - e^{-1 \cdot 5n}) - 1 \cdot 5n - 18kn^2}{n} \right\}$$

where P = ped/h over 100 yards of road including crossing site,
n = veh/s past the crossing site,
I = gap in which pedestrian will cross when not at crossing,
k = relative importance of vehicle to pedestrian times.

The above expression is a minimum when the bracketed part is minimized,
since $P \neq 0$, and the levels of vehicle flow which would give a just positive
saving following the introduction of a crossing are shown in Table 12.4 for
various values of k and I.

These data are also shown graphically in Fig. 12.8.

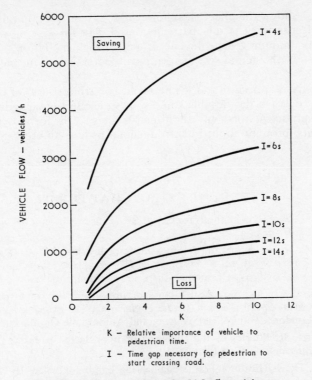

Fig. 12.8. Minimum values of vehicle flow giving an economic saving after the installation of an uncontrolled pedestrian crossing—for various levels of K and I

TABLE 12.4

The minimum value of vehicle flow per hour giving an economic saving* after the installation of an uncontrolled crossing

I (sec)	4	6	8	10	12	14
k:						
1	2412	1008	468	216	72	36
2	3420	1728	1044	684	468	324
3	3996	2124	1332	900	684	504
4	4320	2376	1512	1080	792	612
5	4680	2592	1656	1188	900	684
6	4932	2736	1800	1296	972	756
7	5112	2844	1908	1368	1044	828
8	5256	2988	1980	1440	1116	864
9	5436	3096	2052	1512	1152	936
10	5580	3168	2160	1548	1224	972

* Cost of accident savings is ignored.

Table 12.4 shows the effect the choice of k has on the minimum vehicle flow level criterion. At any particular level, say for $k = 4$, and $I = 10$, where the minimum vehicle flow necessary for the installation of a crossing is 1080 veh/h, the actual size of saving will increase with increasing pedestrian flow.

This analysis concentrates the uncertainty or arbitrariness of the value of pedestrian delay in the variable k and shows the effect of changing its level. The computation ignores any additional savings, in the form of a reduction in accidents, brought about by introducing a pedestrian crossing.

REFERENCES TO CHAPTER 12

1. YATES, F. Sampling methods for censuses and surveys. London, 1960 (Charles Griffin & Co.), p. 43.

2. WEBSTER, F. V. A method for measuring pedestrian delays. *Department of Scientific and Industrial Research, Road Research Laboratory, Research Note* No. RN/2348/FVW. Harmondsworth, 1954 (Unpublished).

3. MOORE, R. L. Psychological factors of importance in traffic engineering. *International Study Week in Traffic Engineering, 1–6 October, 1956, Stresa, Italy*. London, 1956 (World Touring and Automobile Organisation).

4. PRESCHEL, R. Studies of the efficiency of unprotected pedestrian crossings. *Strassentechnik*, 1957, **5** (6), 63–7.

5. EVANS, H. K. (Editor.) Traffic engineering handbook. New Haven, Conn., 1950 (Institute of Traffic Engineers).

6. REIMER, K. Movement on fixed stairways. *Glasers Ann.*, 1954, **78** (2), 50–1.

7. HANKIN, B. D., and R. A. WRIGHT, Passenger flow in subways. *Operat. Res. Quart.*, 1958, **9** (2), 81–8.

8. JENKINS, A. H. Letter to "Engineering". *Engineering*, 1958, **186** (4829), 396.

9. MINISTRY OF LOCAL GOVERNMENT AND PLANNING. Schedule of suggested minimum street widths for carriageways and footways of new streets. London, 1951 (H.M. Stationery Office).

10. MINISTRY OF WAR TRANSPORT. Design and layout of roads in built-up areas. London, 1946 (H.M. Stationery Office).

11. DEPARTMENT OF SCIENTIFIC AND INDUSTRIAL RESEARCH, ROAD RESEARCH LABORATORY. Research on road safety. London, 1963 (H.M. Stationery Office).

12. MACKIE, A. M. Accident risk to pedestrians on and within 50 yards of zebra crossings. *Traff. Engng & Control*, 1962, **4** (8), 448–50.

13. SMEED, R. J. Theoretical studies and operational research on traffic and traffic congestion. *Bull. Inst. int. Statist.*, 1958, **36** (4), 347–75.

14. DIER, R. D. A study of a school crossing hazard. *Traff. Quart.*, 1952, **6**, 102–15.

15. UNDERWOOD, R. T. Tentative warrants for the installation of pedestrian crossings. *Victoria Country Roads Board, Research Memorandum* No. 13. Victoria, 1957 (Victoria Country Roads Board).

16. AMERICAN ASSOCIATION OF STATE HIGHWAY OFFICIALS, INSTITUTE OF TRAFFIC ENGINEERS and NATIONAL CONFERENCE ON STREET AND HIGHWAY SAFETY. Manual on uniform traffic control devices for streets and highways. Washington, D.C., 1948 (U.S. Public Roads Administration).

17. JOINT COMMITTEE OF THE INTERNATIONAL ASSOCIATION OF CHIEFS OF POLICE AND INSTITUTE OF TRAFFIC ENGINEERS. Proceedings, 1947. Report on warrants for traffic officers at school intersections. *Proc. 16th Annual Meeting held at Philadelphia, Pa., Sept.* 17–18, 1945. New Haven, Conn., 1946 (Institute of Traffic Engineers), pp. 118–30.

18. LAWTON, L. Traffic controls in the vicinity of school zones. *Traff. Engng,* 1954, **24** (6), 201–3, 206; (7), 239–41, 244.

19. TANNER, J. C. Delay to pedestrians crossing a road. *Biometrika,* 1951, **38** (3/4), 383–92.

Chapter 13

Layout of Rural Roads

SYNOPSIS

Width of carriageway and numbers of lanes. Other cross-sectional features: verges and kerbs; safety fences; provision for stationary vehicles; central reserves; cycle tracks. Horizontal and vertical profile: design speed; effect of road curvature on accidents, on speeds; gradients; sight distance; surface irregularity. Junctions: extent of the accident problem; manoeuvres and types of accident; accidents and traffic flow; accidents and junction layout; driver behaviour; delays; principles of design.

INTRODUCTION

Nearly three-quarters of the road mileage in Great Britain has no speed limit and lies mostly in rural areas (see Table 13.1). Roads in this category carry nearly one-half of the total vehicle-mileage travelled in the country (see Table 13.1) and account for about one quarter of all road casualties and two-fifths of all fatalities.[1] Rural roads thus figure prominently in the road system and it is important that they should be operated at a high level of efficiency and safety.

This chapter is primarily concerned with presenting the results of research into the effect of rural road layout on accident rates and traffic operations. Although this type of information is of considerable value to those responsible for designing roads and for devising design standards, it falls short of being a comprehensive guide to road design. This is partly due to the limitations of the research work that has been done but an additional factor is that the relation between accidents and certain aspects of road layout appears to be rather complex. Much of the information at present available is inconclusive, and results from different sources often conflict. Further research should help to clarify the problem and fill in the gaps in existing knowledge.

The aspects of road layout considered below fall into three broad categories: cross-section (carriageways, verges, cycle tracks, etc.), alignment (curvature, sight distance, gradients, etc.), and junctions.

WIDTH OF CARRIAGEWAY AND NUMBER OF LANES

Information on the roads and traffic in Great Britain has been provided by a sample survey undertaken between 1957 and 1960 at over 1000 points on the road system,[2] (see Chapter 2). Some of the results are given in Table 13.1 while some additional figures for rural administrative districts are given in Tables 13.2 and 13.3. Table 13.2 shows that trunk roads constituted only 6 per cent of the total mileage of road in rural areas but carried about 30 per cent of the total vehicle mileage. Information on widths and lane markings on rural roads is given in Table 13.3. The estimates in Table 13.3 are subject to considerable sampling error and care must be exercised in interpreting the more detailed results. For example, it is possible that the mileage of dual-carriageway roads was rather greater than that estimated;

TABLE 13.1

Estimated mileage of road and vehicle-mileage in Great Britain, 1960*

(a) Miles of road

	Urban	Rural	Total
With speed limit .	41 855	8020	49 875
Without speed limit .	14 422	98 272	112 694
TOTAL . .	56 277	106 292	162 569

(b) Motor vehicle-miles per day (millions)

	Urban	Rural	Total
With speed limit .	81·73	14·53	96·26
Without speed limit .	19·52	72·52	92·04
TOTAL . .	101·25	87·05	188·30

* About 27 000 miles of very unimportant roads were not covered by the survey.

TABLE 13.2

Estimated mileage and vehicle-mileage on different classes of road in rural areas of Great Britain (1960)

Class of road	Mileage of road	Motor vehicle-miles per day (millions)
Trunk . .	6564	26·0
Class I . .	12 701	28·0
Class II .	13 259	11·5
Class III and unclassified .	73 768	21·5
TOTAL . .	106 292	87·0

TABLE 13.3

Estimated mileage of road in rural districts in Great Britain by type of lane markings and width of carriageway (1957–59)[3]*

(*a*) Trunk and class I roads

Width (ft)	No lane markings	Two lanes		Three lanes	Four lanes	Total
		Continuous line	Broken line			
8–10	153	—	—	—	—	153
10–12	562	—	—	—	—	562
12–14	37	—	—	—	—	37
14–16	290	—	53	—	—	343
16–18	843	—	271	—	—	1114
18–20	1069	361	1902	—	—	3332
20–22	1305	1043	2826	—	—	5174
22–24	1114	679	1944	—	—	3737
24–26	308	629	988	—	—	1925
26–28	151	157	280	—	—	588
28–30	114	131	—	—	—	245
30–32	174	385	379	455	—	1393
32–34	94	132	37	93	—	356
34–36	—	59	—	—	—	59
36–38	—	—	—	—	—	—
38–40	—	—	—	—	—	—
40–50	—	35	116	—	36	187
TOTAL .	6214	3611	8796	548	36	19 205*

* A further 60 miles of road was estimated to have dual carriageways.

(*b*) Class II, class III and unclassified roads

Width (ft)	No lane markings	Two lanes		Total
		Continuous line	Broken line	
8–10	8115	—	—	8115
10–12	15 204	—	—	15 204
12–14	9370	—	—	9370
14–16	14 382	269	136	14 787
16–18	16 372	679	270	17 321
18–20	10 802	882	1782	13 466
20–22	4001	273	617	4891
22–24	1742	—	413	2155
24–26	1113	—	—	1113
26–28	146	136	—	282
28–30	323	—	—	323
30–32	—	—	—	—
32–34	—	—	—	—
34–36	—	—	—	—
36–38	—	—	—	—
38–40	—	—	—	—
40–50	—	—	—	—
TOTAL .	81 570	2239	3218	87 027

in any event, in view of the intensive programme of road building and improvement in recent years, the mileage of dual carriageways has undoubtedly shown a marked increase since 1957–59, when the observations on which Table 13.3 is based were taken. However, there is no reason to doubt the broad implications from these data, e.g. that about 85 per cent of the total mileage of trunk and class I roads had carriageways less than 26 ft wide and thus were incapable of carrying more than two lanes of traffic; nearly 30 per cent had carriageways less than 20 ft wide. The carriageways on class II, class III and unclassified roads were even narrower, the vast majority being less than 26 ft wide. Table 13.3 also shows that a surprisingly high proportion of roads was not marked into lanes.

Table 13.4 gives general information on the numbers of accidents involving serious injury (including fatal) on different types of road in Great Britain not subject to a speed limit. This shows that about one-half of the accidents occurred on roads with two-lane markings and nearly 40 per cent on roads without lane markings. The proportion of accidents at junctions showed considerable variation from one type of road to another, the overall average being about one-third.

TABLE 13.4

Fatal and serious injury accidents in Great Britain, 1961, on roads without speed limits (excluding motorways)

	Single carriageways				Dual carriage-ways	Total
	No lane markings	Two lanes	Three lanes	Four lanes		
Number of accidents:						
at junctions . .	2785	4061	239	86	579	7750
not at junctions .	6525	8521	678	122	669	16 515
TOTAL . .	9310	12 582	917	208	1248	24 265
Number of junction accidents as percentage of total number of accidents.	30	32	26	41	46	32
Of non-junction accidents						
Percentage fatal .	7	11	14	22	15	10
Percentage involving two vehicles travelling in opposite directions (but not including accidents involving more than two vehicles)	27	23	21	16	4	24

The Ministry of Transport recommend the following carriageway widths on trunk and important classified roads for specified ranges of design traffic flows:[3]

2–lane	24 ft
3–lane	33 ft
dual 2–lane	2 × 24 ft
dual 3–lane	2 × 36 ft

Table 13.3 shows that the majority of roads at the time of the survey did not fall into these categories of width, presumably because they were made to conform to earlier standards or because they were built before the principle of standardization was accepted; a further point is that no standards are laid down about carriageway widths on roads other than trunk roads and important classified roads. Despite the heterogeneity of carriageway widths in Table 13.3, it is of interest to note that the distribution of carriageway widths on trunk and class I roads is distinctly bimodal; one mode occurs in the range 20–22 ft and the other in the range 30–32 ft.

The 1000 point survey of the road system referred to above gave information about traffic flows on roads of different width, and provided the means of estimating the degree to which roads are overloaded on the basis of the Ministry of Transport's recommended traffic capacities (supplemented by certain assumptions for road widths not covered by the official recommendations). The main features of these calculations, which are described in detail in Road Research Technical Paper No. 62,[2] are shown in Table 13.5.

TABLE 13.5

Overloading of roads in rural areas (1960)

Class of road	Total mileage	Mileage of overloaded road	Percentage of mileage which was overloaded
Trunk . .	6564	2700	41
Class I . .	12 701	1800	14
Class II .	13 259	400	3
Other . .	73 768	300	0·4
TOTAL .	106 292	5200	5

Table 13.5 indicates that about 40 per cent of trunk roads were overloaded in 1960, the degree of overloading being much less on roads of lower classification. This result justifies the policy adopted in recent years of concentrating expenditure on the more important routes by widening existing roads and building motorways.

An important aspect of research into traffic on rural roads has been concerned with the establishment of speed/flow relations on roads of different widths. This matter is dealt with in Chapter 3, while the traffic capacity of rural roads is considered in Chapter 6. The following five sections of this chapter are therefore largely devoted to accident studies on roads with different numbers of lanes. Many of these studies depend upon comparisons of accident rates on the basis of vehicle-miles, and this concept is explained in Chapter 2 of the Companion Volume.[4]

Two-lane roads

The predominance of two-lane roads in the road system was commented on above and is demonstrated by the figures in Table 13.3 (see Plate 13.1). A study of accident rates on 140 miles of two-lane carriageways on trunk, class I and class II roads in Buckinghamshire produced a relationship between accident rate and width of carriageway given in Table 13.6.

TABLE 13.6

Accident rates on two-lane roads in Buckinghamshire 1946–50

Width of carriageway (ft)	Non-junction injury-accidents per million vehicle-miles (Numbers of accidents shown in brackets)		Average traffic flow (vehicles per day)
16–17	2·3	(21)	460
18–19	2·0	(72)	850
20–21	1·9	(285)	1740
22–24	1·7	(138)	2630
All widths	1·8	(516)	1540

The accident rate decreased as width increased even though the wider roads carried more traffic. It is probable that the effect shown in Table 13.6 is not only one of width since the layout of the narrower roads had a higher frequency of curves and was generally poorer than that of the wider roads. However, it would be expected that a reduction in accidents would follow widening operations, which would normally involve incidental improvements in other layout features. This result would appear to support the policy of using 24-ft wide carriageways on two-lane roads. Similar results have been obtained in other countries including the U.S.A.[5]

Three-lane roads

Table 13.3 shows that about 550 miles of trunk and class I road in rural administrative areas were estimated to have 3-lane markings (see Plate 13.1) and that a further 1200 miles had carriageway widths in the range of 30-34 ft and thus were capable of carrying three lanes, although most of them were marked into two lanes. In Chapter 6 it is shown that on traffic grounds the use of three-lane roads appears to be economically justified at certain levels of traffic flow, and they are officially recommended by the Ministry of Transport.[3] However, three-lane roads are widely criticized on safety grounds and a considerable amount of effort has been expended in examining accident rates on them and comparing them with other types of road. This work has failed to prove a clear-cut case for or against 3-lane roads, and to do so more work would need to be done on the subject. Nevertheless, it is of interest to set down the main features of the available evidence.

A study of accidents on selected classified roads in Lancashire in 1946–47 found that the overall injury-accident rate per million vehicle-miles on 30-ft wide carriageways in rural areas was very similar to those on 22-ft wide roads and on 40-ft wide roads; it was concluded that the 30-ft carriageway did not show any inherent defects in comparison with wider or narrower roads.[6] However, the study also showed that accident rates on roads of a given width appeared to be a function of the traffic flow, and the above conclusion might not apply at any particular level of traffic flow.

In a study of classified roads in Buckinghamshire in 1946–50 it was estimated that there were 2·1 non-junction injury accidents per million vehicle-miles on 3-lane roads (about 30 ft wide) compared with 1·8 on 2-lane roads (16-24 ft wide). A further comparison for 1951 gave similar figures and also showed that the number of non-junction accidents involving serious injury or fatality per million vehicle-miles, was 1·2 on 3-lane roads and 0·9 on 2-lane roads. Thus the differences in accident rates were quite small, even though the 3-lane roads carried over four times as much traffic. The value of this study was limited because the data were not adequate to produce relations between accident rate and flow. Therefore it was not possible to conclude how the two types of road would compare at any specified level of traffic flow.

It is sometimes suggested that three-lane roads are satisfactory at moderate traffic flows but that they become dangerous when the traffic flow exceeds some critical value. This idea receives support from an investigation of 16 000 accidents, mostly in 1941, on 5000 miles of rural highway in 15 states of the U.S.A.[5] In this study there was enough information to permit accident rates on different categories of road to be compared for different levels of traffic flow, and the results are given in Table 13.7. There was a general tendency, with some exceptions, for accident rates (numbers of reported accidents per million vehicle-miles) on different types of road to increase with increasing traffic flows, and the tendency was particularly marked on 3-lane roads. At traffic flows of less than 10 000 vehicles per day accident rates on 3-lane roads compared favourably with those on 2-lane and 4-lane roads, but for flows exceeding 10 000 vehicles per day the accident rate on 3-lane roads rose to a value well in excess of that on other categories of road. Although this result seems plausible, it is important to note that considerable difficulty was caused in this study by the variability from one state to another in the standard of reporting accidents; this raises doubts about the validity of the result. Further comments on this result are given later.

A study in the Netherlands in 1952 also produced relations between accident rate and traffic flow on roads of different types, and the results are given in Table 13.8.[7] These display a general tendency for accident rates at a given level of traffic flow to decrease with increasing width of carriageway and, like the American results in Table 13.7, they also display a general tendency for accident rates on particular types of road to increase with increasing traffic flow. On three-lane roads the increase in accident rate at flows exceeding 10 000 vehicles per day was much less marked than in the

TABLE 13.7

*Reported accidents per million vehicle-miles on straight roads
in 15 states of the U.S.A., by traffic flow and type of road*[5]

(Numbers of accidents on which the rates are based are shown in brackets)

Average daily traffic flow (vehicles per day)	Two-lane roads	Three-lane roads	Four-lane roads		
			Undivided	Divided	Controlled access
Up to 4900 . .	2·1 (5007)	1·6 (79)	1·6 (129)	1·6 (25)	2·0 (265)
5000–9900 . .	3·6 (1396)	2·9 (102)	2·2 (481)	2·4 (388)	2·1 (3)
10 000–14 900 .	3·3 (71)	8·1 (46)	3·5 (422)	3·4 (465)	1·4 (166)
15 000 or more .	—	—	3·6 (317)	4·4 (126)	1·5 (340)
All values . .	2·3 (6474)	2·5 (227)	2·7 (1349)	2·9 (1004)	1·7 (774)

American data, but the two studies are in broad agreement in suggesting that considerable savings in accidents might be achieved by replacing three-lane roads carrying traffic flows of between 10 000 and 15 000 vehicles per day by four-lane undivided roads or dual carriageways. However, this indication can hardly be regarded as conclusive for the following reasons.

TABLE 13.8

*Non-junction accidents per million vehicle-miles on roads
in the Netherlands 1952, by traffic flow and type of road**

(Numbers of accidents on which the rates are based are shown in brackets)

Average daily traffic flow (vehicles per day)	Two-lane roads (15–23 ft)	Three-lane roads (23–31 ft)	Four-lane roads (Over 31 ft)	Dual carriageways (Each carriageway was 20–24 ft wide)
Up to 5000 . .	3·0 (1729)	2·7 (55)	3·1 (29)	0·5 (19)
5000–10 000 . .	3·4 (310)	2·8 (82)	2·1 (70)	1·0 (161)
10 000–15 000 .	—	3·5 (30)	2·1 (117)	1·4 (43)
Over 15 000 .	—	—	4·8 (105)	—
All values . .	3·0 (2039)	2·9 (167)	2·8 (321)	1·1 (223)
Miles of road .	765	30	35	82
Overall average traffic flow . .	2400	5300	9300	6700

* Based upon data published by Van Gils[7]

The accident rates on three-lane roads for flows in the critical range 10 000 to 15 000 vehicles per day in both tables are based upon rather small accident frequencies and are thus subject to considerable sampling error. Moreover, the value of both sets of results is limited because they were not sub-divided according to severity and the results for serious-injury accidents only might well follow a different pattern. Mention has already been made of the variability in reporting in the American study which raises doubts about the validity of the results. A disquieting feature of the Dutch results is that the accident rate on four-lane undivided roads carrying over 15 000 vehicles per day is unusually high; this raises doubt about the wisdom of adding an extra lane to busy three-lane roads. Finally, results from abroad do not necessarily apply in Britain; as will be seen below, a British investigation failed to find a critical level of flow above which accident rates on three-lane roads rose sharply.

An investigation was carried out into accidents on 120 miles of 30-ft carriageways on trunk and class I roads in England during 1957 and 1958;[11] most of the roads had three-lane markings and none was subject to a speed limit. Although this study was more comprehensive than those described above in that accidents were sub-divided according to severity and vehicle movements, and relations between accident rate and traffic flow were derived for different kinds of accident, it suffered from the disadvantage that no corresponding studies were carried out at the same time on other types of road with which the results could be compared. The main features of the results of the study are given in Table 13.9 and Fig. 13.1. Of the 1520

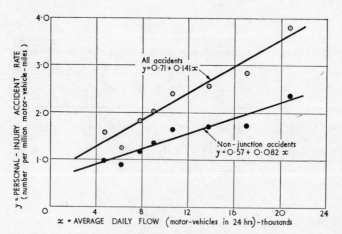

Fig. 13.1. Personal injury accidents rates and traffic flow.
30-ft carriageways, 1957–58

injury-accidents on the roads studied, 534 (i.e. 35 per cent) involved turning vehicles or vehicles crossing the main road at junctions. The remaining 986 non-junction accidents are classified in various ways in Table 13.9, which shows that the accidents were of a very heterogeneous nature. It is not uncommon to judge 3-lane roads on the basis of centre-lane head-on collisions, but Table 13.9 suggests that such events are less common than might be supposed. Collisions between vehicles travelling in opposite directions occurred in 24 per cent of all non-junction injury-accidents (32 per cent of non-junction serious injury accidents), while accidents in which one or more overtaking vehicles were reported to have been involved constituted 33 per cent of the total. Accidents in which vehicles were mentioned as overtaking in opposite directions were rare and constituted only 4 per cent of the total. Since it is possible that the accident reports may not always mention whether vehicles were overtaking, the reports were subjected to a further analysis in which it was assumed that vehicles may have been overtaking unless there was some obvious explanation for the accident (e.g. a vehicle skidded or lost control). This indicated that the true proportion of accidents involving vehicles overtaking in opposite directions might well have been higher than 4 per cent, but it seemed unlikely to be greater than 10 per cent. Another result from this study is given in Fig. 13.1 which shows that the number of injury-accidents per million vehicle-miles increased in a systematic manner with increasing traffic flow over the range 2500 to more than 20 000 vehicles per day.

TABLE 13.9

Movements and collisions in non-junction accidents on 30-ft carriageways, 1957–58

	Per cent of accidents	
	Serious injury accidents	All injury accidents
Movements of vehicles (Not necessarily in collision):		
Overtaking in both directions	4	4
Overtaking movements of any kind	31	33
Opposing traffic—vehicles travelling in opposite directions, with or without overtaking	36	28
No overtaking or opposing traffic	55	57
Collision between:		
Moving vehicles in opposite directions (with or without other kinds of collision)	32	24
Moving vehicle and parked vehicle (with or without other kinds of collision)	14	15
Moving vehicles in one direction only . . .	15	21
Moving vehicle and object or kerb (no collision between vehicles)	13	13
Moving vehicle and pedestrian (no collision between vehicles)	12	11
TOTAL NUMBER OF ACCIDENTS	431	986

Notes:
1. The classification is based on reported information—see text.
2. The percentages given add up to more than 100 per cent because many accidents involved more than one of the features listed.
3. Fatal accidents are included with serious injury-accidents.
4. "Overtaking" includes "passing parked vehicle", or the attempt to do either.

Although it seemed possible that the relations in Fig. 13.1 may have been partly influenced by the suburban nature of the busier roads, similar relations were found when the analysis was confined to accidents not particularly associated with roadside development. Figure 13.1 refers to accidents of all severities, and further work showed that most of the increase in accident rate with increasing flow was attributable to accidents involving slight injury only; the relation for serious-injury accidents was not very marked, while the relation for fatal accidents was not statistically significant.

Although no studies were carried out on other types of road at the same time as the study on 30-ft carriageways in 1957–58, it is of interest to compare the results with those obtained in a study carried out along similar lines on dual-carriageways road in England in 1952–53 (see Companion Volume Chapter 2[4] and Reference 8). To ensure comparability, the comparison was confined to roads which were distinctly rural in character. Neither the 30-ft carriageways nor the dual carriageways falling in the latter category exhibited a statistically significant relation between accident rate and traffic flow, so that it was sufficient to compare overall accident rates (for all levels of traffic flows combined) on the two types of road. The result, which is given in Table 13.10 shows that the fatality rate on 30-ft carriageways was double that on dual carriageways, while the serious-casualty rate was half as much again as on dual carriageways, but the slight-casualty rate and the total injury-accident rate were much the same on both kinds of road: the economic cost of accidents per vehicle-mile was estimated to be half as high again on three-lane roads as on dual carriageways. Table 13.10 demonstrates the importance in studies of this kind of obtaining details of

TABLE 13.10

Accident rates on rural sections of 30-ft carriageways and dual carriageways

(number per million vehicle-miles)

	30-ft single carriageways 1957–58 (Mostly 3-lane markings)	Dual carriageways 1952–53
Injury accidents . . .	1·60	1·60
Casualties: Fatal . . .	0·12	0·06
Serious . . .	0·83	0·59
Slight . . .	1·60	1·60

the numbers and severity of casualties in accidents, wherever possible; if Table 13.10 had been confined to a comparison of the number of injury accidents per million vehicle-miles, the interpretation would have been rather different. In view of the lapse of time between the two studies, there is some doubt about the validity of the comparison, but it would appear that a considerable saving in the more serious casualties would result from converting 30-ft carriageways into dual carriageways.

It is normal practice to replace the three-lane markings on 30 ft carriageways with two-lane markings at junctions and at places with restricted sight distance; on some roads this practice has been extended along the full length of 30-ft carriageways in an attempt to reduce accident frequency, but no evidence has been obtained about the effectiveness of this measure.

Further information about accidents on 3-lane roads is given in Table 13.4 which shows that there were over 900 serious-injury (including fatal) accidents on unrestricted roads with three-lane markings in Britain in 1961; the proportion of these accidents which were fatal was 14 per cent, which is little different from that on dual carriageways. The proportion of accidents on three-lane roads which involved two vehicles travelling in opposite directions was not unduly high, and it was in fact slightly lower than the value for all categories of road combined. These results would appear to contradict the theory that three-lane roads are particularly prone to head-on collisions because of the use of the central lane by vehicles travelling in opposite directions.

Despite the lack of precision in the above results and conflict between results from different sources, some useful conclusions can be drawn. Although some savings in casualties would be expected to result from replacing three-lane roads by dual carriageways, accident rates on three-lane roads show no general tendency to be unduly high and in some of the studies they compare most favourably with other types of road. Evidence from the U.S.A. of the existence of a critical level of traffic flow, above which accident rates on three-lane roads rise sharply, is not substantiated by evidence from Britain.

Four-lane roads

Although four-lane roads are not mentioned in the official recommendations on rural road layout, Table 13.3 shows that this type of road is to be found in rural areas. The estimate of 187 miles of road between 40 and 50 ft wide is, however, open to considerable sampling error. It is likely that most four-lane roads are to be found on the fringes of towns rather than in open country. Table 13.4 shows that in 1961 there were 208 accidents involving serious injury or fatality on unrestricted roads with four-lane markings. The proportion of such accidents which involved a fatality was greater than for any other category of road. Information on accident rates on 4-lane roads in relation to other types of road was produced by the Lancashire study[6] and the main features of the comparison are quoted in the Companion Volume (Chapter 2, p. 22[4]). Comparisons from other sources are quoted in Tables 13.7 and 13.8.

Dual-carriageway roads

The Companion Volume[4] compares accident rates on divided and undivided roads and gives the results of accident studies before and after the provision of short lengths of dual carriageways. All of this evidence indicates that dual carriageways are beneficial in reducing accidents (see Plate 13.2). Further results are given in Tables 13.7 and 13.8. The American data in Table 13.7 show that accident rates at corresponding flows were much the same on 4-lane divided as on 4-lane undivided roads but a similar analysis from the Netherlands (see Table 13.8) confirms the evidence, mentioned above, that accident rates on dual carriageways are appreciably lower than on two-way roads at comparable traffic flows.

Information presented in the Companion Volume indicates that an unusually high proportion of accidents on dual carriageways occurs at junctions or at breaks in the central reserve, and that accidents at junctions may in some circumstances increase following the provision of dual carriageways. This suggests that special care should be exercised in designing junctions on dual carriageway roads and that breaks in the central reserve should be kept to a minimum.

Table 13.4 shows that the proportion of accidents at junctions was greater for dual-carriageway roads than for any other category of road. This result adds emphasis to the preceding comments.

The main advantage of the central reserve is that it reduces the risk of head-on collision and Table 13.4 shows that, although the proportion of accidents involving vehicles travelling in opposite directions is much smaller on dual carriageways than two-way roads, some accidents of this type still occur, presumably largely due to vehicles out of control crossing the central strip. The incidence of such events would be expected to be reduced by providing wider central reserves but no direct evidence is available. In a study of dual-carriageway roads in rural areas of England in 1952–53 the injury-accident rate per million vehicle-miles was estimated at 1·8 on roads with central reserves 20 ft wide or wider, compared with 1·1 where the central reserve was less than 20 ft wide.[8] This curious result must presumably be attributable to other factors not taken into account in the analysis. It emphasizes the difficulty of isolating the effect on accident rates of particular features of highway design. Another method of preventing vehicles from crossing into the other carriageway is to erect safety fences on the central reserve, but there are doubts about the value of such devices. A study in California suggested that certain types of safety fence were likely to worsen the accident situation except on roads carrying high traffic volumes.[9] This was because collisions with the barrier itself usually resulted in severe damage to vehicles, in injury to the occupants and deflection of the vehicles back into the traffic stream. Therefore, unless the traffic was heavy and the chance of hitting an opposing vehicle was high, it appeared to be better to allow the vehicle to run on. Other studies have produced conflicting results (see Chapter 14).

Motorways

The essential features of motorways are dual-carriageways, controlled access, flyover junctions, and prohibition of parking, pedal cycles and pedestrians (see Plate 13.3). There can be little doubt that the capacity of such roads is greatly in excess of all-purpose roads and, despite the high speeds attained (see Chapter 3), there is ample evidence from this and other countries that accident rates on motorways are substantially lower than on ordinary roads (see Companion Volume, Chapter 2).[4] From an examination of accidents on main roads in the area affected by the opening of the 73-mile long London-Birmingham motorway in November 1959, it was estimated that during the first year of operation of the motorway, there was a net saving of nearly 11 000 casualties, including about 400 serious casualties and 30 fatalities. In subsequent years accident savings would be expected to be even greater, in view of increased transfer of traffic to the motorway; for example, traffic in the fourth year of operation was about half as much again as in

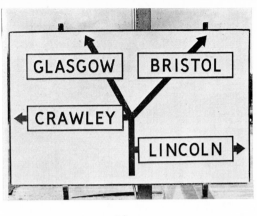

(a)

(b)

(c)

Examples of (a) British, (b) Continental, and (c) American advance direction signs for five-way junctions

PLATE 11.1

(a)   (b)

(c)

**Examples of experimental signs erected by the Ministry of Transport Traffic
Signs Committee 1962 and the signs they were intended to replace: (a) existing
advance direction sign, (b) experimental sign, (c) existing and experimental
warning sign**

PLATE 11.2

Tall direction sign (18 ft 6 in. × 14 ft) illuminated with three floodlights

PLATE 11.3

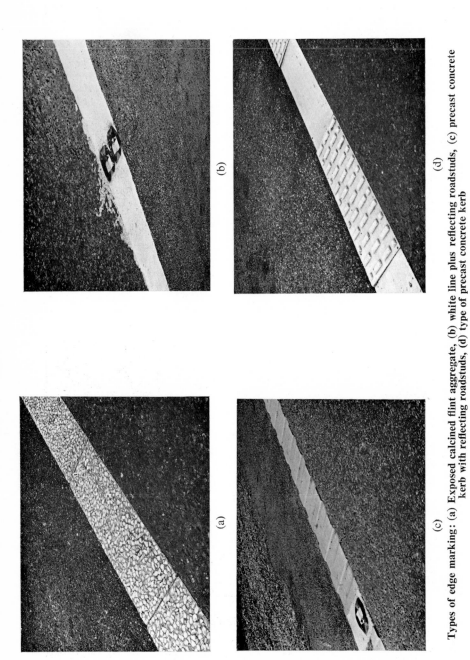

(b)

(d)

(a)

(c)

Types of edge marking: (a) Exposed calcined flint aggregate, (b) white line plus reflecting roadstuds, (c) precast concrete kerb with reflecting roadstuds, (d) type of precast concrete kerb

PLATE 11.4

Pedestrian crossing in Slough, Bucks, in 1948 showing original markings of beacons and lines of studs

PLATE 12.1

Zebra crossing in Hornsey, North London, in 1961, striped experimentally in 1948. Behaviour has been observed here over a number of years

PLATE 12.2

Pedestrian-operated traffic-signal controlled crossing in Slough, Bucks

PLATE 12.3

Pedestrian subway in Stevenage

PLATE 12.4

Pedestrian subway in Birmingham

PLATE 12.5

Pedestrian bridge at Dartford, Kent

PLATE 12.6

(a)

(b)

Examples of (a) two-lane and (b) three-lane roads in Great Britain

PLATE 13.1

(a)

(b)
Examples of dual-carriageway roads in Great Britain
PLATE 13.2

(a)

(b)

Examples of motorways in Great Britain: (a) dual two-lane, (b) dual three-lane

PLATE 13.3

Lorry parked on 8-ft wide shoulder

PLATE 13.4

Roundabout at southern terminal of M.1 near Aldenham, Herts

PLATE 13.5

Over 30 per cent of accidents on rural roads in Great Britain occur on bends

PLATE 13.6

Vehicles turning right out of the major road constitute a major problem at three-way junctions

PLATE 13.7

Modified "Bennett" junction

PLATE 13.8

(a)

(b)

Examples of staggered cross-roads: (a) right-left stagger, (b) left-right stagger

PLATE 13.9

The provision of roundabouts has been found to reduce accidents

PLATE 13.10

T-junction on dual carriageway with acceleration
lane, deceleration lane and turning bay

PLATE 13.11

(a)

(b)

Examples of diamond interchanges: (a) without roundabout, (b) with roundabout

PLATE 13.12

(a)

(b)

Partial cloverleaf interchanges

PLATE 13.13

(a)

(b)

Interchanges for three-way junctions: (a) trumpet layout, (b) roundabout layout

PLATE 13.14

Model of proposed four-level interchange at intersection of M.4 and M.5
(Ministry of Transport photograph)

PLATE 13.15

(a)

(b)

Controlled experiment on rural junction design on Research Track, Crowthorne

PLATE 13.16

View of corrugated metal guard rail

PLATE 14.1

View of Dahl concrete guard rail

PLATE 14.2

Impact with D.A.V. concrete guard rail at 46 mile/h and 20°

PLATE 14.3

Impact with blocked-out metal guard rail at 50 mile/h and 20°

PLATE 14.4

Mounting a Belgian-designed safety kerb after approach at 12 mile/h and 15°

PLATE 14.5

Daytime appearance of experimental anti-glare screen on M.1

PLATE 14.6

the first year. An additional factor is that accident rates in relation to the traffic tended to be lower in the subsequent years; injury-accident rates per million vehicle-miles in each of the first four years are estimated at 0·7, 0·5, 0·5 and 0·6 respectively and fatality rates at 0·07, 0·04, 0·05 and 0·06.

Although accident rates on motorways are lower than on other roads, it is desirable to find methods of reducing them even further by suitable alteration in design standards and other remedial measures. At the time of writing, experience with motorways in Great Britain was rather limited, but some lessons had already been learnt. For example, during the first two months of operation of the London-Birmingham motorway, 23 accidents (including damage only) were reported to have occurred at the five terminal roundabouts. Although the frequency of such accidents subsequently decreased (e.g. during the whole of 1961, the corresponding figure was 28), the experience has raised doubts about the wisdom of using surface roundabouts at the ends of high speed motorways, and has led to consideration of the possible use of grade separation in such circumstances. Another lesson learnt from this motorway relates to the design of the shoulders. The shoulders originally provided were soon recognized to be inadequate in width and strength to accommodate disabled lorries, and they were subsequently strengthened and the width increased from 8 to 10 ft (see Plate 13.4); standards for new motorways were amended accordingly. The London-Birmingham motorway was the first full-length motorway in Britain to be opened to traffic and it is of interest to examine the results of other studies on this road which have a bearing on design problems.

An analysis of accidents which occurred on the London-Birmingham motorway during its first year of operation, with particular reference to the final positions of vehicles, produced the following results:

(1) There were 511 accidents during the year, resulting in damage or injury; in 272 of these (53 per cent) a vehicle ran off the road on to the central reserve or beyond the hard shoulder; in a futher 46 cases (9 per cent) a vehicle ran on to the shoulder.

(2) There were 220 accidents involving one vehicle only in which the vehicle ran off the road, and in 88 of these it collided with a fixed object.

(3) The proportion of accidents in which injuries were sustained was smaller for vehicle/object collisions than for other accidents, but the proportion of these injuries that were fatal or serious was greater.

(4) Overturning occurred in one-third of the accidents away from terminals or interchanges and in half of the accidents in which a vehicle ran beyond the shoulder; three-quaters of the latter type were associated with cuttings or embankments.

(5) In 47 of the 383 non-interchange accidents a vehicle crossed the central reserve into the opposing carriageway, and in six of them collided with an oncoming vehicle.

These results are of interest in connexion with the possible siting of signs, safety fences or lighting columns either on the central reserve or beyond the edges of the hard shoulder. They also emphasize the need for avoiding harmful obstructions close to the carriageway in the form of bridge parapets and abutments, earth mounds and open drains.

Information on the way in which traffic distributes itself among the three traffic lanes on the London-Birmingham motorway is given in Table 13.11. The majority of commercial-vehicle drivers use the nearside lane but more

15

TABLE 13.11

Traffic flows in different traffic lanes on London-Birmingham motorway

(a) Vehicles per hour (August 1960)

Class of vehicle	Nearside lane	Centre lane	Offside lane	All lanes
Cars	94	144	25	263
Light commercial vehicles (up to 30 cwt unladen) . . .	22	12	1	35
Medium commercial vehicles (2-axled)	105	15	0	120
Heavy commercial vehicles (multi-axled)	50	4	0	54
ALL CLASSES	271	175	26	472

(b) Vehicles per hour (August 1962)

	Nearside lane	Centre lane	Offside lane	All lanes
Cars	81	189	59	329
Light commercial vehicles . .	27	26	1	54
Medium commercial vehicles . .	123	27	1	151
Heavy commercial vehicles . .	79	8	0	87
ALL CLASSES	310	250	61	621

(c) Percentage increase in flow from August 1960 to 1962

	Nearside lane	Centre lane	Offside lane	All lanes
Cars	−14	31	136	25
Light commercial vehicles . .	23	117	0	54
Medium commercial vehicles .	17	80	—	26
Heavy commercial vehicles . .	58	100	—	61
ALL CLASSES	14	43	135	32

than half the drivers of cars travel in the centre lane. Table 13.11 also shows that the proportion of vehicles using the centre and offside lanes has increased as the total traffic flow on the motorway has increased. It can be expected that the proportion of vehicles in the offside lane will continue to increase with the passage of time. This has a bearing on the comments made above on the problem of accidents caused by vehicles crossing the central reserve.

A traffic census at interchanges and terminals on the London-Birmingham motorway in April 1961 showed that about one-half of the vehicles using the motorway entered at the 10 interchanges and the other half at one of the four main terminals; the average length of journey on the London-Birmingham motorway was estimated to be 29 miles compared with the maximum possible trip length of 68 miles between Aldenham Terminal and Dunchurch Terminal (see Fig. 13.2).

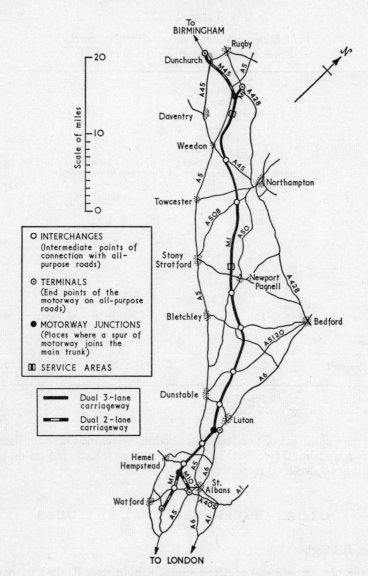

Fig. 13.2. London–Birmingham motorway

The information on traffic flows at access points has been used in conjunction with accident data to estimate the risk of accident to vehicles performing different movements at interchanges and at the four major terminals; Table 13.12, which summarizes the results for 1961, shows that the most dangerous movement at interchanges and terminals was that of leaving the motorway; in both cases the risk to a vehicle performing this movement of being involved in a personal-injury accident was about one in a million.

Table 13.12 also shows that the overall accident rate for all kinds of movement was appreciably lower at interchanges than at terminals. Since

TABLE 13.12

Vehicle accident rates at access points on the
London-Birmingham motorway in 1961

	Interchanges* (10 cases)			Terminals† (4 cases)		
	(1) Vehicles performing movement (millions)	(2) Vehicles involved in personal injury accidents	Rate (2)÷(1)	(1) Vehicles performing movement (millions)	(2) Vehicles involved in personal injury accidents	Rate (2)÷(1)
Leaving motorway	7·49	8	1·1	7·92	9	1·1
Entering motorway	7·49	3	0·4	7·92	1	0·1
Travelling through on motorway .	65·39	15	·2	—	—	—
Travelling through on all-purpose road	16·15	3	·2	9·10	5	0·5
Unknown . .	—	4	—	—	4	—
ALL MOVEMENTS .	96·51	33	0·3	24·93	19	0·8

* Including Pepperstock Junction.
† Excluding Kidney Wood Terminal.

the former consisted of two-level intersections while the latter consisted of surface roundabouts (see Plate 13.5), this result provides an indication of the advantage of two-level treatment.

OTHER CROSS-SECTIONAL FEATURES

Verges and kerbs

In the past, most rural roads in Great Britain were flanked by narrow irregular verges, often obstructed by banks, trees, telegraph poles and other hazards; where kerbs were used, they were almost invariably of the "vertical" type as found in built-up areas. Vertical kerbs are now officially recommended only where busy footways adjoin the carriageway and in a few other cases.[3] In recent years, increasing recognition has been given to the need to minimize damage to vehicles which are forced to leave the road in an emergency or as the result of an accident, and the use of splayed and flush kerbs has increased. In addition to reducing damage the use of splayed and flush kerbs encourages traffic to travel closer to the edge of the carriageway and hence to increase the capacity of the road. Measurements made in 1954–55 of the transverse position of traffic on two-lane roads have shown that, when opposing traffic was present, cars travelled on average $3\frac{1}{2}$ in.

closer to splayed kerbs than to vertical kerbs; when there was no opposing traffic the difference was rather smaller.

The value of wide, level unobstructed verges, preferably hardened, is recognised, not only to assist vehicles which are forced off the carriageway, but also to improve visibility on bends and at junctions, and to encourage traffic to use the full width of the carriageway. Information on conditions encountered in 1957–1959 at the edge of carriageways on the rural road system is given in Table 13.13.

TABLE 13.13

Percentage of road mileage in rural districts with various conditions at edge of carriageway[2]

Condition	Trunk and class I	Other
With kerbs:		
Paved . .	16	5
Flush grass .	6	1
Raised verge .	3	0
Without kerbs:		
Flush grass .	23	28
Raised verge .	33	33
Bank or wall .	19	33
TOTAL .	100	100

Although there is little doubt that the modern approach to the treatment of verges and kerbs makes a contribution to road safety, little direct evidence is available from this country. However, studies have been carried out on a large scale in the United States of America to measure the effect of shoulder width on speeds, lateral positions and accident rates. In a review of studies at over 50 sites on two-lane roads in 15 states, the following conclusions were reached:[10]

"The speed of moving vehicles is not substantially affected by the width of shoulder, providing the shoulder is more than 4 ft in width.

The lateral position of free moving vehicles and the clearances between meeting vehicles bears no significant relation to the shoulder width above 4 ft. Well-maintained grass shoulders have the same effect on the speed and lateral placement of moving vehicles as well-maintained gravel shoulders."

The effect of shoulder width on accident rates is shown in Tables 13.14 and 13.15.

TABLE 13.14

Accident rates on roads in California[11]

Accidents per million vehicle-miles				
Shoulder width (ft)				
0	2–3	4–5	6–7	8 and over
3·42	2·50	1·80	1·80	1·65

TABLE 13.15

Accident rates on two-lane roads in 15 states[5]

	Reported accidents per million vehicle-miles			
	Shoulder width (ft)			
	Less than 5	5–8	8–10	More than 10
Straight roads . .	2·6	2·0	2·4	2·8
Curves . . .	2·8	1·8	1·4	2·3

Table 13.14 shows a steady reduction in accident rate with increasing shoulder width but in Table 13.15 the accident rate increases for shoulder widths in excess of 10 ft. Support for the latter result is provided by the results of another investigation[12] which indicated that the optimum shoulder width was about 6 ft. The author of this latter report suggested that for roads with wider shoulders the higher accident rate might be due to drivers using the shoulder to overtake on the nearside.

Obstructions on the verge have also been found to affect traffic behaviour and accident rates. The effect on transverse position of cars due to the presence of an object on the verge is illustrated in Table 13.16.

TABLE 13.16

*Effect of objects on the shoulder on transverse position
of cars (22 ft wide carriageway)[13]*

Distance of object from edge of carriageway (ft)	Outward movement of mean position of cars (ft)			
	Type of object			
	Parked car	Parked truck	Barricade	Average all types
0	2·6	2·8	2·0	2·5
3	1·0	1·5	0·9	1·1
6	0·5	0·7	0·2	0·5

On this evidence, it is desirable that the edge of the carriageway on important rural roads should be kept clear of obstruction for several feet.

Obstacles such as lighting columns, which are usually mounted only 12 to 18 in. from the edge of the carriageway, are a serious hazard. An analysis of coroners' reports relating to deaths of occupants or drivers of motor vehicles in 1953–55 in England and Wales (including urban areas) showed that 7·1 per cent of all fatalities involved collision with a lighting column, a telegraph pole or a tree. Damage to columns can be considerable.

In a four-year period, 331 columns on a $3\frac{1}{2}$-mile stretch of a largely unrestricted dual-carriageway trunk road sustained 114 collisions resulting in damage to column or lantern. There was about one collision for every million vehicle-miles travelled. It is officially recommended by the Ministry of Transport that on trunk and important roads on new alignments 4 ft of the verge adjacent to the carriageway should be kept clear of all obstructions.[3] (See also Chapter 10 of the Companion Volume.)[4]

Another American result showing the effect on accident rates of bridge parapets obstructing the shoulder is shown in Table 13.17.[5]

TABLE 13.17

Accident rates on bridges and overpasses
*(two-lane roads)**

Width of structure compared with approach roadway	Accidents per ten-million vehicles
Narrower by more than 1 ft	5·7
1 ft narrower to 1 ft wider .	3·6
Wider by 1–3 ft . . .	4·0
3–5 ft . . .	3·1
5–7 ft . . .	1·3
more than 7 ft .	0·5

* A very similar result has also been obtained by Baldwin.[14]

Safety fences

At sharp bends and on sloping ground on hills some form of protection is often used to prevent vehicles from running off the road. This protection ranges from isolated posts to specially designed safety fences of steel rail, concrete, wood or steel cables. Where hard shoulders are in use, as on motorways, safety fences are mounted behind the shoulders, (see Chapter 14).

Provision for stationary vehicles

In the course of a journey, motorists may stop voluntarily or they may be forced to stop because of a breakdown. Out of 621 accidents occurring on three main roads in Buckinghamshire between 1956 and 1958 where there was no speed limit, 16 per cent involved a stationary vehicle.[15] On some roads the proportion is larger still as is shown in Table 13.18, which is based on a detailed examination of personal-injury accidents occurring on 170 miles of road in rural Buckinghamshire and on 80 miles of dual carriageways in rural areas of England and Wales.[16]

TABLE 13.18

Accidents involving stationary vehicles

Type of road	Width of carriageway (ft)	Traffic flow (vehicles per day)	Percentage of non-junction injury accidents involving a stationary vehicle
Two lane (1946–50)	16–17	460	0
	18–19	850	11
	20–21	1740	12
	22–24	2630	13
Three-lane (1946–50)	29–31	6500	23
Dual carriageway (1952–53)	2 × 22	4500	14

A similar type of result has been obtained in Lancashire.[6] It would be expected that, other things being equal, the proportion of accidents involving a stationary vehicle would increase in proportion to the volume of traffic. The evidence of Table 13.18 suggests that something of this kind does occur, although the effect may be partly attributable to a greater tendency on the part of drivers to park on the wider carriageways.

Stationary vehicles may also cause considerable delay to traffic, particularly on a road which is heavily trafficked in relation to its width. An example of this effect is given in Table 13.19.

TABLE 13.19

Effect on a parked lorry on speeds on Road A.5

(Carriageway 24 ft wide. Traffic flow (both directions combined): 580 vehicles per hour)

Class of vehicle	Mean speed (mile/h)	
	Normal operation	Lorry parked 200 yards away
Car . . .	37	27
Light commercial .	34	27
Medium commercial.	31	26
Heavy commercial .	28	23
ALL CLASSES .	33	26

Table 13.19 shows the effect on speeds of a vehicle parked 200 yards away: a greater effect would be expected nearer the parked vehicle.

Although many drivers probably park on the carriageway to rest or take refreshment or for unessential purposes, an appreciable number of stops are made because of breakdown, illness or other emergencies. On the 8-mile long Preston By-pass motorway the number of emergency stops reported to or recorded by the police between December 1958 and October 1959 (inclusive) averaged 1 for each 23 000 vehicle-miles. On the 73 miles long London-Birmingham motorway the numbers of breakdowns attended by the police during the first year of operation were as shown in Table 13.20.

TABLE 13.20

Breakdown rates on the London-Birmingham motorway

Month	Breakdowns (attended by police)	Vehicle-miles (millions)	Breakdowns per million vehicle-miles
November 1959	1101	20·8	53
December .	1117	21·6	52
January 1960 .	1393	20·9	67
February . .	1389	23·0	60
March . .	1531	26·9	57
April . .	1888	30·3	62
May. . .	1884	31·5	60
June. . .	2165	31·8	68
July . .	2407	34·4	70
August . .	2275	34·7	66
September .	2045	35·1	58
October . .	1662	35·5	47
TOTAL .	20 857	346·5	—
AVERAGE	—	—	60

Table 13.20 shows that, on average, there were 60 breakdowns per million vehicle-miles or one breakdown per 17 000 vehicle-miles. Observations between 8 a.m. and 4 p.m. on weekdays have shown that on average there is about one stationary vehicle per six miles of shoulder. Similar results have been reported from the U.S.A. For example on the New Jersey Turnpike the reported breakdown rate during 1959 was one per 24 700 vehicle-miles.[17] All these figures probably exclude stops for which no assistance was required, for instance for a flat tyre. In an investigation in New York State[18] in which about 160 miles of rural road were kept under continuous observation between 8 a.m. and 8 p.m. on a weekday, it was found that emergency stops occurred at the rate of one for every 12 000 vehicle-miles, which corresponded closely to the rate obtained in an earlier study on rural highways in New Jersey.

Observations on eight occasions on a 50-mile stretch of A.4 west of Maidenhead in 1957–58 showed that out of a total of 522 parked cars and commercial vehicles, 204, i.e. 39 per cent, were parked on the carriageway.[15] On the average, vehicles parked on the carriageway were a little over two miles apart. This is an obvious source of danger and in Great Britain it is now officially recommended that the provision of lay-bys, or other suitably hardened areas for the accommodation of parked vehicles, should be regarded as an essential part of the design of rural roads.[3] The recent introduction of "clearways", i.e. selected lengths of road on which provision is made for drivers to stop clear of the carriageways and on which drivers are normally prohibited from stopping on the carriageway, is an important advance in tackling the problem of the stationary vehicle. Although the evidence is at present too limited to reach definite conclusions, the indication is that the measure has been effective in reducing accidents (see Chapter 10). On motorways continuous hard shoulders are provided, the recommended width being 10 ft; from accommodating disabled vehicles these also provide a margin of error for vehicles which are forced off the road in an emergency or as the result of an accident (see pp. 418-22). In the U.S.A. continuous shoulders are a feature not only of motorways but also of all-purpose roads. There is evidence from that country that the presence of shoulders reduces the accident rate (see pp. 422-5).

Central reserves

The practice in recent years has been to provide central reserves without obstructions and flanked by flush or splayed kerbs rather than vertical ones; many of the comments on verges (see pp. 422-5) apply equally to central reserves. This practice probably increases traffic capacity by encouraging traffic to ultilize the full width of the carriageways, The effect on accidents is less certain since central reserves which are easily traversable might be expected to lead to head-on collisions. This and other problems of central reserve design are considered above in the section on dual carriageways and in the section on motorways. The effect of mounting safety fences on central reserves is examined in Chapter 14.

The Ministry of Transport recommend a minimum width of 15 ft for central reserves for roads on new alignments, dropping to 10 ft at difficult sites. Local widening of the central reserve to provide shelter for turning vehicles and cross traffic is also recommended.

At the time of writing, most central reserves on motorways were 15 ft wide including 1-ft wide marginal strips, but on the Preston and Lancaster by-passes the central reserve was made wide enough to permit the addition of an extra traffic lane to each carriageway to provide additional capacity in the future.

Cycle tracks

Since pedal cycles travel more slowly than motor vehicles and are inherently unstable their segregation from other vehicles by the provision of a separate track for their exclusive use would be expected to result in an increase in motor vehicle speeds and in a reduction in accidents. The total mileage of cycle tracks in use in Great Britain, though not known, is certainly very small.

Before considering their effect on accident rates it will be as well to mention the chief reasons which discourage cyclists from using cycle tracks:

(i) The track causes cyclists to cross or merge with other traffic at each junction.

(ii) The right-turn movement becomes difficult (sometimes impossible) for the cyclist.

(iii) The track is easily overlooked or mistaken for the footway by other road users.

(iv) Tracks tend to fall into disrepair.

 (v) Passengers alighting from buses and cars have to cross the track to reach the footway.

(vi) The use of the track by cyclists is not compulsory.

Counts of cyclists using cycle tracks were made by the Laboratory on eight sections of main road, mostly near London, in 1954 and it was found that at least 90 per cent of the cyclists on these roads used the tracks that were in good condition. Where the track was in poor condition, with patches of broken concrete and bad joints, little more than half the cyclists used the tracks. At one site the proportion was 90 per cent on a weekday (assumed to be mostly regular travellers on this road) but only two-thirds on a Sunday (occasional users.) There was no obvious relationship between the amount of motor traffic on the main road and the percentage of cyclists using the track.

A study of cycle accidents in Lancashire is given in Table 13.21.

TABLE 13.21

Cycle accident rates on parts of A.580 in Lancashire,
1937–1948*

		Cycle accidents per million motor vehicle-miles		
		All accidents	Junction accidents	Non-junction accidents
Roads without cycle tracks	1937–38	1·90	0·53	1·36
	1946–48	1·76	0·38	1·37
	Change (per cent)	−7	−28	+1
No cycle track	1937–38	1·20	0·26	0·93
With cycle track	1946–48	1·00	0·61	0·38*
	Change (per cent)	−17	+135	−59

* All the non-junction accidents on the sections with cycle tracks occurred when the cyclist was not using tracks.

Where cycle tracks were provided the total cycle accident rate fell by 17 per cent compared with 7 per cent elsewhere and non-junction accidents fell by 59 per cent. Junction accidents, however, increased by 135 per cent compared with a decrease of 28 per cent elsewhere.[6]

It appears therefore that while cycle tracks reduce the overall cycle accident rate the benefit is felt only on uninterrupted sections of road whereas the rate may be considerably increased at junctions. This supports the objections to the tracks given above.

There is doubt about the importance of providing more cycle tracks in the road system. Between 1938 and 1958 the estimated mileage travelled by pedal cycles in Great Britain was halved while motor-vehicle mileage doubled.

HORIZONTAL AND VERTICAL PROFILE

Design speed

When designing a road it is usual to determine curvature, superelevation, sight distances and certain other design features on the basis of a "design speed". The use of this concept ensures a balanced design on a given road as well as consistent differences in standards on different types of road, e.g. on roads of different traffic importance. The choice of design speed is usually influenced not only by the importance of the road but also by the character of the terrain, the amount of roadside development and economic considerations. Thus a road in level terrain justifies a higher design speed than one in mountainous terrain, and a road in open country justifies a higher design speed than a road in a suburban or urban area. This does not necessarily mean that design speeds are chosen independently of the wishes and habits of drivers, since the factors mentioned which affect the choice of design speed also influence the speeds at which drivers travel. For example, drivers tend to travel more slowly on a suburban road than on the open road because of roadside development, pedestrians, parked vehicles and possibly the existence of a speed limit. Another example is that in hilly country a driver will appreciate the difficulty in attaining high design standards and will be prepared to travel at lower speeds than on a road of similar importance in level terrain. Furthermore, a driver would not expect to be able to travel as fast on a road of minor traffic importance as, say, on a motorway.

Although most definitions of design speed are rather vague and the value is often chosen without knowledge of the speeds likely to be attained in practice, it would appear that the intention is that the design speed should be higher than the expected average speed of vehicles using the road but not high enough to cater for a small minority of excessively fast vehicles. In an attempt to make the definition more rigorous, Charlesworth and Coburn[16] have suggested that the excluded minority should be defined as the fastest 5 per cent of drivers. Furthermore, to overcome the difficulty of varying traffic composition, they have suggested that this definition should refer only to the speeds of cars. Therefore, design speed may be defined as the 95-percentile of the expected distribution of the speeds of cars.

The 85-percentile speed (i.e. the speed exceeded by the fastest 15 per cent of drivers), is used in some branches of traffic engineering. In the U.S.A., for example, speed limits are often fixed at the 85-percentile speed, while in Great Britain double white line markings which govern overtaking are determined on the basis of the 85-percentile speeds on adjacent sections of road, rounded off to the nearest 5 mile/h.[19]

Although the 95-percentile and 85-percentile speeds are best determined by direct measurement on the road in question or on similar roads elsewhere, the relationships in Fig. 13.3 may be of value for some design and traffic engineering purposes. Figure 13.3, which was obtained by plotting the 95-percentile and the 85-percentile speeds at a number of sites on rural roads

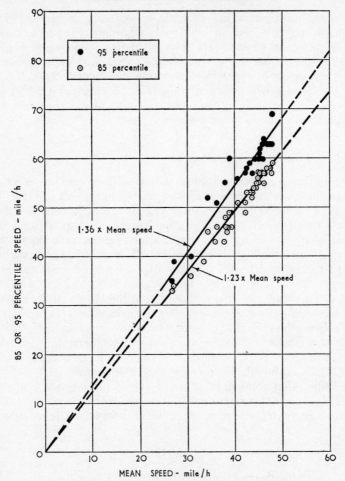

Fig. 13.3. 85-percentile and 95-percentile speeds at different sites against mean speed (cars)

against the mean, shows that the 95-percentile speed was on average 1·36 times the mean while the 85-percentile was 1·23 times the mean. If these factors are used in conjunction with the mean speeds quoted earlier for different types of road, a rough estimate of 95- and 85-percentile speeds will be obtained. For example if 60 mile/h is taken as the mean speed of cars on a motorway, Fig. 13.3 suggests that the 95-percentile speed (or design speed) would be 81·6 mile/h (say, 80), and the 85-percentile would be 73·8 mile/h (say, 75).

The relations in Fig. 13.3 are based on measurements taken between 1951 and 1955, and measurements in 1960 produced very similar results; the ratio of the 85-percentile to the mean was estimated at 1·19, while the ratio of the 95-percentile to the mean was estimated at 1·32. Since these values are slightly lower than those in Fig. 13.3, there is an indication that the spread of speeds has been reduced over the years.

Design speed, as described above, is primarily used in determining curvature and sight distances but for some aspects of design other speed values may be more appropriate. For example, in designing deceleration lanes, it is not unreasonable to assume that drivers intending to leave the main road would be travelling more slowly than usual; the speed value used might therefore be lower than the normal design speed. Another example is that one authority on the design of road curvature and superelevation has suggested that the speed at which the centrifugal force is balanced out by the effect of the superelevation should be chosen independently of the normal design speed and that it should be near the lower end of the speed distribution.[20]

Effect of road curvature on accidents

Since accidents on bends constitute over 40 per cent of non-junction accidents (and over 30 per cent of all accidents) on roads in Great Britain not subject to a speed limit (see Table 13.22), particular emphasis has been placed on investigations into the relation between horizontal curvature and accidents. (see Plate 13.6) "Before-and-after" studies have shown that the numbers of accidents have been substantially reduced at places where the curvature has been reduced or where other types of improvement have been made to bends. The results are given in Table 13.23.

Studies of accident rates per vehicle-mile in Buckinghamshire and in Lancashire have shown a distinct tendency for accidents to cluster on bends, particularly on the very sharp bends. The results given in Tables 13.24 and 13.25 show a marked increase in accident rate with increasing curvature.

A similar type of result was obtained on American roads and is quoted in Table 13.26. Although the figures in this table confirm the findings of the British studies, that accident rates are higher on sharp bends than on slight bends, it also shows that rates on straights were higher than on slight bends; in fact for some categories of road, accident rates on straights were higher

TABLE 13.22

Numbers of accidents on roads in Great Britain
without a speed limit [22,23]

Character of road	1953 all injury accidents	1958 fatal and serious accidents only
Slight Curve	5714	
Bend	6621	
Blind Bend	2190	6841
Humpback bridge on hillcrest . .	585	
Straight	17 854	8997
Junction	11 696	5261
Open space, lay-by and unknown .	189	108
TOTAL	44 849	21 207

TABLE 13.23

Results of improvements at bends

Type of improvement	Reduction in injury-accidents (per cent)
Re-alignment of isolated bend (17 cases) . .	80*
Superelevation of isolated bend (6 cases) . .	60
Improved visibility at isolated bend (6 cases) . .	63
Major re-alignment of lengths of road (7 cases) .	95*

* Statistically significant at the 5 per cent level.

than the average for all bends. An investigation in Belgium has also found a higher accident rate on straights than on curves.[21] Thus it would appear that the relation between curvature and accidents may not be a simple one and a British study on 30-ft carriageways has confirmed this difficulty. In this study accident rates were calculated for straights and for curves of different radii but an additional feature was that the figures were subdivided according to the general curvature of the roads concerned over lengths of about two miles on average. The results are given in Table 13.27. Although these data show that accidents tended to cluster on sharp bends, they also show that the accident rate on straights appears to depend on the length of straight; accident rates on straights were low on roads on which bends were frequent (and which, therefore, had high average curvature) and high on roads on which bends were infrequent. In fact, overall accident rates (for straights and curves combined) were distinctly lower on the more "bendy" roads than on the less "bendy" roads. The rates quoted in Table 13.27 refer to non-junction injury-accidents involving motor vehicles only but separate analysis suggested that substantially similar results would hold for all injury accidents or for serious-injury accidents. It was thought that the high accident rate on straighter sections of road might be due to the fact that the straighter sections had higher flows, which, as shown in the section on three-lane roads (pp. 411-7) appeared to be associated with higher accident rates. However when allowance was made for different levels of flow, the main features of the relations in Table 13.27 were not affected. A separate investigation on trunk roads in Great Britain also indicated that accident rates were lower on the more "bendy" lengths of road than on the less "bendy" ones.

A possible interpretation of the above evidence is that, although reductions in the curvature of bends would produce local reduction in accidents, the number of accidents over a greater length of road might well increase, presumably because of the higher speeds attained (see pp. 436-7). The evidence would also appear to support the policy of designing roads without excessively long straights. However, it is doubtful whether these interpretations can be regarded as conclusive in the present state of knowledge and there is an obvious need for more work on this subject.

TABLE 13.24

Effect of curvature on accident rates on rural roads in Buckinghamshire 1946–48 (Two- and three-lane carriageways)[16]

Radius (ft)	Injury-accidents per million vehicle-miles (Numbers of accidents shown in brackets)	
Over 2900 (including straights) .	2·5	(177)
2900–1450	3·0	(48)
1450–950.	3·5	(21)
950–550	3·8	(9)
Less than 550	14·1	(18)

TABLE 13.25

Effect of curvature on accident rates on rural roads in Lancashire 1946–47[6]

Radius (ft)	Injury-accidents per million vehicle-miles
Over 2000	1·5
2000–1000	2·5
1000–500.	4·0
500–200	3·7
Less than 200	16·7

TABLE 13.26

Accident rates on bends and on straights on main rural highways in 15 states of the U.S.A. (Mostly in 1941)[5]

Radius (ft)	Accidents per million vehicle-miles (Numbers of accidents shown in brackets)			
	2-lane roads	3-lane roads	4-lane roads undivided	4-lane roads divided
Over 1950 (excluding straights) .	1·6 (504)	1·7 (11)	1·9 (98)	1·8 (95)
1950–960 . .	2·5 (596)	2·8 (11)	2·6 (90)	2·4 (65)
960–580 . .	2·8 (338)	3·5 (6)	3·3 (16)	3·1 (5)
Less than 580 .	3·5 (354)	7·3 (11)	1·2 (3)	6·7 (12)
All bends . .	2·3 (1792)	2·8 (39)	2·2 (207)	2·1 (177)
Straights . .	2·3 (6474)	2·5 (227)	2·7 (1348)	2·9 (982)

TABLE 13.27

*Accident rates on straights, and on bends of different radii,
on sections of 30-ft carriageway with different levels of
average curvature, England, 1957–58*

Non-junction injury accidents involving motor vehicles only

Average* curvature (degrees per mile)	Accidents per million vehicle-miles (and numbers of accidents)				
	STRAIGHTS and bends of radius more than 5000 ft	BENDS			TOTAL
		radius 5000 ft– 2000 ft	radius 2000 ft– 1000 ft	radius less than 1000 ft	
0–40 . .	1·2 (284)	1·2 (33)	1·0 (4)	8·6 (18)	1·3 (339)
40–80 . .	0·9 (142)	0·9 (37)	0·9 (23)	1·5 (14)	0·9 (216)
80–120. .	0·7 (69)	0·5 (11)	0·9 (16)	1·6 (24)	0·8 (120)
Over 120 .	0·4 (15)	0·5 (3)	1·0 (19)	1·2 (19)	0·7 (56)
TOTAL .	1·0 (510)	0·9 (84)	1·0 (62)	1·8 (75)	1·0 (731)

* Defined in the next section

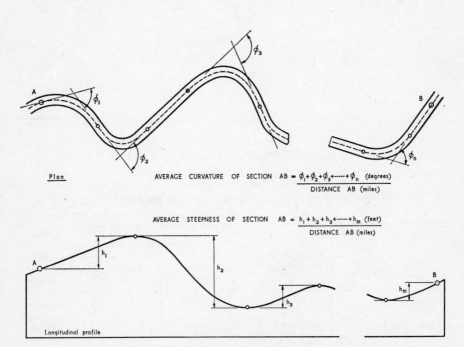

**Fig. 13.4. Method of specifying the average curvature and average gradient of a
section of road**

Effect of road curvature on speeds

The effect of road curvature has been measured by timing vehicles along 34 sections of relatively lightly-trafficked road in Buckinghamshire of average length 1¼ miles, the tortuousness of each section being specified by the sum of the deflections of all the horizontal curves divided by the length of the section (Fig. 13.4). Although this method of specifying average curvature ignores the sharpness of individual curves it was chosen because of its simplicity: it is almost as effective as other more complicated methods. After allowing for the effect of other features of layout, using standard statistical procedures, it was estimated that each 100 degrees of average curvature per mile accounted for 2·31 miles per hour reduction in the mean speed of all vehicles. The values of average curvature on the roads studied ranged from zero on a completely straight section of road to over 500 degrees per mile on a very tortuous section of class II road; this means that curvature was responsible for reductions in mean speed of up to about 12 mile/h. This result refers to the mean speed of all vehicles but, as shown in Table 13.28, the effect on cars was found to be about twice as great as that on commercial vehicles.

TABLE 13.28
Effect of curvature and gradients on speeds on roads in Buckinghamshire (1951)

Class of vehicle	Reduction in mean speed (in mile/h) for each 100 degrees of average curvature per mile	Reduction in mean speed (in mile/h) for each 100 ft of "rise and fall" per mile
Cars	3·07	0·86
Commercial vehicles	1·67	2·22
ALL VEHICLES	2·31	1·49

A useful application of the results is the estimation of the effect of straightening roads. The effect for the roads studied is shown in Table 13.29.

TABLE 13.29
Estimated effect of straightening roads in Buckinghamshire (1951)

Class of road	Average curvature (degrees per mile)	Change due to straightening		
		Speed (per cent)	Length (per cent)	Journey time (per cent)
Trunk road	63	+ 4	−2	− 6
Class I road	137	+ 9	−3·5	−12
Class II road	201	+16	− 7	−20

The effect is twofold. Not only would speeds increase because of the removal of the bends but the road would also be shortened in length. Some of the roads in the study were already straight or almost straight and if a selection were made of the more tortuous sections the benefits would be even greater than shown in the table. Although it would probably be impracticable to straighten roads in the way implied by Table 13.29, an appreciable increase in speed could be achieved by replacing the sharp curves by flatter ones.

In this investigation in Buckinghamshire no measurements of sight distance were made and its effect is included with that of curvature. It is probable that a large amount of the effect attributed to curvature is, in fact, due to low visibility.

The above results are based upon measurements in 1951 and it is probable that the curvature of many of the roads studied has been reduced since then.

The main value of the above results is in producing estimates of savings in delay to be expected from realignment schemes, for use in economic assessments and in assigning priorities (see Chapter 15). However, since they refer to average speeds and average curvatures over lengths of road they cannot be used to relate speeds on bends to their radii or to provide guidance on the design of road curvature. Very little work has been done in the latter field but in a controlled experiment by Warren and Hazeldine[24] in 1939 it was estimated that drivers adjusted their speeds on unsuperelevated bends to produce a centrifugal acceleration of 0·25g on average. In another study reported by Leeming and Black, in 1950[25] measurements were taken of lateral acceleration (centrifugal acceleration minus the effect of superelevation) of vehicles travelling on public roads. The lateral acceleration varied over a wide range and it was concluded that the commonly accepted value of 0·15g was a reasonable basis for design;[20] the latter value is used in the Ministry of Transport's recommendations on the minimum radii of bends on rural roads.[3] These remarks do not apply to junctions, where higher lateral accelerations are acceptable (see pp. 452-4). The study by Leeming and Black cast doubt on the commonly accepted method of designing transition curves, based upon a rate of change of centrigufal acceleration of 1 ft/sec³. The rates of change of acceleration obtained in the study were in practice very variable and on average they were rather greater than this value. As a result of these studies Leeming has proposed a less rigid method of design, in which the total length of transition curve (entry and exit combined) is not more than two-thirds of the total length of the bend (including the circular portion).[20]

Gradients

By analogy with the method of specifying average curvature, the average steepness of a section of road may be specified by the sum of the vertical distances between successive crests and troughs (i.e. the "rise and fall") divided by the length of section (Fig. 13.4). For the relatively lightly-trafficked roads in Buckinghamshire it was estimated that the mean speed along a section was reduced by 1·49 mile/h for every 100 ft of "rise and fall" per mile. The most hilly section in the study had a "rise and fall" of almost 300 ft per mile, accounting for a reduction in average speed of about 4·5 mile/h.

This result refers to the mean speed of all vehicles and Table 13.28 shows, as one would expect, the effect of gradients was greater on commercial vehicles than on cars: this is contrary to the effect of curves, which affect cars more than commercial vehicles.

Most of the sections studied consisted of a succession of short upgrades and downgrades and the values quoted would probably underestimate the effect of a section consisting of one long gradient. However the results can be used in such cases to give an approximate estimate of the effect of the gradient on the mean speed of vehicles in both directions. The effect on uphill speeds would be about twice the average, since the available evidence from gradients in this country suggests that downhill speeds are very similar to speeds on a level road. This is confirmed by American investigations.[26]

The above results were obtained under light traffic conditions and probably relate only to the direct effect of the gradient on vehicle performance. However, on more heavily-trafficked roads a further effect is encountered, namely, the congestion caused by slow-moving vehicles on ascending gradients. Table 13.30 compares mean speeds ascending a gradient of 1 in 20 with those on an adjoining level section, on a two-lane road carrying about 400 vehicles per hour in both directions.

TABLE 13.30

Effect of a gradient of 1 in 20 (1 mile long) on speeds, 1953

Traffic flow 400 vehicles per hour in both directions
(over 40 per cent commercial)

Class of vehicle	Mean speed (mile/h)		Difference (mile/h)
	Level section	Ascending gradient	
Cars	42	35	7
Light commercial vehicles (up to 30 cwt unladen) .	36	30	6
Medium commercial vehicles (30 cwt–3 tons unladen) .	34	25	9
Heavy commercial vehicles (over 3 tons unladen) .	29	20	9

The heavy commercial vehicles had an average speed of only 20 mile/h ascending the gradient and this affected the speeds of the lighter vehicles. The mean speed of cars uphill was 7 mile/h less than on level ground and it has been estimated that, if the commercial vehicles had been absent, this difference would have been only about 2 mile/h.

These results indicate the kind of benefits that can be derived from providing an extra climbing lane for slow vehicles ascending a gradient.

Sight distance

It is desirable that the sight distance on horizontal and vertical curves should be adequate to permit safe overtaking by the majority of vehicles. In formulating design standards it is of value to obtain information about the times and distances required for overtaking; this has been provided by a controlled experiment on a two-lane track. Drivers in a $2\frac{1}{4}$-litre saloon car made runs in which they followed and later overtook another car travelling at a specified speed. During the test a third car was travelling in the opposite direction along the two-lane track and the test driver was asked to carry out overtaking upon receiving a signal, if he considered the gap to be adequate. The main features of the results (averaged over eight drivers) are given in Fig. 13.5, which shows that the distance taken to overtake (and to a lesser degree the time taken) increased as the speed of vehicle being overtaken increased. The peak speed during overtaking was roughly 10 mile/h

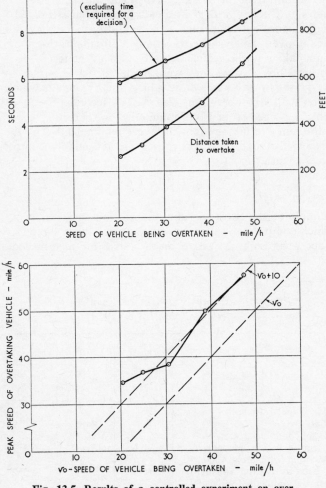

Fig. 13.5. Results of a controlled experiment on over-taking performance

higher than that of the vehicle being overtaken. Full details of this experiment and of other measurements of overtaking times are given in the Companion Volume, Chapter 4.[4]

If these results were used as a basis of design it would be reasonable to cater for a vehicle travelling at the design speed, overtaking another vehicle at a speed of 10 mile/h less (this assumption is in fact made in American practice).[27] Thus the overtaking distance for a design speed of 60 mile/h would be about 700 ft. On a three-lane road it would seem desirable to allow for the possibility of vehicles in opposite directions starting to overtake simultaneously, so that the sight distance would have to be 1400 ft. On a two-lane road it seems reasonable to allow for a vehicle travelling at the design speed in the opposite direction; the distance travelled by this vehicle during the 8·6 seconds required for the overtaking would be $8·6 \times 88 = 750$ ft (approx.) so that the sight distance should be $700 + 750 = 1450$, which is little different from the result for the three-lane road.

The results in Fig. 13.5 refer to a $2\frac{1}{4}$-litre car, which was capable of more rapid acceleration than the average British car, and it might be considered fairer to design for a typical $1\frac{1}{2}$-litre car. It has been estimated from published performance data that such a car would probably have taken about 10 seconds to overtake a vehicle travelling at 50 mile/h; this compares with 8·6 seconds taken by the vehicle actually used in the tests.

In another study observations were made during a journey in a 800 cc car of overtaking times taken by this vehicle and by vehicles which overtook it. The average of 40 observations was about 8 seconds; the speeds of overtaken vehicles ranged from 20 to 50 mile/h.

The minimum overtaking sight distances recommended by the Ministry of Transport[3] for road design purposes are reasonably compatible with the above evidence.

Surface irregularity

An example of the effect of riding quality on speeds is given in Table 13.31, which compares mean speeds before and after a temporary "burnt-off" surface was resurfaced with a machine-laid bitumen macadam carpet.

TABLE 13.31

Effect of resurfacing a straight, level 30-ft wide section of Road A.5 (1953)

	Before	After	Difference
Index of irregularity "r" (in./mile)	219	141	−78
Mean speeds (mile/h):			
Cars	38·4	44·3	+5·9
Light commercial vehicles (up to 30 cwt unladen)	34·6	38·3	+3·7
Medium commercial vehicles (30 cwt to 3 tons unladen)	31·3	33·5	+2·2
Heavy commercial vehicles (over 3 tons unladen)	26·9	28·6	+1·7

The resurfacing brought about a reduction in the index of irregularity "r" measured with the "bump integrator"[4] from 219 to 141 in. per mile, and this was accompanied by an increase of 5·9 mile/h in the mean speed of cars with smaller increases in the speeds of commercial vehicles. Simultaneous measurements at a "control" site on the same road showed much smaller changes in speed and it may be concluded that the differences in Table 13.31 are largely attributable to the improvement in riding quality.

A similar effect was observed on a 1000-yd long section of A.38 where, after resurfacing (which included some kerbing, superelevation and widening), the index of irregularity decreased from 190 to 133 in. per mile and average speed of cars increased by 3 to 4 mile/h.

Studies of accidents on several lengths of road before and after they were resurfaced in the course of normal maintenance have revealed that there was a tendency for accidents to increase following resurfacing, particularly where the riding quality of the surface was substantially improved.[32] The higher speeds attained on the improved surfaces would be expected to be largely responsible for this tendency.

JUNCTIONS

The design of junctions in rural areas so as to minimize the frequency of accidents and to ease traffic flow is a subject that has attracted a considerable amount of attention. Most of the work done so far has been concerned with accidents and much more remains to be discovered, as regards the relative merits of alternative forms of layout and the details of design for each of the various forms. After reviewing the extent and nature of the junction accident problem, and the results of some of the investigations that have been made in recent years, the implications of these results for junction design will be discussed.

Extent of the accident problem

About one-quarter of accidents on rural roads occur at junctions and in 1958, for example, 5261 of the 21 207 accidents involving serious injury or fatality on roads without a speed limit took place at or within 20 yards of a junction.[23] Table 13.32, which analyses these junction accidents according to type of junction and number of vehicles involved, shows that more than 60 per cent were at three-way junctions and nearly 70 per cent involved two vehicles. The majority of accidents involved two vehicles and occurred either at three-way or four-way junctions.

It may be of interest to record here some information on the number of junctions in Great Britain. Table 13.33 gives estimates of the numbers of different types of three-way and four-way junction in rural areas.[2]

It can be seen from Table 13.33 that more than 80 per cent of junctions were three-way junctions and of these the majority were T-junctions. It should be noted that the results shown in Table 13.33 are subject to considerable sampling error and there are also other reasons for not making direct comparisons with the numbers of accidents shown in Table 13.32.

TABLE 13.32

Numbers of fatal or serious accidents at various types of rural junction in 1958[23]

Type of junction	Involving one vehicle	Involving two vehicles	Involving three or more vehicles	Total
Roundabout .	117	26	4	147
T or Y . .	906	2151	179	3236
Cross-road .	282	1301	96	1679
Other . .	39	145	15	199
TOTAL .	1344	3623	294	5261

TABLE 13.33

Numbers of different types of junction in rural districts of Great Britain (1957–59)

ROUNDABOUTS	190
3-way	
Right-hand splay. .	12 000
T-junction . .	81 000
Left-hand splay . .	6500
Y-junction . . .	8400
Other. . .	4000
TOTAL (rounded off) .	110 000
4-way	
Cross-roads . .	14 000
Staggered cross-roads .	490
Other. . .	710
TOTAL (rounded off) .	15 000
Other, more than 4-way .	170
TOTAL, all types (rounded off). . . .	130 000

Manoeuvres and types of accident

Table 13.32 shows the numbers of fatal or serious accidents at the different kinds of junction. It has already been noted that the most common type of accident is the two-vehicle accident. However, Table 13.32 shows also that more than three-quarters of accidents at roundabouts involved only one vehicle; presumably in many of these cases vehicles hit the central island. It will also be seen that whereas 28 per cent of accidents at three-way junctions involve only one vehicle, only 17 per cent of accidents at crossroads are of this type. Summing up, the results indicate that each type of layout appears to have special risks to which it is particularly prone; while these are largely inherent in the nature of the layout, the study of these special risks may well suggest remedial measures.

In several special investigations detailed analyses have been made of accident types at certain types of junctions: three-way junctions, in particular, have received considerable attention. Table 13.34, based on results by Summerfield[28] and Tanner,[29] shows the percentages of various types of accident (including damage-only) in which a turning vehicle was involved, firstly in an analysis of 368 accidents at rural three-way junctions in Oxfordshire and secondly in a similar analysis of 523 accidents in various parts of the country, made earlier by the Laboratory. A few of the junctions may be included in both analyses.

It will be seen that most of the accidents involved one vehicle turning and one vehicle going straight on along the major road; most of the turning vehicles were turning right. The most frequent single combination of movements was the collision between one vehicle turning right out of the major road and another either following or attempting to overtake (see Plate 13.7). In one of the investigations this type of accident accounted for 25 per cent of the total, in the other, 45 per cent. Similar information has also been obtained by Bennett[30] and Pike[31].

TABLE 13.34

Analysis of accident types at rural 3-way junctions

(Includes damage-only accidents)
(Based on Summerfield[28] and Tanner[29])
Oxon: 368 accidents in Oxfordshire, 1946–54
RRL: 523 accidents in various counties, mostly 1945–51

	Left out	Left in	Right out	Right in
No other vehicle	Oxon 0% RRL 3%	Oxon 2% RRL 4%	Oxon 2% RRL 3%	Oxon 0% RRL 3%
With oncoming vehicle	Oxon 0% RRL 1%	Oxon 3% RRL 4%	Oxon 15% RRL 12%	Oxon 12% RRL 17%
With following vehicle	Oxon 1% RRL 2%	Oxon 7% RRL 6%	Oxon 45% RRL 25%	Oxon 8% RRL 8%
Two turning vehicles			Oxon 4% RRL 12%	

Accidents at junctions on rural dual-carriageway roads are analysed in Table 13.35. Again, the most common type of junction collision was the one in which a vehicle turning right was hit by a vehicle travelling straight along the major road. The turning vehicle was more frequently hit by a following or overtaking vehicle on the first carriageway than by an opposing vehicle as it entered or crossed the second carriageway.[8]

TABLE 13.35

Types of accident at junctions on a sample
of rural dual carriageways (1952–53)

(Injury-accidents only)

Type of accident	Number
One vehicle and pedestrian . . .	1
One vehicle and bus passenger . . .	1
Other one-vehicle accident . . .	17
Two vehicles: one turning right from d.c. .	47
one turning left from d.c. .	5
one entering d.c. . .	11
head-tail collisions . .	3
at roundabouts . . .	3
other or not known . .	13
More than two vehicles	0
TOTAL	101

It has been shown by Tanner[29] that vehicles turning left from the major road are particularly liable to collide with pedal cycles travelling straight along the major road. Motorcycles proceeding in either direction along the major road are particularly liable to collide with vehicles turning right to leave the major road. Motorcycles turning left are particularly frequent among one-vehicle accidents.

Accidents and traffic flow

From the analysis of 523 accidents at three-way rural junctions in various counties referred to above,[29] it was deduced that the number of accidents in a given period, between a vehicle on the major road and a vehicle turning into or out of the minor road, was approximately proportional to the square root of the product of the flows concerned in that period. This applied to junctions carrying moderately heavy flows on the major road (seldom less than 1000 veh/day) and volumes appreciably less on the minor roads but usually more than 200 veh/day. These results may be expressed as follows:

The expected number of collisions per year between vehicles turning round the right shoulder and those on the main road is

$$A_r = \frac{4 \cdot 5 \sqrt{(q_r Q)}}{10\ 000}$$

Similarly, for the left shoulder the expected number is

$$A_l = \frac{7 \cdot 5 \sqrt{(q_l Q)}}{10\ 000}$$

where Q, q_l and q_r are the flows per day in each direction along the main road and round the left and right shoulders of the junction respectively (Fig. 13.6).

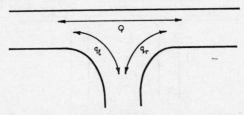

Fig. 13.6. Vehicle streams to which Q, q_l and q_r refer

These two types of accident account for 75 per cent of the accidents in the sample. The constants, of course, depend on the layout and various other factors and may not be of general application but their ratio and the form of the relationships probably are. Further, they refer to conditions soon after the war; Q, q_l and q_r being flows in motor vehicles per 16-hour day in August 1938.

It will be noticed that the number of accidents is not proportional to qQ (the number of encounters) but only to $\sqrt{Qq}$, from which it would appear that drivers are more careful at busy junctions.

Cross-roads are sometimes staggered in order to slow down traffic on the minor road with the intention of reducing accidents. The above analysis enables a comparison to be made between a left-right and a right-left stagger (Fig. 13.7 and Plate 13.9). If all users of the minor road wish to cross the

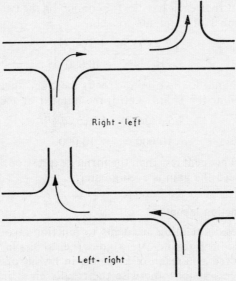

Right - left

Left - right

Fig. 13.7. Two types of staggered cross-roads

major road and not turn into it then at a left-right stagger the number of accidents will be proportional to A_l and at a right-left stagger they will be proportional to A_r. The latter is therefore safer by a factor of 7·5 to 4·5, i.e. by 1·7 to 1, and is in fact the stagger normally used in practice.

Another use of the formulae is to show the advantage of restricting access to main roads. Suppose two minor roads lead on to a main road

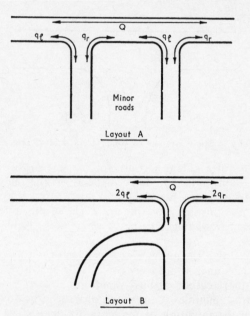

Fig. 13.8. Alternative layouts giving access from two minor roads to a major road

(Fig. 13.8(a)) and that each has flows q_l and q_r on the two shoulders. Then the expected number of accidents will be:

$$2\left\{\frac{7·5\sqrt{q_lQ}}{10\ 000}+\frac{4·5\sqrt{q_rQ}}{10\ 000}\right\}$$

If, on the other hand, the two minor roads meet and then enter the main road at a single junction (Fig. 13.8(b)) the number of accidents will be:

$$\frac{7·5\sqrt{(2q_lQ)}}{10\ 000}+\frac{4·5\sqrt{(2q_rQ)}}{10\ 000}$$

which is about 30 per cent less than the former expression. If more than two roads are combined the gain is even greater.

Accidents and junction layout

Most of the results relating accidents to junction layout have been obtained as a result of before-and-after studies (i.e. studies in which changes in accidents were noted as a result of a change in layout of the junction, see Chapter 16). Unless stated otherwise the results given in this section are based on sufficient data to be reasonably reliable.

REALIGNMENT OF THREE-WAY JUNCTIONS

Twenty-seven junctions have been studied under this heading, including seven studied by Bennett[30] before the 1939–45 war. They have been divided into four sub-groups which are listed below. Squaring of the junctions was achieved by alterations to kerb lines and provision of islands and refuges, and in most cases turning movements round both shoulders were made sharper, usually, it is believed, in order to control the traffic entering rather than leaving the major road.

The modified "Bennett" junction was arrived at after discussion by the Road Research Board of a design put forward by Bennett[30] in 1947. Its main features illustrated in Fig. 13.9 and Plate 13.8 are the gradual turns

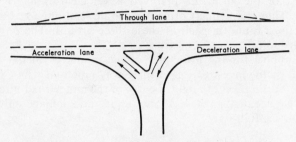

Fig. 13.9. Layout of modified "Bennett" junction

for vehicles turning right out of the major road or left into it, but a nearly square layout for vehicles turning right into the major road. The estimated effects on injury-accidents (not involving pedestrians) are as follows:

(*a*) Squaring of left-hand splay junctions* (seven cases) average reduction 20 per cent.

(*b*) Squaring of right-hand splay junctions* (12 cases) average increase 90 per cent.

(*c*) Making turning movements more sharp at junctions already square (six cases) average reduction 20 per cent.

(*d*) Construction of modified "Bennett" junctions in place of square junctions (two cases) average reduction 30 per cent.

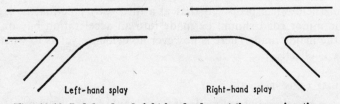

Fig. 13.10. Left-hand and right-hand splays at three-way junctions.

The 90 per cent increase in accidents resulting from the squaring of right-hand splay junctions* is based on enough data to make it most probable that the effect was real, but the other three changes could easily have arisen from chance variations.

* For explanation of left-hand and right-hand splay junctions see Fig. 13.10.

In some of the changes studied, information on the severity of the accidents is available. These data, though not conclusive, tend to show that the proportion of injury-accidents resulting in fatal or serious injury is somewhat smaller for square junctions (where the layout has a slowing-down effect on vehicles) than at splay junctions. If this effect is real it reduces the advantage of the gradual right turn out of the major road, though even for fatal and serious accidents the evidence is slightly in its favour.

The above results are on the whole in accordance with the principles underlying the modified "Bennett" junction. Incomplete data indicate that at the squared right-hand splays and at the Bennett junctions (sub-groups (b) and (d) above) most of the accidents involved a vehicle turning right out of the major road, while at the squared left-hand splays (sub-group (a) above) most of the accidents involved a vehicle turning right into the major road. Thus the Bennett principles would lead one to expect changes in the directions found in each of these three groups. The position as regards sub-group (c) is not so clear.

Further support for the principles of the modified "Bennett" junction are provided by the investigation of three-way junctions which included an examination of the effect of angle of entry of the minor road into the major road. Relative accident rates (personal-injury and damage-only accidents) were obtained as follows:

	Relative accident rate. Vehicle on major road and vehicle turning round:	
	right shoulder	left shoulder
Left-hand splay	(i) 5.0	(iv) 6.2
Square . .	(ii) 3.6	(v) 7.6
Right-hand splay.	(iii) 3.0	(vi) 5.4

The principles would lead one to expect that rate (ii) would be less than rate (i), and that rate (vi) would be less than rate (v).

Summerfield[28] has proposed that at a three-way junction the right turn from the minor road should be made into an acceleration bay on the far side of the major road. There is however no evidence yet as to whether this measure is effective.

STAGGERED CROSS-ROADS

Mention has already been made of the advantages from an accident point of view of staggered cross-roads. Further evidence has been given by Garwood and Tanner[32] who estimated a reduction of 85 per cent in accidents after straight-over cross-roads were converted into right-left staggers. These results, together with some more recent before-and-after studies, give on the average a reduction of about 60 per cent for injury-accidents and probably more for serious accidents.

In addition to the above results, Bennett[30] in an investigation undertaken before the 1939–45 war studied the effect of staggering 19 cross-roads in Oxfordshire to the right-left layout and 10 to the left-right layout (see Fig. 13.7 and Plate 13.9). The accident frequencies were rather small but they showed an average reduction of 55 per cent for injury-accidents; this appeared to be mainly due to the right-left staggers, the others showing only a slight reduction.

ROUNDABOUTS

The layout of intersections as roundabouts was found by Garwood and Tanner [32] to produce an estimated reduction of about 60 per cent for injury-accidents (see Plate 13.10). (This investigation included some roundabouts in built-up areas). Reductions of about the same magnitude have also been found in more recent data.

DUAL CARRIAGEWAYS

In the course of studying the effects on accidents of providing dual carriageways on various lengths of road, it was noted that marked increases in accident frequency occurred at some of the junctions on the improved sections.[32] Although, in some cases of these, further changes in the layout have now caused the accident figures to fall again, it appears that special care is required in the design of junctions on dual-carriageway roads if increases in accident frequency on these roads are to be avoided (see Plate 13.11).

Detailed examination of the individual cases tends to support the following conclusions:

(i) Right-turn exits from the fast lane of a dual carriageway should not be made at very low speeds; this can be prevented either by allowing a fairly large turning radius or by providing a deceleration lane in the reserve.

(ii) Vehicles emerging from the side road and entering or crossing the further stream should cross the near stream at right angles, not in a weaving manoeuvre.

(iii) At cross-roads a right-left stagger with a gap in the central reserve opposite each arm is preferable to a straightover layout (see Fig. 13.11(*b*)).

FLYOVER JUNCTIONS

In Great Britain, flyover junctions are confined largely to motorways and the basic type is that in which the motorway crosses the minor road roughly at right angles, one connecting road or "slip road" being built in each of the four quadrants to produce the characteristic "diamond" shape (see Plate 13.12). This arrangement avoids direct right turns on the major road but not on the minor road. At busier junctions a roundabout may be incorporated on the minor road (see Plate 13.12). Where site conditions prevent the building of slip roads in all four quadrants or where the major and minor roads cross obliquely, one or two of the slip roads may be transferred to other quadrants. In such cases the transferred slip roads must be looped (see Plate 13.13). Sometimes two slip roads in the same quadrant are amalgamated over part of their length to provide two-way working. Many other

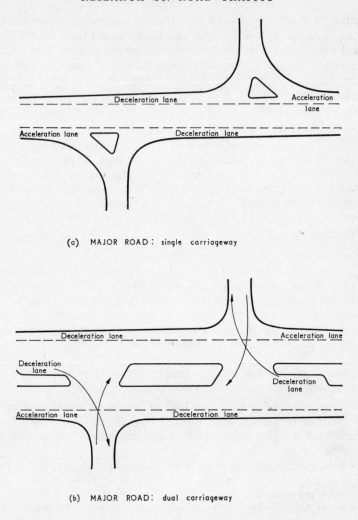

(a) MAJOR ROAD : single carriageway

(b) MAJOR ROAD: dual carriageway

**Fig. 13.11. Diagrammatic layout of staggered cross-roads
illustrating principles of design**

arrangements are possible depending upon the importance of the minor road
whether all possible turning movements are permitted, and whether direct
right turns are permitted. At three-way junctions the "trumpet" design may
be used (see Plate 13.14). Where two motorways cross the full "clover-leaf"
may be considered suitable (with four loops and four direct slip roads for
left turns), but an alternative design is the "double-diamond" in which
eight slip roads are connected to a roundabout suspended between the two
motorways. Another design which is being considered for use in Great
Britain requires four-level treatment (see Plate 13.15).

Because of the gradients on slip roads and the presence of bridge abutments and parapets, a problem characteristic of flyover junction design is

the difficulty of providing adequate visibility for traffic leaving the motor-way. Another problem is that of obtaining adequate weaving lengths in the roundabouts.

Experience with flyover junctions in Britain is, at present, too limited to produce conclusive findings about details of design, but some of the results of the Laboratory's studies of accidents on the London-Birmingham motor-way are given in pp. 418-22 and in Reference 33.

IMPROVEMENTS TO VISIBILITY

Twenty junctions have been studied[32] where improvement of visibility was the main feature. In some cases, however, small changes in layout were made. Fifteen of the junctions were taken from the pre-war work of Bennett.[30] The improvements were achieved by realignment or the removal or setting back of buildings, walls, hedges etc. On the average, the improvements led to a reduction of about 30 per cent in injury-acci-dents. Reductions occurred at both 3-way junctions and at cross-roads.

TRAFFIC CONTROL SIGNS

Although it has been shown by before-and-after studies that the provis-ion of "HALT" or "SLOW" signs can produce substantial reductions in accidents (at least 75 per cent), the sample of sites studied was largely in built-up areas. The investigation of rural 3-way junctions, already referred to, did, however, make some estimate of the effect of these signs in rural areas, and it was concluded that Halt signs probably reduced accidents involving vehicles emerging from the minor road by nearly a half, but that Slow signs had little effect.

An investigation[34] of the effect on accidents of providing "YIELD" signs failed to show any definite changes attributable to the signs.

Driver behaviour

DRIVERS ENTERING THE MAJOR ROAD

In a study of the speed at which drivers approached the major road at a few junctions (mostly in built-up areas), it was concluded that speeds were between 8 and 12 mile/h at about 20 ft from the intersection. It was also concluded that the smallest gap all emerging drivers would accept in the major road traffic was 6 to 7 seconds.

Observations at three junctions in the Slough area indicated that the min-imum interval in the major traffic stream accepted by all drivers was about 18 seconds; 50 per cent would accept about 8 seconds or more.

In another study it was found that the mean speed of vehicles over the 100 ft between 150 and 50 ft from the major road was 14·6 mile/h. For vehicles which did not stop at the major road, the average speed over the last 50 ft before the major road was 7.4 mile/h. The minimum gap in the main stream accepted by all minor road vehicles was about 12 seconds. However, many drivers would accept much smaller gaps.

Yet another study showed that at junctions with Halt signs, about 50 per cent of drivers emerging from the side would accept a 7-second gap in the major road traffic; at Slow signs, the corresponding figure was six sec-onds. Gaps of 12 seconds were rarely refused.

16

DRIVERS LEAVING THE MAJOR ROAD

Observations have been made of driver behaviour at square and Bennett three-way junctions. With the splay form, average speeds of right turners from the major road were 15 to 20 mile/h at the junction and were several mile/h faster than with the square form. With the square right turn, smaller time gaps in the opposing main stream were accepted than with the splay turn. The minimum gap which all drivers would accept was about nine seconds.

Summerfield[28] recorded speeds of vehicles turning left from the major road and using a deceleration lane. Average speeds decreased from about 29 mile/h 200 ft from the junction to 17 mile/h at the junction.

The results of a controlled experiment, carried out at the Laboratory's test track at Crowthorne on the design of rural junctions with respect to the movement of turning left from the major road (see Plate 13.16) are summarized in Table 13.36.[33]

Table 13.36 shows that the cornering speed increased systematically with the radius and with the proportion of transition curve (see Fig. 13.12); the

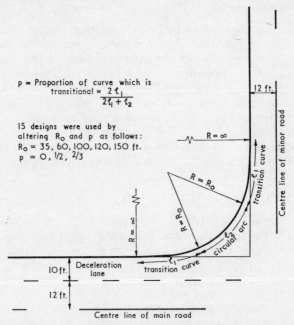

Fig. 13.12. Experimental junction layout for studying
left turns from the major road

mean minimum speed ranged from less than 12 mile/h for a 35 ft radius without transition to about 24 mile/h for a 150-ft radius, with two-thirds transition. The speed was, in fact, roughly proportional to the square root of the radius. The lateral acceleration imposed on the vehicle when cornering varied only slightly for different radii and proportions of transition. Thus it would appear that each driver adjusted his speed in relation to the geometry of the curve, so as to keep the maximum lateral acceleration attained roughly constant. Another result was that the proportion of drivers who allowed the vehicle to cross the centre line of the minor road after cornering was greater for the smaller radii. Table 13.36 also shows that the area of road space required to provide the curve is appreciably higher for the greater radii, the area being proportional to the square of the radius. The one-half transitional design requires 11 per cent more area and the two-thirds transitional design 24 per cent more than the design without transition. Although the measurements made in this study suggest that the provision of transition curves has only a slight effect on driver behaviour, there are other reasons for incorporating these features in design; they facilitate the application of superelevation and they probably improve the appearance of the curve.

TABLE 13.36

Summary of results obtained in controlled experiment on rural junction design

Proportion of total length of curve which was transitional	Radius of circular arc (ft)					
	35	60	100	120	150	Average all radii
Mean minimum speed* (mile/h)						
0	11·5	15·6	20·8	21·1	23·5	18·5
½	12·2	16·7	19·6	22·1	23·6	18·8
⅔	12·3	17·0	20·7	22·8	24·1	19·4
Average all values . .	12·0	16·4	20·3	22·0	23·7	18·9
Mean maximum lateral acceleration† (percentage of g)						
0	33	36	37	33	33	34
½	33	40	35	36	34	35
⅔	34	36	34	33	32	34
Average all values . .	33	37	35	34	33	35
Per cent of drivers crossing centre line of minor road						
0	20	25	15	5	0	13
½	25	15	5	0	5	10
⅔	20	30	10	10	0	14
Average all values . .	22	23	10	5	2	12
Area of road space required to provide the curve‡ (sq. ft)						
0	263	773	2146	3090	4829	2220
½	291	855	2375	3420	5344	2457
⅔	326	959	2663	3835	5992	2755
Average all values . .	293	862	2398	3448	5388	2477

* The minimum speed reached by each driver on cornering, averaged over all drivers.
† The maximum lateral acceleration reached by each driver on cornering, averaged over all drivers.
‡ The extra road space required by comparison with a right-angled corner without a curve.

Although the experiment indicated that each driver tended to attain a particular maximum value of lateral acceleration, there was considerable variation in the standard set by different drivers. The lateral acceleration attained by individual drivers, averaged over all designs, ranged from 0·25g to 0·44g; the overall average for all drivers was 0·35g with a standard error of 0·012g.

It is believed that the results of this experiment may be of value in practical design problems. For example, if 20 mile/h were selected as being a suitable minimum turning speed for left turns off the major road, the results in Table 13.36 suggest that the radius should be about 100 ft.

THE USE OF ACCELERATION AND DECELERATION LANES

Observations of traffic entering and leaving the major road at a square three-way junction by means of acceleration and deceleration lanes about 200 ft long and tapering from 16 ft width showed that, whereas 10 per cent of vehicles turning left into the major road were still wholly within the acceleration lane at a distance of 75 ft from the centre line of the minor road, none of the vehicles turning left into the minor road had wholly entered the deceleration lane at this distance.

The junction at which these observations were made was later made into a right-hand splay after which vehicles turning left into the major road would enter during smaller time gaps in the main stream and merge with that stream at higher speeds, i.e. at speeds nearer those of the main stream.

SIGNS AND CARRIAGEWAY MARKINGS

Observations at several junctions with "HALT" signs showed that drivers were more likely to stop at these places than at junctions without signs or with "SLOW" signs. When "HALT" was painted on the carriageway in large letters at junctions with "HALT" signs at the roadside, more people stopped before entering the major road. Accidents are also fewer where "HALT" or "STOP" is painted on the carriageway,[35] see Chapter 11.

When a square junction was converted to a modified Bennett layout, drivers at first made wrong turns. There was a substantial reduction in these wrong turns after large arrows were marked on the carriageway and improvements were made to direction signs.

Delays

Although a considerable amount of research has been carried out into delays at junctions in urban and suburban areas, particularly at intersections controlled by traffic signals, very little observational information is available for rural junctions. However some theoretical work has been done by Tanner[36] who set up a theoretical model for estimating delays at uncontrolled priority junctions, in terms of flows on the major and minor roads and the minimum gap acceptable to traffic entering the major road. Tabulations have been produced for various values of these and other quantities. The relations obtained suggest the existence of a critical level of flow above which the delay to vehicles joining or crossing the main road becomes very great, indicating the need for some other form of treatment.

An important feature of the roundabout is that its presence delays all traffic, including through traffic on the major road, regardless of the loading of the roundabout. Theoretical considerations suggest that on a fast rural dual-carriageway road, this delay may be of the order of 15 seconds per vehicle. Comparison with priority treatment suggests that, unless the junction is very busy, roundabouts may produce greater overall delay than priority treatment. However, at the busier junctions, roundabouts will prevent the excessive delay found with priority treatment; delays will be minimized by building the junction on more than one level but at higher cost. This theoretical work has been used to produce indications of the economic form of treatment at junctions on rural dual carriageways in terms of major and minor-road flows. The assumptions made will need to be checked by direct measurement before more precise rules can be formulated.

Principles of design

The information so far available appears to point to or to be consistent with the following principles of design.

(a) The number of junctions on major roads should be kept to a minimum (vehicle-vehicle accidents proportional to square root of flow product).

(b) Equal attention should be paid to entry to and exit from the major road and special attention should be given to vehicles turning right (accidents involve a turning movement into and out of the major road about equally often).

(c) Layouts should be so arranged that the speeds of traffic streams which are merging are about equal. Similarly the layout should enable streams which are diverging to start to diverge at about the same speed (roundabouts, Bennett junctions).

(d) On single-carriageway roads, the layout should enable the right-hand exit from the major road to be made obliquely (Bennett junction). Where the major road is a dual carriageway, the layout should enable vehicles turning right from the major road to do so without impeding the traffic stream from which they are turning.

(e) To help the driver's view along the major road, the layout should be such that the manoeuvre of emerging from the minor road and turning right should not be made at too oblique an angle.

(f) The driver on the minor road should be made aware of the major road ahead and at a cross-road should be prevented from making a direct crossing. ("HALT" signs, staggered junctions, improved visibility, roundabouts.)

(g) Carriageway markings and traffic signs should be used to guide drivers into the desired paths. ("HALT" on the carriageway, arrows on the carriageway.)

(h) Where necessary the major carriageway should be widened, if possible, so that an extra lane can be provided to accommodate vehicles waiting to make the right turn from the major road.

Some of these ideas are illustrated diagrammatically in Figs. 13.9 and 13.11. Some points relating to the detailed design of junction layout are given below.

(a) Kerb radii are often too small; 60 ft is probably the minimum to use, at least on main roads and 100 ft would probably be necessary to permit an average turning speed of 20 mile/h. It is possible that small radii and the size of acceleration and deceleration lanes at present in use tend to discourage the use of these lanes by left-turning traffic.

(b) It seems reasonable that a driver on the major road travelling at the design speed should be able to see, at a distance equal to his stopping distance, whether a vehicle is about to emerge from a side road. Further, a driver on the minor road should be able to see, on approaching the major road, a distance at least equal to the minimum gap into or through which he is able to drive without dangerously obstructing vehicles on the major road. The second requirement is probably more stringent than the first. For gaps in the major road of eight seconds (acceptable to the majority of drivers) and 12 seconds (acceptable to all but the extremely cautious) the following visibility distances are obtained:

Design speed (mile/h)	Visibility distance required (ft)	
	8-second gap	12-second gap
40	475	700
50	575	875
60	700	1050
70	825	1225

(c) Drivers on the minor road cover the last 50 ft before the major road at an average speed of about 10 mile/h. During this time a vehicle on the main road travelling at the design speed, S mile/h, will travel $5S$ ft.

(d) A stagger at a cross-roads of about 120 ft recommended in Ministry of Transport Memo 575 seems satisfactory.

(e) Warning signs denoting junctions are not always adequate, especially signs indicating roundabouts at night.

While it is clear that the frequency of accidents at a junction depends to a considerable extent on its layout and traffic flow, and some broad outlines of the dependence have been presented, it is also evident that the problem of the safe and economical design of junctions is very far from solved. If money and land were freely available, then safe and convenient layouts could be designed by building on two or more levels, although even multi-level junctions will still have accidents.

REFERENCES TO CHAPTER 13

1. MINISTRY OF TRANSPORT and SCOTTISH DEVELOPMENT DEPARTMENT. Road accidents 1961. London, 1962 (H.M. Stationery Office).

2. TANNER, J. C., H. D. JOHNSON and J. R. SCOTT. Sample survey of the roads and traffic of Great Britain. *Department of Scientific and Industrial Research, Road Research Technical Paper No. 62.* London, 1962 (H.M. Stationery Office).

3. MINISTRY OF TRANSPORT. Memorandum on the design of roads in rural areas (superseding Memoranda 653, 715 and Circular 727). *Memorandum No. 780.* London, 1961 (H.M. Stationery Office).

4. DEPARTMENT OF SCIENTIFIC AND INDUSTRIAL RESEARCH, ROAD RESEARCH LABORATORY. Research on road safety. London, 1963 (H.M. Stationery Office).

5. RAFF, M. S. Interstate highway-accident study. *Bull. Highw. Res. Bd, Wash.*, 1953, (74), 18–45.

6. DRAKE, J. Road plan for Lancashire. Preston, 1949 (Lancashire County Council), Appendix J.

7. GILS, J. F. L. VAN. Accident rates on different types of road. *Second International Course in Traffic Engineering, Switzerland, 1954*. London, 1954. (World Touring and Automobile Organisation.)

8. TURNER, J. K. Accident rates on dual carriageways. *Department of Scientific and Industrial Research, Road Research Laboratory Research Note* No. RN/2847/JKT. Harmondsworth, 1956 (Unpublished).

9. CALIFORNIA DEPARTMENT OF PUBLIC WORKS, DIVISION OF HIGHWAYS. Median accident study 1958. Sacramento, California 1958 (State Printing Office.)

10. TARAGIN, A., and H. G. ECKHARDT. Effect of shoulders on speed and lateral placement of motor vehicles. *Proc. Highw. Res. Bd, Wash.*, 1953, **32**, 371–82.

11. WILLIAMS, S. J., and C. E. FRITTS. Let's build safety into our highways. *Publ. Saf.*, 1955, **47**, (5), 19–23, 38.

12. BELMONT, D. M. Effect of shoulder width on accidents on two-lane tangents. *Bull. Highw. Res. Bd, Wash.*, 1954, (91).

13. TARAGIN, A. Driver behaviour as affected by objects on highway shoulders. *Proc. Highw. Res. Bd, Wash.*, 1955, **34**, 453–72.

14. BALDWIN, D. M. Accident facts for highway design. *Publ. Saf.*, 1947, **31** (2), 10–1.

15. GRIME, G. Parked vehicles in rural roads. *Traff. Engng & Control*, 1961, **2** (12), 724–6.

16. CHARLESWORTH, G., and T. M. COBURN. The influence of road layout on speeds and accidents in rural areas. *J. Instn munic. Engrs*, 1957, **83** (7), 221–40, 252.

17. NEW JERSEY TURNPIKE AUTHORITY. Eleventh Annual Report 1959. New Brunswick, New Jersey, 1960 (New Jersey Turnpike Authority), p.13.

18. BILLION, C. E. Shoulder occupancy on rural highways. *Proc. Highw. Res. Bd, Wash.*, 1959, **38**, 547–69; Discussion, 570–5.

19. MINISTRY OF TRANSPORT. Carriageway markings: criteria used in installing double white lines, warning lines and lane lines. *Circular No.* 764. London, 1960 (Ministry of Transport).

20. LEEMING, J. J. Road curvature and superelevation. London, 1951 (Contractors Record and Municipal Engineering).

21. CLAES, G. A study of accident rates in Belgium. *Internat. Rd Saf. Traff. Rev.*, 1955, **3** (3), 25–32.

22. MINISTRY OF TRANSPORT AND CIVIL AVIATION. Road Accidents 1953. London, 1955 (H.M. Stationery Office).

23. MINISTRY OF TRANSPORT AND CIVIL AVIATION and SCOTTISH HOME DEPARTMENT. Road accidents 1958. London 1959 (H.M. Stationery Office.)

24. WARREN, H. A., and R. HAZELDINE. Experimental transition curves. *J. Instn munic. Co. Engrs*, 1939, **65**, (21), 1021–6.

25. LEEMING, J. J., and A. M. BLACK. Road curvature and superelevation: experiments on comfort and driving practice. *J. Instn munic. Engrs*. 1950, **76** (8), 522–39; Discussion, 540–3.

26. ARIZONA STATE HIGHWAY DEPARTMENT and U.S. BUREAU OF PUBLIC ROADS. Downhill speeds of trucks on mountain grades. Phoenix, Arizona, 1950 (Arizona State Highway Department).

27. AMERICAN ASSOCIATION OF STATE HIGHWAY OFFICIALS. A policy of geometric design for rural highways. Washington, D.C., 1954 (American Association of State Highway Officials), p.118.

28. SUMMERFIELD, K. Design of road intersections. *Proc. Instn civ. Engrs, Part II*, 1956, **5** (3), 332–60; Discussion, 360–78.

29. TANNER, J. C. Accidents at rural three-way junctions. *J. Instn Highw. Engrs*, 1953, **2** (11), 56–67.

30. BENNETT, G. T. Road junctions: suggestions for improved designs. *Publ. Wks Rds & Transp. Congr.*, 1947, *Final Report*, 175–92.

31. PIKE, B. D. F. Vehicle manoeuvres resulting in traffic accidents. *Army Operational Research Report* No. 3/48. London, 1948. (Unpublished).

32. GARWOOD, F., and J. C. TANNER. Accident studies before and after road changes. *Publ. Wks munic. Services Congr.*, 1956, *Final report*, 329–54; Discussion, 374–80.

33. DEPARTMENT OF SCIENTIFIC AND INDUSTRIAL RESEARCH. Road Research 1962. The report of the Road Research Board with the report of the Director of Road Research, London, 1963 (H.M. Stationery Office), pp. 43–8.

34. INWOOD, J., and R. F. NEWBY. "Yield" signs. *Surveyor, Lond.*, 1959, **118** (3524), 1065–6.

35. OLDER, S. J. Effect on driver behaviour of painting "Halt" or "Stop" on the road at junctions with "Halt" signs. *Surveyor, Lond.*, 1960, **119** (3537), 279–82.

36. TANNER, J. C. A theoretical analysis of delays at an uncontrolled intersection. *Biometrika*, 1962, **49** (1/2), 163–70.

Chapter 14

Safety Fences and Kerbs

SYNOPSIS

Roadside barriers; vehicle guard rails; corrugated metal rails; concrete guard rails; median barriers; cable and chain-link fence; blocked-out beam barrier; parabolic deflector barrier; median barriers and accidents; Safety kerbs. Energy-absorbing barriers. Anti-glare screens.

INTRODUCTION

Most safety fences which have been erected in Great Britain are intended to prevent vehicles leaving the carriageway at locations where to do so would endanger the occupants, common sitings being at sharp bends and precipitous slopes. In the U.S.A. and in some continental European countries similar fences are also extensively used on dual-carriageway roads to prevent vehicles crossing narrow central reserves. These fences which are designed to withstand vehicle impacts are known as guard rails. More recently fences which have as their primary function the prevention of headlamp dazzle have been installed on central reserves at a few selected sites in this country. Evaluations of these fences both at the Laboratory and elsewhere are described in this chapter, together with the results of tests to determine the effectiveness of safety kerbs.

ROADSIDE BARRIERS

Vehicle guard rails

Guard rails should prevent vehicles having access to areas where they cannot safely travel, with a minimum of risk to the occupants. The guard rail should redirect the vehicle on to a course parallel to the rail with a lateral deceleration tolerable to the passengers. For many years the most common form of construction of guard rails in Britain and the U.S.A. has been corrugated metal beams bolted together to form a continuous ribbon, mounted on stout wooden posts buried in the soil so that the upper edge of the rail is 2 ft above ground. Somewhat lower guard rails consisting of concrete beams attached to concrete posts have found favour in continental Europe, where corrugated metal rails, some of which present a flat face to the traffic, are also used. Whatever the system, the behaviour of the rails under vehicle impact should be matched to that of the support posts to avoid high localized stresses and consequent violent vehicle reaction.

Corrugated metal rails

Metal beams are corrugated longitudinally in profile to provide lateral stiffness without resorting to heavy gauge metal, the usual thickness being

459

either 10, 11 or 12 gauge. An additional advantage is that the depth of the beam tends to hold the vehicle away from the posts. All profiles are variants of a W-section, either rounded at the folds, or angular with flat peaks to the corrugations; the former is known as the A-profile in the U.S.A., and the latter as the B-profile in Germany. The width of the rail is usually about 12 in. and the depth of the corrugations about 3 in. They are manufactured in lengths of 11-13 ft which are bolted together on site, and attached directly to the posts by means of a single high tensile steel bolt passing through the central trough of the beam (Plate 14.1). Typical support posts are 6 in × 8 in., or 8 in. square softwood, 6 in. square hardwood, or precast concrete, buried in soil to a depth of 4 ft, the height to the centre of the rail being 18 in. Usual post spacings are either 12 ft 6 in. or 10 ft 6 in. Generally the post spacings are either 12 ft 6 in. or 10 ft 6 in. Generally the posts deflect in the soil without fracture, so that the yielding properties of the fence under impact are determined by the shear strength of the soil and the deformation of the metal rail. The shear strength varies with the type of soil, its moisture content and degree of compaction, and is difficult to control. Detailed specifications relating to steel rails were issued by the American Association of State Highway Officials in 1951. The requirements for beam strength are that a rail simply supported at 150 in. centres must sustain a concentrated central loading of 2000 lb with a deflection not greater than $3\frac{1}{2}$ in., that a 10-gauge rail must withstand a tensile load of 70 000 lb, and a 12-gauge rail must withstand at least 50 000 lb.

Dynamic tests on corrugated steel rails using American cars weighing about 4000 lb were carried out by Beaton and Field,[1] and Cichowski, Skeels, and Hawkins.[2] Beaton and Field found that for impacts at 60 mile/h and 30° approach angle the rail pocketed into curves of small radius between the posts, which themselves overturned in the soil sufficiently to pull the rail down below the height of the centre of gravity of the test cars (about 2 ft). The combined effect of these two actions was to impart a transverse couple to the vehicle such that on reflection from the rail it rolled over laterally towards the fence with disastrous results. This corkscrew motion is characteristic of severe impacts in which the centre of pressure is below the centre of gravity of the vehicle.

Cichowski, Skeels and Hawkins carried out many less severe tests from which it is evident that the corrugated guard rails are effective at impact speeds up to at least 35 mile/h and angles of incidence up to 20°. They recommended that both ends of the rail should be ramped and anchored into the ground, to ensure that the full ribbon tensile strength was developed over the length of the installations which, if less than 100 ft, might otherwise collapse towards the impact point.

Concrete guard rails

The most widely known concrete guard rail is the Danish designed Dansk Auto Vaern (D.A.V.), which has been used in most of the countries of Western Europe, the Soviet Union and Japan. In Britain it has been known as the Dahl safety kerb. It consists of a reinforced concrete beam with a convex face, tilted so that the lower edge makes first contact with the vehicle wheels (Plate 14.2). It is supplied in 6-ft sections and mounted on concrete posts so that the lower edge of the beam is about 6 in. above the road. The height of the top of the rail is 20 in. above ground. The under-lying idea behind the design is that upon impact the front wheel of the vehicle will be deflected to rub against the rail without damage to the body-work, the friction between the tyre and the lower edge of the rail reducing the speed of the vehicle, while the bulge of the tyre under the rail prevents any wheel climb.

Dynamic tests have been carried out on this design of D.A.V. rail in Sweden[3] and Japan.[4] The Swedish tests showed that the rail repulsed a 4000 lb light truck striking at 28 mile/h and 23°, but that it was demolished by a 20 000 lb lorry striking at 30 mile/h and 25°. The most interesting Japanese test was carried out with a British car weighing 3750 lb which struck the rail at a speed of 34 mile/h and an angle of 20°. The vehicle was reflected without overturning and sustained damage to the impacting wheel and the lower parts of the bodywork. The dynamic deflection of the rail was $6\frac{1}{2}$ in. and the permanent set $4\frac{1}{4}$ in.

In the mid 1950's D.A.V. guard rails were erected on a number of sites in Great Britain, on bends judged to be dangerous either on the basis of actual accident records, or on an estimate of the likelihood of serious accident if a vehicle left the road at these points. The sites included bends of varying curvature. The behaviour of drivers was studied at 10 sites before and after the installation of the rail.

It was found that at sharp bends, drivers of cars and commercial vehicles tended to keep well away from the kerb and nearer the centre of the road. An accident investigation at 19 sites proved inconclusive. Compared with the general trend in rural accidents, over all the sites there was a significant reduction of 60 per cent in all personal-injury accidents, but serious and fatal accidents increased, but this may have been due to chance.[5]

Recently new designs of D.A.V. guard rails have been developed in Germany and Italy; both have the same dimensions but whereas the German beams are of reinforced concrete, the Italian beams are pre-stressed. They are 13 ft in length and are roughly triangular in section, the vertical height of the convex face being 12 in. A length of the German rail, known as Dywidag, has been tested at the Laboratory. Its overall height was 22 in., with a 10 in. gap under the rail. Dynamic tests using British cars weighing 3000 lb showed that the guard rail was effective up to a 31 mile/h approach speed at 20°. A vehicle striking the rail at 46 mile/h and an angle of 20° overturned laterally towards the rail in the corkscrew motion mentioned earlier (Plate 14.3). The rail itself was badly damaged.

Median barriers

An American study of cross-median accidents was carried out by Hurd[6] on roads with varying widths of traversable median, i.e. a median with no physical barriers. It was found that cross-median accidents formed 10 per cent of total accidents for 5-ft medians, 5 per cent for 18 ft, 2 per cent for 30 ft, and 1 per cent for 50 ft and above. These figures suggest that an unpaved median without barriers must be at least 50-ft wide before it can be regarded as non-traversable. Narrow medians can be made non-travers-able by installing suitable guard rails, a practice which is increasing in the U.S.A. and Germany, the two countries with the greatest experience of high-speed roads. In Germany double-sided versions of the metal and concrete guard rails already described are installed on heavily-trafficked roads. In the U.S.A., Beaton and Field[1] carried out a comprehensive series of tests on possible median fences and recommended two designs, one a new concept of a flexible barrier designed to entrap the offending vehicle on the median and the other a modification of the corrugated beam guard rail. The flexible barrier was recommended for medians which would allow an 8-ft deflection, and the metal beam barrier for narrow medians down to 3 ft.

Cable and chain-link fence

In its original form shown in Fig. 14.1, the flexible barrier consisted of two $\frac{3}{4}$ in. steel cables supported at 30 in. above the ground by light "I"-section 4.1 lb/ft steel posts set in concrete at 8 ft centres, with an additional cable 9 in. above ground. Chain-link mesh 36 in. wide completed the fence whose overall height was 3 ft 9 in. The cables were attached to the posts

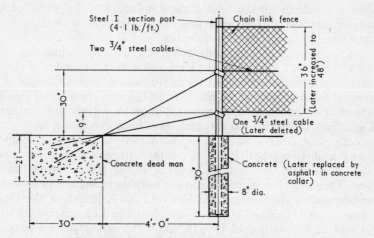

Fig. 14.1. Chain-link and cable median barrier

by means of "U" bolts, the chain-link being trapped between them. The cable ends were anchored below ground in large concrete blocks, and turnbuckles were recommended at 500 ft intervals to maintain the cables in a condition of little or no stress. This design of fence successfully contained 4000-lb cars colliding at 60 mile/h and 30°, and also a 17 500-lb single-decker bus at 42 mile/h and 34°. Posts ahead of the colliding vehicle are bent over at ground level either by direct impact or by the tension developed in the upper cables, which slide off the posts but maintain their original height at the vehicle by cutting into the bodywork. The chain-link mesh is severed and gathered progressively in front of the vehicle throughout the collision to provide extra resistance.

Cichowski, Skeels and Hawkins[2] carried out tests on this Californian design at 65 mile/h and approach angles of 17° and 8°. They reported that the fence worked satisfactorily at these lower impact angles, except when the bunched mesh caught on a turnbuckle on the cable and violently decelerated the car. Their comment on the fence was that in a comparatively minor collision (35 mile/h and 8°) the car was much more severely damaged than it would have been against a corrugated metal guard rail.

A critical appraisal of this design of safety fence was made on the basis of one year's use, by Beaton, Field and Moskowitz.[7] This showed that at high speeds and low angles there was a tendency for the contacting wheels to mount the barrier by means of a ramp formed by a post and the firmly secured chain-link fabric, combined with the lower cable. At these high speeds and low angles there was also a tendency for vehicles to spin out from the fence into the road. Further tests were therefore undertaken at speeds of 70–80 mile/h and angles of approach less than 10°. The height of the fence in these tests was increased from 3 ft 9 in. to 4 ft 9 in., but the cables remained at the 30-in. level.

It was concluded that the lower cable could be omitted from the fence to overcome the ramp effect, without otherwise affecting barrier behaviour. The original intention had been that the lower cable would stiffen the fence and also trap the contacting wheel to retain the vehicle within the median. Fastening the mesh outside the cable overcame snagging at turnbuckles, when the vehicle struck the side containing the mesh. No tests were made with the mesh on the reverse side to the impact however, a condition in which the desired bunching of the mesh may not occur. No remedy was found for the final violent spin out at high speed low angle impacts. In one reported accident a sports car struck the fence at an angle greater than 30° and passed under the 30 in. cables. In view of these experiences it would be prudent to resolve the doubts about the snagging action of the mesh, and about the optimum cable height to contain small cars, before applying this promising median fence to British roads.

Blocked-out beam barrier

The barrier recommended by Beaton and Field for narrow medians is known as the blocked-out beam type. Its final form is shown in Fig. 14.2.

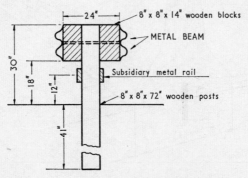

Fig. 14.2. Blocked-out metal beam median barrier

Compared with the usual construction of single-sided barrier the rail is 6 in. higher and blocked-out 8 in. from the posts, post spacing is halved to 6 ft 3 in., and a lower auxiliary rail is included. Blocking-out of the rail has two benefits; it increases the clearance between the vehicle and the posts, and also tends to maintain rail height when the posts are forced back. This latter effect together with the increased height of the rail minimize the tendency of the colliding vehicle to roll over after impact. The lower rail prevents the wheels and parts of the bodywork forced under the corrugated beam from snagging on the posts. This barrier successfully reflected a car colliding at 60 mile/h and 32°, and also a single-decker bus at 41 mile/h and 36°.

A less costly version of the fence has been evaluated at the Laboratory. Corrugated steel rails were blocked out 9 in. from posts at a height of 21 in. to the rail centre instead of 24 in., in order to dispense with the auxiliary rail. The post spacing was 10 ft 6 in., and midway between posts wooden blocks connected the two rails to increase their stiffness without recourse to extra posts. This barrier successfully deflected a 3000-lb car impacting at speeds and angles of up to and including 50 mile/h and 20° (Plate 14.4) with no rolling action of the vehicle. In severe impacts of this order the decelerations experienced by the vehicle occupants are about three times as great with beam-type guard rails as with the flexible cable barrier.

Parabolic deflector barrier

In urban areas road widths are restricted and traffic volumes frequently exceed their planned capacity. This is the case in much of the State of New Jersey, where in 1955 the Highway Department, after erecting adjacent narrow median treatments for study purposes, concluded that an 18-in. high parabolic concrete kerb was superior to steel beams, concrete beams, and a 12-in. high concrete kerb.[8] Subsequently the height of the parabolic deflector was increased to 32 in. (Fig. 14.3); from the top where it is about

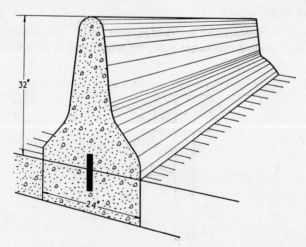

Fig. 14.3. Concrete median deflector barrier

6 in. wide it curves outwards to a ground width of 24 in., the shape being determined by the distance the body of a vehicle overhangs the wheels, to ensure that no part of the bodywork touches the barrier at small impact angles. In New Jersey this type of barrier is replacing the conventional

central grassed island bounded by low kerbs. It does not appear to have been subjected to controlled impact tests.

Median barriers and accidents

The rigid concrete median divider used in New Jersey has eliminated cross-median accidents without increasing other kinds of accident.[8] A possible explanation of this success is that in heavy traffic the risk attached to crossing a traversable median is high, whereas the chance of striking a median barrier at both high speed and high angle is fairly remote.

Steel beam guard rails erected on the more heavily-trafficked German autobahnen, which have median widths comparable to those of British motorways, are also reported to reduce accidents.[9] The installation on the Frankfurt-Mannheim autobahn is claimed to have reduced total accidents involving the median by 15 per cent, and the more serious of these accidents by as much as 67 per cent. On the other hand, although the installation of blocked-out beam and cable barriers in California virtually eliminated cross-median accidents, total accidents and injury accidents increased at the barrier sites (based on one year's experience).[7] Experimental median barriers installed on the M.1 motorway will provide data for British conditions.

SAFETY KERBS

High kerbs have been used in a number of countries to prevent vehicles leaving the road. Generally they are successful only at angles of approach of the order of 5° for realistic vehicle speeds. At larger angles the tyre tread, the wheel rim, or both, provide enough friction for the kerb to be climbed. Undercutting the kerb minimizes the climbing action of the tyre by reducing the contact area and possibly by trapping the bulge of the tyre wall. Beaton and Peterson[10] showed that friction may also be reduced with steel kerb facings, a car approaching at 40 mile/h and 15° being successfully reflected by a 9 in. metal-faced kerb, but without appreciable speed reduction. Fig. 14.4 shows a 10 in. undercut kerb considered by Beaton and

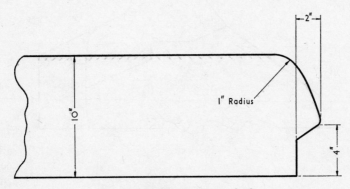

Fig. 14.4. Undercut concrete kerb

Peterson to provide the best compromise between the prevention of climbing and the provision of sufficient friction to decelerate the vehicle.

Beaton and Field[11] studied the effect of kerbs mounted in front of vehicle barriers. They concluded that at high speeds a 6-in. kerb had little or no effect on either the rise or deflection of the collision car, the body of the car maintaining its travelling elevation while the raise of the kerb was absorbed in the deflection of the tyre and the springing system. This effect was only true where the travel time between the kerb and barrier was short, the car soon recovering its original elevation relative to the ground, and rebounding above it for a short time. Where the kerb was 8 in. or more in height, an immediate dynamic jump was imparted to the car. To minimize the chance of the vehicle leaping a bridge railing, Beaton and Field recommended that the basic rail height of 27 in. above the kerb should be increased by 5 in. for each 12 in. of setback from the kerb face, to a maximum height of 48 in.

In the New Jersey study of experimental median barriers it was noted that an outlying kerb caused vehicles to strike the centre barriers in an unfavourable manner, and that a driver, after mounting the low kerb, might be thrown about sufficiently to lose control of the vehicle. For these reasons it was concluded that any kerb in front of a vehicle barrier was potentially dangerous.

A Belgian designed safety kerb has been tested at the Laboratory. It stands about 12 in. above the road, and consists of a shallow ramp terminating in a convex rubbing edge. (Fig. 14.5). With a Standard Vanguard car (overall wheel diameter 27 in.) the critical speeds at which the contacting wheel climbed over the kerb were 18 mile/h at a 10° approach, and 12 mile/h at a 15° approach (Plate 14.5). When the kerb and tyres were wet the critical climbing speed at 15° increased to 20 mile/h, demonstrating the influence of friction on the climbing action. The performance of the kerb

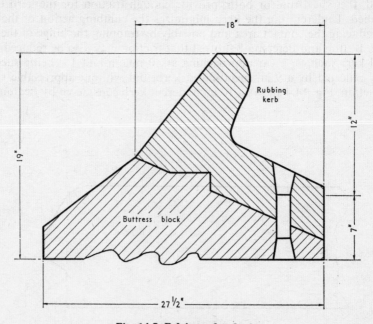

Fig. 14.5. Belgian safety kerb

can be approximately summarized in terms of the component of the approach velocity perpendicular to the barrier. This was about 3 mile/h in dry conditions, i.e. if the velocity perpendicular to the kerb in any approach exceeds this value the kerb will be climbed. The relationship between critical speed and angle of approach based upon this simple assumption is shown in Fig. 14.6 and gave good agreement with observed values at angles of approach greater than about 7½°. However, at an angle of 5° successful reflection of the vehicle occurred at 40 mile/h, which is somewhat better than the predicted critical speed of 36 mile/h. A possible explanation is that at small approach angles only the side wall of the tyre contacts the kerb, whereas at larger angles part of the tyre tread pattern is brought into play.

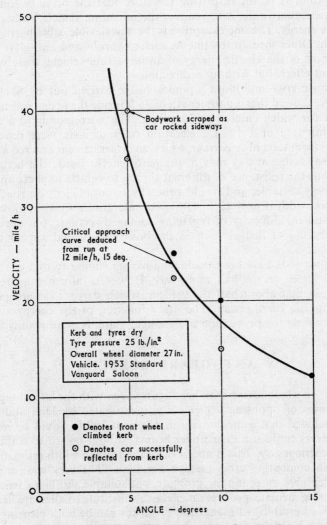

Fig. 14.6. Critical velocities and angles of approach to mount Belgian safety kerb

In the foregoing tests no attempt was made to narrow the angle of approach by turning the steering wheel just before impact. In one test where this was done deliberately, the kerb successfully reflected the car when the approach path was originally at 15° and 41 mile/h. Tests carried out in this way have little value, however, for the reasons that they do not enable reliable comparisons to be made between barriers, and the driver of an out-of-control vehicle could not be relied upon to narrow the impact angle of the front wheel to the best advantage.

ENERGY-ABSORBING BARRIERS

The kinetic energy of a car weighing $1\frac{1}{2}$ tons and travelling at 50 mile/h is 125 ft tons. It is not surprising therefore that the primary function of most vehicle guard rails is to redirect the offending vehicle, rather than to absorb its energy. The one exception is the new flexible cable barrier, which does both. Other median treatments such as shrubs and anti-glare screens, absorb some of the kinetic energy of an impacting vehicle, thereby having a deterrent effect, but without redirection.

Tests on a rosa multiflora japonica hedge carried out by Skelton[12] in the U.S.A. showed that a path length of 76 ft inside the hedge was necessary to stop a car which entered at 50 mile/h. This corresponds to a constant deceleration rate of 1·1g. Deceleration rates of 5–8g were reported by Zurcher[13] from tests in Austria in which an American car entered a Lycium (box thorn) hedge at $37\frac{1}{2}$ mile/h, the path lengths inside the hedge being 6–9 ft. Thus the resistance of different shrubs to vehicle impacts appears to be extremely variable, and would generally be insufficient on roads where the median width is only 13 ft. Other considerations are their slow rate of growth, and the difficulty of replacing damaged sections, but nevertheless the possibilities of hedges such as the box thorn would appear to merit further study.

No impact tests have been made on a barrier similar to that of the metal anti-glare screen on the M.1 motorway. However, information from accidents shows that about half the vehicles which strike it do not penetrate to the opposite carriageway. The other function of the energy-absorbing barriers, namely the prevention of headlight glare, is more readily fulfilled.

ANTI-GLARE SCREENS

The way in which seeing with headlights varies with the lateral separation of the beams of opposing vehicles was investigated by Jehu and Hirst.[14] They concluded that a median width of about 100 ft would be necessary before drivers could use their upper beams without regard to traffic in the opposite carriageway. This is about twice the median width estimated to be effective in combating cross-median accidents. The very wide median is rarely acceptable on economic grounds, but suitable shrubs or fences sited along existing medians provide an effective substitute to alleviate headlight-glare. A well established plantation of shrubs can be both pleasing by day and effective by night; fences are effective on medians too narrow to support shrubs. Where a gap in an anti-glare screen allows crossing traffic, alignment must be such as to allow adequate sight-distance for the crossing manoeuvre. This usually entails terminating the screen some considerable distance from the opening, but on a wide enough median angling the screen away from the direction of the obscured through traffic may suffice.

A metal anti-glare fence almost two miles in length was erected as an experiment on the M.1 motorway in January 1960, at a site which contained a variety of topographical features including the crest of a hill, a trough or valley, left and right-hand bends and a length of straight road. The fence comprises expanded steel mesh panels mounted on tubular steel posts set in concrete, the upper edge of the screen being at 5 ft 8 in. and the lower edge 1 ft 8 in. above the carriageway level, to benefit drivers of heavy vehicles as well as those in cars (Plate 14.6). Mesh sizes were chosen to give complete cut-off of oncoming headlight beams up to 20° from their straight ahead direction, on both straight and curved road sections, so that glaring intensities experienced by an oncoming driver were less than 1000 cd. Glare protection was found to be satisfactory except when approaching the hilltop, when lamps were visible through the gap under the screen; this situation was remedied by extending the mesh to ground level near the summit. At angles greater than 20° oncoming lamps are still partially screened by the mesh, and for this reason a later screen erected on the A.40 trunk road at Denham has a cut-off angle of 15°. A criticism of the fence on the M.1 motorway has been loss of daylight amenity, but the improved night driving conditions it provides are generally acknowledged. The installation is too short however to influence night-time accidents, the rate for which is about twice that of accidents by day on this road. Similar screens have since been erected in several American States.

SUMMARY

In this chapter an attempt has been made to compare the effectiveness of vehicle guard rails and safety kerbs. An example of safety kerbing has been shown to be an effective barrier for cars provided the component of the approach velocity perpendicular to the kerb is not more than about 3 mile/h, the end point being the climbing of the kerb by the contacting wheel. Tests on a concrete guard rail show that the corresponding critical velocity perpendicular to the rail is somewhat in excess of 10 mile/h, the end point being the rolling action towards the rail imparted to the car upon impact. From American work it appears that conventional corrugated steel guard rails mounted directly on to the support posts have a corresponding critical velocity of at least 12 mile/h. Both concrete and steel guard rails appear to be capable of some improvement by a better matching of post and beam strengths, and steel guard rails are also improved by blocking-out the beam from the posts. It appears from work in the U.S.A. that a low kerb in front of a guard rail reduces its effectiveness.

Three types of barrier have been developed recently in the U.S.A. for various widths of median, the rigid concrete deflector for very narrow medians on heavily-trafficked roads, the semi-rigid blocked-out corrugated beam for slightly wider medians, and the flexible cable and chain-link fence for medians about 16 ft wide. The concrete deflector is best suited to urban areas where there will usually be road lighting; the blocked-out beam and cable barriers are more applicable to rural roads which may not be lighted, and both could be modified to provide protection from headlight glare. Most shrubs appear to offer insufficient resistance to impacting vehicles to be effective on the 13 ft medians of existing British motorways, but tests in Austria suggest that a type of box thorn hedge may be an exception, and there may be others.

The effect of these guard rails and kerbs on accidents is not known with certainty. It seems probable that although most cross-median accidents are prevented, a number of accidents of other types may be generated by striking the guard rail; the overall effect may therefore depend on the particular conditions of traffic and the geometrical design of the road. In this connexion, it should be realized that no guard rail or kerb, however well designed, can be guaranteed never to give rise to an accident; this must always remain a possibility when a vehicle travelling at high speed is deflected from its original path. Ideally, the efficiency of a guard rail at a particular speed might be expressed in terms of the proportion of occasions in which a vehicle was deflected by the rail without loss of control; in practice, it is too expensive to do the required number of tests to establish the efficiency in this way for even one type of vehicle. It remains a possibility that a narrow median equipped with the most effective barrier yet designed ((1963) may not be as effective in preventing accidents as a wide (40 ft +)), flat, median free from dangerous obstacles. Furthermore, it may be noted that any sort of metal crash barrier would present a serious hazard to a motorcyclist, who would be well advised to give it a wide berth.

REFERENCES TO CHAPTER 14

1. BEATON, J. L., and R. N. FIELD. Dynamic full-scale tests of median barriers. *Bull. Highw. Res. Bd, Wash.*, 1960, (266), 78–125.

2. CICHOWSKI, W. G., P. C. SKEELS and W. R. HAWKINS. Appraisal of guard rail installations by car impact and laboratory tests. *Proc. Highw. Res. Bd, Wash.*, 1961, **40**, 137–78.

3. STATENS VÄGINSTITUT. Vägrackesförsök utiförda, år 1954 av. *Kungl Väg- och Vattenbyggnadsstyrelsen and Statens Väginstitut, Special Rapport* 4. Stockholm, 1955 (Statens Väginstitut).

4. TAKAHASHI, N. Report on D.A.V. Auto-guard strength tests/field tests by automobiles. Tokio, 1960 (Transport Technical Research Institute and Ministry of Transportation).

5. TRESIDDER, J. O. An investigation into the use of a special safety kerb on dangerous bends. *Department of Scientific and Industrial Research, Road Research Laboratory Research Note* RN/3244/JOT. Harmondsworth, 1958 (Unpublished).

6. HURD, F. W. Accident experience with traversable medians of different widths. *Bull. Highw. Res. Bd, Wash.*, 1956, (137), 18–26.

7. BEATON, J. L., R. N. FIELD and K. MOSKOWITZ. Median barriers: one year's experience and further controlled full-scale tests. *Proc. Highw. Res. Bd, Wash.*, 1962, **41**, 433–68.

8. PALMER, D. R. G. Center barriers save lives. Trenton, New Jersey, 1962 (New Jersey State Highway Department, Bureau of Public Information).

9. HOEG, M. Modern steel barriers. *Dansk Vejtidsskr.*, 1962, **39** (4), 77–80.

10. BEATON, J. L., and H. PETERSON. Roadway barrier curb investigation. *California Department of Public Works, Division of Highways*. Sacramento, California, 1953 (State Printing Office).

11. BEATON, J. L., and R. N. FIELD. Final report of full scale dynamic tests of bridge curbs and rails. *California Department of Public Works, Division of Highways*. Sacramento, California, 1957 (State Printing Office).

12. SKELTON, R. R. Crash barrier tests on multiflora rose hedges. *Bull. Highw. Res. Bd, Wash.*, 1958, (185), 1–18.

13. ZURCHER, H. Typen, Berechnung und Wirkungsweise von Leitplanken. *Eidgenössische Technische Hochschule, Zürich, Institut für Strassenbau*. Zurich, 1961 (Eidgenössische Technische Hochschule Zürich).

14. JEHU, V. J., and G. HIRST. Problem of headlight glare. Effect of lateral separation of beams of opposing vehicles on seeing with headlights. *Traff. Engng & Control*, 1962, 3 (9), 545–7, 552.

Chapter 15

Economics

SYNOPSIS

Investment in road inprovements; comparison of different investment criteria; benefits; costs; comparison of costs and benefits. Road pricing.

INTRODUCTION

The book so far has discussed a large number of topics connected with traffic, mainly concerned with finding ways of improving the conditions in which traffic operates. Few, if any, of these improvements can be carried out without incurring costs, usually in the form of direct monetary costs and sometimes in the form of costs imposed upon road users.

Economics is concerned with the allocation of the community's scarce resources—land, labour, capital—between an almost unlimited number of different uses and activities in order to obtain the maximum benefit to the community from those resources. In the British economy, and in most advanced economies, the usual way of channelling resources is by means of the price system whereby individuals can sell their labour and other surplus resources for a common currency and can use that currency to purchase their requirements, thus influencing the allocation of resources. But the price system is not normally applied in the case of roads; road users do not pay directly for roads at the time and place that they use them (except to a very limited extent in the case of parking meters and toll roads). Consequently there is no semi-automatic mechanism for adjusting road space and traffic to each other and for indicating where and when the road space that road users would prefer to other things should be provided.

Much of the economics of roads therefore is concerned with remedying this deficiency and with supplying criteria by which to estimate and judge the effective demands of the community for road space.

The economic problems of roads and road traffic cover a wide range of subjects: the relative merits of different forms of transport, parking policies, and the costs of road construction, to name just a few. Here the concern is with two main subjects, though there are many ramifications of each: investing in improvements to the road system, and making a more economic use of the existing road system by ensuring that journeys are not undertaken unless the road users are willing to pay the full cost.

INVESTMENT IN ROAD IMPROVEMENTS

Comparison of different investment criteria

The road problem is sometimes thought of as almost entirely one of investment. What factors usually determine the amount of investment that is undertaken in different sectors of the economy? In the case of private

472

industry the main consideration is profit. In the case of gove.
vestment in, for example, schools and hospitals, no income is ea.
the investment, and it is very difficult to assess the benefits. (To quote
"Public Investment in Great Britain October 1961".—"Commercial prob
ability in the normal sense is often not relevant to public-service capital
expenditure; expenditure decisions have to be taken on broad grounds of
public interest".)

With investment in roads, however, although the use of the roads is
not charged for, improvements to the road system usually yield a number
of direct economic benefits. These benefits do not accrue to those responsible for making the investment but to the road users, they can however
be measured and compared with the cost of the investment. Such comparisons should be made to indicate not only whether an improvement
scheme is worthwhile but also to compare with other schemes. This may
affect the order in which various schemes are undertaken.

In its simplest form the procedure for carrying out an economic investment is to measure the benefits, measure the costs and then compare them.

Benefits

CLASS OF BENEFITS TO BE CONSIDERED

Road improvements are designed to bring benefits to road users in the
form of cheaper, quicker and safer travel. The value of this basic benefit
is received by the road user but is often passed on to other persons. Provided
that the full value of the basic benefit is measured it would be double
counting to include any of the "passed on" or indirect benefits. For instance,
it is often argued that by not including increases in land value that appear
to be caused by the road improvements the total benefits are underestimated. The land increases in value because it has become more accessible and this gain in accessibility is measured by the gains to traffic through
time savings and reduced running costs. If the traveller had to pay the road
authority the full value of the net benefits that he received as a result of the
road improvement he would still make the journey but the value of the
land would then not alter. In assessing the economic return from road
improvements the concern is with calculating the total benefits to the
community not with how the benefits are distributed. In a normal private
investment the concern is with the benefits which accrue to the investor
although other benefits, including negative ones, frequently exist.

The benefits which are relevant can be divided into those resulting from
a change in operating costs of which the most important element is the
saving in time and changes in accidents. In addition there are often a
number of amenity benefits such as a reduction of noise or fumes which
cannot be precisely valued.

The traffic to be considered falls into one or more of the following
categories:

(i) that which already uses the road being improved;
(ii) that which will divert to the improved road from other roads;
(iii) that which will remain on roads from which traffic is diverted, e.g.
a road which is now by-passed;
(iv) generated traffic, i.e. journeys which would not have taken place
without the improvement.

Moreover as the benefits are assessed over a number of years the future growth of traffic must also be allowed for.

SAVINGS IN OPERATING COSTS

The reduction in operating costs can be subdivided into two main categories: time saving and vehicle running costs. Running costs cover the consumption of fuel and lubricants, and the maintenance and depreciation of vehicles and tyres.

TIME SAVINGS. It is frequently contended that there is no value in the saving of a few minutes or fractions of a minute as this time cannot be put to any useful purpose and, therefore, it is wrong to place a value on the aggregate of these savings for a number of people. There is some truth in this premise in a number of individual cases, but on the other hand a small saving of time may enable some activity to be undertaken which in total takes much longer. For example, a saving of a few minutes on a long distance lorry journey might frequently be spent by the driver in a cafe or dawdling over part of the route (the former alternative has some benefit, the latter possibly only a dis-benefit), but in a number of cases the result might be that a return journey could be made on the same day or that an overnight stop, with lodging allowances and delays, could be avoided, the value of which would far outweigh the value of the sum of the few minutes which was the direct saving.

The other argument for valuing all time savings is that they have a cumulative effect, a few minutes here and there adding up to hours and having undoubted value. Almost all transport improvements, even the most radical ones, such as areoplanes replacing trains, result in only small time savings at first. In the short run these savings may have little value but over a longer period they have a considerable value. It must be admitted however that some of the benefits from time savings might not accrue immediately and therefore the total benefits may be slightly overestimated in the short run.

Time is saved, as a result of road or traffic improvements, by the vehicle, by its driver and passengers and by any load being carried. It is difficult, and in most cases not possible, to place a value on the time savings of goods in transit and frequently it will be of little importance, though the possible cumulative effect of a large number of small savings must not be forgotten. The time that goods spend in transit represents capital locked up; the saving of this time is therefore a gain and improved transport facilities by being either quicker or more regular, may result in lower stocks being required.

The saving in time by vehicles has a value because the same fixed costs (overheads) including depreciation of the vehicle can be spread over a greater number of vehicle-miles, or conversely the overall cost per vehicle-mile will fall. A reduction in the time a vehicle takes to do any particular journey will result in more time being spent in the garage, the same vehicle doing more vehicle-miles, fewer vehicles doing the same vehicle-miles, or some combination of these results. It is not possible to forecast what the result will be in any particular case but if it is assumed that the time saved is put to good use then the benefits are the same whether calculated on a basis of more vehicle-miles or less vehicles. In practice it is more convenient to calculate on the basis of a saving of vehicles.

Often the chief gain from a road improvement is the saving of the time of persons travelling, but there is frequently disagreement as to how this should be valued. Time saved whilst travelling is usually divided into (1) working time, and (2) non-working time, which includes time spent travelling to and from work. The value of working time is taken as the income earned during the relevant period of time.

It is sometimes contended that saving of working time results in extra productive work being done thus adding to the national income but that no such result follows from the saving of non-working time. This argument attaches undue weight to the value of production as against the value of leisure and utility, which is the ultimate aim of all production.

It is obvious that in a very large number of cases non-working time has a value to the person concerned. This can be seen clearly in situations where a motorist has the choice between paying money to save time by using a ferry or toll route and travelling via a longer route and thus saving money. Attempts have been made, where such conditions occur, to assess the value that motorists place on their non-working time but it is never possible completely to isolate the influence of time. The results indicate that the value of non-working time is approximately equal to the value of working time. This answer is not inconsistent with theoretical considerations. The evidence is, however, not very strong and a number of problems arise such as the value to be placed on the time of non-workers (e.g. housewives, children and the retired). Until more accurate information is available a somewhat arbitrary valuation must be placed on non-working time and a figure of three quarters the appropriate rate for working time has therefore been adopted.

MEASUREMENT OF CHANGES IN JOURNEY TIMES AND ANNUAL VEHICLE-MILEAGE. The aim at this stage in carrying out economic assessments of road improvements is to estimate, for traffic affected by the improvement, the annual vehicle-mileage and journey speed, or annual traffic flow and average delay in the case of intersections, in conditions with and without the improvement, at the time when the improvement is completed and for a period of years. This entails applying several of the methods and techniques which have been discussed in the earlier chapters of this book. The measurement of speeds and the effects of changes in width, in gradient and in horizontal curvature on speed are discussed in Chapters 3 and 13, the estimation of delays at intersections in Chapter 9, origin-and-destination surveys in Chapter 4, and the measurement of traffic volumes, the estimation of annual volumes and of the future increase in traffic in Chapter 2.

Although estimates of benefits are made in terms of annual vehicle-mileages the calculations of speeds should not be based on the average hourly flow over the whole year. For when, as is frequently the case, a small proportion of the total hours have a much greater than average flow the total benefits will be underestimated if this variation is ignored. On the other hand it may well be difficult or unnecessary to make calculations for each hour separately, as the requisite data will not be available and the work entailed would be enormous. The grouping of hours in any particular case will depend on the variation that exists and the available data.

For improvements to existing roads it is necessary to measure any change in road distance as a result of realignments, and to estimate what the speeds and flows would be on the unimproved and the improved road at the time the improvement is carried out and in future years.

For new roads it is necessary to determine the origins and destinations of traffic using the existing road network from which traffic is likely to be drawn to the new road, and to measure or estimate journey speeds and journey times between these origins and destinations via existing routes and via the new road. Traffic may then be assigned between the existing routes and the new road by assuming that vehicles will choose the route giving either the least journey time, or the lowest cost. In making assessments, time is a more convenient and less ambiguous basis than cost. Annual vehicle-mileage and journey speeds with and without the improvement may then be estimated both for traffic transferring to the new road and for traffic remaining on the existing roads. For a simple by-pass which will save time and to which there is no intermediate access a survey need only discover whether or not the traffic wishes to enter the area to be by-passed, and traffic can be assigned to the by-pass, or to existing roads accordingly.

VALUATION OF CHANGES IN OPERATING COSTS. In assessing the value of the benefits from a change in operating costs the vehicle operating cost and time costs can be considered together. To value the changes in operating costs it is necessary to estimate the total annual vehicle-mileage with and without the improvement and the appropriate speeds, and to value each total at representative costs per vehicle-mile. The costs per vehicle-mile consist of a basic cost plus costs that vary with time; the time costs can be divided by speed in order to get total costs per vehicle-mile. These costs are given in Table 15.1 for five vehicles, each of which is taken as being typical of a wide class.

The benefits to be valued are the benefits to the community as a whole and therefore indirect taxes, such as fuel tax, purchase tax on vehicles and licence fees, are excluded since, although they are a cost to the individual road user, they do not represent a real cost to the community but only a transfer within the community, and the revenue represented by these taxes would probably have to be raised in any case. Insurance premiums should also be excluded from the calculations since to include these and to value savings in accidents would be double-counting.

The principal costs that may be assumed to vary directly with time are the cost of the working time of vehicle occupants and the overhead costs of commercially-operated vehicles which may be allocated to the working time of the vehicle, e.g. interest on the capital invested in the vehicle.

These costs have been obtained from various sources. The proportion of car occupants travelling in working time and average car occupancies from the Ministry of Transport's survey of motoring,[1] the incomes of the occupants of cars, taxis and buses were found in the London Travel Survey carried out in 1954,[2] and overhead costs per vehicle-hour of operation and the occupancies of commercial vehicles were derived from the economic study of the London-Birmingham motorway.[3]

In addition to costs that vary directly with time, it was found on research into the effect of road conditions on fuel consumption and other vehicle operating costs that, up to certain limits, fuel consumption per mile tended to decrease as speed increased. Tyre wear, and a proportion of maintenance and depreciation costs are assumed to vary with speed in a way similar to fuel costs.[4] Thus an element of operating costs could be assumed to vary directly with journey time over a given distance up to speeds of about 40 mile/h for cars and light commercial vehicles and up to 30 mile/h for heavier vehicles. Two formulae are given for cars and public-service vehicles: one attaching no value to non-working time and one valuing non-working time at three quarters of the rate applicable to working time.

TABLE 15.1

Average total costs per vehicle-mile
(pence/mile)

Class of vehicle	"Typical" vehicle		Costs for different range of speed (v)	
			$v < 40$ *mile/h*	$40 < v$ *mile/h*
Car . . .	1750 cc	(a)	$3 \cdot 9 + 76/v$	$4 \cdot 5 + 52/v$
		(b)	$3 \cdot 9 + 221/v$	$4 \cdot 5 + 197/v$
Light commercial vehicle . . .	10 cwt carrying capacity Petrol		$3 \cdot 9 + 104/v$	$4 \cdot 2 + 91/v$
			$v < 30$ *mile/h*	$30 < v < 40$ *mile/h*
Medium commercial vehicle . . .	4 tons carrying capacity Diesel		$5 \cdot 1 + 110/v$	$5 \cdot 6 + 95/v$
Heavy commercial vehicle . . .	8 tons carrying capacity Diesel		$7 \cdot 2 + 145/v$	$8 \cdot 0 + 121/v$
Public-service vehicle .	44 seater Diesel	(a)	$9 \cdot 3 + 283/v$	$10 \cdot 5 + 249/v$
		(b)	$9 \cdot 3 + 1097/v$	$10 \cdot 5 + 1063/v$

(*a*) non-working time valued at zero.
(*b*) non-working time valued at three quarters the value of working time.

In table 15.1 the basic costs per vehicle-mile independent of speed (fuel, lubricants, tyres, maintenance and depreciation) are obtained from tables of vehicle operating costs.[5,6] For lower speeds, as explained above, some of these costs vary with speed and are, therefore, transferred from the basic to the variable part of the formula by assuming that the operating costs (net of tax) given in the tables for vehicles typical of their classes occur at 40 mile/h (light vehicles) and at 30 mile/h (heavy vehicles). Above speeds of about 40 mile/h (light vehicles) and about 30 mile/h (heavy vehicles) operating costs per mile do not decrease with increase in speed and, in fact, there is a tendency for them to increase slightly with speed above these levels.

From the above data an average cost per vehicle-mile can be calculated. Based on the average composition of traffic on all roads in 1963 (69 per cent cars and taxis, 3 per cent buses and coaches, 14 per cent light commercial vehicles and 14 per cent other commercial vehicles) and placing no value on non-working time, the formulae are:

$$4 \cdot 4 + \frac{93}{v} \text{ if } v < 37 \text{ mile/h}$$

or

$$5 \cdot 0 + \frac{71}{v} \text{ if } v > 37 \text{ mile/h}$$

where v = average speed of all traffic in mile/h. 37 mile/h for all traffic, of this composition is equivalent to 40 mile/h for cars.[7] When non-working time is valued at three quarters of the rate for working time the formulae become:

$$4{\cdot}4 + \frac{218}{v} \text{ if } v < 37 \text{ mile/h}$$

or

$$5{\cdot}0 + \frac{196}{v} \text{ if } v > 37 \text{ mile/h}$$

From the average cost per vehicle-mile multiplied by the annual vehicle-mileage, with and without the improvement, it is possible to calculate the annual change in operating costs as a result of the improvement.

The above cost figures do not apply directly to intersections where traffic costs can be expressed in terms of delay. The relevant cost of delay per vehicle-hour for a traffic flow of the standard composition given above, is 218 pence (93 pence if no value is given to non-working time). This figure may be applied directly to the annual change in delay expected from an improvement to an intersection to give the annual savings from the improvement.

REDUCTION IN ACCIDENTS

To measure the benefits resulting from accident reduction it is necessary first to estimate the reduction in the accident rate, (usually expressed in terms of personal-injury accidents per million vehicle-miles). This can be done from the results of before-and-after studies which indicate the changes which may be expected from different types of improvement (see Chapter 16 and Reference 8) or from the accident rates on different classes of road.[9]

ACCIDENT COSTS. A road accident always results in some costs, some of which are measurable in monetary terms and some such as suffering and bereavement which are not. Investment in road improvements often leads to a change in the number of accidents (usually, it is hoped, to a decrease), and an estimate of the monetary value of this change should be included in the calculation of the benefits.

It is possible to adopt different criteria in defining the total cost of accidents, and estimates have been made by different methods and for a number of different countries. The method used at the Laboratory, which could be defined as the National Income approach, is based on one which was first put forward by the Government Actuary in Appendix III to Jones.[10] The costs which are included in this method can be divided into two broad groups: those that cause a diversion of current resources (repairing the damage to vehicles and other property, the costs of medical treatment and administrative costs) and the loss of future output because people are killed or injured in road accidents.

A further item, which is difficult to measure and is therefore usually excluded from the estimates, is the cost to other road users of the delay which frequently results from road accidents.

The measure required for the loss of output is the present-day value of the net loss. This is calculated by estimating the difference between the future loss of output of those killed and injured, given a normal expectation of working life, and the future consumption of those killed, given a normal expectation of life, both discounted back to give present-day values. The Laboratory estimates for 1952 are given by Reynolds[11] and these have been extrapolated for the ensuing years.

In the study of costs, account must be taken of the difference between a casualty (who is an individual) and an accident (which is an event).

TABLE 15.2

Cost of road accidents in Great Britain in 1962

(i) *Total costs*

	£ million
Costs of medical treatment	13
Damage to vehicles and other property	45
Administration expenses	26
Loss of output	91
	175

(ii) *Average unit costs*

	£
Medical costs and cost of loss of output per:	
Fatal casualty	3080
Serious casualty	800
Slight casualty	50
Costs of damage to property per accident	55
Administrative cost per:	
Injury accident	90
Damage only accident	10

In practice the figure usually used to assess the value of savings in accidents is the average value of all accidents per personal-injury accident (i.e. the total cost of person-injury and damage-only accidents divided by the number of personal-injury accidents). This average for 1962 is £650. The reasons for using an average in this form is that records of damage-only accidents are often very inadequate and, except over a wide area, there will in any year be only a few accidents of any degree of severity (certainly of fatal and serious ones) and any changes in these numbers will probably not be significant.

It should be remembered that apart from this measureable economic cost there are costs in the form of suffering and bereavement which are impossible to measure, though this does not preclude an arbitrary value being included in the assessment as the result of an administrative decision.

GENERATED TRAFFIC

Apart from traffic that already uses the roads that are affected directly or indirectly by a road improvement, traffic will frequently be generated by the improvement. Generated traffic arises from journeys that were not worthwhile before but which are worthwhile under the improved conditions. Generation is likely to be of particular importance in very congested areas where there is probably a large frustrated demand ready to take advantage of any improvement in the situation.

To estimate the generated traffic consequent on a change in the cost of travelling between two areas, it is necessary to know the fundamental relation between the cost of travel (including such "costs" as the value of time, discomfort, etc.) and the volume of traffic. This depends on a large number of factors which are largely unknown: population, inhabitants' incomes, the travel pattern, and the business and social relations, actual and potential, between areas surrounding the improvement. Attempts have been made to establish a general law expressing the relation between the distance (or other factor expressing the cost of travel) between two points and traffic flow. This usually assumes the form

$$Q_{ij} = \frac{k P_i P_j}{d^n}$$

where Q_{ij} = traffic flow per unit time by a given means of transport between areas i and j;

k = a constant;

P_i and P_j = the populations of the areas i and j;

d = distance or some other indication of the cost of travel between the two points, (journey time is usually of more significance than distance);

n = a positive exponent. It has been found empirically to vary between $0 \cdot 6$ and $3 \cdot 4$

This suggests that total traffic will be multiplied by $(t_1/t_2)^n$ where t_1 and t_2 refer respectively to the journey times with and without the improvement. The times to be considered are the total journey times and not just the time taken to travel the length of the improvement. Since the value of the exponent n is not known for typical situations, the use of this relation to estimate generated traffic is subject to a wide margin of error. For traffic between towns n has usually been found to lie between 2 and 3.

Tanner[12] has shown that a more theoretically sound formula is obtained by replacing $1/d^n$ by $e^{-\lambda d}/d^n$.

The benefits to generated traffic arise in the following way. If the cost of travel between two points is reduced from C_1 to C_2, travellers would then find it worthwhile to carry out journeys which were worth less than C_1 but more than C_2; if the cost had remained at C_1 these journeys would not be worthwhile and would not be carried out. Of the additional journeys made possible by the reduction in cost, the most valuable will be worth C_1 and will cost C_2 leaving a gain of $C_1 - C_2$ to the person carrying out that journey. The least valuable additional journey will be worth C_2 and will cost C_2 leaving no gain to the person carrying out that journey. Assuming a straight line relation between "worthwhileness" of journeys and number of journeys, the average savings per vehicle will be given by $\frac{1}{2}(C_1 - C_2)$ and the total gains to generated traffic will be given by $\frac{1}{2} Q_g (C_1 - C_2)$, where Q_g is the amount of generated traffic. Therefore benefits to generated traffic should be valued at half the rate for existing traffic.

In the majority of cases of rural improvements the amount of generated traffic and the benefits to it are likely to be small and can safely be ignored but in the case of large schemes such as new motorways it must be allowed for. (An example of this is given in the calculations for the London-Birmingham motorway.)[3] In the case of urban improvements an allowance should be made, although the position is often more complex because the number of journeys made at the moment is restricted not only by the costs but also by the road capacity. So even comparatively small schemes are likely to produce an appreciable amount of generated traffic. Generally speaking, however, generated traffic tends to increase the gains from improvement to open rural roads where speeds are high, and tends to reduce the gains from improvement in congested urban areas where speeds (even after improvement) are low. These tendencies should be borne in mind when comparing the gains from different road improvement schemes.

The effect of generated traffic on the speed of existing traffic must be allowed for when estimating the benefits that accrue to this traffic.

The estimated benefits to generated traffic must be added to the savings in operating costs to existing traffic and to accident savings to give total benefits.

Costs

The capital cost of the improvement should include all costs attributable to the construction of the road at the price level obtaining on the date on which the improvement is carried out. Any land previously acquired should be included at the estimated amount that it could be sold for at the time when the improvement is to be carried out. The original cost of the land, or the cost of surrounding land are both immaterial; it is the price foregone by using this land for road building that has to be considered. The current cost of any land purchased now for future use should be included.

A further cost that should be considered, but is often overlooked, is the cost of delay and accidents which is frequently imposed on traffic whilst the improvement is being carried out.

Allowance must be made for changes in maintenance costs; these should include the costs of periodic resurfacing, cleaning, lighting, verge maintenance and traffic control.

Comparison of cost and benefits

There are some limitations on the exclusive reliance on economic assessments in comparing a road programme owing to the weight that needs to be given to factors outside the scope of economic analysis.

INTERDEPENDENCE OF DIFFERENT SCHEMES

When comparing different schemes it must be remembered that many schemes are inter-related. Any pair of schemes falls into one of three categories: independent, complementary or competitive. Schemes are independent where the benefits from one scheme are completely unaffected by whether or not the other scheme is carried out. Complementary schemes are those where the implementation of one scheme will increase the benefits from the other, i.e. the total benefit if both schemes are carried out is greater than the sum of the benefits calculated independently. Competitive schemes are those where the carrying out of one will detract from the return expected from the other; the extreme example is where the schemes are alternatives or mutually exclusive, say different lines for a by-pass or a motorway when the building of one would make the other almost entirely redundant.

PRINCIPLES OF A LONG TERM RATE OF RETURN

A road will last for a great number of years, almost indefinitely if properly maintained. If traffic was not expected to change then the benefits from the improved road would remain constant and it would only be necessary to calculate the return for one year. Traffic has however been increasing continuously (except for interruptions due to the two world wars) ever since the first automobile travelled on a road and is expected to increase over the foreseeable future. From past trends in the increase in the number of vehicles and vehicle-miles, it should be possible to forecast the future growth of traffic with a reasonable degree of accuracy although forecasts for any particular road are likely to be less accurate than those for the country as a whole. The benefits from an improvement will not usually increase at the same rate as the traffic and, even when for different improvements the traffic is expected to increase at the same rate, the benefits may change at different rates.

To calculate the rate of return over a number of years, costs and benefits must be calculated for future years. As costs and benefits in the future are worth less than they are today they must be discounted to give present-day values. It is considered sufficient to make the calculations for 30 years; beyond this date the accuracy of the forecast will not be very reliable and the discounted values will be small. (It is not necessary to calculate the benefits for each year; normally it will be sufficient to make calculations for each tenth year and to interpolate for the others.)

To assess whether a scheme is worthwhile and to compare the relative merits of different schemes the "present value" of the improvement should be calculated. Future costs and benefits in each year should be calculated and the present value of the investment is the excess of the discounted benefits over the discounted cost. Algebraically the present value is expressed as:

$$P_0 = (B_0 - C_0) + \frac{(B_1 - C_1)}{(1+i)} + \frac{(B_2 - C_2)}{(1+i)^2} \cdots \frac{(Bn - C_n)}{(1+i)^n}$$

P_o = the present value of the investment in the year 0,

= the value of the benefits which occur in the year t,

the costs which occur in the year t,

discount rate per annum,

n = the number of years for which the return is to be calculated.

If resources are unlimited then all the schemes which have a positive present value would be worth undertaking subject to the proviso that the annual rate of return for the first year of operation is greater than the rate of interest. If the annual rate of return is less than the rate of interest than the present value will be increased by postponing the investment. An annual rate of return is the net benefit in the year in question expressed as a percentage of the capital cost; the net benefit being the sum of the savings in the cost of the annual vehicle-mileage and the change in the costs of accidents less the increase in maintenance costs.

When the funds available are not sufficient to carry out all schemes that are judged worth-while the aim is to select a programme which maximizes the present-day value of the return from the programme as a whole.

To do this the present value/cost ratio should be calculated for each scheme—this is the present value of the scheme expressed as a percentage of the discounted capital cost. All schemes being considered should be listed in descending order of their present value/cost ratios and schemes selected until the total available funds are accounted for. The return on the last scheme to be accepted is the marginal present value/cost ratio. When any scheme is accepted the rates for any dependent schemes must be adjusted, this will probably entail moving competitive schemes to a lower and complementary schemes to a higher place on the list.

INCREMENTAL RATE OF RETURN

Frequently when an improvement has been decided on there is a choice between a number of possible ways of carrying it out. Then the scheme with the highest present value should be adopted provided that the incremental present value/cost ratio calculated from the difference between the present value of one and that of the other and the difference between the capital cost of the two schemes, exceeds the marginal present value/cost ratio. For example if an improvement can be carried out at costs $x_1, x_2 \ldots$ with present values of $y_1, y_2 \ldots$ then the decision whether to adopt the more expensive scheme x_2 instead of x_1 depends on whether $(y_2 - y_1)/(x_2 - x_1)$ is greater than the marginal present value/cost ratio. If it is not greater, then it would be better to invest x_1 in this scheme and $(x_2 - x_1)$ in some other improvement.

PHASING ROAD INVESTMENTS

In many cases there may be a choice between building the improvement to its final standard in one stage or carrying out the work in two or more stages separated by a period of years. For example in the case of a motorway which will eventually need to be three lanes there may be a choice between building three lanes in the first instance or building two lanes with provision for future widening and building the third lane some years later when the traffic has increased. The total undiscounted costs will obviously be greater if construction is carried out in stages and the benefits will probably be smaller but the present value of the investment may be greater. When it is practical to build in stages each possibility should be investigated as if it was a separate scheme.

COMPARISON WITH A COMMERCIAL RATE OF RETURN

Returns from road improvements are not calculated on the same basis as those from most other forms of investment. The income from a commercial investment will be based on the sale of a number of commodities at a standard price or at a price which is fixed for a very wide range. Many who buy at this price would in fact have been prepared to pay more and thus the price charged is not a full measure of the benefit received. On the other hand a number of people would wish to buy at a lower price than that asked; they would receive a benefit from owning the commodity in question but the benefit to them would be less than the price asked. In the case of a road improvement the benefits are measured at their full amount and will therefore, other things being equal, be greater than those which would be calculated if the roads were run on strictly commercial lines. Other factors may enter into the comparison, such as the value to be placed on amenity, and it is not possible to make any estimate of the precise relationship between the two types of measurement.

17*

ROAD PRICING

Earlier chapters in this book have discussed various methods of making efficient use of the existing road system. Where significant expenditure is required an economic decision has to be made, namely, whether the expenditure is worthwhile. This is the investment problem which has just been discussed. But there is also the problem of allocation: who is going to enjoy the use of the facilities which have been provided? Who is to use the roads, for what purposes, under what conditions? There are innumerable possibilities, which will produce different distributions of benefit and loss throughout the entire affected population. Can a way be devised of using the road system so as to maximize the net benefits to the community?

One of the most important means of influencing the distribution of goods and services is through the price system. At the present time no prices are charged for the use of the roads, but there are taxes, namely fuel tax, annual vehicle tax and the purchase tax on vehicles. In 1962, a panel was set up by the Ministry of Transport to study the technical feasibility of various methods for improving the pricing system relating to the use of the roads, and relevant economic considerations. The Panel's report was published in June 1964.[13]

In its conclusions the Panel pointed out deficiencies of present taxation methods as a way of employing the price system, notably their inability to restrain people from making journeys which impose high costs on other people, and they suggested that road charges could usefully take more account than they do of the large differences that exist in congestion costs between one journey and another.

The Panel examined a number of possible charging methods, including new methods of charging directly for movement on the roads. They found little advantage in two measures sometimes proposed: the differential fuel tax, which could not be related at all closely to congestion costs, and the poll tax on employees in congested areas, which—whatever its merit in other fields—would have little effect on road congestion.

They concluded that parking taxes could bring significant benefits, in spite of their "inequitable results" and their undesirable effects in en-encouraging non-parking traffic and penalizing local traffic. They thought that a system of daily licences might be preferable to parking taxes, since it would embrace all traffic in the areas concerned; but it would give rise to difficult boundary problems.

Whatever the merits of parking taxes and daily licences, the Panel concluded that considerably superior results were potentially obtainable from direct pricing systems. By charging more when costs are high and less when costs are low, it was estimated that a practicable system in urban areas could yield economic benefits from reduced congestion of £100 to £150 million a year under present traffic conditions; and this estimate excluded some important items which could not be measured.

The Panel examined a number of proposals for direct charging methods, and described six meter systems—two manual and four automatic—which, with development, they thought could be made effective. Their main conclusion, was that there was every possibility that at least one of these proposals could be developed into an efficient charging system and could yield substantial benefits on congested roads.

REFERENCES TO CHAPTER 15

1. CENTRAL STATISTICAL OFFICE. Motor car ownership and use. *Economic Trends*, No. 116. London 1963 (H.M. Stationery Office).

2. DAWSON, R. F. F., and J. G. WARDROP. Passenger-mileage by road in Greater London. *Department of Scientific and Industrial Research, Road Research Technical Paper* No. 59. London, 1962 (H.M. Stationery Office).

3. COBURN. T. M., M. E. BEESLEY and D. J. REYNOLDS. The London-Birmingham motorway. Traffic and economics. *Department of Scientific and Industrial Research, Road Research Technical Paper* No. 46. London, 1960 (H.M. Stationery Office).

4. CHARLESWORTH, G., and J. L. PAISLEY. The economic assessment of returns from road works. *Proc. Instn civ. Engrs*, 1959, **14**, 229–54.

5. COMMERCIAL MOTOR. Tables of operating costs for commercial vehicles 1963. London, 1963 (Temple Press), 47th edition.

6. AUTOMOBILE ASSOCIATION. Schedule of estimated vehicle running costs based on new car values. London, 1963 (Automobile Association).

7. CHARLESWORTH, G., and T. M. COBURN. The influence of road layout on speeds and accidents in rural areas. *J. Instn munic. Engrs*, 1957, **83**, (7), 221–40.

8. GARWOOD, F., and J. C. TANNER. Accident studies before and after road changes. *Publ. Wks munic. Services Congr.* 1956, Final Report, 329–54.

9. DEPARTMENT OF SCIENTIFIC AND INDUSTRIAL RESEARCH, ROAD RESEARCH LABORATORY. Research on road safety. London, 1963 (H.M. Stationery Office).

10. JONES, J. H. Road accidents. Report submitted to the Minister of Transport. London, 1946 (H.M. Stationery Office).

11. REYNOLDS, D. J. The cost of road accidents. *J. roy. statist. Soc. Series A (General)*, 1956, **119** (4), 393–408.

12. TANNER, J. C. Factors affecting the amount of travel. *Department of Scientific and Industrial Research, Road Research Technical Paper* No. 51. London, 1961 (H.M. Stationery Office).

13. MINISTRY OF TRANSPORT. Road pricing: the economic and technical possibilities. London, 1964 (H.M. Stationery Office).

Chapter 16

Accident Studies Before and After Road Changes

SYNOPSIS

Notation. Analysis for a single site. Analysis when real effects at all sites may
be assumed equal. Tests for equality of real effects. Results.

INTRODUCTION

To estimate the effect of a change in road conditions at a particular
site on the frequency of accidents there, the usual procedure is to obtain
details of accidents at the site in convenient periods before and after and
to compare the ratio after to before with the corresponding ratio for a large
control area. The latter may be the whole of the police district in which
the site lies, or some other area from which trends due to external factors
can be reliably assessed. The significance of the difference between the
two ratios can be tested in the usual way by means of χ^2 with 1 degree of
freedom (see below).

Frequently, however, one wishes to combine the data from a representative sample of changes of a given type, since the frequencies for any single
change are usually too small to enable useful conclusions to be drawn.
This raises three problems. In the first place, unless all the before periods,
and also all the after periods, are of the same length (or more generally, if
the "control ratios" after to before are the same at all sites), it is not
immediately obvious how the average effect of the type of change concerned
should be estimated. Secondly, it is desirable to test whether the effect of
a given type of change is the same at all sites. Thirdly, if there is reason to
suppose that it varies then complications arise in testing the significance
of the average change.

This chapter discusses these matters and suggests appropriate methods
of estimation and significance tests. These methods have already been
applied extensively (see Tables 16.1 and 16.2), and a general survey of
them has been given by Garwood and Tanner;[1] more details of the theory
are given by Tanner.[2] For readers who are interested in the elementary
part of the theory of statistics reference should be made to a textbook
on the subject, e.g. References 3, 4, 5, 6, 7; the latter contains many
applications in the field of road traffic and safety.

NOTATION

N Number of sites from which data are to be combined.

b_i Number of accidents in the before period at site i ($i = 1, 2, \ldots, N$).

a_i Number of accidents in the after period at site i ($i = 1, 2, \ldots, N$).

C_i Ratio of accidents after to before in the control area for site i (generally assumed free from error).

$n_i = a_i + b_i$.

$k_i = a_i/(b_iC_i)$. This measures the apparent effect of the change at site i. It is the ratio of accidents after to the number that would have been expected if the change had no effect.

It is assumed throughout that b_i and a_i are drawn from a binomial distribution:

$$\left(\frac{1}{1+\kappa_iC_i}+\frac{\kappa_iC_i}{1+\kappa_iC_i}\right)^{n_i},$$

in which n_i is regarded as fixed. κ_i is the "true" value of k_i, i.e. the value that k_i would take if b_i and a_i took their expected values.

Throughout this chapter, the summation sign Σ denotes summation over sites, from $i = 1$ to $i = N$. These limits are omitted to save space.

ANALYSIS FOR A SINGLE SITE

When data from only one site are available, there is little choice of method. The obvious procedure is to use $k = a/bC$ as an estimate of κ. A value of k greater than unity denotes an increase compared with the control area, while a value less than unity denotes a decrease.

To test the significance of the change, one can calculate χ^2 with one degree of freedom in the usual way, as follows:

$$\chi^2 = \frac{[b-n/(1+C)]^2}{n/(1+C)}+\frac{[a-n/(1+C)]^2}{nC/(1+C)}$$

$$= \frac{(a-bC)^2}{nC} \qquad \qquad \qquad . \qquad (1)$$

The change is then judged to be real (at the 5 per cent level of significance) if χ^2 exceeds $3\cdot84$. It should be noted that this tests whether there was an effect due to the particular change at the particular site, not whether the type of change of which this was a representative is effective.

Example 1

In a period of two years there were 21 accidents at a cross-roads. This was re-designed with a staggered layout, and in the two years afterwards there were 10 accidents. In the whole police district in which the junction was situated there were 500 and 550 accidents in the two periods respectively.

Thus $a = 10$, $b = 21$, $n = 31$ and $C = 1\cdot1$, the figures for the control area being large enough for their ratio to be assumed free from error.

Substitution in equation (1) gives

$$\chi^2 = 5\cdot03.$$

As this exceeds the 5 per cent significance level ($3\cdot84$) by a considerable amount, the data provide strong evidence that the new design was effective in making conditions safer, and that the change was unlikely to have been due to chance.

Example 2

The same test can be used to compare the accident rates on two roads, or on the same road in two periods.

For example, on the London-Birmingham Motorway the following injury accidents and vehicle-mileage occurred in the years 1961 and 1963:

	1961	1963
Injury accidents	223	316
Motor-vehicles miles (millions) . .	433	530
Accident rate per million vehicle-miles .	0·52	0·60

As the accident rates are being compared the control ratio C, calculated from the vehicle-mileage figures, is $530/433 = 1·22$. Putting $a = 316$ and $b = 223$ in (1) therefore gives

$$\chi^2 = \frac{(316-223 \times 1·22)^2}{539 \times 1·22} = 2·94$$

As χ^2 is less than $3·84$ it is concluded that the difference between the accident rates in the two years could easily have arisen by chance.

Where the control site is not large enough for the ratio of the accident frequencies there to be assumed free from error, the test takes the usual form

$$\chi^2 = \frac{T(ad-bc)^2}{(a+b)(c+d)(a+c)(b+d)} \qquad \qquad . \quad . \quad . \quad . \quad (2)$$

where c and d are the control frequencies before and after, and $T =$ total number of accidents $= a+b = c+d$.

Example 3

In a town which conducted a dipped headlights campaign the numbers of road users killed during the campaign and in a comparable "before" period were as follows:

	Before	During
Dark hours	24	14
Light hours	12	15

Here we wish to test whether the reduction in deaths during dark hours was significantly different from the change in daylight hours, assuming that any other factors operating in the dark also operated to the same extent during the daylight hours.

Substituting $a = 14$, $b = 24$, $c = 15$, $d = 12$ in (2) we find that

$$\chi^2 = 2·24$$

As χ^2 is considerably less than $3·84$ we conclude that the difference between the light and dark changes could easily have arisen by chance.

If χ^2 is near the critical significance level, it is usual to apply "Yates correction", giving

$$\chi^2 = \frac{T|ad-bc| - \frac{1}{2}T)^2}{(a+b)(c+d)(a+c)(b+d)} \qquad . \quad . \quad . \quad . \quad (3)$$

ANALYSIS WHEN REAL EFFECTS AT ALL SITES MAY BE ASSUMED EQUAL

We consider here the method of estimation and the test of significance to be used when prior considerations or internal evidence in the data suggest that there is no variation between the real effects κ_i at the various sites.

The quantity k, estimate of κ, and of the average of the κ_i, is the solution of the equation

$$\sum \frac{n_i}{1+kC_i} = \sum b_i \qquad \qquad . \quad . \quad . \quad . \quad . \quad . \quad (4)$$

This equation has to be solved by successive approximation. The sampling distribution of $\log k$ is less skew, and more nearly normal, than that of k itself, and it is preferable to use the former for testing purposes. It can be shown that, approximately,

$$\text{variance } (\log k) = \frac{1+2/\sum n_i}{\sum \dfrac{\kappa C_i n_i}{(1+\kappa C_i)^2}} \qquad . \quad . \quad . \quad . \quad . \quad (5)$$

The procedure thus consists in (i) finding k, the estimated effect of the change, from equation (4); (ii) testing whether there has been a significant effect by comparing $\log k$ with zero, using its estimated standard error (i.e. the square root of the variance) from equation (5), in which κ is put equal to unity; (iii) if a significant change is found, confidence limits can be put on the estimated effect of the change from equation (5), in which κ is then replaced by k.

Example 4

A comparison was made between the numbers of injury accidents in certain periods on eight lengths of road before and after they were marked with double white lines. The numbers of casualties in the surrounding police districts in corresponding periods were used to calculate control ratios for each site. The data were as follows:

Site	Injury accidents		Control ratio
	Before	After	
1	149	146	1·091
2	159	160	1·135
3	44	20	0·395
4	41	13	0·291
5	14	19	1·382
6	6	7	1·069
7	0	2	1·051
8	103	130	1·073
	516	497	

Using these data, (4) gives $k = 0 \cdot 98$ and hence $\log_e k = -0 \cdot 0202$. Substituting in (5) gives var $(\log_e k) = 0 \cdot 00394$ and its standard error (i.e. the square root of the variance) is therefore $0 \cdot 0628$.

We now calculate the ratio between $\log_e k$ and its standard error, which is

$$-\frac{0 \cdot 0202}{0 \cdot 0628} = -0 \cdot 32$$

To be significant at the 5 per cent level this ratio should be outside the range $\pm 1 \cdot 96$. In the above case it lies within this range and the conclusion is therefore that for this group of roads as a whole there was no significant reduction in the number of injury accidents after the introduction of double white lines.

TEST FOR EQUALITY OF REAL EFFECTS

The appropriate test in this case is to calculate

$$\chi^2 = \sum \frac{(a_i - k b_i C_i)^2}{k C_i n_i}$$

where k is the estimate obtained from equation (4). If this is significant with $N-1$ degrees of freedom, it may be concluded that there are differences between the κ_i, i.e. the changes at the various sites are not producing the same effects on accident rates. The estimate of the mean effect is obtained in the same way as before, i.e. by solving equation (4), but the appropriate sampling errors are a little more complicated and are dealt with in Reference (2).

RESULTS

It is convenient to summarize here the results of the various before and after accident studies which have been made by the Laboratory, and in which the above methods have been used. Table 16.1 records the changes which have been judged to bring about significant reductions in the accident rate. The level of significance is 5 per cent, but it should be noted that in some cases the application of the tests is not always straightforward. Table 16.2 lists changes which result in increased accident rates.

The method of studying changes was generally to ask highway authorities for information about specific types of change which were carried out in their areas. Emphasis was laid on the need for unselected information, and this was achieved in many cases by including changes which had not, at the time of listing, actually been carried out or which had only recently been made. The estimated effect for any one type of accident is thus an estimate of what the future effect is likely to be for an average change of the same type, assuming, of course, that changes in the general conditions such as the speed and flow of traffic are not likely to be important.

One reservation to be made here is that the sites which have been changed may have been those in greater need of improvement. For example, the junctions which have been staggered may tend to have been the more dangerous ones. In so far as this factor has been operating then future changes will tend to have a smaller effect, but it is not thought that this tendency will be very important.

A somewhat related point is that the groups of changes for which average effects have been estimated contain in some cases wide variations in the

TABLE 16.1

Changes which have reduced accident rates

Description of change	Percentage effect	Type of accident
Reconstruction of short lengths of road on new line	−95	Injury accidents
Providing dual-carriageways in place of 2-way roads	−30	Injury accidents
Provision of by-passes to small towns	−25	Injury accidents
Improved alignment at bends . .	−80	Injury accidents
Provision of roundabouts . . .	−50	Injury accidents
Staggering of cross roads . . .	−60	Injury accidents
Provision of "Halt" signs . . .	−80	Injury accidents involving emerging vehicles
Provision of "Slow" signs . . .	−75	Injury accidents
Automatic traffic signals . . .	−40	Injury accidents
Addition of "all red" period at 4-way junctions with traffic signals . .	−40	Injury accidents
Improving slippery surfaces . . .	−80	All accidents on wet roads (injury and damage only)
	−45	All accidents
Removal of tram tracks . . .	−10	Injury accidents
Improvement of street lighting . .	−30	Injury accidents in dark
Striping of pedestrian crossings in 1951	− 7	Pedestrian casualties in G.B.
Imposition of 30 mile/h. speed limit in built-up areas of N. Ireland . .	−24	Injury accidents in built-up areas
40 mile/h. speed limit on main roads near London formerly unrestricted . .	−19	Injury accidents
	−28	Fatal and serious accidents
"No-waiting" regulations	Up to 30	Injury accidents
One-way systems	−30	Injury accidents on all roads affected
Replacement of trams by buses in London	− 9	Injury accidents on roads concerned
Power operated doors on buses . .	−90	Injury accidents involving boarding and alighting
Experimental police patrol scheme (1938).	− 7	All casualties
Reconstruction of bridges and culverts .	−70	Injury accidents
Improving visibility at bends . .	variable	Injury accidents
Improving visibility at junctions . .	−30	Injury accidents
Provision of pedestrian guard rails .	−10	Pedestrian accidents
Imposing 30 mile/h. speed limit in fringe areas of towns	−10*	Injury accidents

* This change was on its own not significant but there is supporting evidence which justifies its inclusion in this table (See Table 16.2).

TABLE 16.2

Changes which have increased accident rates

Description of change	Percentage effect	Type of accident
Reconstruction of length of road on same line	+120	Injury and damage only
Squaring rural right-hand splay junctions	+ 90	Non-pedestrian accidents
Major resurfacing improvements on rural roads (other than of slippery roads) .	+ 65	Injury accidents
Relaxation of lighting on parked vehicles	+ 50	Fatal and serious injury accidents at night involving parked vehicles of type permitted to park without lights
Removing 30 mile/h. speed limit in fringe areas of towns	+ 45*	Injury accidents

* This change is not significant but there is supporting evidence which justifies its inclusion in this table (See Table 16.1).

details of the changes and conclusions can then only be stated in general terms.

Another possible source of bias in the estimated effects arises from the way in which decisions were taken to make the changes at the various sites. At any site the number of accidents will, by chance factors alone, vary from year to year. On short or lightly trafficked lengths of road, for example, there will be no accidents in most years, one accident in a few years, and two or more accidents occasionally. In deciding whether or not a change is to be carried out it is usual to study the past accident record; when there are more accidents, there will be a greater chance that the scheme will be sanctioned than when there are fewer accidents. It follows that a particular improvement is more likely to be carried out after a period with a chance high number of accidents than after a period with average or a chance low number of accidents. After the change has been carried out, however, there is no reason to expect the chance high frequency of accidents to continue; there is an equal chance that they will be above and below average (a different average if the change had any effect). This means that there will, on the whole, be a tendency for there to be a lower frequency of accidents after than before a change, even though the change had no effect. Although the difference between the before and after periods due to this effect will rarely be statistically significant, it may be so when the figures for a large number of similar changes are combined. This source of error in the interpretation of the data, though widespread, is not often likely to lead to serious results.

One group of types of change which tend to show increases in accident frequency have some features in common. These types are:

Resurfacing other than of slippery roads.
Reconstruction on the same line.

In addition, removal of speed limits and widening of carriageway show on the average some increase in accidents, but the information available is very limited. In all four cases the main reason for the changes is not safety, but to improve the flow of traffic or increase driving comfort, as noted in Chapter 13. This might be expected to lead to an increase in speeds or a decrease in care on the part of drivers, and hence, unless there are any compensating features of the change, to an increase in accidents. In the first and third cases, at least, there are no obvious compensating features of importance, though in the other two cases there may be.

Apart from the above changes the only others which resulted in an increase in accidents were some of those at three-way junctions. These are also discussed in Chapter 13.

REFERENCES TO CHAPTER 16

1. GARWOOD, F., and J. C. TANNER. Accident studies before and after road changes. *Publ. Wks munic. Services Congr.*, 1956. *Final report*, 329–54; Discussion, 374–80.
2. TANNER, J. C. A problem in the combination of accident frequencies. *Biometrika*, 1958, **45** (3/4), 331–42.
3. MORONEY, M. J. Facts from figures. Harmondsworth, 1951 (Penguin Books Limited).
4. BROWNLEE, K. A. Industrial experimentation. *Ministry of Supply*. London, 1949 (H.M. Stationery Office).
5. BROOKES, B. C., and W. F. L. DICK. Introduction to statistical method. London, 1951 (Heinemann).
6. LEVY, H., and E. E. PREIDEL. Elementary statistics. London, 1947 (Thomas Nelson and Sons, Limited).
7. LEEMING, J. J. Statistical methods for engineers. London, 1963 (Blackie).

INDEX

Acceptance gaps at priority intersections, 284

Accidents,
  before and after studies, 412, 486
  benefits from road improvements, 478
  by-passes, 491
  cost of, 1, 478
  critical levels of flow, 411
  design of rural junctions, 441
  dual carriageways, 491
  effect of
    all-night parking in London, 335
    cycle tracks, 428
    linked traffic signals, 327
    objects on verge, 419, 424
    one-way systems, 336
    parking meters, 334
    road curvature, 432
    shoulder width, 423
    speed limits, 324
  junction design, 491, 492
  on rural roads, 409, 411
  on three-lane roads, 411
  on two-lane roads, 411
  roundabouts, 491
  staggering cross-roads, 491
  street lighting, 491
  studies, 412, 486
  to pedestrians, 327, 336, 398
  to vehicles crossing median barriers, 461
Advance direction signs, 369
Ametron speedmeter, 89
Anti-glare screens, 468
Assignment curves, 137
Assignment of traffic to alternative routes,
  see Traffic assignment
Automatic diversion of traffic, 351
  equipment, 353
  experiments, 354
    Blackwall Tunnel, 355
    Congress Street Expressway, 356
    John Lodge Freeway, 355
    Malton, Yorkshire, 354
    M4, Chiswick, 355
    on-ramp control, 356, 357
Automatic measurement of concentration, 352
Automatic traffic counters, 7
  bicycle check, 13
  causes of over- and undercounting, 15
  check count, 13
  contact gap, 12
  detectors, 7
  see also Detectors, traffic counter
  inspection on site, 14
  inspection reports, 13

Automatic traffic counters—*contd.*
  installation, 12
  maintenance, 14
  sites for, 10
  type,
    Decca Trafficometry system, 9
    Fischer and Porter counter, 9
    Streeter Amet RCH counter, 9
    SYX-RRL vehicle counter No. 4A, 8
  use in 50-point traffic census, 28
Automatic vehicle control, 357
Automatic vehicle guidance, 357
Automatic weighbridge, 18
Average daily flow
  analysis of results, 26
  estimation of, 20
  public holidays, 46
  traffic patterns, 43
Average-factor method, use in traffic surveys, 132
Axle types of lorries, 18

Before and after studies, 412, 486
Benefits from road improvements, 478
Bennett type junction, 283, 447
Bicycle check for traffic counters, 13
Blackwall Tunnel, 355
Blocked-out beam barrier, 463
Bottlenecks,
  effect on capacity, 210, 238
Bristol, 249
By-passes, accidents, 491

Cable and chain-link fence, 462
Capacity of a lane,
  effect of curvature, 193
Capacity of priority intersections,
  Halt and slow signs, 228
Capacity of roads, 196
  economic, 198, 204
  effect of
    bottlenecks, 210, 238
    carriageway width, 210
    commercial vehicles, 203, 207, 212
    intersections, 214
    parked vehicles, 211
    pedestrians, 212
    weather, 213
  one-way streets, 336
  ring roads, 257
  road space for journey, 257
  rural roads, 201, 422
  theoretical studies, 178, 186, 196
  urban, 209